DIOPHANTUS OF ALEXANDRIA

A STUDY IN THE HISTORY

OF

GREEK ALGEBRA

BY

SIR THOMAS L. HEATH, K.C.B.,

SC.D., SOMETIME FELLOW OF TRINITY COLLEGE, CAMBRIDGE

SECOND EDITION

WITH A SUPPLEMENT CONTAINING AN ACCOUNT OF FERMAT'S THEOREMS AND PROBLEMS CONNECTED WITH DIOPHANTINE ANALYSIS AND SOME SOLUTIONS OF DIOPHANTINE PROBLEMS BY EULER

DOVER PUBLICATIONS, INC., NEW YORK

Published simultaneously in Canada by General Publishing Co., Ltd., 222 Adelaide St. W., Toronto, Canada.

Published in the United Kingdom by Constable and Company Limited, 10 Orange Street, London W. C. 2.

This Dover edition, first published in 1964, is an unabridged and corrected republication of the Second (1910) edition of the work first published by the Cambridge University Press in 1885.

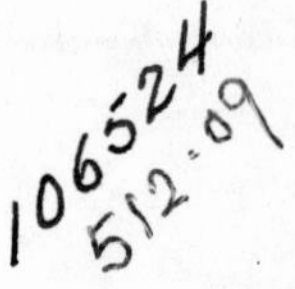

Library of Congress Catalog Card Number: 64-18851

Manufactured in the United States of America

Dover Publications, Inc.
180 Varick Street
New York 14, N. Y.

PREFACE

THE first edition of this book, which was the first English Diophantus, appeared in 1885, and has long been out of print. Inquiries made for it at different times suggested to me that it was a pity that a treatise so unique and in many respects so attractive as the *Arithmetica* should once more have become practically inaccessible to the English reader. At the same time I could not but recognise that, after twenty-five years in which so much has been done for the history of mathematics, the book needed to be brought up to date. Some matters which in 1885 were still subject of controversy, such as the date of Diophantus, may be regarded as settled, and some points which then had to be laboured can now be dismissed more briefly. Practically the whole of the Introduction, except the chapters on the editions of Diophantus, his methods of solution, and the porisms and other assumptions found in his work, has been entirely rewritten and much shortened, while the chapters on the methods and on the porisms etc., have been made fuller than before. The new text of Tannery (Teubner 1893, 1895) has enabled a number of obscure passages, particularly in Books V and VI, to be cleared up and, as a basis for a reproduction of the whole work, is much superior to the text of Bachet. I have taken the opportunity to make my version of the actual treatise somewhat fuller and somewhat closer to the language of the original. In other respects also I thought I could improve upon a youthful work which was my first essay in the history of Greek mathematics. When writing it I was solely concerned to make Diophantus himself known to mathematicians, and I did not pay sufficient attention to Fermat's notes on the various problems. It is well known that it is in these notes that many of the great propositions discovered by Fermat in the theory of numbers are enshrined; but, although the notes are literally translated in Wertheim's edition, they do not seem to have appeared in English; moreover they need to be supplemented by passages from the correspondence of Fermat and from the *Doctrinae analyticae Inventum Novum* of Jacques de Billy. The histories of mathematics furnish only a very inadequate description of Fermat's work, and it seemed desirable to attempt to give as full an account of his theorems and problems in or connected with Diophantine analysis as it is possible to compile from the scattered material available in Tannery and Henry's edition of the *Oeuvres de Fermat* (1891—1896). So much of this material as could not be conveniently given in the notes to particular problems of Diophantus I have put together in the Supplement, which is thus intended to supply a missing chapter in the history of mathematics. Lastly, in order to make the book more complete, I thought it right to add some of the more remarkable solutions of difficult Diophantine problems given by Euler, for whom such problems had a great fascination; the last section of the Supplement is therefore devoted to these solutions.

T. L. H.

October, 1910.

CONTENTS

INTRODUCTION

THE ARITHMETICA

SUPPLEMENT

INTRODUCTION

CHAPTER I

DIOPHANTUS AND HIS WORKS

THE divergences between writers on Diophantus used to begin, as Cossali said[1], with the last syllable of his name. There is now, however, no longer any doubt that the name was Diophant*os*, not Diophant*es*[2].

The question of his date is more difficult. Abū'lfaraj, the Arabian historian, in his *History of the Dynasties*, places Diophantus under the Emperor Julian (A.D. 361–3), but without giving any authority; and it may be that the statement is due simply to a confusion of our Diophantus with a rhetorician of that name, mentioned in another article of Suidas, who lived in the time of Julian[3]. On the other hand, Rafael Bombelli in his Algebra,

[1] Cossali, *Origine, trasporto in Italia, primi progressi in essa dell' Algebra* (Parma, 1797–9), I. p. 61: "Su la desinenza del nome comincia la diversità tra gli scrittori."

[2] Greek authority is overwhelmingly in favour of Diophant*os*. The following is the evidence, which is collected in the second volume of Tannery's edition of Diophantus (henceforward to be quoted as "Dioph.," "Dioph. II. p. 36" indicating page 36 of Vol. II., while "Dioph. II. 20" will mean *proposition* 20 of Book II.): Suidas s.v. Ὑπατία (Dioph. II. p. 36), Theon of Alexandria, on Ptolemy's *Syntaxis* Book I. c. 9 (Dioph. II. p. 35), Anthology, Epigram on Diophantus (Ep. XIV. 126; Dioph. II. p. 60), Anonymi prolegomena in Introductionem arithmeticam Nicomachi (Dioph. II. p. 73), Georgii Pachymerae paraphrasis (Dioph. II. p. 122), Scholia of Maximus Planudes (Dioph. II. pp. 148, 177, 178 etc.), Scholium on Iamblichus *In Nicomachi arithm. introd.*, ed. Pistelli, p. 127 (Dioph. II. p. 72), a Scholium on Dioph. II. 8 from the MS. "*A*" (Dioph. II. p. 260), which is otherwise amusing (Ἡ ψυχή σου, Διόφαντε, εἴη μετὰ τοῦ Σατανᾶ ἕνεκα τῆς δυσκολίας τῶν τε ἄλλων σου θεωρημάτων καὶ δὴ καὶ τοῦ παρόντος θεωρήματος, "Your soul to perdition, Diophantus, for the difficulty of your problems in general and of this one in particular"); John of Jerusalem (10th c.) alone (*Vita Ioannis Damasceni* XI.: Dioph. II. p. 36), if the reading of the MS. Parisinus 1559 is right, wrote, in the plural, ὡς Πυθαγόραι ἢ Διόφανται, where however Διόφανται is clearly a mistake for Διόφαντοι.

[3] Λιβάνιος, σοφιστὴς Ἀντιοχεύς, τῶν ἐπὶ Ἰουλιανοῦ τοῦ βασιλέως χρόνων, καὶ μέχρι Θεοδοσίου τοῦ πρεσβυτέρου· Φασγανίου πατρός, μαθητὴς Διοφάντου.

published in 1572, says dogmatically that Diophantus lived under Antoninus Pius (138–161 A.D.), but there is no confirmation of this date either.

The positive evidence on the subject can be given very shortly. An upper limit is indicated by the fact that Diophantus, in his book on Polygonal Numbers, quotes from Hypsicles a definition of such a number[1]. Hypsicles was also the writer of the supplement to Euclid's Book XIII. on the Regular Solids known as Book XIV. of the *Elements*; hence Diophantus must have written later than, say, 150 B.C. A lower limit is furnished by the fact that Diophantus is quoted by Theon of Alexandria[2]; hence Diophantus wrote before, say, 350 A.D. There is a wide interval between 150 B.C. and 350 A.D., but fortunately the limits can be brought closer. We have a letter of Psellus (11th c.) in which Diophantus and Anatolius are mentioned as writers on the Egyptian method of reckoning. "Diophantus," says Psellus[3], "dealt with it more accurately, but the very learned Anatolius collected the most essential parts of the doctrine as stated by Diophantus in a different way (reading ἑτέρως) and in the most succinct form, dedicating (προσεφώνησε) his work to Diophantus." It would appear, therefore, that Diophantus and Anatolius were contemporaries, and it is most likely that the former would be to the latter in the relation of master to pupil. Now Anatolius wrote about 278–9 A.D., and was Bishop of Laodicea about 280 A.D. We may therefore safely say that Diophantus flourished about 250 A.D. or not much later. This agrees well with the fact that he is not quoted by Nicomachus (about 100 A.D.), Theon of Smyrna (about 130 A.D.) or Iamblichus (end of 3rd c.).

[1] Dioph. I. p. 470–2.

[2] Theo Alexandrinus in primum librum Ptolemaei Mathematicae Compositionis (on c. IX.): see Dioph. II. p. 35, *καθ' ἃ καὶ Διόφαντός φησι· τῆς γὰρ μονάδος ἀμεταθέτου οὔσης καὶ ἑστώσης πάντοτε, τὸ πολλαπλασιαζόμενον εἶδος ἐπ' αὐτὴν αὐτὸ τὸ εἶδος ἔσται κ.τ.έ.*

[3] Dioph. II. p. 38–9: *περὶ δὲ τῆς αἰγυπτιακῆς μεθόδου ταύτης Διόφαντος μὲν διέλαβεν ἀκριβέστερον, ὁ δὲ λογιώτατος Ἀνατόλιος τὰ συνεκτικώτατα μέρη τῆς κατ' ἐκεῖνον ἐπιστήμης ἀπολεξάμενος ἑτέρω* (? *ἑτέρως* or *ἑταίρῳ*) *Διοφάντῳ συνοπτικώτατα προσεφώνησε.* The MSS. read *ἑτέρω*, which is apparently a mistake for *ἑτέρως* or possibly for *ἑταίρῳ*. Tannery conjectures *τῷ ἑταίρῳ*, but this is very doubtful; if the article had been there, *Διοφάντῳ τῷ ἑταίρῳ* would have been better. On the basis of *ἑταίρῳ* Tannery builds the further hypothesis that the Dionysius to whom the *Arithmetica* is dedicated is none other than Dionysius who was at the head of the Catechist school at Alexandria 232–247 and was Bishop there 248–265 A.D. Tannery conjectures then that Diophantus was a Christian and a pupil of Dionysius (Tannery, "Sur la religion des derniers mathématiciens de l'antiquité," Extrait des *Annales de Philosophie Chrétienne*, 1896, p. 13 sqq.). It is however difficult to establish this (Hultsch, art. "Diophantos aus Alexandreia" in Pauly-Wissowa's *Real-Encyclopädie der classischen Altertumswissenchaften*).

The only personal particulars about Diophantus which are known are those contained in the epigram-problem relating to him in the Anthology[1]. The solution gives 84 as the age at which he died. His boyhood lasted 14 years, his beard grew at 21, he married at 33; a son was born to him five years later and died, at the age of 42, when his father was 80 years old. Diophantus' own death followed four years later[2]. It is clear that the epigram was written, not long after his death, by an intimate personal friend with knowledge of and taste for the science which Diophantus made his life-work[3].

The works on which the fame of Diophantus rests are:

(1) The *Arithmetica* (originally in thirteen Books).

(2) A tract *On Polygonal Numbers*.

Six Books of the former and part of the latter survive.

Allusions in the *Arithmetica* imply the existence of

(3) A collection of propositions under the title of Porisms; in three propositions (3, 5 and 16) of Book V. Diophantus quotes as known certain propositions in the Theory of Numbers, prefixing to the statement of them the words "We have it in the *Porisms* that......" (ἔχομεν ἐν τοῖς Πορίσμασιν ὅτι κ.τ.ἑ.).

A scholium on a passage of Iamblichus where he quotes a dictum of certain Pythagoreans about the unit being the dividing line (μεθόριον) between number and aliquot parts, says "thus Diophantus in the *Moriastica*[4]......for he describes as 'parts' the progression without limit in the direction of less than the unit." Tannery thinks the Μοριαστικά may be ancient scholia (now lost) on Diophantus I. Def. 3 sqq.[5]; but in that case why should *Diophantus* be supposed to be speaking? And, as Hultsch

[1] Anthology, Ep. XIV. 126; Dioph. II. pp. 60–1.

[2] The epigram actually says that his boyhood lasted $\frac{1}{6}$ of his life; his beard grew after $\frac{1}{12}$ more; after $\frac{1}{7}$ more he married, and his son was born five years later; the son lived to half his father's age, and the father died four years after his son. Cantor (*Gesch. d. Math.* I_3, p. 465) quotes a suggestion of Heinrich Weber that a better solution is obtained if we assume that the son died at the time when his father's age was double his, not at an age equal to half the age at which his father died. In that case

$$\tfrac{1}{6}x+\tfrac{1}{12}x+\tfrac{1}{7}x+5+\tfrac{1}{2}(x-4)+4=x, \text{ or } 3x=196 \text{ and } x=65\tfrac{1}{3}.$$

This would substitute $10\frac{8}{9}$ for 14, $16\frac{1}{3}$ for 21, $25\frac{2}{3}$ for 33, $30\frac{2}{3}$ for 42, $61\frac{1}{3}$ for 80, and $65\frac{1}{3}$ for 84 above. I do not see any advantage in this solution. On the contrary, I think the fractional results are an objection to it, and it is to be observed that the scholiast has the solution 84, derived from the equation

$$\tfrac{1}{6}x+\tfrac{1}{12}x+\tfrac{1}{7}x+5+\tfrac{1}{2}x+4=x.$$

[3] Hultsch, art. Diophantos in Pauly-Wissowa's *Real-Encyclopädie*.

[4] Iamblichus *In Nicomachi arithm. introd.* p. 127 (ed. Pistelli); Dioph. II. p. 72.

[5] Dioph. II. p. 72 note.

remarks, such scholia would more naturally have been quoted as *σχόλια* and not by the separate title Μοριαστικά[1]. It may have been a separate work by Diophantus giving rules for reckoning with fractions; but I do not feel clear that the reference may not simply be to the definitions at the beginning of the *Arithmetica*.

With reference to the title of the *Arithmetica*, we may observe that the meaning of the word ἀριθμητικά here is slightly different from that assigned to it by more ancient writers. The ancients drew a marked distinction between ἀριθμητική and λογιστική, though both were concerned with numbers. Thus Plato states that ἀριθμητική is concerned with the abstract properties of numbers (as odd and even, etc.), whereas λογιστική deals with the same odd and even, but in relation to one another[2]. Geminus also distinguishes the two terms[3]. According to him ἀριθμητική deals with numbers *in themselves*, distinguishing linear, plane and solid numbers, in fact all the forms of number, starting from the unit, and dealing with the generation of plane numbers, similar and dissimilar, and then with numbers of three dimensions, etc. λογιστική on the other hand deals, not with the abstract properties of numbers in themselves, but with numbers of concrete things (*αἰσθητῶν*, sensible objects), whence it calls them by the names of the things measured, *e.g.* it calls some by the names μηλίτης and φιαλίτης[4]. But in Diophantus the calculations take an abstract form (except in V. 30, where the question is to find the number of measures of *wine* at two given prices respectively), so that the distinction between λογιστική and ἀριθμητική is lost.

We find the *Arithmetica* quoted under slightly different titles. Thus the anonymous author of prolegomena to Nicomachus' *Introductio Arithmetica* speaks of Diophantus' "thirteen Books of Arithmetic[5]." A scholium on Iamblichus refers to "the last theorem of the first Book of Diophantus' Elements of Arithmetic

[1] Hultsch, *loc. cit.*

[2] *Gorgias*, 451 B, C: τὰ μὲν ἄλλα καθάπερ ἡ ἀριθμητικὴ ἡ λογιστικὴ ἔχει· περὶ τὸ αὐτὸ γάρ ἐστι, τό τε ἄρτιον καὶ τὸ περιττόν· διαφέρει δὲ τοσοῦτον, ὅτι καὶ πρὸς αὑτὰ καὶ πρὸς ἄλληλα πῶς ἔχει πλήθους ἐπισκοπεῖ τὸ περιττὸν καὶ τὸ ἄρτιον ἡ λογιστική.

[3] Proclus, Comment. on Euclid I., p. 39, 14–40, 7.

[4] Cf. Plato, *Laws* 819 B, C, on the advantage of combining amusement with instruction in arithmetical calculation, *e.g.* by distributing apples or garlands (μήλων τέ τινων διανομαὶ καὶ στεφάνων) and the use of different bowls of silver, gold, or brass etc. (φιάλας ἅμα χρύσου καὶ χαλκοῦ καὶ ἀργύρου καὶ τοιούτων τινῶν ἄλλων κεραννύντες, οἱ δὲ ὅλας πως διαδιδόντες, ὅπερ εἶπον, εἰς παιδιὰν ἐναρμόττοντες τὰς τῶν ἀναγκαίων ἀριθμῶν χρήσεις).

[5] Dioph. II. p. 73, 26.

(ἀριθμητικῆς στοιχειώσεως)[1]." A scholium on one of the epigrams in Metrodorus' collection similarly speaks of the "Elements of Diophantus[2]."

None of the MSS. which we possess contain more than the first six Books of the *Arithmetica*, the only variation being that some few divide the six Books into seven[3], while one or two give the fragment on Polygonal Numbers with the number VIII. The idea that Regiomontanus saw, or said he saw, a MS. containing the thirteen Books complete is due to a misapprehension. There is no doubt that the missing Books were lost at a very early date. Tannery[4] suggests that Hypatia's commentary extended only to the first six Books, and that she left untouched the remaining seven, which accordingly were first forgotten and then lost; he compares the case of Apollonius' *Conics*, the first four Books of which were preserved by Eutocius, who wrote a commentary on them, while the rest, which he did not include in his commentary, were lost so far as the Greek text is concerned. While, however, three of the last four Books of the *Conics* have fortunately reached us through the Arabic, there is no sign that even the Arabians ever possessed the missing Books of Diophantus. Thus the second part of an algebraic treatise called the *Fakhrī* by Abū Bekr Muḥ. b. al-Ḥasan al-Karkhī (d. about 1029) is a collection of problems in determinate and indeterminate analysis which not only show that their author had deeply studied Diophantus, but in many cases are taken direct from the *Arithmetica*, with the change, occasionally, of some of the constants. In the fourth section of this work, which begins and ends with problems corresponding to problems in Diophantus Books II. and III. respectively, are 25 problems not found in Diophantus; but the differences from Diophantus in essential features (*e.g.* several of the problems lead to equations giving irrational results, which are always avoided by Diophantus), as well as other internal evidence, exclude the hypothesis that we have here a lost Book of Diophantus[5]. Nor is there any sign that more of the work than we possess was known

[1] Dioph. II. p. 72, 17; Iamblichus (ed. Pistelli), p. 132, 12.

[2] Dioph. II. p. 62, 25.

[3] *e.g.* Vaticanus gr. 200, Scorialensis Ω-I-15, and the Broscius MS. in the University Library of Cracow; the two last divide the first Book into two, the second beginning immediately after the explanation of the sign for *minus* (Dioph. I. p. 14, 1).

[4] Dioph. II. p. xvii, xviii.

[5] See F. Woepcke, *Extrait du Fakhrī, traité d'Algèbre par Abou Bekr Mohammed ben Alhaçan Alkarkhī* (*manuscrit* 952, *supplément arabe de la bibliothèque Impériale*), Paris, 1853.

to Abū'l Wafā al-Būzjānī (940–998 A.D.), who wrote a "commentary (*tafsīr*) on the algebra of Diophantus" as well as a "Book of proofs of the propositions used by Diophantus in his work..." These facts again point to the conclusion that the lost Books were lost before the 10th c.

Tannery's suggestion that Hypatia's commentary was limited to the six Books, and the parallel of Eutocius' commentary on Apollonius' *Conics*, imply that it is the *last seven* Books, and the most difficult, which are lost. This view is in strong contrast to that which had previously found most acceptance among competent authorities. The latter view was most clearly put, and most ably supported, by Nesselmann[1], though Colebrooke[2] had already put forward a conjecture to the same effect; and historians of mathematics such as Hankel, Moritz Cantor, and Günther have accepted Nesselmann's conclusions, which, stated in his own words, are as follows: (1) that much less of Diophantus is wanting than would naturally be supposed on the basis of the numerical proportion of 6 to 13; (2) that the missing portion is not to be looked for at the end but in the middle of the work, and indeed mostly between the first and second Books. Nesselmann's general argument is that, if we carefully read the last four Books, from the third to the sixth, we find that Diophantus moves in a rigidly defined and limited circle of methods and artifices, and that any attempts which he makes to free himself are futile; "as often as he gives the impression that he wishes to spring over the magic circle drawn round him, he is invariably thrown back by an invisible hand on the old domain already known; we see, similarly, in half-darkness, behind the clever artifices which he seeks to use in order to free himself, the chains which fetter his genius, we hear their rattling, whenever, in dealing with difficulties only too freely imposed upon himself, he knows of no other means of extricating himself except to cut through the knot instead of untying it." Moreover, the sixth Book forms a natural conclusion to the whole, in that it consists of exemplifications of methods explained and used in the preceding Books. The subject is the finding of right-angled triangles in rational numbers such that the sides and area satisfy given conditions, the geometrical property of the right-angled triangle being introduced as a fresh condition additional to the purely arithmetical conditions which have to be satisfied in the

[1] *Algebra der Griechen*, pp. 264–273.
[2] *Algebra of the Hindus*, Note M, p. lxi.

problems of the earlier Books. But, assuming that Diophantus' resources are at an end in the sixth Book, Nesselmann has to suggest possible topics which would have formed approximately adequate material for the equivalent of seven Books of the *Arithmetica.* The first step is to consider what is actually wanting which we should expect to find, either as foreshadowed by the author himself or as necessary for the elucidation or completion of the whole subject. Now the first Book contains problems leading to determinate equations of the first degree; the remainder of the work is a collection of problems which, with few exceptions, lead to indeterminate equations of the second degree, beginning with simpler cases and advancing step by step to more complicated questions. There would have been room therefore for problems involving (1) determinate equations of the *second* degree and (2) indeterminate equations of the *first.* There is indeed nothing to show that (2) formed part of the writer's plan; but on the other hand the writer's own words in Def. 11 at the beginning of the work promise a discussion of the solution of the complete or *adfected* quadratic, and it is clear that he employed his method of solution in the later Books, where in some cases he simply states the solution without working it out, while in others, where the roots are "irrational," he gives approximations which indicate that he was in possession of a scientific method. *Pure* quadratics Diophantus regarded as simple equations, taking no account of the negative root. Indeed it would seem that he adopted as his ground for the classification of quadratics, not the index of the highest power of the unknown quantity contained in it, but the *number of terms* left in it when reduced to its simplest form. His words are[1]: "If the same powers of the unknown occur on both sides, but with different coefficients (μὴ ὁμοπληθῆ δέ), we must take like from like until we have one single expression equal to another. If there are on both sides, or on either side, any terms with negative coefficients (ἐν ἐλλείψεσί τινα εἴδη), the defects must be added on both sides until the terms on both sides have none but positive coefficients (ἐνυπάρχοντα), when we must again take like from like until there remains one term on each side. This should be the object aimed at in framing the hypotheses of propositions, that is to say, to reduce the equations, if possible, until one term is left equated to one term. But afterwards I will

[1] Dioph. I. Def. 11, p. 14.

show you also how, when two terms are left equal to one term, such an equation is solved." That is to say, reduce the quadratic, if possible, to one of the forms $ax^2 = bx$, $ax^2 = c$, or $bx = c$; I will show later how to solve the equation when three terms are left of which any two are equal to the third, *i.e.* the complete quadratic $ax^2 \pm bx \pm c = 0$, excluding the case $ax^2 + bx + c = 0$. The exclusion of the latter case is natural, since it is of the essence of the work to find rational and positive solutions. Nesselmann might have added that Diophantus' requirement that the equation, as finally stated, shall contain only positive terms, of which two are equated to the third, suggests that his solution would deal separately with the three possible cases (just as Euclid makes separate cases of the equations in his propositions VI. 28, 29), so that the exposition might occupy some little space. The suitable place for it would be between the first and second Books. There is no evidence tending to confirm Nesselmann's further argument that the six Books may originally have been divided into even more than seven Books. He argues from the fact that there are often better natural divisions in the middle of the Books (*e.g.* at II. 19) than between them as they now stand; thus there is no sign of a marked division between Books I. and II. and between Books II. and III., the first five problems of Book II. and the first four of Book III. recalling similar problems in the preceding Books respectively. But the latter circumstances are better explained, as Tannery explains them, by the supposition that the first problems of Books II. and III. are interpolated from some ancient commentary. Next Nesselmann points out that there are a number of imperfections in the text, Book V. especially having been "treated by Mother Time in a very stepmotherly fashion"; thus it seems probable that at V. 19 three problems have dropped out altogether. Still he is far from accounting for seven whole Books; he has therefore to press into the service the lost "Porisms" and the tract on Polygonal Numbers.

If the phrase which, as we have said, occurs three times in Book V., "We have it in the Porisms that ...," indicates that the "Porisms" were a definite collection of propositions concerning the properties of certain numbers, their divisibility into a certain number of squares, and so on, it is possible that it was from the same collection that Diophantus took the numerous other propositions which he assumes, either explicitly enunciating them, or implicitly taking them for granted. May we not then, says

Nesselmann, reasonably suppose the "Porisms" to have formed an introduction to the indeterminate and semi-determinate analysis of the second degree which forms the main subject of the *Arithmetica*, and to have been an integral part of the thirteen Books, intervening, probably, between Books I. and II.? Schulz, on the other hand, considered this improbable, and in recent years Hultsch[1] has definitely rejected the theory that Diophantus filled one or more Books of his *Arithmetica* exclusively with Porisms. Schulz's argument is, indeed, not conclusive. It is based on the consideration that "Diophantus expressly says that his work deals with *arithmetical problems*[2]"; but what Diophantus actually says is "Knowing you, O Dionysius, to be anxious to learn the solution (or, perhaps, 'discovery,' εὕρεσιν) of problems in numbers, I have endeavoured, beginning from the foundations on which the study is built up, to expound (ὑποστῆσαι = to lay down) the nature and force subsisting in numbers," the last of which words would easily cover propositions in the theory of numbers, while "propositions," not "problems," is the word used at the end of the Preface, where he says, "let us now proceed to the propositions (προτάσεις) ...... which have been treated in thirteen Books."

On reconsideration of the whole matter, I now agree in the view of Hultsch that the Porisms were not a separate portion of the *Arithmetica* or included in the *Arithmetica* at all. If they had been, I think the expression "we have it in the Porisms" would have been inappropriate. In the first place, the Greek mathematicians do not usually give references in such a form as this to propositions which they cite when they come from the same work as that in which they are cited; as a rule the propositions are quoted without any references at all. The references in this case would, on the assumption that the Porisms were a portion of the thirteen Books, more naturally have been to particular propositions of particular Books (cf. Eucl. XII. 2, "For it was proved

[1] Hultsch, *loc. cit.*

[2] The whole passage of Schulz is as follows (pref. xxi): "Es ist daher nicht unwahrscheinlich, dass diese Porismen eine eigene Schrift unseres Diophantus waren, welche vorzüglich die Zusammensetzung der Zahlen aus gewissen Bestandtheilen zu ihrem Gegenstande hatten. Könnte man diese Schrift als einen Bestandtheil des grossen in dreizehn Büchern abgefassten arithmetischen Werkes ansehen, so wäre es sehr erklärbar, dass gerade dieser Theil, der den blossen Liebhaber weniger anzog, verloren ging. Da indess Diophantus ausdrücklich sagt, sein Werk behandele *arithmetische Probleme*, so hat wenigstens die letztere Annahme nur einen geringen Grad von Wahrscheinlichkeit."

in the first theorem of the 10th Book that...."). But a still vaguer reference would have been enough, even if Diophantus had chosen to give any at all; if the propositions quoted had preceded those in which they are used, some expression like τοῦτο γὰρ προγέγραπται, "for this has already been proved," or δέδεικται γὰρ τοῦτο, "for this has been shown," would have sufficed, or, if the propositions occurred later, some expression like ὡς ἑξῆς δειχθήσεται or δειχθήσεται ὑφ' ἡμῶν ὕστερον, "as will be proved in due course" or "later." The expression "we have it in the Porisms" (in the plural) would have been still more inappropriate if the "Porisms" had been, as Tannery supposes[1], not collected together as one or more Books of the *Arithmetica*, but scattered about in the work as *corollaries* to particular propositions[2]. And, as Hultsch says, it is hard, on Tannery's supposition, to explain why the three particular theorems quoted from "the Porisms" were lost, while a fair number of other additions survived, partly under the title πόρισμα (cf. I. 34, I. 38), partly as "lemmas to what follows," λῆμμα εἰς τὸ ἑξῆς (cf. lemmas before IV. 34, 35, 36, V. 7, 8, VI. 12, 15). On the other hand, there is nothing improbable in the supposition that Diophantus was induced by the difficulty of his problems to give place in a separate work to the "porisms" necessary to their solution.

The hypothesis that the Porisms formed part of the *Arithmetica* being thus given up, we can hardly hold any longer to Nesselmann's view of the contents of the lost Books and their place in the treatise; and I am now much more inclined to the opinion of Tannery that it is the last and the most difficult Books which are lost. Tannery's argument seems to me to be very attractive and to deserve quotation in full, as finally put in the preface to Vol. II. of his Diophantus[3]. He replies first to the assumption that Diophantus could not have proceeded to problems more difficult than those of Book V. "But if the fifth or the sixth Book of the *Arithmetica* had been lost, who, pray, among us would have believed that such problems had ever been attempted by the Greeks? It would be the greatest error, in any case in which a

[1] Dioph. II. p. xix.

[2] Thus Tannery holds (*loc. cit.*) that the solution of the complete quadratic was given in the form of corollaries to I. 27, 30; and he refers the three "porisms" quoted in V. 3, 5, 16 respectively to a second (lost) solution of III. 10, to III. 15, and to IV. 1, 2.

[3] Dioph. II. p. xx.

thing cannot clearly be proved to have been unknown to all the ancients, to maintain that it could not have been known to some Greek mathematician. If we do not know to what lengths Archimedes brought the theory of numbers (to say nothing of other things), let us admit our ignorance. But, between the famous problem of the cattle and the most difficult of Diophantus' problems, is there not a sufficient gap to require seven Books to fill it? And, without attributing to the ancients what modern mathematicians have discovered, may not a number of the things attributed to the Indians and Arabs have been drawn from Greek sources? May not the same be said of a problem solved by Leonardo of Pisa, which is very similar to those of Diophantus but is not now to be found in the *Arithmetica*? In fact, it may fairly be said that, when Chasles made his reasonably probable restitution of the *Porisms* of Euclid, he, notwithstanding the fact that he had Pappus' lemmas to help him, undertook a more difficult task than he would have undertaken if he had attempted to fill up seven Diophantine Books with numerical problems which the Greeks may reasonably be supposed to have solved."

On the assumption that the lost portion came at the end of the existing six Books, Schulz supposed that it contained new methods of solution in addition to those used in Books I. to VI., and in particular extended the method of solution by means of the *double equation* (διπλῆ ἰσότης or διπλοϊσότης). By means of the double equation Diophantus shows how to find a value of the unknown which will make two expressions (linear or quadratic) containing it simultaneously squares. Schulz then thinks that he went on, in the lost Books, to make *three* such expressions simultaneously squares, *i.e.* advanced to a *triple equation.* But this explanation does not in any case take us very far.

Bombelli thought that Diophantus went on to solve determinate equations of the third and fourth degree[1]; this view, however, though natural at that date, when the solution of cubic and biquadratic equations filled so large a space in contemporary investigations and in Bombelli's own studies, has nothing to support it.

Hultsch[2] seems to find the key to the question in the fragment of the treatise on Polygonal Numbers and the developments to

[1] Cossali, I. pp. 75, 76.

[2] Hultsch, *loc. cit.*

which it might have been expected to lead. In this he differs from Tannery, who says that, as Serenus' treatise on the sections of cones and cylinders was added to the mutilated *Conics* of Apollonius consisting of four Books only, in order to make up a convenient volume, so the tract on Polygonal Numbers was added to the remains of the *Arithmetica*, though forming no part of the larger work[1]. Thus Tannery would seem to deny the genuineness of the whole tract on Polygonal Numbers, though in his text he only signalises the portion beginning with the enunciation of the problem "Given a number, to find in how many ways it can be a polygonal number" as a "vain attempt by a commentator" to solve this problem. Hultsch, on the other hand, thinks we may conclude that Diophantus really solved the problem. He points out moreover that the beginning of the tract is like the beginning of Book I. of the *Arithmetica* in containing definitions and preliminary propositions. Then came the difficult problem quoted, the discussion of which breaks off in our text after a few pages; and to this it would be easy to tack on a great variety of other problems. Again, says Hultsch, the supplementary propositions added by Bachet may serve to give an approximate idea of the difficulty of the problems which were probably treated in Books VII. and the following. And between these and the bold combination of a triangular and a square number in the Cattle-Problem stretches, as Tannery says, a wide domain which was certainly not unknown to Diophantus, but was his hunting-ground for the most various problems. Whether Diophantus dealt with plane numbers, and with other figured numbers, such as prisms and tetrahedra, is uncertain.

The name of Diophantus was used, as were the names of Euclid, Archimedes and Heron in their turn, for the purpose of palming off the compilations of much later authors. Tannery prints in his edition three fragments under the head of "Diophantus Pseudepigraphus." The first[2], which is not "from the Arithmetic of Diophantus" as its heading states, is worth notice as containing some particulars of one of "two methods of finding the square root of any square number"; we are told to begin by writing the number "according to the arrangement of the Indian method," *i.e.* according to the Indian numerical notation which reached us through the Arabs. The fragment is taken from a Paris MS.

[1] Dioph. II. p. xviii.

[2] Dioph. II. p. 3, 3–14.

(Supplem. gr. 387), where it follows a work with the title Ἀρχὴ τῆς μεγάλης καὶ Ἰνδικῆς ψηφιφορίας (*i.e.* ψηφοφορίας), written in 1252 and raided about half a century later by Maximus Planudes. The second fragment[1] is the work edited by C. Henry in 1879 as *Opusculum de multiplicatione et divisione sexagesimalibus Diophanto vel Pappo attribuendum.* The third[2], beginning with Διοφάντου ἐπιπεδομετρικά, is a compilation made in the Byzantine period out of late reproductions of the γεωμετρούμενα and στερεομετρούμενα of Heron. The second and third fragments, like the first, have nothing to do with Diophantus.

[1] Dioph. II. p. 3, 15–15, 17.

[2] Dioph. II. p. 15, 18–31, 22.

CHAPTER II

THE MSS. OF AND WRITERS ON DIOPHANTUS

FOR full details of the various MSS. and of their mutual relations, reference should be made to the prefaces to the first and second volumes of Tannery's edition[1]. Tannery's account needs only to be supplemented by a description given by Gollob[2] of another MS. supposed by Tannery to be non-existent, but actually rediscovered in the Library of the University of Cracow (Nr 544). Only the shortest possible summary of the essential facts will be given here.

After the loss of Egypt the work of Diophantus long remained almost unknown among the Byzantines; perhaps one copy only survived (of the Hypatian recension), which was seen by Michael Psellus and possibly by the scholiast to Iamblichus, but of which no trace can be found after the capture of Constantinople in 1204. From this one copy (denoted by the letter *a* in Tannery's table of the MSS.) another MS. (α) was copied in the 8th or 9th century; this again is lost, but is the true archetype of our MSS. The copyist apparently intended to omit all scholia, but, the distinction between text and scholia being sometimes difficult to draw, he included a good deal which should have been left out. For example, Hypatia, and perhaps scholiasts after her, seem to have added some alternative solutions and a number of new problems; some of these latter, such as II. 1–7, 17, 18, were admitted into the text as genuine.

The MSS. fall into two main classes, the ante-Planudes class, as we may call it, and the Planudean. The most ancient and the best of all is Matritensis 48 (Tannery's *A*), which was written in the 13th century and belongs to the first class; it is evidently a most faithful copy of the lost archetype (α). Maximus Planudes wrote a systematic commentary on Books I. and II., and his scholia,

[1] Dioph. I. pp. iii–v, II. pp. xxii–xxxiv.

[2] Eduard Gollob, "Ein wiedergefundener Diophantuscodex" in *Zeitschrift für Math. u. Physik*, XLIV. (1899), hist.-litt. Abtheilung, pp. 137–140.

which are edited by Tannery for the first time, are preserved in the oldest representative which we possess of the Planudean class, namely, Marcianus 308 (Tannery's B_1), itself apparently copied from an archetype of the 14th century now lost, with the exception of ten leaves which survive in Ambrosianus Et 157 sup.

Tannery shows the relation of the MSS. in the following diagram:

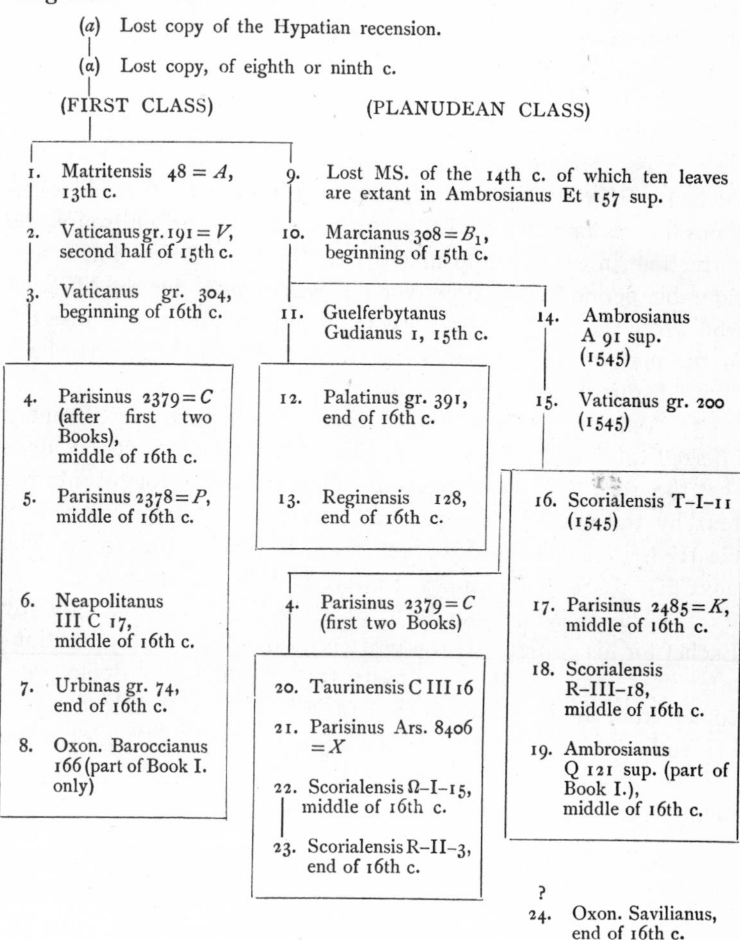

Auria's recension made up out of MSS. 2, 3, 15 above and Xylander's translation:

25. Parisinus 2380 = *D*.
26. Ambrosianus E 5 sup.

27. MS. (Patavinus) of Broscius (Brozek) now at Cracow.
28. Lost MS. of Cardinal du Perron.

The addition of a few notes as regards the most important and interesting of the MSS., in the order of their numbers in Tannery's arrangement, will now sufficiently complete the story.

1. The best and most ancient MS., that of Madrid (Tannery's *A*), was unfortunately spoiled at a late date by corrections made, especially in the first two Books, from some MS. of the Planudean class, in such a way that the original reading is sometimes entirely erased or made quite illegible. In these cases recourse must be had to the Vatican MS. 191.

2. The MS. Vaticanus graecus 191 was copied from *A* before it had suffered the general alteration by means of a MS. of the other class, though not before various other corrections had been made in different hands not easily distinguished; thus *V* sometimes has readings which Tannery found to have arisen from some correction in *A*. *A* appears to have been at Rome for a considerable period at the time when *V* was copied; for the librarian who wrote the old table of contents[1] at the beginning of *V* inserted in the margin in one place[2] the word ἀρξάμενος, which had been omitted, direct from the original (*A*).

3. Vat. gr. 304 was copied from *V*, not from *A*; Tannery inferred this mainly from a collation of the scholia, and he notes that the word ἀρξάμενος above mentioned is here brought into the text by the erasure of some letters. This MS. 304, being very clearly written, was used thenceforward to make copies from. The next five MSS. do not appear to have had any older source.

4. The MS. Parisinus 2379 (Tannery's *C*) was that used by Bachet for his edition. It was written by one Ioannes Hydruntinus after 1545, and has the peculiarity that the first two Books were copied from the MS. Vat. gr. 200 (a MS. of the Planudean class), evidently in order to include the commentary of Planudes, while the MS. Vat. gr. 304 belonging to the pre-Planudes class was followed in the remaining Books, no doubt because it was considered superior. Thus the class of which *C* is the chief representative is a sort of mixed class.

5, 6. Parisinus 2378 = *P*, and Neapolitanus III C 17, were copied by Angelus Vergetius. In the latter Vergetius puts the

[1] The MS. *V* was made up of various MSS. before separated. The old table of contents has Διοφάντου ἀριθμητική· ἁρμονικὰ διάφορα. The ἁρμονικὰ include the *Introduction to Harmony* by Cleonides, but without any author's name. This fact sufficiently explains the error of Ramus in saying, *Schola mathematica*, Bk I. p. 35, "Scripserat et Diophantus harmonica."

[2] Dioph. I. p. 2, 5–6.

numbers Α, Β, Γ, Δ, Ε, Ζ, Η at the top of the pages (as we put headlines) corresponding to the different Books, implying that he regarded the tract on Polygonal Numbers as Book VII.

The other MSS. of the first class call for no notice, and we pass to the Planudean class.

9. Tannery, as he tells us, congratulated himself upon finding in Ambrosianus Et 157 sup. ten pages of the archetype of the class, and eagerly sought for new readings. So far, however, as he was able to carry his collation, he found no difference from the principal representative of the class (B_1) next to be mentioned.

10. The MS. Marcianus 308 ($=B_1$) of the 15th century formerly belonged to Cardinal Bessarion, and was seen by Regiomontanus at Venice in 1464. It contains the recension by Planudes with his commentary.

11. It seems certain that the Wolfenbüttel MS. Guelferbytanus Gudianus 1 (15th c.) was that which Xylander used for his translation; Tannery shows that, if this was not the MS. lent to Xylander by Andreas Dudicius Sbardellatus, that MS. must have been lost, and there is no evidence in support of the latter hypothesis. It is not possible to say whether the Wolfenbüttel MS. was copied from Marcianus 308 (B_1) or from the complete MS. of which Ambrosianus Et 157 sup. preserves the ten leaves.

12. Palatinus gr. 391 (end of 16th c.) has notes in German in the margin which show that it was intended to print from it; it was written either by Xylander himself or for him. It is this MS. of which Claudius Salmasius (Claude de Saumaise, 1588–1653) told Bachet that it contained nothing more than the six Books, with the tract on Polygonal Numbers.

13. Reginensis 128 was copied at the end of the 16th century from the Wolfenbüttel MS.

14, 15. Ambrosianus A 91 sup. and Vaticanus gr. 200 both come from B_1; as they agree in omitting V. 28 of Diophantus, one was copied from the other, probably the latter from the former. They were both copied by the same copyist for Mendoza in 1545. Vat. gr. 200 has headings which make eight Books; according to Tannery the first Book is numbered *α'*, the fourth δ^{ov}; before V. 20 (in Bachet's numbering)—should this be IV. 20?—is the heading *Διοφάντου* ε^{ov}, before the fifth Book *Διοφάντου* ς^{ov}, before the sixth *Διοφάντου* ζ^{ov}, and before the tract on Polygonal Numbers *Διοφάντου* η^{ov}; this wrong division occurs in the next three MSS.

(16, 17, 18 in the diagram), all of which seem to be copied from Vat. 200.

The MSS. numbered 20, 21, 22, 23 in the diagram are of the hybrid class derived from Parisinus 2379 (C). Scorialensis Ω–I–15 and Scorialensis R–II–3, the latter copied from the former, have the first Book divided into two (cf. p. 5 above), and so make seven Books of the *Arithmetica* and an eighth Book of the Polygonal Numbers.

27. The Cracow MS. has the same division into Books as the MSS. last mentioned. According to Gollob, the collation of this MS., so far as it was carried in 1899, showed that it agrees in the main with A (the best MS.), B_1 (Marcianus 308) and C (Parisinus 2379); but, as it contains passages not found in the two latter, it cannot have been copied from either of them.

25. Parisinus 2380 appears to be the copy of Auria's Diophantus mentioned by Schulz as having been in the library of Carl von Montchall and bearing the title "Diophanti libri sex, cum scholiis graecis Maximi Planudae, atque liber de numeris polygonis, collati cum Vaticanis codicibus, et latine versi a Josepho Auria[1]."

The first commentator on Diophantus of whom we hear is Hypatia, the daughter of Theon of Alexandria; she was murdered by Christian fanatics in 415 A.D. According to Suidas she wrote commentaries on Diophantus, on the Astronomical Canon (sc. of Ptolemy) and on the Conics of Apollonius[2]. Tannery suggests that the remarks of Michael Psellus (11th c.) at the beginning of his letter about Diophantus, Anatolius, and the Egyptian method of arithmetical reckoning were taken bodily from some MS. of Diophantus containing an ancient and systematic commentary; and he believes this commentary to have been that of Hypatia. I have already mentioned the attractive hypothesis of Tannery that Hypatia's commentary extended only to our six Books, and that this accounts for the loss of the rest.

Georgius Pachymeres (1240 to about 1310) wrote in Greek a paraphrase of at least a portion of Diophantus. Sections 25–44 of

[1] Schulz, Diophantus, pref. xliii.

[2] Suidas s.v. Ὑπατία: *ἔγραψεν ὑπόμνημα εἰς Διόφαντον, <εἰς> τὸν ἀστρονομικὸν κανόνα, εἰς τὰ κωνικὰ Ἀπολλωνίου ὑπόμνημα.* So Tannery reads, following the best MSS.; he gives ample reasons for rejecting Kuster's conjecture *εἰς Διοφάντου τὸν ἀστρονομικὸν κανόνα*, viz. (1) that the order of words would have been *τὸν Διοφάντου ἀστρονομικὸν κανόνα*, (2) that there is nothing connecting Diophantus with astronomy, while Suidas mentions, s.v. Θέων, a commentary *εἰς τὸν Πτολεμαίου πρόχειρον κανόνα*.

this survive and are published by Tannery in his edition of Diophantus[1]. The chapters lost at the beginning may have contained general observations and introductions to the first two paragraphs of Book I.; section 25 begins with the third paragraph (Def. 1), and the rest of the fragment takes us up to the problem in I. 11.

Soon afterwards Maximus Planudes (about 1260–1310) wrote a systematic commentary on Books I., II. This is also included by Tannery in his edition[2].

There are a number of other ancient scholia, very few of which seemed to Tannery to be worth publication[3].

But in the meantime, and long before the date of Georgius Pachymeres, the work of Diophantus had become known in Arabia, where it was evidently the subject of careful study. We are told in the *Fihrist*, the main part of which was written in the year 987 A.D., (1) that Diophantus was a Greek of Alexandria who wrote a book "On the art of algebra[4]," (2) that Abū'l Wafā al-Būzjānī (940–998) wrote (*a*) a commentary (*tafsīr*) on the algebra of Diophantus and (*b*) a book of "proofs to the propositions used by Diophantus in his book and to that which he himself (Abū'l Wafā) stated in his commentary[5]," (3) that Qusṭā b. Lūqā al-Baʿlabakkī (died about 912) wrote a "commentary on three and a half Books of Diophantus' work on arithmetical problems[6]." Qusṭā b. Lūqā, physician, philosopher, astronomer, mathematician and translator, was the author of works on Euclid and of an "introduction to geometry" in the form of question and answer, and translator of the so-called Books XIV., XV. of Euclid; other Arabian authorities credit him with an actual "translation of the book of Diophantus on Algebra[7]." Lastly, we are told by Ibn abī Uṣaibiʿa of "marginal glosses which Isḥāq b. Yūnis (died about 1077), the physician of Cairo, after Ibn al-Haitham, added to the book of Diophantus on algebraic problems." The title is somewhat obscure; probably Ibn al-Haitham (about 965–1039), who wrote several works on Euclid, wrote a commentary on the *Arithmetica* and Isḥāq b. Yūnis added glosses to this commentary[8].

[1] Dioph. II. pp. 78–122. [2] Dioph. II. pp. 125–255.

[3] The few that he gives are in Vol. II. pp. 256–260; as regards the collection in general cf. Hultsch in *Berliner philologische Wochenschrift*, 1896, p. 615.

[4] *Fihrist*, ed. Suter, p. 22. [5] *ibid.* p. 39. [6] *ibid.* p. 43.

[7] Suter, *Die Mathematiker und Astronomen der Araber*, 1900, p. 41.

[8] Suter, *op. cit.* pp. 107–8. Cf. *Bibliotheca Mathematica* IV$_3$, 1903–4, p. 296.

To Regiomontanus belongs the credit of being the first to call attention to the work of Diophantus as being extant in Greek. We find two notices by him during his sojourn in Italy, whither he journeyed after the death of his teacher Georg von Peurbach, which took place on the 8th April, 1461. In connexion with lectures on the astronomy of Alfraganus which he gave at Padua he delivered an *Oratio introductoria in omnes scientias mathematicas*[1]. In this he observed: "No one has yet translated from the Greek into Latin the fine thirteen Books of Diophantus, in which the very flower of the whole of Arithmetic lies hid, the *ars rei et census* which to-day they call by the Arabic name of Algebra[2]." Secondly, he writes to Bianchini, in answer to a letter dated 5th February, 1464, that he has found at Venice "Diofantus," a Greek arithmetician, who has not yet been translated into Latin; that in his preface Diophantus defines the various powers up to the sixth; but whether he followed out all the combinations of these Regiomontanus does not know: "for not more than six Books are found, though in the preface he promises thirteen. If this book, which is really most wonderful and most difficult, could be found entire, I should like to translate it into Latin, for the knowledge of Greek which I have acquired while staying with my most reverend master [Bessarion] would suffice for this...." He goes on to ask Bianchini to try to discover a complete copy and, in the meantime, to advise him whether he should begin to translate the six Books[3]. The exact date of the *Oratio* is not certain. Regiomontanus made some astronomical observations at Viterbo in the summer and autumn of 1462. He is said to have spent a year at Ferrara, and he seems to have gone thence to Venice. Extant letters of his written at Venice bear dates from 27th July, 1463, to 6th July, 1464, and it may have been from Venice that he made his visit to Padua. At all events the *Oratio* at Padua must have been near in time to the discovery of the MS. at Venice.

Notwithstanding that attention was thus called to the work, it

[1] Printed in the work *Rudimenta astronomica Alfragani*, Nürnberg, 1537.

[2] As the *ars rei et census*, the solution of determinate quadratic equations, is not found in our Diophantus, it would seem that at the time of the *Oratio* Regiomontanus had only looked at the MS. cursorily, if at all.

[3] The letter to Bianchini is given on p. 135 of Ch. Th. v. Murr's *Memorabilia*, Norimbergae, 1786, and partly in Doppelmayer's *Historische Nachricht von den Nürnbergischen Mathematicis und Künstlern* (Nürnberg, 1730), p. 5, note *y*.

seems to have remained practically a closed book from the date of Maximus Planudes to about 1570. Luca Paciuolo, towards the end of the 15th c., Cardano and Tartaglia about the middle of the 16th, make no mention of it. Only Joachim Camerarius, in a letter published in 1556[1], mentions that there is a MS. of Diophantus in the Vatican which he is anxious to see. Rafael Bombelli was the first to find a MS. in the Vatican and to conceive the idea of publishing the work. This was towards 1570, for in his Algebra[2] published in 1572 Bombelli tells us that he had *in the years last past* discovered a Greek book on Algebra written by "a certain Diofantes, an Alexandrine Greek author, who lived in the time of Antoninus Pius"; that, thinking highly of the contents of the work, he and Antonio Maria Pazzi determined to translate it; that they actually translated five books out of the seven into which the MS. was divided; but that, before the rest was finished, they were called away from it by other labours. Bombelli did not carry out his plan of publishing Diophantus in a translation, but he took all the problems of the first four Books and some of those of the fifth, and embodied them in his Algebra, interspersing them with his own problems. He took no pains to distinguish Diophantus' problems from his own; but in the case of the former he adhered pretty closely to the original, so that Bachet admits his obligations to him, remarking that in many cases he found

[1] *De Graecis Latinisque numerorum notis et praeterea Saracenis seu Indicis*, etc. etc., studio Joachimi Camerarii, Papeberg, 1556.

[2] Nesselmann tells us that he has not seen this work but takes his information about it from Cossali. I was fortunate enough to find in the British Museum one of the copies dated 1579 (really the same as the original edition of 1572 except that the title-page and date are new, and a dedicatory letter on pp. 3–8 is reprinted; there were not two separate editions). The title is *L'Algebra, opera di Rafael Bombelli da Bologna diuisa in tre Libri*...... In Bologna, Per Giovanni Rossi, MDLXXIX. The original of the passage from the preface is:

"Questi anni passati, essendosi ritrouato una opera greca di questa disciplina nella libraria di Nostro Signore in Vaticano, composta da un certo Diofante Alessandrino Autor Greco, il quale fù à tempo di Antonin Pio, e havendomela fatta vedere Messer Antonio Maria Pazzi Reggiano, publico lettore delle Matematiche in Roma, e giudicatolo con lui Autore assai intelligente de' numeri (ancorche non tratti de' numeri irrationali, ma solo in lui si vede vn perfetto ordine di operare) egli, ed io, per arrichire il mondo di così fatta opera, ci dessimo à tradurlo, e cinque libri (delli sette che sono) tradutti ne habbiamo; lo restante non hauendo potuto finire per gli trauagli auenuti all' uno, e all' altro; e in detta opera habbiamo ritrouato, ch' egli assai volte cita gli Autori Indiani, col che mi ha fatto conoscere, che questa disciplina appo gl' indiani prima fù, che à gli Arabi." The last words stating that Diophantus often quotes from Indian authors are no doubt due to Bombelli's taking for part of Diophantus the tract of Maximus Planudes about the Indian method of reckoning.

Bombelli's translation better than Xylander's and consequently very useful for the purpose of amending the latter[1].

It may be interesting to mention a few points of notation in this work of Bombelli. At the beginning of Book II. he explains that he uses the word "tanto" to denote the unknown quantity, not "cosa" like his predecessors; and his symbol for it is $\overset{1}{\smile}$, the square of the unknown (x^2) is $\overset{2}{\smile}$, the cube $\overset{3}{\smile}$; and so on. For *plus* and *minus* (*più* and *meno*) he uses the initial letters *p* and *m*. Thus corresponding to $x+6$ we should find in Bombelli $1\overset{1}{\smile}$ *p*. 6, and for x^2+5x-4, $1\overset{2}{\smile}$ *p*. $5\overset{1}{\smile}$ *m*. 4. This notation shows, as will be seen later, some advance upon that of Diophantus in one important respect.

The next writer upon Diophantus was Wilhelm Holzmann who published, under the Graecised form of his name, *Xylander*, by which he is generally known, a work bearing the title: *Diophanti Alexandrini Rerum Arithmeticarum Libri sex, quorum primi duo adiecta habent Scholia Maximi (ut coniectura est) Planudis. Item Liber de Numeris Polygonis seu Multangulis. Opus incomparabile, uerae Arithmeticae Logisticae perfectionem continens, paucis adhuc uisum. A Guil. Xylandro Augustano incredibili labore Latinè redditum, et Commentariis explanatum, inque lucem editum, ad Illustriss. Principem Ludovicum Vuirtembergensem. Basileae per Eusebium Episcopium, et Nicolai Fr. haeredes. MDLXXV.* Xylander was according to his own statement a "public teacher of Aristotelian philosophy in the school at Heidelberg[2]." He was a man of almost universal culture[3], and was so thoroughly imbued with the classical literature, that the extraordinary aptness of his quotations and his wealth of expression give exceptional charm to his writing whenever he is free from the shackles of mathematical formulae and technicalities. The *Epistola Nuncupatoria* is addressed to the Prince Ludwig, and Xylander neatly introduces it by the line "Offerimus numeros, numeri sunt principe digni." This preface is very quaint and interesting. He tells us how he first saw the name of Diophantus mentioned in Suidas, and then found that mention

[1] "Sed suas Diophanteis quaestionibus ita immiscuit, ut has ab illis distinguere non sit in promptu, neque vero se fidum satis interpretem praebuit, cum passim verba Diophanti immutet, hisque pleraque addat, pleraque pro arbitrio detrahat. In multis nihilominus interpretationem Bombellii, Xilandriana praestare, et ad hanc emendandam me adjuvisse ingenue fateor." *Ad lectorem.*

[2] "Publicus philosophiae Aristoteleae in schola Heidelbergensi doctor."

[3] Even Bachet, who, as we shall see, was no favourable critic, calls him "Vir omnibus disciplinis excultus."

had been made of his work by Regiomontanus as being extant in an Italian library and having been seen by him. But, as the book had not been edited, he tried to think no more of it but, instead, to absorb himself in the study of such arithmetical books as he could obtain, and in investigations of his own[1]. Self-taught except in so far as he could learn from published works such as those of Christoff Rudolff (of the "Coss"), Michael Stifel, Cardano, Nuñez, he yet progressed so far as to be able to add to, modify and improve what he found in those works. As a result he fell into what Heraclitus called *οἴησιν, ἱερὰν νόσον*, that is, into the conceit of "being somebody" in the field of Arithmetic and "Logistic"; others too, themselves learned men, thought him an arithmetician of exceptional ability. But when he first became acquainted with the problems of Diophantus (he continues) right reason brought such a reaction that he might well doubt whether he ought previously to have regarded himself as an object of pity or of derision. He considers it therefore worth while to confess publicly his own ignorance at the same time that he tries to interest others in the work of Diophantus, which had so opened his eyes. Before this critical time he was so familiar with methods of dealing with surds that he had actually ventured to add something to the discoveries of others relating to them; the subject of surds was considered to be of great importance in arithmetical questions, and its difficulty

[1] I cannot refrain from quoting the whole of this passage: "Sed cùm ederet nemo: cepi desiderium hoc paulatim in animo consopire, et eorum quos consequi poteram Arithmeticorum librorum cognitione, et meditationibus nostris sepelire. Veritatis porrò apud me est autoritas, ut ei coniunctum etiam cum dedecore meo testimonium lubentissimè perhibeam. Quod Cossica seu Algebrica (cum his enim reliqua comparata, id sunt quod umbrae Homericè in Necya ad animam Tiresiae) ea ergo quòd non assequebar modò, quanquam mutis duntaxat usus preceptoribus caetera *αὐτοδίδακτος*, sed et augere, uariare, adeoque corrigere in loco didicissem, quae summi et fidelissimi in docendo uiri Christifer Rodolphus Silesius, Micaelus Stifelius, Cardanus, Nonius, aliique litteris mandauerant: incidi in *οἴησιν, ἱερὰν νόσον*, ut scitè appellauit Heraclitus sapientior multis aliis philosophis, hoc est, in Arithmetica, et uera Logistica, putaui me esse aliquid: itaque de me passim etiam a multis, iisque doctis uiris iudicatum fuit, me non de grege Arithmeticum esse. Verum ubi primùm in Diophantea incidi: ita me recta ratio circumegit, ut flendúsne mihi ipsi anteà, an uerò ridendus fuissem, haud iniuria dubitauerim. Operae precium est hoc loco et meam inscitiam inuulgare, et Diophantei operis, quod mihi nebulosam istam caliginem ab oculis detersit, immò eos in coenum barbaricum defossos eleuauit et repurgauit, gustum aliquem exhibere. Surdorum ego numerorum tractationem ita tenebam, ut etiam addere aliorum inuentis aliquid non poenitendum auderem, atque id quidem in rebus arithmeticis magnum habetur, et difficultas istarum rerum multos a mathematibus deterret. Quanto autem hoc est praeclarius, in iis problematis, quae surdis etiam numeris uix posse uidentur explicari, rem eo deducere, ut quasi solum arithmeticum uertere iussi obsurdescant illi planè, et ne mentio quidem eorum in tractatione ingeniosissimarum quaestionum admittatur."

was even such as to deter many from the study of mathematics. "But how much more splendid," says Xylander, "in the case of problems which seem to be hardly capable of solution even with the help of surds, to bring the matter to the point that, while the surds, when bidden (so to speak) to plough the arithmetic soil, become true to their name and deaf to entreaty, they are not so much as mentioned in these most ingenious solutions!" He then describes the enormous difficulties which beset his work owing to the corruptions in his text. In dealing, however, with the mistakes and carelessness of copyists he was, as he says, no novice; for proof of which he appeals to his editions of Plutarch, Stephanus and Strabo. This passage, which is good reading, but too long to reproduce here, I give in full in the note[1]. Next Xylander tells us how he came to get possession of a manuscript of Diophantus. In October of the year 1571 he made a journey to Wittenberg; while there he had conversations on mathematical subjects with two professors, Sebastian Theodoric and Wolfgang Schuler by name, who showed him a few pages of a Greek

[1] "Id uerò mihi accidit durum et uix superabile incommodum, quòd mirificè deprauata omnia inueni, cùm neque problematum expositio interdum integra esset, ac passim numeri (in quibus sita omnia esse in hoc argumento, quis ignorat?) tam problematum quàm solutionum siue explicationum corruptissimi. Non pudebit me ingenuè fateri, qualem me heic gesserim. Audacter, et summo cum feruore potius quàm alacritate animi opus ipsum initio sum aggressus, laborque mihi omnis uoluptati fuit, tantus est meus rerum arithmeticarum amor. quin et gratiam magnam me apud omnes liberalium scientiarum amatores ac patronos initurum, et praeclare de rep. litteraria meriturum intelligebam, eamque rem mihi laudi (quam à bonis profectam nemo prudens aspernatur) gloriaeque fortasse etiam emolumento fore sperabam. Progressus aliquantulum, in salebras incidi: quae tantum abest ut alacritatem meam retuderint, ut etiam animos mihi addiderint, neque enim mihi novum aut insolens est aduersus librariorum incuriam certamen, et hac in re militaui, (ut Horatii nostri uerbis utar) non sine gloria. quod me non arroganter dicere, Dio, Plutarchus, Strabo, Stephanusque nostri testantur. Sed cum mox in ipsum pelagus monstris scatens me cursus abripuit: non despondi equidem animum, neque manus dedi, sed tamen saepius ad oram unde soluissem respexi, quàm portum in quem esset euadendum cogitando prospicerem, depraehendique non minus uerè quàm eleganter ea cecinisse Alcaeum, quae (si possum) Latinè in hac quasi uotiua mea tabula scribam.

Qui uela uentis uult dare, dum licet,
Cautus futuri praeuideat modum
Cursus. mare ingressus, marino
Nauiget arbitrio necesse est.

Sanè quod de Echeneide pisce fertur, eum nauim cui se adplicet remorari, poenè credibile fecit mihi mea cymba tot mendorum remoris retardata. Expediui tamen me ita, ut facilè omnes mediocri de his rebus iudicio praediti, intellecturi sint incredibilem me laborem et aerumnas difficilimas superasse: pudore etiam stimulatum oneris quod ultro mihi imposuissem, non perferendi. Paucula quaedam non planè explicata, studio et certis de causis in alium locum reiecimus. Opus quidem ipsum ita absoluimus ut neque eius nos pudere debeat, et Arithmeticae Logisticesque studiosi nobis se plurimum debere sint haud dubie professuri."

manuscript of Diophantus and informed him that it belonged to Andreas Dudicius whom Xylander describes as "Andreas Dudicius Sbardellatus, hoc tempore Imperatoris Romanorum apud Polonos orator." On his departure from Wittenberg Xylander wrote out and took with him the solution of a single problem of Diophantus, to amuse himself with on his journey. This he showed at Leipzig to Simon Simonius Lucensis, a professor at that place, who wrote to Dudicius on his behalf. A few months afterwards Dudicius sent the MS. to Xylander and encouraged him to persevere in his undertaking to translate the *Arithmetica* into Latin. Accordingly Xylander insists that the glory of the whole achievement belongs in no less but rather in a greater degree to Dudicius than to himself. Finally he commends the work to the favour of Prince Ludwig, extolling the pursuit of arithmetical and algebraical science and dwelling in enthusiastic anticipation on the influence which the Prince's patronage would have in helping and advancing the study of Arithmetic[1]. This *Epistola Nuncupatoria* bears the date 14th August, 1574[2]. Xylander died on the 10th of February in the year following that of the publication, 1576.

Tannery has shown that the MS. used by Xylander was Guelferbytanus Gudianus I. Bachet observes that he has not been able to find out whether Xylander ever published the Greek text, though parts of his commentary seem to imply that he had, or at least intended to do so. It is now clear that he intended to bring out the text, but did not carry out his intention. Tannery observes that the MS. Palatinus gr. 391 seems to have been written either by Xylander himself or for him, and there are German notes in the margin showing that it was intended to print from it.

Xylander's achievement has been, as a rule, quite inadequately appreciated. Very few writers on Diophantus seem to have studied the book itself: a fact which may be partly accounted for by its rarity. Even Nesselmann, whose book appeared in 1842, says that he has never been able to find a copy. Nesselmann however seems to have come nearest to a proper appreciation of the value of the work: he says "Xylander's work remains, in spite of the various

[1] "Hoc non modò tibi, Princeps Illustrissime, honorificum erit, atque gloriosum; sed te labores nostros approbante, arithmeticae studium cùm alibi, tum in tua Academia et Gymnasiis, excitabitur, confirmabitur, prouehetur, et ad perfectam eius scientiam multi tuis auspiciis, nostro labore perducti, magnam hac re tuis in remp. beneficiis accessionem factam esse gratissima commemoratione praedicabunt."

[2] "Heidelberga. postrid. Eidus Sextiles CIↃ IↃ LXXIV."

defects which are unavoidable in a first edition of so difficult an author, especially when based on only one MS. and that full of errors, a highly meritorious achievement, and does not deserve the severe strictures which it has sometimes had passed upon it. It is true that Xylander has in many places not understood his author, and has misrepresented him in others; his translation is often rough and un-Latin, this being due to a too conscientious adherence to the actual wording of the original; but the result was none the less brilliant on that account. The mathematical public was put in possession of Diophantus' work, and the appearance of the translation had an immediate and enormous influence on the development and shaping of Algebra[1]." As a rule, the accounts of Xylander's work seem to have been based on what Bachet says about it and about his obligations to it. When I came to read Bachet myself and saw how disparaging, as a rule, his remarks upon Xylander were, I could not but suspect that they were unfair. His repeated and almost violent repudiation of obligation to Xylander suggested to me the very thing which he disclaimed, that he was under too great obligation to his predecessor to acknowledge it duly. I was therefore delighted at my good fortune in finding in the Library of Trinity College, Cambridge, a copy of Xylander, and so being able to judge for myself of the relation of the later to the earlier work. The result was to confirm entirely what I had suspected as to the unfair attitude taken up by Bachet towards his predecessor. I found it everywhere; even where it is obvious that Xylander's mistakes or difficulties are due only to the hopeless state of his solitary MS. Bachet seems to make no allowance for the fact. The truth is that Bachet's work could not have been as good as it was but for the pioneer work of Xylander; and it is the great blot in Bachet's otherwise excellent edition that he did not see fit to acknowledge the fact.

I must now pass to Bachet's work itself. It was the first edition published which contained the Greek text, and appeared in 1621 bearing the title: *Diophanti Alexandrini Arithmeticorum libri sex, et de numeris multangulis liber unus. Nunc primùm Graecè et Latinè editi, atque absolutissimis Commentariis illustrati. Auctore Claudio Gaspare Bacheto Meziriaco Sebusiano, V.C. Lutetiae Parisiorum, Sumptibus Hieronymi Drovart*[2], *via Jacobaea, sub Scuto*

[1] Nesselmann, p. 279–80.

[2] For "sumptibus Hieronymi Drovart etc." some copies have "sumptibus Sebastiani

Solari. MDCXXI. Bachet's Greek text is based, as he tells us, upon a MS. which he calls "codex Regius," now in the Bibliothèque Nationale at Paris (Parisinus 2379); this MS. is his sole authority, except that Jacobus Sirmondus had part of a Vatican MS. (Vat. gr. 304) transcribed for him. He professes to have produced a good Greek text, having spent incalculable labour upon its emendation, to have inserted in brackets all additions which he made to it, and to have given notice of all corrections, except those of an obvious or trifling nature; a few passages he has left asterisked, in cases where correction could not be safely ventured upon. He is careful to tell us what previous works relating to the subject he had been able to consult. First he mentions Xylander (he spells the name as X*i*lander throughout), who had translated the whole of Diophantus, and commented upon him throughout, "except that he scarcely touched a considerable part of the fifth book, the whole of the sixth and the treatise on multangular numbers, and even the rest of his work was not very successful, as he himself admits that he did not thoroughly understand a number of points." Then he speaks of Bombelli (as already mentioned) and of the *Zetetica* of Vieta (in which the author treats in his own way a large number of Diophantus' problems: Bachet thinks that he so treated them because he despaired of restoring the book completely). Neither Bombelli nor Vieta (says Bachet) made any attempt to demonstrate the difficult porisms and abstruse theorems in numbers which Diophantus assumes as known in many places, or sufficiently explained the causes of his operations and artifices. All these omissions on the part of his predecessors he thinks he has supplied in his notes to the various problems and in the three books of "Porisms" which he prefixed to the work[1]. As regards his Latin translation, he says that he gives us Diophantus in Latin from the version of Xylander most carefully corrected, in which he would have us know that he has done two things in particular, first,

Cramoisy, via Jacobaea, sub Ciconiis." The copy (from the Library of Trinity College, Cambridge) which I used in preparing my first edition has the former words; a copy in the Library of the Athenaeum Club has the latter.

[1] On the nature of some of Bachet's proofs Nicholas Saunderson (formerly Lucasian Professor) remarks in *Elements of Algebra*, 1740, àpropos of Dioph. III. 15: "M. Bachet indeed in the 16th and 17th props. of his second book of Porisms has given us demonstrations, such as they are, of the theorems in the problem: but in the first place he demonstrates but one single case of those theorems, and in the next place the demonstrations he gives are only synthetical, and so abominably perplexed withal, that in each demonstration he makes use of all the letters in the alphabet except I and O, singly to represent the quantities he has there occasion for."

corrected what was wrong and filled the numerous lacunae, secondly, explained more clearly what Xylander had given in obscure or ambiguous language; "I confess however," he says, "that this made so much change necessary, that it is almost fairer to attribute the translation to me than to Xilander. But if anyone prefers to consider it as his, because I have held fast, tooth and nail, to his words when they do not misrepresent Diophantus, I have no objection[1]." Such sentences as these, which are no rarity in Bachet's book, are certainly not calculated to increase our respect for the author. According to Montucla[2], "the historian of the French Academy tells us" that Bachet worked at this edition during the course of a quartan fever, and that he himself said that, disheartened as he was by the difficulty of the work, he would never have completed it, had it not been for the stubbornness which his malady generated in him.

As the first edition of the Greek text of Diophantus, this work, in spite of any imperfections we may find in it, does its author all honour.

The same edition was reprinted and published with the addition of Fermat's notes in 1670: *Diophanti Alexandrini Arithmeticorum libri sex, et de numeris multangulis liber unus. Cum commentariis C. G. Bacheti V.C. et obseruationibus D. P. de Fermat Senatoris Tolosani. Accessit Doctrinae Analyticae inuentum nouum, collectum ex variis eiusdem D. de Fermat Epistolis. Tolosae, Excudebat Bernardus Bosc, è Regione Collegii Societatis Jesu. MDCLXX.* This edition was not published by Fermat himself, but by his son after his death. S. Fermat tells us in the preface that this publication of Fermat's notes to Diophantus[3] was part of an attempt to collect together from his letters and elsewhere his contributions to mathematics. The "Doctrinae Analyticae Inuentum nouum" is a collection made by Jacobus de Billy[4]

[1] Deinde Latinum damus tibi Diophantum ex Xilandri versione accuratissimè castigata, in qua duo potissimum nos praestitisse scias velim, nam et deprauata correximus, hiantesque passim lacunas repleuimus: et quae subobscurè, vel ambiguè fuerat interpretatus Xilander, dilucidius exposuimus; fateor tamen, inde tantam inductam esse mutationem, vt propemodum aequius sit versionem istam nobis quàm Xilandro tribuere. Si quis autem potius ad eum pertinere contendat, quòd eius verba, quatenus Diophanto fraudi non erant, mordicus retinuimus, per me licet."

[2] I. 323.

[3] Now published in *Œuvres de Fermat* by P. Tannery and C. Henry, Vol. I. (1891), pp. 289–342 (the Latin original), and Vol. III. (1896), pp. 241–274 (French translation).

[4] Now published in *Œuvres de Fermat*, III. 323–398 (French translation). De Billy had already published in 1660 a book under the title *Diophantus geometra sive opus contextum ex arithmetica et geometria.*

from various letters which Fermat sent to him at different times. The notes upon Diophantus' problems, which his son hopes will prove of value very much more than commensurate with their bulk, were (he says) collected from the margin of his copy of Diophantus. From their brevity they were obviously intended for the benefit of experts[1], or even perhaps solely for Fermat's own, he being a man who preferred the pleasure which he had in the work itself to any reputation which it might bring him. Fermat never cared to publish his investigations, but was always perfectly ready, as we see from his letters, to acquaint his friends and contemporaries with his results. Of the notes themselves this is not the place to speak in detail. This edition of Diophantus is rendered valuable only by the additions in it due to Fermat; for the rest it is a mere reprint of that of 1621. So far as the Greek text is concerned, it is very much inferior to the first edition. There is a far greater number of misprints, omissions of words, confusions of numerals; and, most serious of all, the brackets which Bachet inserted in the edition of 1621 to mark the insertion of words in the text are in this later edition altogether omitted. These imperfections have been already noticed by Nesselmann[2]. Thus the reprinted edition of 1670 is untrustworthy as regards the text.

In 1585 Simon Stevin published a French version of the first four books of Diophantus[3]. It was based on Xylander and was a free reproduction, not a translation, Stevin himself observing that the MS. used by Xylander was so full of mistakes that the text of

[1] *Lectori Beneuolo*, p. iii: "Doctis tantum quibus pauca sufficiunt, harum obseruationum auctor scribebat, vel potius ipse sibi scribens, his studiis exerceri malebat quam gloriari; adeo autem ille ab omni ostentatione alienus erat, vt nec lucubrationes suas typis mandari curauerit, et suorum quandoque responsorum autographa nullo seruato exemplari petentibus vltrò miserit; norunt scilicet plerique celeberrimorum huius saeculi Geometrarum, quam libenter ille et quantâ humanitate, sua iis inuenta patefecerit."

[2] "Was dieser Abdruck an äusserer Eleganz gewonnen hat (denn die Bachet'sche Ausgabe ist mit äusserst unangenehmen, namentlich Griechischen Lettern gedruckt), das hat sie an innerm Werthe in Bezug auf den Text verloren. Sie ist nicht bloss voller Druckfehler in einzelnen Worten und Zeichen (z. B. durchgehends π statt ϡ, 900) sondern auch ganze Zeilen sind ausgelassen oder doppelt gedruckt (z. B. III. 12 eine Zeile doppelt, IV. 25 eine doppelt und gleich hinterher eine ausgelassen, IV. 52 eine doppelt, V. 11 eine ausgelassen, desgleichen V. 14, 25, 33, VI. 8, 13 und so weiter), die Zahlen verstümmelt, was aber das Aergste ist, die Bachet'schen kritischen Zeichen sind fast überall, die Klammer durchgängig weggefallen, so dass diese Ausgabe als Text des Diophant völlig unbrauchbar geworden ist," p. 283.

[3] Included in *L'Arithmetique de Simon Stevin de Bruges*...A Leyde, De l'Imprimerie de Christophle Plantin, CIↃ . IↃ . LXXXV.

Diophantus could not be given word for word[1]. Albert Girard added the fifth and sixth books to the four, and this complete version appeared in 1625[2].

In 1810 was published an excellent translation (with additions) of the fragment upon Polygonal Numbers by Poselger: *Diophantus von Alexandrien über die Polygonal-Zahlen. Uebersetzt mit Zusätzen von F. Th. Poselger. Leipzig*, 1810.

In 1822 Otto Schulz, professor in Berlin, published a very meritorious German translation with notes: *Diophantus von Alexandria arithmetische Aufgaben nebst dessen Schrift über die Polygon-Zahlen. Aus dem Griechischen übersetzt und mit Anmerkungen begleitet von Otto Schulz, Professor am Berlinisch-Cölnischen Gymnasium zum grauen Kloster. Berlin*, 1822. *In der Schlesingerschen Buch- und Musikhandlung.* The work of Poselger just mentioned was with the consent of its author incorporated in Schulz's edition along with his own translation and notes upon the larger treatise, the *Arithmetica.* According to Nesselmann Schulz was not a mathematician by profession; he produced, however, a thoroughly useful edition, with notes chiefly upon the matter of Diophantus and not on the text (with the exception of a very few emendations): notes which, almost invariably correct, help much to understand the author. Schulz's translation is based upon the edition of Bachet's text published in 1670.

Another German translation was published by G. Wertheim in 1890: *Die Arithmetik und die Schrift über Polygonalzahlen des Diophantus von Alexandria. Übersetzt und mit Anmerkungen begleitet von G. Wertheim* (Teubner). Though it appeared before the issue of Tannery's definitive text, it is an excellent translation, the translator being thoroughly equipped for his task; it is valuable also as containing Fermat's notes, also translated into German, with a large number of other notes by the translator elucidating both Diophantus and Fermat, and generalising a number of the problems which, with very few exceptions, receive only particular solutions from Diophantus himself. Wertheim has also included 46 epigram-problems from the Greek anthology and the enunciation of the famous Cattle-Problem attributed to Archimedes.

[1] See *Bibliotheca Mathematica* VII$_3$, 1906–7, p. 59.

[2] *L'Arithmetique de Simon Stevin de Brvges, Reueuë, corrigee & augmentee de plusieurs traictez et annotation par Albert Girard Samielois Mathematicien.* A Leide, de l'Imprimerie des Elzeviers CIↃ.IↃ.CXXV. Reproduced in the edition of *Les Œuvres Mathematiques de Simon Stevin de Bruges. Par Albert Girard.* Leyde, CIↃ.IↃ.CXXXIV.

No description is necessary of the latest edition, by Tannery, in which we at last have a definitive Greek text of Diophantus with the ancient commentaries, etc., *Diophanti Alexandrini opera omnia cum Graecis commentariis. Edidit et Latine interpretatus est Paulus Tannery* (Teubner). The first volume (1893) contains the text of Diophantus, the second (1895) the Pseudepigrapha, Testimonia veterum, Pachymeres' paraphrase, Planudes' commentary, various ancient scholia, etc., and 38 arithmetical epigrams in the original Greek with scholia. Any further edition will necessarily be based on Tannery, who has added all that is required in the shape of introductions, etc.

Lastly we hear of other works on Diophantus which, if they were ever written, are lost or remain unpublished. First, we find it asserted by Vossius (as some have understood him) that the Englishman John Pell wrote an unpublished Commentary upon Diophantus. John Pell (1611–1685) was at one time professor of mathematics at Amsterdam and gave lectures there on Diophantus, but what Vossius says about his commentary may well be only a recommendation to undertake a commentary, rather than a historical assertion of its completion. Secondly, Schulz states in his preface that he had lately found a note in Schmeisser's *Orthodidaktik der Mathematik* that Hofrath Kausler by command of the Russian Academy prepared an edition of Diophantus[1]. This seems however to be a misapprehension on the part of Schulz. Kausler is probably referring, not to a translation of Diophantus, but to his memoir of 1798 published in *Nova Acta Acad. Petropol.* XI. p. 125, which might easily be described as an *Ausarbeitung* of Diophantus' work.

I find a statement in the *New American Cyclopaedia* (New York, D. Appleton and Company), Vol. VI., that "a complete translation of his (Diophantus') works into English was made by the late Miss Abigail Lousada, but has not been published."

[1] The whole passage of Schmeisser is: "Die mechanische, geistlose Behandlung der Algebra ist ins besondere von Herrn Hofrath Kausler stark gerügt worden. In der Vorrede zu seiner Ausgabe des *Uflakerschen Exempelbuchs* beginnt er so: 'Seit mehreren Jahren arbeitete ich für die Russisch-Kaiserliche Akademie der Wissenschaften Diophants unsterbliches Werk über die Arithmetik aus, und fand darin einen solchen Schatz von den feinsten, scharfsinnigsten algebraischen Auflösungen, dass mir die mechanische, geistlose Methode der neuen Algebra mit jedem Tage mehr ekelte u.s.w.'" (p. 33).

CHAPTER III

NOTATION AND DEFINITIONS OF DIOPHANTUS

As it is my intention, for the sake of brevity and perspicuity, to make use of the modern algebraical notation in giving my account of Diophantus' problems and general methods, it is necessary to describe once for all the machinery which our author uses for working out the solutions of his problems, or the notation by which he expresses such relations as would be represented in our time by algebraical equations, and, in particular, to illustrate the extent to which he is able to manipulate unknown quantities. Apart, however, from the necessity of such a description for the proper and adequate comprehension of Diophantus, the general question of the historical development of algebraical notation possesses great intrinsic interest. Into the general history of this subject I cannot enter in this essay, my object being the elucidation of Diophantus; I shall accordingly in general confine myself to an account of his notation solely, except in so far as it is interesting to compare it with the corresponding notation of his editors and (in certain cases) that of other writers, as, for example, certain of the early Arabian algebraists.

First, as to the representation of an unknown quantity. The unknown quantity, which Diophantus defines as containing *πλῆθος μονάδων ἀόριστον*, *i.e.* an undefined number of units (def. 2), is denoted throughout by what was printed in the editions before Tannery's as the Greek letter ς with an accent, thus ς′, or in the form ς^{ό}. This symbol in verbal description he calls *ὁ ἀριθμός*, "the number," *i.e.*, by implication, the number *par excellence* of the problem in question. In the cases where the symbol is used to denote inflected forms, *e.g.*, the accusative singular or the dative plural, the terminations which would have been added to the stem of the full word *ἀριθμός* were printed above the symbol ς in the manner of an exponent, thus ϛ'' (for ἀριθμόν, as τ'' for τόν), ϛ^{οῦ}, the symbol being in addition doubled in the plural cases, thus ϛϛ^{οί}, ϛϛ^{ούς}, ϛϛ^{ῶν}, ϛϛ^{οῖς}, for ἀριθμοί κ.τ.έ. When the symbol is used in practice, the coefficient is expressed by putting the required Greek numeral immediately after it, thus ϛϛ^{οὶ} $\overline{ια}$ corresponds to $11x$, ϛ' $\bar{α}$ to x and so on.

Tannery discusses the question whether in the archetype (a) of the MSS. this duplication of the sign for the plural and this addition of the terminations of the various cases really occurred[1]. He observes that any one accustomed to reading Greek MSS. will admit that the marks of cases are common in the later MSS. but are very frequently omitted in the more ancient. Further, the practice of duplicating a sign to express the plural is more ancient than that of adding the case-terminations. Tannery concludes that the case-terminations (like the final syllables of abbreviations used for other words) were very generally, if not always, wanting in the archetype (a). If this seems inconsistent with the regularity with which they appear in our MSS., it is has to be remembered that A and B_1 do not represent the archetype (a) but the readings of α, the copyist of which probably took it upon himself to substitute the full word for the sign or to add the case-terminations. Tannery's main argument is the frequent occurrence of instances where the wrong case-ending has been added, *e.g.*, the nominative for the genitive; the conclusion is also confirmed by instances in which different cases of the word ἀριθμός, *e.g.* ἀριθμοῦ, ἀριθμόν, and even ἀριθμῶν written in full are put by mistake for καί owing to the resemblance between the common abbreviation for καί and the sign for ἀριθμός, and of course in such cases the abbreviation would not have had the endings. As regards the duplication of the sign for the plural, Tannery admits that this was the practice of the Byzantines; but he considers that the evidence is against supposing that Diophantus duplicated the sign; he does not do so with any other of his technical abbreviations, those for μονάς, δύναμις, etc. Accordingly in his text of Diophantus Tannery has omitted the case-endings and written the single sign for ἀριθμός whether in the singular or in the plural; in his second volume, however, containing the scholia, etc., he has retained the duplicated sign.

On the assumption that the sign was the Greek final sigma, it was natural that Nesselmann should explain it by the supposition

[1] Dioph. II. pp. xxxiv–xxxix.

that Diophantus, in search of a convenient symbol for his unknown quantity, would select the only letter of the Greek alphabet which was not already appropriated as a numeral[1]. But he made the acute observation[2] that, as the symbol occurred in many places (of course in Bachet's text) for *ἀριθμός* used in the ordinary untechnical sense, and was therefore, as it appeared, not exclusively used to designate the unknown quantity, the technical *ἀριθμός*, it must after all be more of the nature of an abbreviation than an algebraical symbol like our *x*. It is true that this uncertainty in the use of the sign in the MSS. is put an end to by Tannery, who uses it for the technical *ἀριθμός* alone and writes the untechnical *ἀριθμός* in full; but, even if Diophantus' practice was as strict as this, I do not think this argues any difference in the nature of the abbreviation. There is also a doubt whether the final sigma, ς, was developed as distinct from the form *σ* so early as the date of the MSS. of Diophantus, or rather so early as the first copy of his work, if the author himself really gave the explanation of the sign as found in our text of his second definition. These considerations suggested to me that the sign was not the final sigma at all, but must be explained in some other way. I had to look for confirmation of this to the precise shape of the sign as found in extant MSS. The only MS. which I had the opportunity of inspecting personally was the MS. of the first ten problems of Diophantus in the Bodleian; but here I found strong confirmation of my view in the fact that the sign appeared as ’ς̄, quite different in shape from, and much larger than, the final sigma at the end of words in the same MS. (There is in the Oxford MS. the same irregularity as was pointed out by Nesselmann in the use of the sign sometimes for the technical, and sometimes for the untechnical, *ἀριθμός*[3].) But I found evidence that the sign appeared elsewhere in somewhat different forms. Thus Rodet in the *Journal Asiatique* of January, 1878, quoted certain passages from Diophantus for the purpose of comparison with the algebra of Muḥammad b. Mūsā al-Khuwārazmī. Rodet says he copied these passages exactly from Bachet's MS.; but, while he generally gives the sign as the final sigma, he has in one case ϥϥ^οι for *ἀριθμοί*. In this last case

[1] Nesselmann, pp. 290–1. [2] *ibid.* pp. 300–1.

[3] An extreme case is *ἔταξα τὸ τοῦ δευτέρου* ’ς̄ *ἀριθμοῦ ἑνός*, where the sign (contrary to what would be expected) means the untechnical *ἀριθμός*, and the technical is written in full. Also in the definition *ὁ δὲ μηδὲν τούτων τῶν ἰδιωμάτων κτησάμενος...ἀριθμὸς καλεῖται* the word *ἀριθμός* is itself denoted by the symbol, showing that the word and the symbol are absolutely convertible.

Bachet himself reads ϛϛ^οι. But the same form ΥΥ^οι which Rodet gives is actually found in three places in Bachet's own edition. (1) In his note to IV. 3 he gives a reading from his own MS. which he has corrected in his own text and in which the signs Υᾱ and ΥΥη̄ occur, evidently meaning ἀριθμὸς ᾱ and ἀριθμοὶ η̄, though the sign should have been that for ἀριθμοστόν (= $1/x$). (2) In the text of IV. 13 there is a sentence (marked by Bachet as interpolated) which contains the expression ΥΥϛ̄, where the context again shows that ΥΥ is for ἀριθμοί. (3) At the beginning of V. 9 there is a difficulty in the text, and Bachet notes that his MS. has μήτε ὁ διπλασίων αὐτοῦ Υ where a Vatican MS. reads ἀριθμόν (Xylander notes that his MS. had in this place μήτε ὁ διπλασίων αὐτοῦ ἀρ μō ᾱ ...). It is thus clear that the MS. (Paris. 2379) which Bachet used sometimes has the sign for ἀριθμός in a form which is at least sufficiently like Υ to be taken for it. Tannery states that the form of the sign found in the Madrid MS. (A) is Υ, while B_1 has it in a form (ς) nearly approaching Bachet's reproduction of it.

It appeared also that the use of the sign, or something like it, was not confined to MSS. of Diophantus; on reference to Gardthausen, *Griechische Palaeographie*, I found under the head "hieroglyphisch-conventionell" an abbreviation ς̊, ς̊ς for ἀριθμός, -οί, which is given as occurring in the Bodleian MS. of Euclid (D'Orville 301) of the 9th century. Similarly Lehmann[1] notes as a sign for ἀριθμός found in that MS. a curved line similar to that which was used as an abbreviation for καί. He adds that the ending is placed above it and the sign is doubled for the plural. Lehmann's facsimile is like the form given by Gardthausen, but has the angle a little more rounded. The form ΥΥ^οι above mentioned is also given by Lehmann, with the remark that it seems to be only a modification of the other. Again, from the critical notes to Heiberg's texts of the *Arenarius* of Archimedes it is clear that the sign for ἀριθμός occurred several times in the MSS. in a form approximating to that of the final sigma, and that there was the usual confusion caused by the similarity of the signs for ἀριθμός and καί[2]. In Hultsch's edition of Heron, similarly, the critical notes to the *Geodaesia* show that one MS. had an abbreviation for

[1] Lehmann, *Die tachygraphischen Abkürzungen der griechischen Handschriften*, 1880, p. 107: "Von Sigeln, welchen ich auch anderwärts begegnet bin, sind zu nennen ἀριθμός, das in der Oxforder Euclidhandschrift mit einer der Note καί ähnlichen Schlangenlinie bezeichnet wird."

[2] Cf. Heiberg, *Quaestiones Archimedeae*, pp. 172, 174, 187, 188, 191, 192; *Archimedis opera omnia*, II., pp. 268 sqq.

ἀριθμός in various forms with the case-endings superposed; sometimes they resembled the letter ζ, sometimes ρ, sometimes ○ and once ξ[1]. Lastly, the sign for ἀριθμός resembling the final sigma evidently appeared in a MS. of Theon of Smyrna[2].

All these facts strongly support the assumption that the sign was a mere tachygraphic abbreviation and not an algebraical symbol like our *x*, though discharging much the same function. The next question is, what is its origin? The facts (1) that the sign has the breathing prefixed in the Bodleian MS., which writes 'ς° for ἀριθμός, and (2) that in one place Xylander's MS. read ἀρ for the full word, suggested to me the question whether it could be a contraction of the first two letters of ἀριθμός; and, on consideration, this seemed to me quite possible when I found a contraction for αρ given by Gardthausen, namely αρ. It is easy to see that a simplification of this in different ways would readily produce signs like the different forms shown above. This then was the hypothesis which I put forward twenty-five years ago, and which I still hold to be the easiest and best explanation. Two alternatives are possible. (1) Diophantus may not have made the contraction himself. In that case I suppose the sign to be a cursive contraction made by scribes; and I conceive it to have come about through the intermediate form ϛ. The loss of the downward stroke, or of the loop, would produce a close approximation to the forms which we know. (2) Diophantus may have used a sign approximately, if not exactly, like that which we find in the MSS. For it is from a papyrus of 154 A.D., in writing of the class which Gardthausen calls the "Majuskelcursive," that the contraction αρ for the two letters is taken. The great advantage of my hypothesis is that it makes the sign for ἀριθμός exactly parallel to those for the powers of the unknown, *e.g.*, Δ^{Y} for δύναμις and K^{Y} for κύβος, and to that for the unit μονάς which is denoted by $\overset{o}{M}$, with the sole difference that the letters coalesce into one instead of being written separately.

Tannery's views on the subject are, I think, not very consistent, and certainly they do not commend themselves to me. He seems to suggest that the sign is the ancient letter Koppa, perhaps slightly modified; he first says that the sign in Diophantus is peculiar to him and that, although the word ἀριθμός is very often

[1] Heron, ed. Hultsch, pp. 146, 148, 149, 150.
[2] Theon of Smyrna, ed. Hiller, p. 56, critical notes.

represented in mathematical MSS. by an abbreviation, it has much oftener the form ϙ or something similar, closely resembling the ancient Koppa. In the next sentence he seems to say that "on the contrary the Diophantine abbreviation is an inverted digamma"; yet lower down he says that the copyist of α (copied from the archetype *a*) got the form ϥ by simplifying the more complicated Koppa. And, just before the last remark, he has stated that in the archetype *a* the form must have been ƨ or very like it, as is shown by the confusion with the sign for καί. (If this is so, it can hardly have been peculiar to Diophantus, seeing that the same confusion occurs fairly often in the MSS. of other authors, as above shown.) I think the last consideration (the confusion with καί) is very much against the Koppa-hypothesis; and, in any case, it seems to me very unlikely that a sign would be used by Diophantus for the unknown which was already appropriated to the number 90. And I confess I am unable to see in the sign any resemblance to an inverted digamma.

Hultsch[1] regards it as not impossible that Diophantus may have adopted one of the signs used by the Egyptians for their unknown quantity *hau*, which, if turned round from left to right, would give ϒ; but here again I see no particular resemblance. Prof. D'Arcy Thompson[2] has a suggestion that the sign might be the first letter of σωρός, a heap. But, apart from the fact that the *final* sigma (ς) is not that first letter, there is no trace whatever in Diophantus of such a use of the word σωρός; and, when Pachymeres[3] speaks of a number being σωρεία μονάδων, he means no more than the πλῆθος μονάδων which he is explaining: his words have no connexion with the Egyptian *hau*.

Notwithstanding that the sign is not the final sigma, I shall not hesitate to use ς for it in the sequel, for convenience of printing. Tannery prints it rather differently as ƨ.

We pass to the notation which Diophantus used to express the different powers of the unknown quantity, corresponding to x^2, x^3, and so on. He calls the square of the unknown quantity δύναμις, and denotes it by the abbreviation Δ^{Y}. The word δύναμις, literally "power," is constantly used in Greek mathematics for

[1] Art. Diophantus in Pauly-Wissowa's *Real-Encyclopädie der classischen Altertumswissenschaften*.

[2] *Transactions of the Royal Society of Edinburgh*, Vol. XXXVIII. (1896), pp. 607–9.

[3] Dioph. II. p. 78, 4. Cf. Iamblichus, ed. Pistelli, p. 7, 7; 34, 3; 81, 14, where σωρεία is similarly used to elucidate πλῆθος.

square[1]. With Diophantus, however, it is not any square, but only the square of the unknown; where he speaks of any particular square number, it is τετράγωνος ἀριθμός. The higher powers of the unknown quantity which Diophantus makes use of he calls κύβος, δυναμοδύναμις, δυναμόκυβος, κυβόκυβος, corresponding respectively to x^3, x^4, x^5, x^6. Beyond the sixth power he does not go, having no occasion for higher powers in the solutions of his problems. For these powers he uses the abbreviations K^{Y}, $\Delta^{Y}\Delta$, ΔK^{Y}, $K^{Y}K$ respectively. There is a difference between Diophantus' use of the word δύναμις and of the complete words for the third and higher powers, namely that the latter are not always restricted like δύναμις to powers of the *unknown*, but may denote powers of ordinary known numbers as well. This is no doubt owing to the fact that, while there are two words δύναμις and τετράγωνος which both signify "square," there is only one word for a third power, namely κύβος. It is important, however, to observe that the abbreviations K^{Y}, $\Delta^{Y}\Delta$, ΔK^{Y}, $K^{Y}K$, are, like δύναμις and Δ^{Y}, *only* used to denote powers of the unknown. The coefficients of the different powers of the unknown, like that of the unknown itself, are expressed by the addition of the Greek letters denoting numerals, *e.g.*, $\Delta K^{Y}\ \overline{\kappa\varsigma}$ corresponds to $26x^5$. Thus in Diophantus' system of notation the signs Δ^{Y} and the rest represent not merely the exponent of a power like the 2 in x^2, but the whole expression x^2. There is no obvious connexion between the symbol Δ^{Y} and the symbol ς of which it is the square, as there is between x^2 and x, and in this lies the great inconvenience of the notation. But upon this notation no advance was made by Xylander, or even by Bachet and Fermat. They wrote N (which was short for *Numerus*) for the ς of Diophantus, Q (*Quadratus*) for Δ^{Y}, C (*Cubus*) for K^{Y}, so that we find, for example, $1Q + 5N = 24$, corresponding to $x^2 + 5x = 24$. Other symbols were however used even before the publication of Xylander's Diophantus, *e.g.* in Bombelli's Algebra. Bombelli denotes the unknown and its powers by the symbols $\overset{1}{\smile}$ $\overset{2}{\smile}$, $\overset{3}{\smile}$, and so on. But it is certain that up to this time (1572) the common symbols had been R (*Radix* or *Res*), Z (*Zensus*, *i.e.* square), C (*Cubus*). Apparently the first important step towards x^2, x^3, etc., was taken by Vieta (1540—

[1] In Plato we have δύναμις used for a square number (*Timaeus*, 31) and also (*Theaetetus*, 147 D) for a *square root* of a number which is not a complete square, *i.e.* for a surd; but the commonest use is in geometry, in the form δυνάμει, "in square," *e.g.* "AB is δυνάμει double of BC" means "$AB^2 = 2BC^2$."

1603), who wrote *Aq*, *Ac*, *Aqq*, etc. (abbreviated for *A quadratus* and so on) for the powers of *A*. This system, besides showing the con exion between the different powers, has the infinite advantage that by means of it we can use in one and the same solution any number of unknown quantities. This is absolutely impossible with the notation used by Diophantus and the earlier algebraists. Diophantus in fact never uses more than one unknown quantity in the solution of a problem, namely the ἀριθμός or ς.

Diophantus has no symbol for the operation of multiplication; it is rendered unnecessary by the fact that his coefficients are all definite numbers or fractions, and the results are simply put down without any preliminary step which would call for the use of a symbol. On the ground that Diophantus uses only numerical expressions for coefficients instead of general symbols, it might occur to a superficial observer that there must be a great want of generality in his methods, and that his problems, being solved with reference to particular numbers only, would possess the attraction of a clever puzzle rather than any more general interest. The answer to this is that, in the first place, it was absolutely impossible that Diophantus should have used any other than numerical coefficients, for the reason that the available symbols of notation were already employed, the letters of the Greek alphabet always doing duty as numerals, with the exception of the final ς. In the second place, it is not the case that the use of none but numerical coefficients makes his solutions any the less general. This will be clearly seen when I come to give an account of his problems and methods.

Next as to Diophantus' expressions for the operations of addition and subtraction. For the former no symbol at all is used: it is expressed by mere juxtaposition, thus $K^{Y}\bar{\alpha}\,\Delta^{Y}\overline{\iota\gamma}\,\varsigma\,\bar{\epsilon}$ corresponds to $x^3 + 13x^2 + 5x$. In this expression, however, there is no absolute term, and the addition of a simple numeral, as for instance $\bar{\beta}$, directly after $\bar{\epsilon}$, the coefficient of ς, would cause confusion. This fact makes it necessary to have some expression to distinguish the absolute term from the variable terms. For this purpose Diophantus uses the word μονάδες, or units, and denotes them after his usual manner by the abbreviation $\overset{\circ}{M}$. The *number* of units is expressed as a coefficient. Thus corresponding to the expression $x^3 + 13x^2 + 5x + 2$ we should find in Diophantus $K^{Y}\bar{\alpha}\,\Delta^{Y}\overline{\iota\gamma}\,\varsigma\,\bar{\epsilon}\,\overset{\circ}{M}\,\bar{\beta}$. As Bachet uses the sign + for addition, he has no occasion for a distinct symbol to mark an absolute term. He accordingly writes $1C + 13Q + 5N + 2$. It is worth observing, however, that the Italians do use a symbol in this case, namely *N* (*Numero*), the first power of the unknown being with them *R* (*Radice*). Cossali[1] makes an interesting comparison between the terms used by Diophantus for the successive powers of the unknown and those employed by the Italians after their instructors, the Arabians. He observes that Fra Luca (Paciuolo), Tartaglia, and Cardano begin their scale of powers from the power 0, not from the power 1, as does Diophantus, and he compares the scales thus:

		Scala Diofantea.		*Scala Araba.*
		....	1.	Numero...il Noto.
x	1.	Numero...l' Ignoto.	2.	Cosa, Radice, Lato.
x^2	2.	Podestà.	3.	Censo.
x^3	3.	Cubo.	4.	Cubo.
x^4	4.	Podestà-Podestà.	5.	Censo di Censo.
x^5	5.	Podestà-Cubo.	6.	Relato 1°.
x^6	6.	Cubo-Cubo.	7.	Censo di Cubo, o Cubo di Censo.
x^7	7.	....	8.	Relato 2°.
x^8	8.	....	9.	Censo di Censo di Censo.
x^9	9.	....	10.	Cubo di Cubo.

and so on. So far, however, as this is meant to be a comparison between Diophantus and the early Arabian algebraists themselves (as the title "Scala *Araba*" would seem to imply), there appears to be no reason why Cossali should not have placed some term to express Diophantus' μονάδες in the same line with *Numero* in the Arabian scale, and moved the numbers 1, 2, 3, etc. one place upwards in the first scale, or downwards in the second. As Diophantus does not go beyond the sixth power, the last three places in the first scale are left blank. An examination of these two scales will show also that the evolution of the successive powers differs in the two systems. The Diophantine terms for them are based on the *addition* of exponents, the Arabic on

[1] Upon Wallis' comparison of the Diophantine with the Arabian scale Cossali remarks: "ma egli non ha riflettuto a due altre differenze tra le scale medesime. La prima si è, che laddove Diofanto denomina con singolarità *Numero* il numero ignoto, denominando *Monade* il numero dato di comparazione: gli antichi italiani degli arabi seguaci denominano questo il *Numero*; e *Radice*, o *Lato*, o *Cosa* il numero sconosciuto. La seconda è, che Diofanto comincia la scala dal numero ignoto; e Fra Luca, Tartaglia, Cardano la incominciano dal numero noto. Ecco le due scale di rincontro, onde meglio risaltino all' occhio le differenze loro", I. p. 195.

their *multiplication*[1]. Thus the "cube-cube" means in Diophantus x^6, while the Italian and Arabian system uses the expression "cube of cube" and applies it to x^9. The first system may (says Cossali) be described as the method of representing each power by the product of the two lesser powers which are the nearest to it, *the method of multiplication*; the second the *method of elevation, i.e.* the method which forms by the process of squaring and cubing all powers which can be so formed, as the 4th, 6th, 8th, 9th, etc. The intermediate powers which cannot be so formed are called in Italian *Relati*. Thus the fifth power is Relato 1°, x^7 is Relato 2°, x^{10} is Censo di Relato 1°, x^{11} is Relato 3°, and so on. Another name for the Relati in use among European algebraists in the 16th and 17th centuries was *sursolida*, with the variants *supersolida* and *surdesolida*.

It is interesting to compare with these systems the Egyptian method described by Psellus[2]. The next power after the fourth (δυναμοδύναμις), *i.e.* x^5, the Egyptians called "the first undescribed" (ἄλογος here apparently meaning that of which no account can be given), because it is neither a square nor a cube; alternatively they called it "the fifth number," corresponding to the fifth power of x. The sixth power they apparently called "cube-cube"; but the seventh was "the second undescribed" (ἄλογος δεύτερος), as being the product of the square and the "first undescribed," or, alternatively, the "seventh number." The eighth power was the "quadruple-square" (τετραπλῆ δύναμις), the ninth the "extended cube" (κύβος ἐξελικτός). Thus the "first undescribed" and the "second undescribed" correspond to "Relato 1°" and "Relato 2°" respectively, but the "quadruple-square" exhibits the additive principle.

For subtraction Diophantus uses a symbol. His full term for *negation* or *wanting* is λεῖψις, corresponding to ὕπαρξις which denotes the opposite. The symbol used to denote it in the MSS., and corresponding to our − for *minus*, is (Def. 9 καὶ τῆς λείψεως σημεῖον Ψ ἐλλιπὲς κάτω νεῦον, ⋔) "an inverted Ψ with the top

[1] This statement of Cossali's needs qualification however. There is at least one Arabian algebraist, al-Karkhī (died probably about 1029), the author of the *Fakhrī*, who uses the Diophantine system of powers of the unknown depending on the *addition* of exponents. Al-Karkhī, namely, expresses all powers of the unknown above the third by means of *māl*, his term for the square, and *ka'b*, his term for the cube of the unknown, as follows. The fourth power is with him *māl māl*, the fifth *māl ka'b*, the sixth *ka'b ka'b*, the seventh *māl māl ka'b*, the eighth *māl ka'b ka'b*, the ninth *ka'b ka'b ka'b*, and so on. Among the Italians too there was an exception, Leonardo of Pisa, who proceeded on the additive principle (*Bibliotheca Mathematica*, VI_3, 1905–6, p. 310).

[2] Dioph. II. p. 37–38.

shortened, ⋔." As Diophantus uses no distinct sign for +, it is clearly necessary, in order to avoid confusion, that all the negative terms in an expression should be placed together after all the positive terms. And so in fact he does place them. Thus corresponding to $x^3 - 5x^2 + 8x - 1$, Diophantus would write $K^{Y}\bar{\alpha}\,\varsigma\,\bar{\eta}$ ⋔ $\Delta^{Y}\bar{\epsilon}\,\overset{\circ}{M}\,\bar{\alpha}$. With respect to this curious sign, given in the MSS. as ⋔ and described as an inverted truncated Ψ, I believe that I was the first to suggest that it could not be what it is represented as being. Even when, as in Bachet's edition, the sign was printed as ⋔ I could not believe that Diophantus used so fantastic a sign for *minus* as an inverted truncated Ψ. In the first place, an inverted Ψ seems too far-fetched; to one who was looking for a symbol to express *minus* many others more natural and less fantastic than ⋔ must have suggested themselves. Secondly, given that Diophantus used an inverted Ψ, why should he truncate it? Surely that must have been unnecessary; we could hardly have expected it unless, without it, confusion was likely to arise; but ⋔ could not well have been confused with anything. This very truncation itself appears to throw doubt on the description of the symbol as we find it in the MS. I concluded that the conception of this symbol as an inverted truncated Ψ was a mistake, and that the description of it as such is not Diophantus' description, but an explanation by a scribe of a symbol which he did not understand[1]. I believe that the true explanation is the following. Diophantus here took the same course as in the case of the other symbols which we have discussed (those for ἀριθμός, δύναμις, etc.). As in those cases he took for his abbreviation the first letter of the word with such an addition as would make confusion with numbers impossible (namely the second letter of the word, which in each of the cases happens to come later in the alphabet than the corresponding first letter), so, in seeking an abbreviation for λεῖψις and cognate inflected forms developed from λιπ, he began by taking the initial letter of the word. The uncial[2] form is Λ. Clearly Λ by itself would not serve his purpose, since it denotes a number. Therefore an addition is necessary. The second letter is Ε, but ΛΕ is equally a number. The second letter of the stem

[1] I am not even sure that the description can be made to mean all that it is intended to mean. ἐλλιπὲς scarcely seems to be sufficiently precise. Might it not be applied to ⋔ with any part cut off, and not only the top?

[2] I adhere to the uncial form above for clearness' sake. If Diophantus used the "Majuskelcursive" form, the explanation will equally apply, the difference of form being for our purpose negligible.

λιπ is Ι, but ΛΙ is open to objection when so written. Hence Diophantus placed the Ι *inside* the Λ, thus, ⩚. Of the possibility of this I entertain no doubt, because there are undoubted cases of combination, even in uncial writing, of two letters into one sign. I would refer in particular to Ⲧ, which is an uncial abbreviation for ΤΑΛΑΝΤΟΝ. Now this sign, ⩚, is an inverted and truncated Ψ (written in the uncial form, ᛘ); and we can, on this assumption, easily account for the explanation of the sign for *minus* which is given in the text.

The above suggestion, made by me twenty-five years ago, seems to be distinctly supported by what Tannery says of the form in which the sign appears in the MSS.[1] Thus he remarks (1) that the sign in the MSS. is often made to lean to the right so that it resembles the letter Lambda, (2) that Planudes certainly wrote λ as if he meant to write the first letter of λείψει, and (3) that the letter Λ appears twice in *A* where it seems to mean λοιπός. Yet in his edition of Diophantus Tannery did not adopt my explanation or even mention it, but explained the sign as being in reality adapted from the old letter Sampi (ϡ), the objection to which suggestion is the same as that to which the identification of ϛ with Koppa is open, namely that ϡ represented the number 900, as ϙ represented 90. Tannery however afterwards[2] saw reason to abandon his suggestion that the symbol was originally an archaic form of the Greek Sampi rather than "un monogramme se rattachant à la racine de λεῖψις." The occasion for this change of view was furnished by the appearance of the same sign in the critical notes to Schöne's edition of the *Metrica* of Heron[3], which led Tannery to re-examine the evidence of the MSS. of Diophantus as to the sign and as to the exact word or words which it represented in different places, as well as to search for any similar expressions denoting subtraction which might occur in the works of other Greek mathematicians. In the MSS. of Diophantus, when the sign is resolved by writing a full word instead of it, it is generally resolved into λείψει, the dative of λεῖψις; in such cases the only grammatical possibility is to construct it with the genitive case of the quantity subtracted, the meaning then being "with the wanting, or deduction, *of* ...". But the best MS. (*A*)

[1] Dioph. II. p. xli.

[2] *Bibliotheca Mathematica* V_3, 1904–5, pp. 5–8.

[3] *Heronis Alexandrini opera*, Vol. III., 1903, pp. 156, 8, 10. The MS. reading is μονάδων οδ ⩚ ιʹ δʹ, the meaning of which is $74 - \frac{1}{14}$.

has in some places the nominative λεῖψις, while in others it has the symbol instead of parts of the verb λείπειν, namely λιπών or λείψας and once even λίπωσι; hence we may conclude that in the cases where *A* and B_1 have λείψει followed by the *accusative* (which is impossible grammatically) the sign was wrongly resolved, and the full word should have been a participle or other part of the verb λείπειν governing the accusative. The question therefore arises whether Diophantus himself used the dative λείψει at all or whether it was introduced into the MSS. later. Certain it is that the use is foreign to Classical Greek; but, even if it began with Diophantus, it did not finally hold the field before the time of Planudes. No evidence for it can be found in Greek mathematicians before Diophantus. Ptolemy has in two places λεῖψαν and λείπουσαν respectively, followed by the accusative, and in one case τὸ ἀπὸ τῆς ΓΛ λειφθὲν ὑπὸ τοῦ ἀπὸ τῆς ΖΓ (where the meaning is $ZΓ^2 - ΓΛ^2$). Consequently we cannot suppose that the sign where it occurs in the *Metrica* of Heron represents the dative λείψει; it must rather stand for a participle, active or passive. Tannery suggests that the full expression in that passage was μονάδων $\overline{οδ}$ λειφθέντος τεσσαρακαιδεκάτου, the participle being passive and the construction being the genitive absolute; but I think a perhaps better alternative would be μονάδων $\overline{οδ}$ λειψασῶν τεσσαρακαιδέκατον, where the active participle would govern the accusative case of the term subtracted. From all this we may infer that the sign had no exclusive reference to the substantive λεῖψις, still less to the dative case of that substantive, but was a conventional abbreviation associated with the root of the verb λείπειν. In these circumstances I think I may now fairly claim Tannery as, substantially, a convert to my view of the nature of the sign.

For division it often happens that no symbol is necessary, *i.e.* in the cases where the divisor divides the dividend without a remainder. In other cases the quotient has to be expressed as a fraction, whether the divisor is a specific number or contains the variable. The case of division comes then under that of fractions.

Fractions are represented in different ways according as they are submultiples (fractions with unity as numerator) or not. In the case of submultiples the Greeks did not write the numerator, but only the denominator, distinguishing the submultiple from the cardinal number itself by affixing a certain sign. In more recent

MSS. a double accent was used for this purpose: thus $\gamma'' = \frac{1}{3}$. Diophantus follows this plan in the hypothesis and analysis of his problems, though in the solutions he seems to have written the numerator *α* and assimilated the notation to that used for other fractions. The sign, however, added to the cardinal number to express the submultiple takes somewhat different forms in *A*: sometimes it is a simple accent, sometimes more elaborate, as ^ above the letter and to the right, or actually forming a continuation of the numeral sign, *e.g.* θ̂ $= \frac{1}{9}$. Tannery adopts as the genuine mark in Diophantus the affix $^{\times}$ in place of the accent: thus $\gamma^{\times} = \frac{1}{3}$. For $\frac{1}{2}$ he writes ∠′ as being most suitable for the time of Diophantus, though *A* has ◡̇, sometimes without the dot.

Of the other class of fractions (numerator not unity) $\frac{2}{3}$ stands by itself, having a peculiar sign of its own; curiously enough it occurs only four times in Diophantus. *A* has a sign for it which was confused with that for ἀριθμός in one place; Tannery judges from the Greek mathematical papyrus of Achmīm[1] that its original form was ϧ; he himself writes in his text the common form ω̸. In the rare cases where the first hand in the oldest MS. (*A*) has fractions as such with numerator and denominator written in full, the denominator is written above the numerator. Tannery therefore adopts, in his text, this way of writing fractions, separating the numerator and denominator by a horizontal line: thus $\frac{\iota\varsigma}{\rho\kappa\alpha} = \frac{121}{16}$.

It is however better to omit the horizontal line (cf. $\overset{\rho\kappa\eta}{\rho}$ in Kenyon Papyri II. No. cclxv. 40; also the fractions in Schöne's edition of Heron's *Metrica*). Once we find in the same MS. (*A*) in the first hand the form $\iota\epsilon^{\delta} = \frac{15}{4}$. In this latter method of writing fractions the denominator is written as we write exponents; and this is the method adopted by Planudes and by Bachet in his edition. Another alternative is to write the numerator first, and then the denominator after it in the same line, marking the denominator with the submultiple sign in some form; thus $\bar{\gamma}\,\delta'$ would mean $\frac{3}{4}$; this is the most convenient method for purposes of printing. Or the denominator may be written as an abbreviation for the *ordinal* number, and the case-termination may be added higher up; *e.g.* $\bar{\nu}\ \kappa\gamma^{\omega\nu} = 50$ twenty-thirds. But the denominators are nearly always omitted

[1] Published by Baillet in *Mémoires publiés par les Membres de la Mission archéologique française au Caire*, T. lx, Fascicule 1, pp. 1–88. Paris, 1892.

altogether in the first hand of *A*; in the first two Books B_1 and the second hand of *A* give the denominator in the place in which we write an exponent, following the method of Planudes; in the last four Books both MSS. almost invariably omit the denominator. In some cases the omission is not unnatural, *i.e.* where the denominator has once been given, and it is almost superfluous to repeat it in other fractions immediately following which have the same denominator; in other cases it was probably omitted because the superposed denominator was taken by the copyist to be an interlinear scholium. A few examples of fractions from Diophantus may be added:

$$\overset{ιβ}{ιζ} = \frac{17}{12}\ (\text{V. 10});\quad \overset{φιβ}{,βυνϛ} = \frac{2456}{512}\ (\text{IV. 28});\quad \overset{α.σα}{,ετνη} = \frac{5358}{10201}\ (\text{V. 9});$$

$$\overset{,βψδ}{γ.\,,ϛχκα} = \frac{36621}{2704}\ (\text{IV. 16});\quad ρκα^{ων}\ \overline{,αωλδ∠'} = \frac{1834\frac{1}{2}}{121}\ (\text{IV. 39});$$

$$\overset{ρνβ}{τπθ∠'} = \frac{389\frac{1}{2}}{152}\ (\text{V. 2}).$$

Diophantus however often expresses fractions by putting ἐν μορίῳ or μορίου between the numerator and denominator, *i.e.* he says one number divided by another. Cf. $\overset{Y}{M}\,\overline{ρν}\,.\,\overline{,ζϡπδ}$ μορίου $\overline{κϛ}\,.\,\overline{,βρμδ} = 1507984/262144$ (IV. 28), where of course $\overset{Y}{M}$ = μυριάδες (tens of thousands); $\overline{β}\,.\,\overline{,εχ}$ ἐν μορίῳ $\overline{ρκβ}\,.\,\overline{,ακε} = 25600/1221025$ (V. 22). As we said, the most orthodox way of writing a submultiple was to omit the numerator (unity) and use the denominator with a distinguishing sign attached, *e.g.* $ϛ^{x}$ or $ϛ' = \frac{1}{6}$. But in his solutions Diophantus often uses the form applicable to fractions other than submultiples; *e.g.* he writes $\overset{φιβ}{α}$ for $\frac{1}{512}$ (IV. 28).

Numbers partly integral and partly fractional, where the fraction is a submultiple or the sum of submultiples, are written much as we write them, the fraction simply following the integer; *e.g.* $\bar{α}\,γ^{x} = 1\frac{1}{3}$; in the Lemma to V. 8 we have $\bar{β}\,∠'\,ϛ' = 2\,\frac{1}{2}\,\frac{1}{6}$ or $2\frac{2}{3}$, where $\frac{2}{3}$ is decomposed into submultiples as in Heron. Cf. also (III. 11) $\overline{το}\,∠'\,ιϛ^{x} = 370\,\frac{1}{2}\,\frac{1}{16}$.

Before leaving the subject of numerical notation, it may be convenient to refer to the method of writing large numbers. Myriads (tens of thousands) are expressed by $\overset{Y}{M}$, myriads to the second power by MM^Y or, in words, *δευτέρα μυριάς*. The denominator 187474560 in V. 8 would thus be written *μορίου δευτέρας μυριάδος* $\overline{\alpha}$ *καὶ μυριάδων πρώτων* $\overline{,\eta\psi\mu\zeta}$ *καὶ* $\overset{\circ}{M}$ $\overline{,\delta\phi\xi}$, and the fraction 131299224/1629586560 would be written *δευτέρα μυριὰς* $\overline{\alpha}$ *πρῶται* (*μυριάδες*) $\overline{,\gamma\rho\kappa\theta}$ $\overset{\circ}{M}$ $\overline{,\theta\sigma\kappa\delta}$ *μορίου δευτέρων μυριάδων* $\overline{\iota ϛ}$ *πρώτων* (*μυριάδων*) $\overline{,\beta ϡ \nu\eta}$ $\overset{\circ}{M}$ $\overline{,ϛ\phi\xi}$[1].

But there is another kind of fraction, besides the purely numerical one, which is continually occurring in the *Arithmetica*, such fractions namely as involve the unknown quantity in some form or other in their denominators. The simplest case is that in which the denominator is merely a power of the unknown, ϛ. Concerning fractions of this kind Diophantus says (Def. 3): "As fractions named after numbers have similar names to those of the numbers themselves (thus a third is named from three, a fourth from four), so the fractions homonymous with the numbers just defined are called after them; thus from *ἀριθμός* we name the fraction *ἀριθμοστόν* [*i.e.* $1/x$ from x], *τὸ δυναμοστόν* from *δύναμις*, *τὸ κυβοστόν* from *κύβος*, *τὸ δυναμοδυναμοστόν* from *δυναμοδύναμις*, *τὸ δυναμοκυβοστόν* from *δυναμόκυβος*, and *τὸ κυβοκυβοστόν* from *κυβόκυβος*. And every such fraction shall have, above the sign for the homonymous number, a line to indicate the species." Thus we find, for example, IV. 3, $ϛ^{\chi}\ \overline{\eta}$ corresponding to $8/x$ and, IV. 15, $ϛ^{\chi}\ \overline{\lambda\epsilon}$ for $35/x$. Cf. $\Delta^{Y\chi}\ \overline{\sigma\nu}$ for $250/x^2$.

Where the denominator is a compound expression involving the unknown and its powers, Diophantus uses the expedient which he often adopts with numerical fractions when the numerators and denominators are large numbers, namely the insertion of *ἐν μορίῳ* or *μορίου* between the expressions for the numerator and denominator. Thus in VI. 12 we have

$$\Delta^Y \overline{\xi}\ \overset{\circ}{M}\ \overline{,\beta\phi\kappa}\ \text{ἐν μορίῳ}\ \Delta^Y\Delta\ \overline{\alpha}\ \overset{\circ}{M}\ \overline{ϡ}\ ⋔\ \Delta^Y \overline{\xi}$$
$$= (60x^2 + 2520)/(x^4 + 900 - 60x^2),$$

and in VI. 14

$$\Delta^Y \overline{\iota\epsilon}\ ⋔\ \overset{\circ}{M}\ \overline{\lambda ϛ}\ \text{ἐν μορίῳ}\ \Delta^Y\Delta\ \overline{\alpha}\ \overset{\circ}{M}\ \overline{\lambda ϛ}\ ⋔\ \Delta^Y\ \overline{\iota\beta}$$
$$= (15x^2 - 36)/(x^4 + 36 - 12x^2).$$

For *ἴσος*, equal, connecting the two sides of an equation, the sign in the archetype seems to have been ι^{σ}; but copyists intro-

[1] Hultsch, *loc. cit.*

duced a sign which was sometimes confused with the sign ϥ for ἀριθμός; this was no doubt the same abbreviation ϥ as that shown (with terminations of cases added above) in the list given at the end of Codex Parisinus 2360 (Archimedes) of contractions found in the "very ancient" MS. from which it was copied and which was at one time the property of Georgius Valla[1].

Diophantus evidently put down his equations in the ordinary course of writing, *i.e.* they were written straight on, as are the steps in the propositions of Euclid, and not put in separate lines for each step in the process of simplification. In the scholia of Maximus Planudes however we find conspectuses of the problems with steps in separate lines which, except for the slightly more cumbrous notation, make the work scarcely more difficult to follow than it is in our notation[2]. Though in the MSS. we have the abbreviation ἴσ to denote equality, Bachet makes no use of any symbol for the purpose in his Latin translation. He uses throughout the full Latin word. It is interesting however to observe that in the notes to his earlier translation (1575) Xylander had already used a symbol to denote equality, namely ||, two short vertical parallel lines. Thus we find, for example (p. 76),

$$1Q + 12 \,\|\, 1Q + 6N + 9,$$

which we should express by $x^2 + 12 = x^2 + 6x + 9$.

Now that we have described in detail Diophantus' method of expressing algebraical quantities and relations, it is clear that it is essentially different in its character from the modern notation. While in modern times signs and symbols have been developed

[1] Heiberg, *Quaestiones Archimedeae*, p. 115.

[2] One instance will suffice. On the left Planudes has abbreviations for the words showing the nature of the steps or the operations they involve, *e.g.* ἔκθ. = ἔκθεσις (setting-out), τετρ. = τετραγωνισμός (squaring), σύνθ. = σύνθεσις (adding), ἀφ. = ἀφαίρεσις (subtraction), μερ. = μερισμός (division), ὕπ. = ὕπαρξις (resulting fact).

Dioph. I. 28.

	Planudes.			*Modern equivalent.*
	$\bar{\kappa}$		$\overline{\sigma\eta}$	[Given numbers] 20, 208
ἔκθ.	$s\bar{\alpha}\ \mu^{o}\bar{\iota}$		$\mu^{o}\bar{\iota} \pitchfork s\bar{\alpha}$	Put for the numbers $x+10$, $10-x$.
τετρ.	$\Delta^{Y}\bar{\alpha}\, ss\bar{\kappa}\, \mu^{o}\bar{\rho}$		$\Delta^{Y}\mu^{o}\bar{\rho} \pitchfork ss\bar{\kappa}$	Squaring, we have $x^2+20x+100$, $x^2+100-20x$.
σύνθ.	$\Delta^{Y}\bar{\beta}\mu^{o}\bar{\sigma}$	ἴσ	$\mu^{o}\overline{\sigma\eta}$	Adding, $2x^2+200=208$.
ἀφ.	$\Delta^{Y}\bar{\beta}$	ἴσ	$\mu^{o}\bar{\eta}$	Subtracting, $2x^2=8$.
μερ.	$\Delta^{Y}\bar{\alpha}$	ἴσ	$\mu^{o}\bar{\delta}$	Dividing, $x^2=4$.
	$s\bar{\alpha}$	ἴσ	$\mu^{o}\bar{\beta}$	$x=2$.
ὕπ.	$\mu^{o}\overline{\iota\beta}$		$\mu^{o}\bar{\eta}$	Result: [the numbers are] 12, 8.

which have no intrinsic relationship to the things which they represent, but depend for their use upon convention, the case is quite different in Diophantus, where algebraic notation takes the form of mere abbreviation of words which are considered as pronounced or implied.

In order to show in what place, in respect of systems of algebraic notation, Diophantus stands, Nesselmann observes that we can, as regards the form of exposition of algebraic operations and equations, distinguish three historical stages of development, well marked and easily discernible. (1) The first stage Nesselmann represents by the name *Rhetorical Algebra* or "reckoning by complete words." The characteristic of this stage is the absolute want of all symbols, the whole of the calculation being carried on by means of complete words, and forming in fact continuous prose. As representatives of this first stage Nesselmann mentions Iamblichus (of whose algebraical work he quotes a specimen in his fifth chapter) "and all Arabian and Persian algebraists who are at present known." In their works we find no vestige of algebraic symbols; the same may be said of the oldest Italian algebraists and their followers, and among them Regiomontanus. (2) The second stage Nesselmann proposes to call the *Syncopated Algebra*. This stage is essentially *rhetorical*, and therein like the first in its treatment of questions; but we now find for often-recurring operations and quantities certain abbreviational symbols. To this stage belong Diophantus and, after him, all the later Europeans until about the middle of the seventeenth century (with the exception of Vieta, who was the first to establish, under the name of *Logistica speciosa*, as distinct from *Logistica numerosa*, a regular system of reckoning with letters denoting magnitudes and not numbers only). (3) To the third stage Nesselmann gives the name *Symbolic Algebra*, which uses a complete system of notation by signs having no visible connexion with the words or things which they represent, a complete language of symbols, which supplants entirely the *rhetorical* system, it being possible to work out a solution without using a single word of the ordinary written language, with the exception (for clearness' sake) of a connecting word or two here and there, and so on[1]. Neither

[1] It may be convenient to note here the beginnings of some of our ordinary algebraical symbols. The signs + and − first appeared in print in Johann Widman's arithmetic (1489), where however they are scarcely used as regular symbols of operation; next they are found in the Rechenbuch of Henricus Grammateus (Schreiber), written in 1518 but perhaps not published till 1521, and then regularly in Stifel's *Arithmetica integra* (1544)

is it the Europeans from the middle of the seventeenth century onwards who were the first to use *symbolic* forms of Algebra. In this they were anticipated by the Indians.

Nesselmann illustrates these three stages by three examples, quoting word for word the solution of a quadratic equation by Muḥammad b. Mūsā as an example of the first stage, and the solution of a problem from Diophantus as representing the second.

First Stage. Example from Muḥammad b. Mūsā (ed. Rosen, p. 5). "A *square* and ten of its *roots* are equal to nine and thirty dirhems, that is, if you add ten *roots* to one *square*, the sum is equal to nine and thirty. The solution is as follows. Take half the number of *roots*, that is in this case five; then multiply this by itself, and the result is five and twenty. Add this to the nine and thirty, which gives sixty-four; take the square root, or eight, and subtract from it half the number of *roots*, namely five, and there remain three: this is the *root* of the *square* which was required, and the square itself is *nine*[1]."

Here we observe that not even are symbols used for numbers, so that this example is even more "*rhetorical*" than the work of Iamblichus who does use the Greek symbols for his numbers.

---

as well as in his edition of Rudolff's Coss (1553). Vieta (1540–1603) has, in addition, = for ~. Robert Recorde (1510–1558) had already in his Algebra (*The Whetstone of Witte*, 1557) used = (but with much longer lines) to denote equality ("bicause noe .2. thynges, can be moare equalle"). Harriot (1560–1621) denoted multiplication by a dot, and also by mere juxtaposition of letters; Stifel (1487–1567) had however already expressed the product of two magnitudes by the juxtaposition of the two letters representing them. Oughtred (1574–1660) used the sign × for multiplication. Harriot also introduced the signs > and < for greater and less respectively. ÷ for division is found in Rahn's Algebra (1659). Descartes introduced in his Geometry (1637) our method of writing powers, as a^3, a^4 etc. (except a^2, for which he wrote aa); but this notation was practically anticipated by Pierre Hérigone (*Cours mathématique*, 1634), who wrote $a2$, $a3$, $a4$, etc., and the idea is even to be found in the Rechenbuch of Grammateus above mentioned, where the successive powers of the unknown are denoted by pri, se, ter, etc. The use of x for the unknown quantity began with Descartes, who first used z, then y, and then x for this purpose, showing that he intentionally chose his unknowns from the last letters of the alphabet. $\surd$ for the square root is traceable to Rudolff, with whom it had only two strokes, the first (down) stroke being short, and the other relatively long.

[1] Thus Muḥammad b. Mūsā states in words the following solution.

$$x^2 + 10x = 39,$$

$$x^2 + 10x + 25 = 64;$$

therefore

$$x + 5 = 8,$$

$$x = 3.$$

Second Stage. As an example of Diophantus I give a translation word for word of II. 8. So as to make the symbols correspond exactly I use S (*Square*) for Δ^{Y} (δύναμις), N (*Number*) for ς, U (*Units*) for $\overset{\circ}{M}$ (μονάδες).

"To divide the proposed square into two squares. Let it be proposed then to divide 16 into two squares. And let the first be supposed to be $1\,S$; therefore the second will be $16\,U - 1\,S$. Thus $16\,U - 1\,S$ must be equal to a square. I form the square from any number of N's minus as many U's as there are in the side of 16 U's. Suppose this to be $2N - 4U$. Thus the square itself will be $4S\ 16U - 16N$. These are equal to $16\,U - 1\,S$. Add to each the negative term (ἡ λεῖψις, the deficiency) and take likes from likes. Thus $5\,S$ are equal to $16N$, and the N is 16 fifths. One [square] will be $\frac{256}{25}$, and the other $\frac{144}{25}$, and the sum of the two makes up $\frac{400}{25}$, or $16\,U$, and each of the two is a square."

Of the *third stage* any exemplification is unnecessary.

To the form of Diophantus' notation is due the fact that he is unable to introduce into his solutions more than one unknown quantity. This limitation has made his procedure often very different from our modern work. In the first place we can begin with any number of unknown quantities denoted by different symbols, and eliminate all of them but one by gradual steps in the course of the work; Diophantus on the other hand has to perform all his eliminations beforehand, as a preliminary to the actual work, by expressing every quantity which occurs in the problem in terms of only one unknown. This is the case in the great majority of questions of the first Book, which involve the solution of determinate simultaneous equations of the first degree with two, three, or four variables; all these Diophantus expresses in terms of one unknown, and then proceeds to find it from a simple equation. Secondly, however, this limitation affects much of Diophantus' work injuriously; for, when he handles problems which are by nature indeterminate and would lead with our notation to an indeterminate equation containing two or three unknowns, he is compelled by limitation of notation to assume for one or other of these some particular number arbitrarily chosen, the effect of the assumption being to make the problem a determinate one. However, it is but fair to say that Diophantus, in assigning an arbitrary value to a quantity, is careful to tell us so, saying, "for such and such a quantity we put any number whatever, say such and such a number." Thus it can hardly be said that there is (as a rule) any loss of generality. We may say, then, that in general Diophantus is obliged to express all his unknowns in terms, or as functions, of one variable. He compels our admiration by the clever devices by which he contrives so to express them in terms of his single unknown, ς, as to satisfy by that very expression of them all conditions of the problem except one, which then enables us to complete the solution by determining the value of ς. Another consequence of Diophantus' want of other symbols besides ς to express more variables than one is that, when (as often happens) it is necessary in the course of a problem to work out a subsidiary problem in order to obtain the coefficients etc. in the functions of ς which express the numbers to be found, the unknown quantity which it is the object of the new subsidiary problem to find is also in its turn denoted by the same symbol ς; hence we often have in the same problem the same variable ς used with two different meanings. This is an obvious inconvenience and might lead to confusion in the mind of a careless reader. Again we find two cases, II. 28 and 29, where for the proper working-out of the problem two unknowns are imperatively necessary. We should of course use x and y; but Diophantus calls the first ς as usual; the second, for want of a term, he agrees to call "*one unit*," *i.e.* 1. Then, later, having completed the part of the solution necessary to find ς, he substitutes its value, and uses ς over again to denote what he had originally called "1"—the second variable—and so finds it. This is the most curious case of all, and the way in which Diophantus, after having worked with this "1" along with other numerals, is yet able to put his finger upon the particular place where it has passed to, so as to substitute ς for it, is very remarkable. This could only be possible in particular cases such as those which I have mentioned; but, even here, it seems scarcely possible now to work out the problem by using x and 1 for the variables as originally taken by Diophantus without falling into confusion. Perhaps, however, in working out the problems before writing them down as we have them Diophantus may have given the "1" which stood for a variable some mark by which he could recognise it and distinguish it from other numbers.

Diophantus will have in his solutions no numbers whatever except "rational" numbers; and in pursuance of this restriction he excludes not only surds and imaginary quantities, but also *negative* quantities. Of a negative quantity *per se*, *i.e.* without some positive quantity to subtract it from, Diophantus had apparently no conception. Such equations then as lead to surd, imaginary, or negative roots he regards as useless for his purpose: the solution is in these cases ἀδύνατος, impossible. So we find him (v. 2) describing the equation $4 = 4x + 20$ as ἄτοπος, absurd, because it would give $x = -4$. Diophantus makes it his object throughout to obtain solutions in rational numbers, and we find him frequently giving, as a preliminary, the conditions which must be satisfied in order to secure a result rational in his sense of the word. In the great majority of cases, when Diophantus arrives in the course of a solution at an equation which would give an irrational result, he retraces his steps and finds out how his equation has arisen, and how he may, by altering the previous work, substitute for it another which shall give a rational result. This gives rise, in general, to a subsidiary problem the solution of which ensures a rational result for the problem itself. Though, however, Diophantus has no notation for a surd, and does not admit surd results, it is scarcely true to say that he makes no use of quadratic equations which lead to such results. Thus, for example, in V. 30 he solves such an equation so far as to be able to see to what integers the solution would approximate most nearly.

CHAPTER IV

DIOPHANTUS' METHODS OF SOLUTION

BEFORE I give an account in detail of the different methods which Diophantus employs for the solution of his problems, so far as they can be classified, it is worth while to quote some remarks which Hankel has made in his account of Diophantus[1]. Hankel, writing with his usual brilliancy, says in the place referred to, "The reader will now be desirous to become acquainted with the classes of indeterminate problems which Diophantus treats of, and with his methods of solution. As regards the first point, we must observe that included in the 130 (or so) indeterminate problems, of which Diophantus treats in his great work, there are over 50 different classes of problems, strung together on no recognisable principle of grouping, except that the solution of the earlier problems facilitates that of the later. The first Book is confined to determinate algebraic equations; Books II. to V. contain for the most part indeterminate problems, in which expressions involving in the first or second degree two or more variables are to be made squares or cubes. Lastly, Book VI. is concerned with right-angled triangles regarded purely arithmetically, in which some linear or quadratic function of the sides is to be made a square or a cube. That is all that we can pronounce about this varied series of problems without exhibiting singly each of the fifty classes. Almost more different in kind than the problems are their solutions, and we are completely unable to give an even tolerably exhaustive review of the different turns which his procedure takes. Of more general comprehensive methods there is in our author no trace discoverable: every question requires a quite special method, which often will not serve even for the most closely allied problems. It is on that

[1] *Zur Geschichte der Mathematik in Alterthum und Mittelalter*, Leipzig, 1874, pp. 164–5.

account difficult for a modern mathematician even after studying 100 Diophantine solutions to solve the 101st problem; and if we have made the attempt, and after some vain endeavours read Diophantus' own solution, we shall be astonished to see how suddenly he leaves the broad high-road, dashes into a side-path and with a quick turn reaches the goal, often enough a goal with reaching which we should not be content; we expected to have to climb a toilsome path, but to be rewarded at the end by an extensive view; instead of which our guide leads by narrow, strange, but smooth ways to a small eminence; he has finished! He lacks the calm and concentrated energy for a deep plunge into a single important problem; and in this way the reader also hurries with inward unrest from problem to problem, as in a game of riddles, without being able to enjoy the individual one. Diophantus dazzles more than he delights. He is in a wonderful measure shrewd, clever, quick-sighted, indefatigable, but does not penetrate thoroughly or deeply into the root of the matter. As his problems seem framed in obedience to no obvious scientific necessity, but often only for the sake of the solution, the solution itself also lacks completeness and deeper signification. He is a brilliant performer in the *art* of indeterminate analysis invented by him, but the *science* has nevertheless been indebted, at least directly, to this brilliant genius for few methods, because he was deficient in the speculative thought which sees in the True more than the Correct. That is the general impression which I have derived from a thorough and repeated study of Diophantus' arithmetic."

It might be inferred from these remarks of Hankel that Diophantus' object was less to teach methods than to obtain a multitude of mere results. On the other hand Nesselmann observes[1] that Diophantus, while using (as he must) specific numbers for numbers which are "given" or have to be arbitrarily assumed, always makes it clear how by varying our initial assumptions we can obtain any number of particular solutions of the problem, showing "that his whole attention is directed to the explanation of the *method*, to which end numerical examples only serve as means"; this is proved by his frequently stopping short, when the method has been made sufficiently clear, and the remainder of the work is mere straightforward calculation. The truth seems to be that there is as much in the shape of general

[1] *Algebra der Griechen*, pp. 308–9.

methods to be found in Diophantus as his notation and the nature of the subject admitted of. On this point I can quote no better authority than Euler, who says[1]: "Diophantus himself, it is true, gives only the most special solutions of all the questions which he treats, and he is generally content with indicating numbers which furnish one single solution. But it must not be supposed that his method was restricted to these very special solutions. In his time the use of letters to denote undetermined numbers was not yet established, and consequently the more general solutions which we are now enabled to give by means of such notation could not be expected from him. Nevertheless, the actual methods which he uses for solving any of his problems are as general as those which are in use today; nay, we are obliged to admit that there is hardly any method yet invented in this kind of analysis of which there are not sufficiently distinct traces to be discovered in Diophantus."

In his 8th chapter, entitled "Diophantus' treatment of equations[2]," Nesselmann gives an account of Diophantus' solutions of (1) Determinate, (2) Indeterminate equations, classified according to their kind. In chapter 9, entitled "Diophantus' methods of solution[3]," he classifies these "methods" as follows[4]: (1) "The adroit assumption of unknowns," (2) "Method of reckoning backwards and auxiliary questions," (3) "Use of the symbol for the unknown in different significations," (4) "Method of Limits," (5) "Solution by mere reflection," (6) "Solution in general expressions," (7) "Arbitrary determinations and assumptions," (8) "Use of the right-angled triangle."

At the end of chapter 8 Nesselmann observes that it is not his solutions of equations that we have to wonder at, but the art, amounting to virtuosity, which enabled Diophantus to avoid such equations as he could not technically solve. We look (says Nesselmann) with astonishment at his operations, when he reduces the most difficult problems by some surprising turn to a quite simple

[1] *Novi Commentarii Academiae Petropolitanae*, 1756–7, Vol. VI. (1761), p. 155 = *Commentationes arithmeticae collectae* (ed. Fuss), 1849, I. p. 193.

[2] "Diophant's Behandlung der Gleichungen."

[3] "Diophant's Auflösungsmethoden."

[4] (1) "Die geschickte Annahme der Unbekannten," (2) "Methode der Zurückrechnung und Nebenaufgabe," (3) "Gebrauch des Symbols für die Unbekannte in verschiedenen Bedeutungen," (4) "Methode der Grenzen," (5) "Auflösung durch blosse Reflexion," (6) "Auflösung in allgemeinen Ausdrücken," (7) "Willkührliche Bestimmungen und Annahmen," (8) "Gebrauch des rechtwinkligen Dreiecks."

equation. Then, when in the 9th chapter Nesselmann passes to the "methods," he prefaces it by saying: "To give a complete picture of Diophantus' methods in all their variety would mean nothing else than copying his book outright. The individual characteristics of almost every problem give him occasion to try upon it a peculiar procedure or found upon it an artifice which cannot be applied to any other problem....Meanwhile, though it may be impossible to exhibit all his methods in any short space, yet I will try to describe some operations which occur more often or are particularly remarkable for their elegance, and (where possible) to bring out the underlying scientific principle by a general exposition and by a suitable grouping of similar cases under common aspects or characters." Now the possibility of giving a satisfactory account of the methods of Diophantus must depend largely upon the meaning we attach to the word "method." Nesselmann's arrangement seems to me to be faulty inasmuch as (1) he has treated Diophantus' solutions of equations, which certainly proceeded on fixed rules, and therefore by "*method*," separately from what he calls "methods of solution," thereby making it appear as though he did not look upon the "treatment of equations" as "methods"; (2) the classification of the "Methods of solution" seems unsatisfactory. Some of the latter can hardly be said to be *methods* of solution at all; thus the third, "Use of the symbol for the unknown in different significations," might be more justly described as a "hindrance to the solution"; it is an *inconvenience* to which Diophantus was subjected owing to the want of notation. Indeed, on the assumption of the eight "methods," as Nesselmann describes them, it is really not surprising that no complete account of them could be given without copying the whole book. To take the first, "the adroit assumption of unknowns." Supposing that a number of essentially different problems are proposed, the differences make a different choice of an unknown in each case absolutely necessary. That being so, how could a rule be given for all cases? The best that can be done is to give a number of typical instances. Precisely the same remark applies to "methods" (2), (5), (6), (7). The case of (4), "Method of Limits," is different; here we have a "method" in the true sense of the term, *i.e.* in the sense of an *instrument* for solution. And accordingly in this case the method can be exhibited, as I hope to show later on; (8) also deserves to some extent the name of a "method."

In one particular case, Diophantus formally states a method or rule; this is his rule for solving what he calls a "double-equation," and will be found in II. 11, where such an equation appears for the first time. Apart from this, we do not find in Diophantus' work statements of method put generally as book-work to be applied to examples. Thus we do not find the separate rules and limitations for the solution of different kinds of equations systematically arranged, but we have to seek them out laboriously from the whole of his work, gathering scattered indications here and there, and to formulate them in the best way that we can.

I shall now attempt to give a short account of those methods running through Diophantus which admit of general statement. For the reasons which I have stated, my arrangement will be different from that of Nesselmann; I shall omit some of the heads in his classification of "methods of solution"; and, in accordance with his remark that these "methods" can only be adequately described by a transcription of the entire work, I shall leave them to be gathered from a perusal of my reproduction of Diophantus' book.

I shall begin my account with

I. Diophantus' treatment of equations.

This subject falls naturally into two divisions: (A) Determinate equations of different degrees, (B) Indeterminate equations.

(A) Determinate equations.

Diophantus was able without difficulty to solve determinate equations of the first and second degrees; of a cubic equation we find in his *Arithmetica* only one example, and that is a very special case. The solution of simple equations we may pass over; we have then to consider Diophantus' methods of solution in the case of (1) Pure equations, (2) Adfected, or mixed, *quadratics*.

(1) *Pure determinate equations.*

By *pure* equations I mean those equations which contain only one power of the unknown, whatever the degree. The solution is effected in the same way whatever the exponent of the term in the unknown; and Diophantus treats pure equations of any degree as if they were simple equations of the first degree.

He gives a general rule for this case without regard to the degree[1]: "If a problem leads to an equation in which any terms are equal to the same terms but have different coefficients, we must take like from like on both sides, until we get one term equal to one term. But, if there are on one side or on both sides any negative terms, the deficient terms must be added on both sides until all the terms on both sides are positive. Then we must take like from like until one term is left on each side." After these operations have been performed, the equation is reduced to the form $Ax^m = B$ and is considered solved. The cases which occur in Diophantus are cases in which the value of x is found to be a rational number, integral or fractional. Diophantus only recognises one value of x which satisfies this equation; thus, if m is even, he gives only the positive value, excluding a negative value as "impossible." In the same way, when an equation can be reduced in degree by dividing throughout by any power of x, the possible values, $x = 0$, thus arising are not taken into account. Thus an equation of the form $x^2 = ax$, which is of common occurrence in the earlier part of the book, is taken to be merely equivalent to the simple equation $x=a$.

It may be observed that the greater proportion of the problems in Book I. are such that more than one unknown quantity is sought. Now, when there are two unknowns and two conditions, both unknowns can easily be expressed in terms of one symbol. But, when there are three or four quantities to be found, this reduction is much more difficult, and Diophantus shows great adroitness in effecting it: the ultimate result being that it is only necessary to solve a simple equation with one unknown quantity.

(2) *Mixed quadratic equations.*

After the remarks in Def. 11 upon the reduction of equations until we have one term equal to another term, Diophantus adds[2]: "But we will show you afterwards how, in the case also when two terms are left equal to a single term, such an equation can be solved." That is to say, he promises to explain the solution of a mixed quadratic equation. In the *Arithmetica*, as we possess the book, this promise is not fulfilled. The first

[1] Def. 11.

[2] *ὕστερον δέ σοι δείξομεν καὶ πῶς δύο εἰδῶν ἴσων ἑνὶ καταλειφθέντων τὸ τοιοῦτον λύεται.*

indications we have on the subject are a number of cases in which the equation is given, and the solution written down, or stated to be rational, without any work being shown. Thus

(IV. 22) $x^2 = 4x - 4$, therefore $x = 2$;

(IV. 31) $325x^2 = 3x + 18$, therefore $x = \frac{78}{325}$ or $\frac{6}{25}$;

(VI. 6) $84x^2 + 7x = 7$, whence $x = \frac{1}{4}$;

(VI. 7) $84x^2 - 7x = 7$, hence $x = \frac{1}{3}$;

(VI. 9) $630x^2 - 73x = 6$, therefore $x = \frac{6}{35}$;

and (VI. 8) $630x^2 + 73x = 6$, and x is rational.

These examples, though proving that Diophantus had somehow arrived at the result, are not in themselves sufficient to show that he was necessarily acquainted with a regular method for the solution of quadratics; these solutions might (though their variety makes it somewhat unlikely) have been obtained by mere *trial*. That, however, Diophantus' solutions of mixed quadratics were not merely empirical is shown by instances in V. 30. In this problem he shows that he could approximate to the root in cases where it is not "rational." As this is an important point, I give the substance of the passage in question: "This is not generally possible unless we contrive to make $x > \frac{1}{8}(x^2 - 60)$ and $< \frac{1}{5}(x^2 - 60)$. Let then $x^2 - 60$ be $> 5x$, but $x^2 - 60 < 8x$. Since then $x^2 - 60 > 5x$, let 60 be added to both sides, so that $x^2 > 5x + 60$, or $x^2 = 5x +$ some number > 60; therefore x must not be less than 11." In like manner Diophantus concludes that "$x^2 = 8x +$ some number less than 60; therefore x must be found to be not greater than 12."

Now, solving for the positive roots of these two equations, we have

$$x > \tfrac{1}{2}(5 + \sqrt{265}) \text{ and } x < 4 + \sqrt{76},$$

or $$x > 10{\cdot}6394\ldots \text{ and } x < 12{\cdot}7177\ldots.$$

It is clear that x may be < 11 or > 12, and therefore Diophantus' limits are not strictly accurate. As however it was doubtless his object to find *integral* limits, the limits 11 and 12 are those which are obviously adapted for his purpose, and are *a fortiori* safe.

In the above equations the other roots obtained by prefixing the negative sign to the radical are negative and therefore would be of no use to Diophantus. In other cases of the kind occurring in Book V. the equations have both roots positive, and we have to consider why Diophantus took no account of the smaller roots in those cases.

We will take first the equations in V. 10 where the inequalities to be satisfied are

$$72x > 17x^2 + 17 \quad \text{.........................(1).}$$

$$72x < 19x^2 + 19 \quad \text{.........................(2).}$$

Now, if α, β be the roots of the equation

$$x^2 - px + q = 0 \ (p, q \text{ both positive}),$$

and if $\alpha > \beta$, then

(a) in order that $x^2 - px + q$ may be > 0 we must have $x > \alpha$ or $< \beta$,

and (b) in order that $x^2 - px + q$ may be < 0 we must have $x < \alpha$ and $> \beta$.

(1) The roots of the equation

$$17x^2 - 72x + 17 = 0$$

are $\dfrac{36 \pm \sqrt{1007}}{17}$; that is, $\dfrac{67{\cdot}73\ldots}{17}$ and $\dfrac{4{\cdot}26\ldots}{17}$;

and, in order that $17x^2 - 72x + 17$ may be < 0, we must have

$$x < \frac{67{\cdot}73\ldots}{17} \text{ but} > \frac{4{\cdot}26\ldots}{17}.$$

(2) The roots of the equation

$$19x^2 - 72x + 19 = 0$$

are $\dfrac{36 \pm \sqrt{935}}{19}$; that is, $\dfrac{66{\cdot}577\ldots}{19}$ and $\dfrac{5{\cdot}422\ldots}{19}$;

and, in order that $19x^2 - 72x + 19$ may be > 0, we must have

$$x > \frac{66{\cdot}577\ldots}{19} \text{ or} < \frac{5{\cdot}422\ldots}{19}.$$

Diophantus says that x must not be greater than $\frac{67}{17}$ or less than $\frac{66}{19}$. These are again doubtless intended to be *a fortiori* limits; but $\frac{66}{19}$ should have been $\frac{67}{19}$, and the more correct way of stating the case would be to say that, if x is not greater than $\frac{67}{17}$ and not less than $\frac{67}{19}$, the given conditions are *a fortiori* satisfied.

Now consider what alternative (if any) could be obtained, on Diophantus' principles, if we used the lesser positive roots of the equations. If, like Diophantus, we were to take *a fortiori* limits, we should have to say

$$x < \tfrac{5}{19} \text{ but } > \tfrac{5}{17},$$

which is of course an impossibility. Therefore the smaller roots are here useless from his point of view.

This is, however, not so in the case of another pair of inequalities, used later in V. 30 for finding an auxiliary x, namely

$$x^2 + 60 > 22x,$$
$$x^2 + 60 < 24x.$$

The roots of the equation

$$x^2 - 22x + 60 = 0$$

are $11 \pm \sqrt{61}$; that is, 18·81... and 3·18...;

and the roots of the equation $x^2 - 24x + 60 = 0$

are $12 \pm \sqrt{84}$; that is, 21·16... and 2·83....

In order therefore to satisfy the above inequalities we must have

$$x > 18{\cdot}81 \ldots \text{ or } < 3{\cdot}18\ldots,$$

and $$x < 21{\cdot}16 \ldots \text{ but } > 2{\cdot}83.$$

Diophantus, taking *a fortiori* integral limits furnished by the greater roots, says that x must not be less than 19 but must be less than 21. But he could also have obtained from the smaller roots an integral value of x satisfying the necessary conditions, namely the value $x = 3$; and this would have had the advantage of giving a smaller value for the auxiliary x than that actually taken, namely 20[1]. Accordingly the question has been raised[2] whether we have not here, perhaps, a valid reason for believing that Diophantus only knew of the existence of roots obtained by using the positive sign with the radical, and was unaware of the solution obtained by using the negative sign. But in truth we can derive no certain knowledge on this point from Diophantus' treatment of the particular equations in question. Thus, *e.g.*, if he chose to use the first of the two equations

$$72x > 17x^2 + 17,$$
$$72x < 19x^2 + 19,$$

for the purpose of obtaining an upper limit *only*, and the second

[1] This is remarked by Loria (*Le scienze esatte dell' antica Grecia*, V. p. 128). But in fact, whether we take 20 or 3 as the value of the auxiliary unknown, we get the same value for the original x of the problem. For the original x has to be found from $x^2 - 60 = (x - m)^2$ where m is the auxiliary x; and we obtain $x = 11\tfrac{1}{2}$ whether we put $x^2 - 60 = (x - 20)^2$ or $x^2 - 60 = (x - 3)^2$.

[2] Loria, *op. cit.* p. 129.

for the purpose of obtaining a lower limit *only*, he could *only* use the values obtained by using the positive sign. Similarly, if, with the equations

$$x^2 + 60 > 22x,$$
$$x^2 + 60 < 24x,$$

he chose to use the first in order to find a lower limit *only*, and the second in order to find an upper limit *only*, it was not open to him to use the values corresponding to the negative sign[1].

For my part, I find it difficult or impossible to believe that Diophantus was unaware of the existence of two real roots in such cases. The numerical solution of quadratic equations by the Greeks immediately followed, if it did not precede, their geometrical solution. We find the geometrical equivalent of the solution of a quadratic assumed as early as the fifth century B.C., namely by Hippocrates of Chios in his *Quadrature of lunes*[2], the algebraic form of the particular equation being $x^2 + \sqrt{\frac{3}{2}} \cdot ax = a^2$. The complete geometrical solution was given by Euclid in VI. 27–29: and the construction of VI. 28 corresponds in fact to the *negative* sign before the radical in the case of the particular equation there solved, while a quite obvious and slight variation of the construction would give the solution corresponding to the *positive* sign. In VI. 29 the solution corresponds to the positive sign before the radical; in the case of the equation there dealt with the other sign would not give a "real" solution[3]. It is true that we do not find the negative sign taken in Heron any more than in Diophantus, though we find Heron[4] stating an approximate solution of the equation

$$x(14 - x) = 6720/144,$$

without showing how he arrived at it; x is, he says, approximately equal to $8\frac{1}{2}$. It is clear however that Heron already possessed a scientific method of solution. Again, the author of the so-called *Geometry* of Heron[5] practically states the solution of the equation

$$\frac{11}{14}x^2 + \frac{29}{7}x = 212$$

in the form
$$x = \frac{\sqrt{(154 \times 212 + 841)} - 29}{11},$$

[1] Eneström in *Bibliotheca Mathematica* IX_3, 1908–9, pp. 71–2.

[2] Simplicius, *Comment. in Aristot. Phys.*, ed. Diels, p. 64, 18; Rudio, *Der Bericht des Simplicius über die Quadraturen des Antiphon und des Hippokrates*, 1907, p. 58, 8–11.

[3] *The Thirteen Books of Euclid's Elements*, Cambridge, 1908, Vol. II. pp. 257–267.

[4] Heron, *Metrica*, ed. Schöne, pp. 148–151. The text has 8 as the approximate solution, but the correction is easy, as the inference immediately drawn is that $14 - x = 5\frac{1}{2}$.

[5] Heron, ed. Hultsch, p. 133, 10–23. See M. Cantor, *Geschichte der Math.* I_3, p. 405.

showing pretty clearly the rule followed after the equation had been written in the form

$$121x^2 + 638x = 212 \times 154.$$

We cannot credit Diophantus with less than a similar uniform method; and, if he did not trouble to give two roots where both were real, this seems quite explicable when it is remembered that he did not write a text-book of algebra, and that his object throughout is to obtain a single solution of his problems, not to multiply solutions or to show how many can be found in each case.

In solving such an equation as

$$ax^2 - bx + c = 0,$$

it is our modern practice to divide out by a in order to make the first term a square. It does not appear that Diophantus divided out by a; rather he multiplied by a so as to bring the equation into the form

$$a^2x^2 - abx + ac = 0;$$

then, solving, he found

$$ax = \tfrac{1}{2}b \pm \sqrt{(\tfrac{1}{4}b^2 - ac)},$$

and wrote the solution in the form

$$x = \frac{\tfrac{1}{2}b \pm \sqrt{(\tfrac{1}{4}b^2 - ac)}}{a},$$

wherein his method corresponds to that of the Pseudo-Heron above referred to.

From the rule given in Def. 11 for removing by means of addition any negative terms on either side of an equation and taking equals from equals (operations called by the Arabians *aljabr* and *almukābala*) it is clear that, as a preliminary to solution, Diophantus so arranged his equation that all the terms were positive. Thus, from his point of view, there are three cases of mixed quadratic equations.

Case I. Form $mx^2 + px = q$; the root is

$$\frac{-\tfrac{1}{2}p + \sqrt{(\tfrac{1}{4}p^2 + mq)}}{m},$$

according to Diophantus. An instance is afforded by VI. 6. Diophantus namely arrives at the equation $6x^2 + 3x = 7$, which, if it is to be of any service to his solution, should give a rational value of x; whereupon he says "the square of half the coefficient[1] of x

[1] For "coefficient" Diophantus simply uses πλῆθος, multitude or number; thus "number of ἀριθμοί" = coeff. of x. The absolute term is described as the "units."

together with the product of the absolute term and the coefficient of x^2 must be a square number; but it is not," *i.e.* $\frac{1}{4}p^2 + mq$, or in this case $(\frac{3}{2})^2 + 42$, must be a square in order that the root may be rational, which in this case it is not.

Case 2. Form $mx^2 = px + q$. Diophantus takes

$$x = \frac{\frac{1}{2}p + \sqrt{(\frac{1}{4}p^2 + mq)}}{m}.$$

An example is IV. 39, where $2x^2 > 6x + 18$. Diophantus says: "To solve this take the square of half the coefficient of x, *i.e.* 9, and the product of the absolute term and the coefficient of x^2, *i.e.* 36. Adding, we have 45, the square root[1] of which is not[2] < 7. Add half the coefficient of x, [and divide by the coefficient of x^2]; whence x is not < 5." Here the form of the root is given completely; and the whole operation of finding it is revealed. Cf. IV. 31, where Diophantus remarks that the equation $5x^2 = 3x + 18$ "is not rational. But 5, the coefficient of x^2, is a square plus 1, and it is necessary that this coefficient multiplied by the 18 units and then added to the square of half the coefficient of x, namely 3, that is to say $2\frac{1}{4}$, shall make a square."

Case 3. Form $mx^2 + q = px$. Diophantus' root is

$$\frac{\frac{1}{2}p + \sqrt{(\frac{1}{4}p^2 - mq)}}{m}.$$

Cf. in V. 10 the equation already mentioned, $17x^2 + 17 < 72x$. Diophantus says: "Multiply half the coefficient of x into itself and we have 1296; subtract the product of the coefficient of x^2 and the absolute term, or 289. The remainder is 1007, the square root of which is not[3] > 31. Add half the coefficient of x, and the result is not > 67. Divide by the coefficient of x^2, and x is not $> 67/17$." Here again we have the complete solution given. Cf. VI. 22, where, having arrived at the equation $172x = 336x^2 + 24$, Diophantus remarks that "this is not always possible, unless half the coefficient of x multiplied into itself, *minus* the product of the coefficient of x^2 and the units, makes a square."

For the purpose of comparison with Diophantus' solutions of quadratic equations we may refer to a few of his solutions of

[1] The "square root" is with Diophantus πλευρά, or "side."

[2] 7, though not accurate, is clearly the nearest integral limit which will serve the purpose.

[3] As before, the nearest *integral* limit.

(3) *Simultaneous equations involving quadratics.*

Under this heading come the pairs of equations

$$\left.\begin{aligned} \xi + \eta &= 2a \\ \xi\eta &= B \end{aligned}\right\}, \qquad \text{(I. 27.)}$$

$$\left.\begin{aligned} \xi + \eta &= 2a \\ \xi^2 + \eta^2 &= B \end{aligned}\right\}, \qquad \text{(I. 28.)}$$

$$\left.\begin{aligned} \xi - \eta &= 2a \\ \xi\eta &= B \end{aligned}\right\}. \qquad \text{(I. 30.)}$$

I use Greek letters to distinguish the numbers which the problem requires us to find from the one unknown which Diophantus uses and which I shall call x.

In the first two of the above problems, he chooses his x thus. Let, he says,

$$\xi - \eta = 2x \quad (\xi > \eta).$$

Then it follows, by addition and subtraction, that

$$\xi = a + x, \quad \eta = a - x.$$

Consequently, in I. 27,

$$\xi\eta = (a + x)(a - x) = a^2 - x^2 = B,$$

and x is found from this "pure" quadratic equation.

If we eliminate ξ from the original equations, we have

$$\eta^2 - 2a\eta + B = 0,$$

which we should solve by completing the square $(a - \eta)^2$, whence

$$(a - \eta)^2 = a^2 - B,$$

which is Diophantus' ultimate equation with $a - \eta$ for x.

Thus Diophantus' method corresponds here again to the ordinary method of solving a mixed quadratic, by which we make it into a pure quadratic with a different x.

In I. 30 Diophantus puts $\xi + \eta = 2x$, and the solution proceeds in the same way as in I. 27.

In I. 28 the resulting equation in x is

$$\xi^2 + \eta^2 = (a + x)^2 + (a - x)^2 = 2(a^2 + x^2) = B.$$

(4) *Cubic equation.*

There is no ground for supposing that Diophantus was acquainted with the algebraical solution of a cubic equation. It is true that there is one cubic equation to be found in the *Arithmetica*, but it is only a very particular case. In VI. 17 the problem leads to the equation

$$x^2 + 2x + 3 = x^3 + 3x - 3x^2 - 1,$$

and Diophantus says simply "whence x is found to be 4." All that can be said of this is that, if we write the equation in true Diophantine fashion, so that all the terms are positive,

$$x^3 + x = 4x^2 + 4.$$

This equation being clearly equivalent to

$$x(x^2 + 1) = 4(x^2 + 1),$$

Diophantus no doubt detected the presence of the common factor on both sides of the equation. The result of dividing by it is $x = 4$, which is Diophantus' solution. Of the other two roots $x = \pm\sqrt{(-1)}$ no account is taken, for the reason stated above.

It is not possible to judge from this example how far Diophantus was acquainted with the solution of equations of a degree higher than the second.

I pass now to the second general division of equations.

(B) Indeterminate equations.

As I have already stated, Diophantus does not, in his *Arithmetica* as we have it, treat of indeterminate equations of the first degree. Those examples in Book I. which would lead to such equations are, by the arbitrary assumption of a specific value for one of the required numbers, converted into determinate equations. Nor is it likely that indeterminate equations of the first degree were treated of in the lost Books. For, as Nesselmann observes, while with indeterminate quadratic equations the object is to obtain a *rational* result, the whole point in solving indeterminate simple equations is to obtain a result in *integral* numbers. But Diophantus does not exclude fractional solutions, and he has therefore only to see that his results are *positive,* which is of course easy. Indeterminate equations of the first degree would therefore, from Diophantus' point of view, have no particular significance. We take therefore, as our first division, indeterminate equations of the second degree.

(a) *Indeterminate equations of the second degree.*

The form in which these equations occur in Diophantus is invariably this: one or two (but never more) functions of the unknown quantity of the form $Ax^2 + Bx + C$ or simpler forms are to be made rational square numbers by finding a suitable value for x. Thus the most general case is that of solving one or two equations of the form $Ax^2 + Bx + C = y^2$.

(1) *Single equation.*

The single equation takes special forms when one or more of the coefficients vanish or satisfy certain conditions. It will be well to give in order the different forms as they can be identified in Diophantus, premising that for "$=y^2$" Diophantus simply uses the formula ἴσον τετραγώνῳ, "is equal to a square," or ποιεῖ τετράγωνον, "makes a square."

1. Equations which can always be solved rationally. This is the case when A or C or both vanish.

Form $Bx=y^2$. Diophantus puts for y^2 any arbitrary square number, say m^2. Then $x=m^2/B$.

Ex. III. 5: $2x=y^2$, y^2 is assumed to be 16, and $x=8$.

Form $Bx+C=y^2$. Diophantus puts for y^2 any square m^2, and $x=(m^2-C)/B$. He admits fractional values of x, only taking care that they are "rational," *i.e.* rational and positive.

Ex. III. 6: $6x+1=y^2=121$, say, and $x=20$.

Form $Ax^2+Bx=y^2$. Diophantus substitutes for y any multiple of x, as $\frac{m}{n}x$; whence $Ax+B=\frac{m^2}{n^2}x$, the factor x disappearing and the root $x=0$ being neglected as usual. Thus $x=\frac{Bn^2}{m^2-An^2}$.

Exx. II. 21: $4x^2+3x=y^2=(3x)^2$, say, and $x=\frac{3}{5}$.

II. 33: $16x^2+7x=y^2=(5x)^2$, say, and $x=\frac{7}{9}$.

2. Equations which can only be rationally solved if certain conditions are fulfilled.

The cases occurring in Diophantus are the following.

Form $Ax^2+C=y^2$. This can be rationally solved according to Diophantus

(α) When A is positive and a square, say a^2.

Thus $a^2x^2+C=y^2$. In this case y^2 is put $=(ax\pm m)^2$;

therefore
$$a^2x^2+C=(ax\pm m)^2,$$

and
$$x=\pm\frac{C-m^2}{2ma},$$

(m and the doubtful sign being always assumed so as to give x a positive value).

(β) When C is positive and a square number, say c^2.

Thus $Ax^2+c^2=y^2$. Here Diophantus puts $y=(mx\pm c)$;

therefore $$Ax^2 + c^2 = (mx \pm c)^2,$$

and $$x = \pm \frac{2mc}{A - m^2}.$$

(γ) When one solution is known, any number of other solutions can be found. This is enunciated in the Lemma to VI. 15 thus, though only for the case in which C is negative: "Given two numbers, if, when one is multiplied by some square and the other is subtracted from the product, the result is a square, then another square also can be found, greater than the aforesaid square which has the same property." It is curious that Diophantus does not give a general enunciation of this proposition, inasmuch as not only is it applicable to the cases $\pm Ax^2 \pm C = y^2$, but also to the general form $Ax^2 + Bx + C = y^2$.

Diophantus' method of finding other greater values of x satisfying the equation $Ax^2 - C = y^2$ when one such value is known is as follows.

Suppose that x_0 is the value already known and that q is the corresponding value of y.

Put $x = x_0 + \xi$ in the original expression, and equate it to $(q - k\xi)^2$, where k is some integer.

Since $$A(x_0 + \xi)^2 - C = (q - k\xi)^2,$$
it follows (because by hypothesis $Ax_0^2 - C = q^2$) that
$$2\xi(Ax_0 + kq) = \xi^2(k^2 - A),$$
whence $$\xi = \frac{2(Ax_0 + kq)}{k^2 - A},$$

and $$x = x_0 + \frac{2(Ax_0 + kq)}{k^2 - A}.$$

In the second Lemma to VI. 12 Diophantus does prove that the equation $Ax^2 + C = y^2$ has an infinite number of solutions when $A + C$ is a square, *i.e.* in the particular case where the value $x = 1$ satisfies the equation. But he does not always bear this in mind; for in III. 10 the equation $52x^2 + 12 = y^2$ is regarded as impossible of solution although $52 + 12 = 64$, a square, and a rational solution is therefore possible. Again in III. 11 the equation $266x^2 - 10 = y^2$ is regarded as impossible though $x = 1$ satisfies it.

The method used by Diophantus in the second Lemma to VI. 12 is like that of the Lemma to VI. 15.

Suppose that $A + C = q^2$.

Put $1 + \xi$ for x in the original expression $Ax^2 + C$, and equate it to $(q - k\xi)^2$, where k is some integer.

Thus $$A(1+\xi)^2+C=(q-k\xi)^2,$$
and it follows that $$2\xi(A+kq)=\xi^2(k^2-A),$$
so that $$\xi=\frac{2(A+kq)}{k^2-A},$$
and $$x=1+\frac{2(A+kq)}{k^2-A}.$$

It is of course necessary to choose k^2 such that $k^2>A$.

It is clear that, if $x=0$ satisfies the equation, C is a square, and therefore this case (γ) includes the previous case (β).

It is to be observed that in VI. 14 Diophantus says that a rational solution of the equation
$$Ax^2-c^2=y^2$$
is impossible *unless A is the sum of two squares.*

[In fact, if $x=p/q$ satisfies the equation, and $Ax^2-c^2=k^2$, we have $$Ap^2=c^2q^2+k^2q^2,$$
or $$A=\left(\frac{cq}{p}\right)^2+\left(\frac{kq}{p}\right)^2.]$$

Lastly, we have to consider

Form $Ax^2+Bx+C=y^2$.

This equation can be reduced by means of a change of variable to the preceding form wanting the second term. For, if we put $x=z-\frac{B}{2A}$, the transformation gives
$$Az^2+\frac{4AC-B^2}{4A}=y^2.$$

Diophantus, however, treats this form of the equation quite separately from the other and less fully. According to him the rational solution is only possible in the following cases.

(α) When A is positive and a square, or the equation is
$$a^2x^2+Bx+C=y^2.$$
Diophantus then puts $y^2=(ax-m)^2$, whence
$$x=\frac{m^2-C}{2am+B}.$$ (Exx. II. 20, 22 etc.)

(β) When C is positive and a square, or the equation is
$$Ax^2+Bx+c^2=y^2.$$
Diophantus puts $y^2=(c-mx)^2$, whence
$$x=\frac{2mc+B}{m^2-A}.$$ (Exx. IV. 8, 9 etc.)

(γ) When $\frac{1}{4}B^2 - AC$ is positive and a square number. Diophantus never expressly enunciates the possibility of this case; but it occurs, as it were unawares, in IV. 31. In that problem

$$3x + 18 - x^2$$

is to be made a square. To solve this Diophantus assumes

$$3x + 18 - x^2 = 4x^2,$$

which leads to the quadratic $3x + 18 - 5x^2 = 0$; but "the equation is not rational." Accordingly the assumption $4x^2$ will not do; "and we must find a square [to replace 4] such that 18 times (this square + 1) + $(\frac{3}{2})^2$ may be a square." Diophantus then solves the auxiliary equation $18(m^2+1)+\frac{9}{4}=y^2$, finding $m = 18$. He then assumes $3x + 18 - x^2 = (18)^2x^2$, which gives $325x^2 - 3x - 18 = 0$, "and $x = \frac{78}{325}$, that is $\frac{6}{25}$."[1]

[1] With this solution should be compared the much simpler solution of this case given by Euler (*Algebra*, tr. Hewlett, 1840, Part II. Arts. 50–53), depending on the separation of the quadratic expression into factors. (Curiously enough Diophantus does not separate quadratic expressions into their factors except in one case, VI. 19, where however his purpose is quite different: he has made the sum of three sides of a right-angled triangle $4x^2+6x+2$, which has to be a cube, and, in order to simplify, he divides throughout by $x+1$, which leaves $4x+2$ to be made a cube.)

Since $\frac{1}{4}B^2 - AC$ is a square, the roots of the quadratic $Ax^2+Bx+C=0$ are real, and the expression has two real linear factors. Take the particular case now in question, where Diophantus actually arrives at $3x+18-x^2$ as the result of multiplying $6-x$ and $3+x$, but makes no use of the factors.

We have
$$3x+18-x^2=(6-x)(3+x).$$

Assume then
$$(6-x)(3+x)=\frac{p^2}{q^2}(6-x)^2,$$

and we have
$$p^2(6-x)=q^2(3+x),$$
$$x=\frac{6p^2-3q^2}{p^2+q^2},$$

where p, q may be any numbers subject to the condition that $2p^2>q^2$. If $p^2=9$, $q^2=16$, we have Diophantus' solution $x=\frac{6}{25}$.

In general, if
$$Ax^2+Bx+C=(f+gx)(h+kx),$$

we can put
$$(f+gx)(h+kx)=\frac{p^2}{q^2}(f+gx)^2,$$

whence
$$q^2(h+kx)=p^2(f+gx),$$

and
$$x=\frac{fp^2-hq^2}{kq^2-gp^2}.$$

This case, says Euler, leads to a fourth case in which $Ax^2+Bx+C=y^2$ can be solved, though neither A nor C is a square, and though B^2-4AC is not a square either. The fourth case is that in which Ax^2+Bx+C is the sum of two parts, one of which is a square and the other is the product of two factors linear in x. For suppose

$$Ax^2+Bx+C=Z^2+XY,$$

where
$$Z=dx+e,\quad X=fx+g,\quad Y=hx+k.$$

It is worth observing that from this example of Diophantus we can deduce the reduction of this general case to the form

$$Ax^2 + C = y^2$$

wanting the middle term.

Assume, with Diophantus, that $Ax^2 + Bx + C = m^2x^2$: therefore by solution we have

$$x = \frac{-\frac{1}{2}B \pm \sqrt{\frac{1}{4}B^2 - AC + Cm^2}}{A - m^2},$$

and x is rational provided that $\frac{1}{4}B^2 - AC + Cm^2$ is a square. This condition can be fulfilled if $\frac{1}{4}B^2 - AC$ is a square, by the pre-

---

We can then put $$Z^2 + XY = \left(Z + \frac{p}{q}X\right)^2,$$

whence $$Y = 2\frac{p}{q}Z + \frac{p^2}{q^2}X,$$

or $$hx + k = 2\frac{p}{q}(dx + e) + \frac{p^2}{q^2}(fx + g),$$

that is, $$x(p^2f + 2pqd - q^2h) = kq^2 - 2pqe - p^2g.$$

Ex. 1. Equation $2x^2 - 1 = y^2$.

Put $$2x^2 - 1 = x^2 + (x+1)(x-1) = \left\{x + \frac{p}{q}(x+1)\right\}^2.$$

Therefore $$x - 1 = 2\frac{p}{q}x + \frac{p^2}{q^2}(x+1),$$

and $$x(p^2 + 2pq - q^2) = -(p^2 + q^2).$$

As x^2 is alone found in our equation, we can take either the positive or negative sign and we may put

$$x = \frac{p^2 + q^2}{p^2 + 2pq - q^2}.$$

Ex. 2. Equation $2x^2 + 2 = y^2$.

Here we put $$2x^2 + 2 = 4 + 2(x+1)(x-1).$$

Equating this to $$\left\{2 + \frac{p}{q}(x+1)\right\}^2,$$

we have $$2(x-1) = 4\frac{p}{q} + \frac{p^2}{q^2}(x+1),$$

or $$x(p^2 - 2q^2) = -(2q^2 + 4pq + p^2),$$

and $$x = \frac{p^2 + 4pq + 2q^2}{2q^2 - p^2}.$$

It is to be observed that this method enables us to solve the equation

$$Ax^2 - c^2 = y^2$$

whenever it can be solved rationally, *i.e.* whenever A is the sum of two squares ($d^2 + e^2$, say). For then

$$Ax^2 - c^2 = d^2x^2 + (ex - c)(ex + c).$$

In cases not covered by any of the above rules our only plan is to try to discover *one* solution empirically. If one solution is thus found, we can find any number of others; if we cannot discover such a solution by trial (even after reducing the equation to the simplest form $A'x'^2 + C = y'^2$), recourse must be had to the method of continued fractions elaborated by Lagrange (cf. *Oeuvres*, II. pp. 377–535 and pp. 655—726; additions to Euler's *Algebra*).

ceding case. If $\frac{1}{4}B^2 - AC$ is not a square, we have to solve (putting, for brevity, D for $\frac{1}{4}B^2 - AC$) the equation

$$D + Cm^2 = y^2,$$

and the reduction is effected.

(2) *Double-equation.*

By the name "double-equation" Diophantus denotes the problem of finding one value of the unknown quantity which will make two different functions of it simultaneously rational square numbers. The Greek term for the "double-equation" occurs variously as διπλοϊσότης, διπλῆ ἰσότης or διπλῆ ἴσωσις. We have then to solve the equations

$$\left.\begin{aligned} mx^2 + \alpha x + a &= u^2 \\ nx^2 + \beta x + b &= w^2 \end{aligned}\right\}$$

in rational numbers. The necessary preliminary condition is that each of the two expressions can severally be made squares. This is always possible when the first term (in x^2) is wanting. This is the simplest case, and we shall accordingly take it first.

1. *Double-equation of the first degree.*

Diophantus has one general method of solving the equations

$$\left.\begin{aligned} \alpha x + a &= u^2 \\ \beta x + b &= w^2 \end{aligned}\right\},$$

taking slightly different forms according to the nature of the coefficients.

(α) First method of solution of

$$\left.\begin{aligned} \alpha x + a &= u^2 \\ \beta x + b &= w^2 \end{aligned}\right\}.$$

This method depends upon the identity

$$\{\tfrac{1}{2}(p+q)\}^2 - \{\tfrac{1}{2}(p-q)\}^2 = pq.$$

If the difference between the two expressions in x can be separated into two factors p, q, the expressions themselves are equated to $\{\frac{1}{2}(p \pm q)\}^2$ respectively. Diophantus himself (II. 11) states his rule thus.

"Observing the difference [between the two expressions], seek two numbers such that their product is equal to this difference; then equate either the square of half the difference of the two factors to the lesser of the expressions or the square of half the sum to the greater."

We will take the general case and investigate to what particular classes of cases the method is applicable, from Diophantus' point of view, remembering that his cases are such that the final quadratic equation in x always reduces to a simple equation.

Take the equations

$$\left.\begin{aligned}\alpha x + a = u^2\\ \beta x + b = w^2\end{aligned}\right\}.$$

Subtracting, we have

$$(\alpha - \beta)x + (a - b) = u^2 - w^2.$$

We have then to separate $(\alpha - \beta)x + (a - b)$ into two factors; let these be p, $\{(\alpha - \beta)x + (a - b)\}/p$.

We write accordingly

$$u \pm w = \frac{(\alpha - \beta)x + a - b}{p},$$

$$u \mp w = p.$$

Thus $$u^2 = \alpha x + a = \frac{1}{4}\left\{\frac{(\alpha - \beta)x + a - b}{p} + p\right\}^2;$$

therefore $$\{(\alpha - \beta)x + a - b + p^2\}^2 = 4p^2(\alpha x + a),$$

or $(\alpha - \beta)^2x^2 + 2x\{(\alpha - \beta)(a - b + p^2) - 2p^2\alpha\} + (a - b + p^2)^2 - 4ap^2 = 0$,

that is, $$(\alpha - \beta)^2x^2 + 2x\{(\alpha - \beta)(a - b) - p^2(\alpha + \beta)\} + (a - b)^2 - 2p^2(a + b) + p^4 = 0.$$

Now, in order that this equation may reduce to a simple equation, either

(1) The coefficient of x^2 must vanish, so that

$$\alpha = \beta,$$

or (2) The absolute term must vanish, that is,

$$p^4 - 2p^2(a + b) + (a - b)^2 = 0,$$

or $$\{p^2 - (a + b)\}^2 = 4ab,$$

so that ab must be a square number.

Therefore either a and b are both squares, in which case we may substitute c^2 and d^2 for them respectively, p being then equal to $c \pm d$, or the ratio of a to b is the ratio of a square to a square.

With respect to (1) we observe that on one condition it is not necessary that $\alpha - \beta$ should vanish, *i.e.* provided we can, before solving the equations, make the coefficients of x the same in both expressions by multiplying either equation or both equations by some square number, an operation which does not affect the problem, since a square multiplied by a square is still a square.

In other words, it is only necessary that the ratio of α to β should be the ratio of a square to a square[1].

Thus, if $\alpha/\beta = m^2/n^2$ or $\alpha n^2 = \beta m^2$, the equations can be solved by multiplying them respectively by n^2 and m^2; we can in fact solve the equations

$$\left.\begin{array}{r}\alpha m^2 x + a = u^2 \\ \alpha n^2 x + b = w^2\end{array}\right\},$$

like the equations

$$\left.\begin{array}{r}\alpha x + a = u'^2 \\ \alpha x + b = w'^2\end{array}\right\},$$

in an infinite number of ways.

Again, the equations under (2)

$$\left.\begin{array}{r}\alpha x + c^2 = u^2 \\ \beta x + d^2 = w^2\end{array}\right\}$$

can be solved in two different ways according as we write them in this form or in the form

$$\left.\begin{array}{r}\alpha d^2 x + c^2 d^2 = u'^2 \\ \beta c^2 x + c^2 d^2 = w'^2\end{array}\right\},$$

obtained by multiplying them respectively by d^2, c^2, in order that the absolute terms may be equal.

I shall now give those of the possible cases which we find solved in Diophantus' own work. These are equations

(1) of the form

$$\left.\begin{array}{r}\alpha m^2 x + a = u^2 \\ \alpha n^2 x + b = w^2\end{array}\right\},$$

[1] Diophantus actually states this condition in the solution of IV. 32 where, on arriving at the equations

$$\left.\begin{array}{r}8 - x = u^2 \\ 8 - 3x = w^2\end{array}\right\},$$

he says: "And this is not rational because the coefficients of x have not to one another the ratio which a square number has to a square number."

Similarly in the second solution of III. 15 he states the same condition along with an alternative condition, namely that a has to b the ratio of a square to a square, which is the second condition arrived at under (2) above. On obtaining the equations

$$\left.\begin{array}{r}4x + 3 = u^2 \\ 6\tfrac{1}{2}x + 5\tfrac{1}{2} = w^2\end{array}\right\},$$

Diophantus observes "But, since the coefficients in one expression are respectively greater than those in the other, neither have they (in either case) the ratio which a square number has to a square number, the hypothesis which we took is useless."

Cf. also IV. 39 where he says that the equations

$$\left.\begin{array}{r}8x + 4 = u^2 \\ 6x + 4 = w^2\end{array}\right\}$$

are possible of solution because there is a square number of units in each expression.

a case which includes the more common one where the coefficients of x in both are *equal*;

(2) of the form

$$\left.\begin{array}{l}\alpha x + c^2 = u^2 \\ \beta x + d^2 = w^2\end{array}\right\},$$

solved in two different ways according as they are written in this form or in the alternative form

$$\left.\begin{array}{l}\alpha d^2 x + c^2 d^2 = u'^2 \\ \beta c^2 x + c^2 d^2 = w'^2\end{array}\right\}.$$

General solution of Form (1) or

$$\left.\begin{array}{l}\alpha m^2 x + a = u^2 \\ \alpha n^2 x + b = w^2\end{array}\right\}.$$

Multiply by n^2, m^2 respectively, and we have to solve the equations

$$\left.\begin{array}{l}\alpha m^2 n^2 x + a n^2 = u'^2 \\ \alpha m^2 n^2 x + b m^2 = w'^2\end{array}\right\}.$$

The difference is $an^2 - bm^2$; suppose this separated into two factors p, q.

Let $\qquad u' \pm w' = p,$

$\qquad\qquad u' \mp w' = q;$

therefore $\qquad u'^2 = \frac{1}{4}(p+q)^2,\ w'^2 = \frac{1}{4}(p-q)^2,$

and $\qquad \alpha m^2 n^2 x + a n^2 = \frac{1}{4}(p+q)^2,$

or $\qquad \alpha m^2 n^2 x + b m^2 = \frac{1}{4}(p-q)^2.$

Either equation gives the same value of x, and

$$x = \frac{\frac{1}{4}(p^2+q^2) - \frac{1}{2}(an^2+bm^2)}{\alpha m^2 n^2},$$

since $pq = an^2 - bm^2$.

Any factors p, q may be chosen provided that the resulting value of x is *positive*.

Ex. from Diophantus:

$$\left.\begin{array}{l}65 - 6x = u^2 \\ 65 - 24x = w^2\end{array}\right\}; \qquad \text{(IV. 32.)}$$

therefore

$$\left.\begin{array}{l}260 - 24x = u'^2 \\ 65 - 24x = w^2\end{array}\right\}.$$

The difference $= 195 = 15 \cdot 13$, say;

therefore $\frac{1}{4}(15-13)^2 = 65 - 24x$; that is, $24x = 64$, and $x = \frac{8}{3}$.

General solution (first method) of Form (2), or

$$\left.\begin{aligned} \alpha x + c^2 &= u'^2 \\ \beta x + d^2 &= w'^2 \end{aligned}\right\}.$$

In order to solve by this method, we multiply by d^2, c^2 respectively and write

$$\left.\begin{aligned} \alpha d^2 x + c^2 d^2 &= u^2 \\ \beta c^2 x + c^2 d^2 &= w^2 \end{aligned}\right\},$$

u being supposed to be the greater.

The difference $= (\alpha d^2 - \beta c^2) x$. Let the factors of this be px, q.

Therefore
$$u^2 = \tfrac{1}{4}(px+q)^2,$$
$$w^2 = \tfrac{1}{4}(px-q)^2.$$

Thus x is found from the equation

$$\alpha d^2 x + c^2 d^2 = \tfrac{1}{4}(px+q)^2.$$

This equation gives

$$p^2 x^2 + 2x(pq - 2\alpha d^2) + q^2 - 4c^2 d^2 = 0,$$

or, since $pq = (\alpha d^2 - \beta c^2)$,

$$p^2 x^2 - 2x(\alpha d^2 + \beta c^2) + q^2 - 4c^2 d^2 = 0.$$

In order that this may reduce to a simple equation, as Diophantus requires, the absolute term must vanish,

or
$$q^2 = 4c^2 d^2,$$
and
$$q = 2cd.$$

Thus our method in this case furnishes us with only *one* solution of the double-equation, q being restricted to the value $2cd$, and the solution is

$$x = \frac{2(\alpha d^2 + \beta c^2)}{p^2} = \frac{8c^2 d^2 (\alpha d^2 + \beta c^2)}{(\alpha d^2 - \beta c^2)^2}.$$

Ex. from Diophantus. This method is only used in one particular case (IV. 39), where $c^2 = d^2$ as the equations originally stand, the equations being

$$\left.\begin{aligned} 8x + 4 &= u^2 \\ 6x + 4 &= w^2 \end{aligned}\right\}.$$

The difference is $2x$, and q is necessarily taken to be $2\sqrt{4}$, or 4; the factors are therefore $\frac{1}{2}x$, 4.

Therefore
$$8x + 4 = \tfrac{1}{4}(\tfrac{1}{2}x + 4)^2,$$
and
$$x = 112.$$

General solution (second method) of Form (2) or

$$\left.\begin{aligned} \alpha x + c^2 &= u^2 \\ \beta x + d^2 &= w^2 \end{aligned}\right\}.$$

The difference $= (\alpha - \beta)\,x + (c^2 - d^2)$.

Let the factors of this be p, $\{(\alpha - \beta)\,x + c^2 - d^2\}/p$.

Then, as before proved (p. 74), p must be equal to $(c \pm d)$.

Therefore the factors are

$$\frac{\alpha - \beta}{c \pm d}x + c \mp d, \quad c \pm d,$$

and we have finally

$$\alpha x + c^2 = \frac{1}{4}\left(\frac{\alpha - \beta}{c \pm d}x + c \mp d + c \pm d\right)^2$$

$$= \frac{1}{4}\left(\frac{\alpha - \beta}{c \pm d}x + 2c\right)^2.$$

Therefore $$\left(\frac{\alpha - \beta}{c \pm d}\right)^2 x^2 + 4x\left\{\frac{c(\alpha - \beta)}{c \pm d} - \alpha\right\} = 0,$$

which equation gives two possible values for x. Thus in this case we can find by our method *two* values of x, since one of the factors p may be either $(c + d)$ or $(c - d)$.

Ex. from Diophantus. To solve the equations

$$\left.\begin{aligned} 10x + 9 &= u^2 \\ 5x + 4 &= w^2 \end{aligned}\right\}. \qquad \text{(III. 15.)}$$

The difference is here $5x + 5$, and Diophantus chooses as the factors 5, $x + 1$. This case therefore corresponds to the value $c + d$ of p. The solution is given by

$$(\tfrac{1}{2}x + 3)^2 = 10x + 9, \text{ whence } x = 28.$$

The other value, $c - d$, of p is in this case excluded, because it would lead to a negative value of x.

The possibility of deriving any number of solutions of a double-equation when one solution is known does not seem to have been noticed by Diophantus, though he uses the principle in certain cases of the single equation (see above, pp. 69, 70). Fermat was the first, apparently, to discover that this might always be done, if one value a of x were known, by substituting $x + a$ for x in the equations. By this means it is possible to find a positive solution, even if a is negative, by successive applications of the principle.

But, nevertheless, Diophantus had certain peculiar artifices by which he could arrive at a second value. One of these artifices (which is made necessary in one case by the unsuitableness of the value of x found by the ordinary method) gives a different way of solving a double-equation from that which has been explained, and is used only in one special case (IV. 39).

(β) Second method of solving a double-equation of the first degree.

Consider only the special case

$$hx + n^2 = u^2,$$
$$(h+f)x + n^2 = w^2.$$

Take these expressions, and n^2, and write them in order of magnitude, denoting them for convenience by A, B, C.

$$A = (h+f)x + n^2, \quad B = hx + n^2, \quad C = n^2.$$

Therefore $$\frac{A-B}{B-C} = \frac{f}{h}, \text{ and } \left.\begin{matrix} A - B = fx \\ B - C = hx \end{matrix}\right\}.$$

Suppose now that $hx + n^2 = (y+n)^2$;

therefore $$hx = y^2 + 2ny,$$

and $$A - B = \frac{f}{h}(y^2 + 2ny),$$

or $$A = (y+n)^2 + \frac{f}{h}(y^2 + 2ny);$$

thus it is only necessary to make this expression a square.

Assume therefore that

$$\left(1 + \frac{f}{h}\right)y^2 + 2n\left(\frac{f}{h} + 1\right)y + n^2 = (py - n)^2;$$

and any number of values for y, and therefore for x, can be found, by varying p.

Ex. from Diophantus (the only one), IV. 39.

In this case there is the additional condition of a limit to the value of x. The double-equation

$$\left.\begin{matrix} 8x + 4 = u^2 \\ 6x + 4 = w^2 \end{matrix}\right\}$$

has to be solved in such a manner that $x < 2$.

Here $\frac{A-B}{B-C} = \frac{1}{3}$, and B is taken[1] to be $(y+2)^2$.

Therefore $$A - B = \tfrac{1}{3}(y^2 + 4y);$$

therefore $$A = \tfrac{1}{3}(y^2 + 4y) + y^2 + 4y + 4$$
$$= \tfrac{4}{3}y^2 + \tfrac{16}{3}y + 4,$$

which must be made a square.

[1] Of course Diophantus uses the same variable x where I have for clearness used y. Then, to express what I have called m later, he says: "I form a square from 3 minus *some number* of x's, and x becomes *some number* multiplied by 6 and then added to 12, divided by the difference by which the square of *the number* exceeds 3."

If we multiply by $\frac{9}{4}$, we must make

$$3y^2 + 12y + 9 = \text{a square},$$

where y must be < 2.

Diophantus assumes

$$3y^2 + 12y + 9 = (3 - my)^2,$$

whence
$$y = \frac{6m + 12}{m^2 - 3},$$

and the value of m is then taken such as to make $y < 2$.

It is in a note on this problem that Bachet shows that the double-equation

$$\left.\begin{aligned} \alpha x + a &= u^2 \\ \beta x + b &= w^2 \end{aligned}\right\}$$

can be rationally solved by a similar method provided that the coefficients satisfy either of two conditions, although none of the coefficients are squares and neither of the ratios $\alpha : \beta$ and $a : b$ is equal to the ratio of a square to a square. Bachet's conditions are:

(1) That, when the difference between the two expressions is multiplied or divided by a suitably-chosen number, and the expression thus obtained is subtracted from the smaller of the original expressions, the result is a square number, or

(2) That, when the difference between the two expressions is multiplied or divided by a suitably-chosen number, and the smaller of the two original expressions is subtracted from the expression obtained by the said multiplication or division, the result is a number bearing to the multiplier or divisor the ratio of a square to a square[1].

[1] Bachet of course does not solve equations in general expressions (his notation does not admit of this), but illustrates his conditions by equations in which the coefficients are specific numbers. I will give one of his illustrations of each condition, and then set the conditions out more generally.

Case (1). Equations
$$\left.\begin{aligned} 3x + 13 &= u^2 \\ x + 7 &= w^2 \end{aligned}\right\};$$
difference
$$2x + 6$$

The suitably-chosen number (to *divide* by in this case) is 2;

$$\tfrac{1}{2}\,(\text{difference}) = x + 3,$$

and (lesser expression) $- \frac{1}{2}$ (difference) $= x + 7 - (x + 3) = 4$, that is, a square.

We have then to find two squares such that

their difference $= 2$ (difference between lesser and 4).

Assume that the lesser $= (y + 2)^2$, 2 being the square root of 4.

Therefore
$$\begin{aligned} (\text{greater square}) &= 3\,(\text{lesser}) - 8 \\ &= 3y^2 + 12y + 4. \end{aligned}$$

2. *Double-equation of the second degree,*

or the general form

$$\left.\begin{aligned} Ax^2 + Bx + C = u^2 \\ A'x^2 + B'x + C' = w^2 \end{aligned}\right\}.$$

These equations are much less thoroughly treated in Diophantus than those of the first degree. Only such special instances

---

To make $3y^2+12y+4$ a square we put

$$3y^2+12y+4=(2-py)^2,$$

where p must lie between certain limits which have next to be found. The equation gives

$$y=\frac{12+4p}{p^2-3}.$$

In order that y may be positive, p^2 must be >3; and in order that the second of the original expressions, assumed equal to $(y+2)^2$, may be greater than 7 (it is in fact $x+7$), we must have $(y+2)>2\frac{3}{4}$ (an *a fortiori* limit, since $2\frac{3}{4}>\sqrt{7}$), or $y>\frac{3}{4}$.

Therefore $$4p+12>\tfrac{3}{4}(p^2-3),$$

or $$16p+57>3p^2.$$

Suppose that $3p^2=16p+53\frac{2}{3}$, which gives $p=7\frac{2}{3}$.

Therefore $$p<7\tfrac{2}{3}, \text{ but } p^2>3.$$

Put $p=3$ in the above equation; therefore

$$3y^2+12y+4=(2-3y)^2,$$

and $$y=4.$$

Therefore $$x=(y+2)^2-7=29.$$

Case (2). Equations

$$\left.\begin{aligned} 6x+25=u^2 \\ 2x+\ \ 3=w^2 \end{aligned}\right\};$$

difference $4x+22$

The suitable-number (again to *divide* by) in this case is 2;

$$\tfrac{1}{2}\,(\text{difference})=2x+11,$$

and $$\tfrac{1}{2}\,(\text{difference})-(\text{lesser expression})=8=2\cdot 4,$$

where 2 is the divisor used and 4 is the ratio of a square to a square.

Hence two squares have to be found such that

(their difference) = 2 (sum of lesser and 8).

If the lesser is y^2, the greater is $3y^2+16=(4-py)^2$, say.

Bachet gives, as limits for p,

$$p \not> 4\tfrac{1}{2}, \quad p^2>3,$$

and puts $p=3$. This gives $y=4$, so that $x=6\frac{1}{2}$.

Let us now state Bachet's conditions generally.

Suppose the equations to be

$$\left.\begin{aligned} \alpha x+a=u^2 \\ \beta x+b=w^2 \end{aligned}\right\}.$$

The difference is $(\alpha-\beta)\,x+(a-b)$.

This has to be multiplied by $\dfrac{\beta}{\alpha-\beta}$ which is the "suitable" factor in this case, and, if we subtract the product from $\beta x+b$, we obtain

$$b-\frac{\beta}{\alpha-\beta}(a-b), \quad \text{or} \quad \frac{\alpha b-a\beta}{\alpha-\beta}.$$

occur as can be easily solved by the methods which we have described for equations of the first degree.

The following types are found.

(1) $$\left.\begin{array}{l}\rho^2x^2+\alpha x+a=u^2\\ \rho^2x^2+\beta x+b=w^2\end{array}\right\}.$$

The difference is $(\alpha-\beta)x+(a-b)$, and, following the usual course, we may, *e.g.*, resolve this into the factors

---

(1) The first of Bachet's conditions is that

$$\frac{ab-a\beta}{a-\beta}=\text{a square}=p^2/q^2\text{, say.}$$

(2) The second condition is that

$$\frac{a\beta-ab}{a-\beta}=\frac{p^2}{q^2}\cdot\frac{\beta}{a-\beta},$$

or $$\frac{a\beta-ab}{\beta}=\text{a ratio of a square to a square.}$$

It is to be observed that the first of these conditions can be obtained by considering the equation

$$(a-\beta)^2x^2+2x\{(a-\beta)(a-b)-p^2(a+\beta)\}+(a-b)^2-2p^2(a+b)+p^4=0,$$

obtained on page 74 above.

Diophantus only considers the cases in which this equation reduces to a simple equation; but the solution of it as a *mixed* quadratic gives a rational value of x provided that

$$\{(a-\beta)(a-b)-p^2(a+\beta)\}^2-(a-\beta)^2\{(a-b)^2-2p^2(a+b)+p^4\}\text{ is a square,}$$

that is, if

$$p^4\{(a+\beta)^2-(a-\beta)^2\}+2p^2\{(a+b)(a-\beta)^2-(a^2-\beta^2)(a-b)\}\text{ is a square,}$$

which reduces to $$a\beta p^2+(a-\beta)(ab-a\beta)=\text{a square} \quad\ldots\ldots\ldots\ldots\ldots\ldots\ldots \text{(A).}$$

This can be solved (cf. p. 68 above), if

$$\frac{ab-a\beta}{a-\beta}\text{ is a square.}\qquad\text{(Bachet's first condition.)}$$

Again take Bachet's second condition

$$\frac{a\beta-ab}{\beta}=\text{a square}=\frac{r^2}{s^2}\text{ say,}$$

and substitute $\beta r^2/s^2$ for $a\beta-ab$ in the equation (A) above.

Therefore $$a\beta p^2-(a-\beta)\beta\frac{r^2}{s^2}=\text{a square,}$$

or $$a\beta p'^2-(a-\beta)\beta=\text{a square.}$$

This is satisfied by $p'=1$; therefore (p. 69) any number of other solutions can be found.

The second condition can also be obtained directly by eliminating x from the equations

$$\left.\begin{array}{l}ax+a=u^2\\ \beta x+b=w^2\end{array}\right\};$$

for the result is $$\frac{a}{\beta}w^2+\frac{a\beta-ab}{\beta}=u^2,$$

which can be rationally solved if

$$\frac{a\beta-ab}{\beta}=\text{a square.}$$

$$(a-b)\left\{\frac{\alpha-\beta}{a-b}x+1\right\};$$

as usual, we put

$$\rho^2x^2+\alpha x+a=\frac{1}{4}\left(\frac{\alpha-\beta}{a-b}x+1+a-b\right)^2,$$

or

$$\rho^2x^2+\beta x+b=\frac{1}{4}\left(\frac{\alpha-\beta}{a-b}x+1-a+b\right)^2.$$

In order that x may be rational a condition is necessary; thus x is rational if

$$\rho=\frac{1}{2}\frac{\alpha-\beta}{a-b}.$$

This is the case in the only instance of the type where a is not equal to b, namely (III. 13)

$$\left.\begin{aligned}4x^2+15x&=u^2\\4x^2-x-4&=w^2\end{aligned}\right\};$$

the difference is $16x+4$, and the resolution of this into the factors 4, $4x+1$ solves the problem.

In the other cases of the type $a=b$; the difference is then $(\alpha-\beta)x$, which is resolved into the factors

$$\frac{\alpha-\beta}{2\rho},\quad 2\rho x;$$

and we put

$$\rho^2x^2+\alpha x+a=\frac{1}{4}\left(\frac{\alpha-\beta}{2\rho}+2\rho x\right)^2,$$

or

$$\rho^2x^2+\beta x+a=\frac{1}{4}\left(\frac{\alpha-\beta}{2\rho}-2\rho x\right)^2,$$

whence

$$\frac{\alpha+\beta}{2}x=\left(\frac{\alpha-\beta}{4\rho}\right)^2-a.$$

Exx. from Diophantus:

$$\left.\begin{aligned}x^2+x-1&=u^2\\x^2-1&=w^2\end{aligned}\right\}\qquad\text{(IV. 23.)}$$

and

$$\left.\begin{aligned}x^2+14x+1&=u^2\\x^2+1&=w^2\end{aligned}\right\}.\qquad\text{(VI. 8.)}$$

(2) The second type found in Diophantus[1] is

$$\left.\begin{aligned}x^2+\alpha x+a&=u^2\\\beta x+a&=w^2\end{aligned}\right\},$$

where one equation has no term in x^2, and $\rho=1$, $a=b$.

[1] It is perhaps worth noting that the method of the "double-equation" has a distinct advantage in this type of case. The alternative is to solve by the method of Euler (who does not use the "double-equation"), *i.e.* to put the linear expression equal to p^2 and then, substituting the value of x (in terms of p) in the quadratic expression, to solve the

The difference $x^2+(\alpha-\beta)x$ is resolved into the factors

$$x(x+\alpha-\beta);$$

and we put
$$\beta x+a=\tfrac{1}{4}(\alpha-\beta)^2,$$
which gives x.

---

resulting equation in p. But the difficulties would generally be great. Take the case of VI. 6 where

$$\left.\begin{matrix}x^2+1\\ 14x+1\end{matrix}\right\}\text{ have to be made squares.}$$

If $14x+1=p^2$, $x=(p^2-1)/14$;

therefore
$$x^2+1=\frac{(p^2-1)^2}{14^2}+1\text{ has to be made a square,}$$
or
$$p^4-2p^2+197=\text{a square.}$$

This does not admit of solution unless we could somehow discover empirically *one* value of p which would satisfy the requirement, and this would be very difficult.

Let us take an easier case for solution by this method,

$$\left.\begin{matrix}x^2+1=u^2\\ x+1=w^2\end{matrix}\right\},$$

which is solved by Euler (*Algebra*, Part II. Art. 222), and let us compare the working of the two methods in this case.

I. *Euler's method.* Assuming $x+1=p^2$ and substituting p^2-1 for x in the quadratic expression, we have

$$p^4-2p^2+2=\text{a square.}$$

This can only be solved generally if we can discover one possible value of p by trial; this however is not difficult in the particular case, for $p=1$ is an obvious solution.

To find others we put $1+q$ instead of p in the expression to be made a square; this gives

$$1+4q^2+4q^3+q^4=\text{a square.}$$

This can be solved in several ways.

1. Suppose
$$1+4q^2+4q^3+q^4=(1+q^2)^2;$$
thus
$$4q^2+4q^3=2q^2,\text{ whence } q=-\frac{1}{2},\ p=\frac{1}{2}\text{ and } x=-\frac{3}{4}.$$

2. Suppose
$$1+4q^2+4q^3+q^4=(1-q^2)^2;$$
thus
$$4q^2+4q^3=-2q^2,\text{ and } q=-\frac{3}{2},\ p=-\frac{1}{2}\text{ and } x=-\frac{3}{4}.$$

3. Suppose
$$1+4q^2+4q^3+q^4=(1\pm 2q\pm q^2)^2;$$
and we find, in either case, that $q=-2$, so that $p=-1$, $x=0$.

4. Suppose
$$1+4q^2+4q^3+q^4=(1+2q^2)^2;$$
and we have $4q^3+q^4=4q^4$, whence $q=\frac{4}{3}$, $p=\frac{7}{3}$ and $x=\left(\frac{7}{3}\right)^2-1=\frac{40}{9}$.

This value of x satisfies the conditions, for

$$x+1=\left(\frac{7}{3}\right)^2,\quad x^2+1=\frac{1681}{81}=\left(\frac{41}{9}\right)^2.$$

The above five suppositions therefore give only two serviceable solutions

$$x=-\frac{3}{4},\quad x=\frac{40}{9}.$$

To find another solution we take one of the values of q already found, say $q=-\frac{1}{2}$, and

Exx. from Diophantus:

$$\left.\begin{aligned} x^2 - 12 &= u^2 \\ 6\tfrac{1}{2}x - 12 &= w^2 \end{aligned}\right\}, \qquad \text{(V. 1.)}$$

$$\left.\begin{aligned} x^2 + 1 &= u^2 \\ 14x + 1 &= w^2 \end{aligned}\right\}, \qquad \text{(VI. 6.)}$$

$$\left.\begin{aligned} x^2 - 6144x + 1048576 &= u^2 \\ x + 64 &= w^2 \end{aligned}\right\}. \qquad \text{(VI. 22.)}$$

---

substitute $r - \frac{1}{2}$ for q. This gives $p = 1 + q = r + \frac{1}{2}$, and we substitute this value for p in the expression $p^4 - 2p^2 + 2$.

We have then $\frac{25}{16} - \frac{3}{2}r - \frac{1}{2}r^2 + 2r^3 + r^4$ to be made a square, or

$$25 - 24r - 8r^2 + 32r^3 + 16r^4 = \text{a square.}$$

1. We take $5 + fr \pm 4r^2$ for the root, so that the absolute term and the term in r^4 may disappear. We can make the term in r disappear also by putting $10f = -24$ or $f = -\frac{12}{5}$. We then have

$$-8r^2 + 32r^3 = r^2(f^2 \pm 40) \pm 8fr^3.$$

(*a*) The upper sign gives

$$-8 + 32r = 40 + f^2 + 8fr,$$

and
$$r = (f^2 + 48)/(32 - 8f) = \frac{21}{20};$$

thus
$$p = \frac{31}{20}, \text{ and } x = p^2 - 1 = \frac{561}{400}.$$

(*b*) The lower sign gives

$$-8 + 32r = -40 + f^2 - 8fr,$$

and
$$r = (f^2 - 32)/(32 + 8f) = -\frac{41}{20};$$

thus
$$p = -\frac{31}{20}, \text{ and } x = \frac{561}{400} \text{ as before.}$$

We have therefore $x + 1 = \left(\frac{31}{20}\right)^2$, and $x^2 + 1 = \left(\frac{689}{400}\right)^2$.

2. Another solution is found by assuming the root to be $5 + fr + gr^2$ and determining f and g so that the absolute term and the terms in r, r^2 may vanish; the result is

$$f = -\frac{12}{5}, \quad g = -\frac{172}{125}, \quad r = \frac{2fg - 32}{16 - g^2} = -\frac{1550}{861},$$

whence
$$p = -\frac{2239}{1722}, \quad x = \frac{2047837}{2965284}, \quad x + 1 = \left(\frac{2239}{1722}\right)^2$$

and
$$x^2 + 1 = \left(\frac{3603685}{2965284}\right)^2.$$

II. *Method of "double-equation."*

$$x^2 + 1 = u^2,$$
$$x + 1 = w^2.$$

The difference $= x^2 - x$.

(1) If we take as factors x, $x - 1$ and, as usual, equate the square of half their difference, or $\frac{1}{4}$, to $x + 1$, we have

$$x + 1 = \frac{1}{4},$$

or
$$x = -\frac{3}{4}.$$

The absolute terms in the last case are made equal by multiplying the second equation by $(128)^2$ or 16384.

(3) One separate case must be mentioned which cannot be solved, from Diophantus' standpoint, by the foregoing method, but which sometimes occurs and is solved by a special artifice.

The form of double-equation is

$$\left.\begin{array}{l}\alpha x^2 + ax = u^2 \\ \beta x^2 + bx = w^2\end{array}\right\} \begin{array}{l}\dots\dots\dots\dots(1), \\ \dots\dots\dots\dots(2).\end{array}$$

Diophantus assumes $\qquad u^2 = m^2x^2,$

whence, by (1), $\qquad x = a/(m^2 - \alpha),$

---

(2) If we take $\frac{1}{2}x$, $2x-2$, as factors, half the sum of which is $\frac{5}{4}x-1$, so that the absolute terms may disappear in the resulting equation, we have

$$\frac{25}{16}x^2 - \frac{5}{2}x = x^2,$$

or

$$\frac{9}{16}x = \frac{5}{2},$$

and

$$x = \frac{40}{9}.$$

(3) To find another value by means of the first, namely $x = -\frac{3}{4}$, we substitute $y - \frac{3}{4}$ for x in the original expressions. We then have to solve

$$y^2 - \frac{3}{2}y + \frac{25}{16} = u^2,$$

$$y + \frac{1}{4} = w^2.$$

Multiply the latter by $\frac{25}{4}$ so as to make the absolute terms the same, and we must have

$$\frac{25}{4}y + \frac{25}{16} = w'^2.$$

Subtract from the first expression, and the difference is $y^2 - \frac{31}{4}y = y\left(y - \frac{31}{4}\right)$; then, equating the square of half the difference of the factors to the smaller expression, we have

$$\frac{1}{4}\left(\frac{31}{4}\right)^2 = \frac{25}{4}y + \frac{25}{16},$$

so that

$$961 = 400y + 100.$$

Therefore

$$y = \frac{861}{400}, \text{ and } x = y - \frac{3}{4} = \frac{561}{400}, \quad x + 1 = \left(\frac{31}{20}\right)^2, \quad x^2 + 1 = \left(\frac{689}{400}\right)^2.$$

(4) If we start from the known value $\frac{40}{9}$ and put $y + \frac{40}{9}$ for x in the equations, we obtain Euler's fourth value of x, namely $\frac{2047837}{2965284}$.

Thus all the four values obtained by Euler are more easily obtained by the method of the "double-equation."

and, by substitution in (2), we derive that

$$\beta\left(\frac{a}{m^2-\alpha}\right)^2+\frac{ba}{m^2-\alpha} \text{ must be a square,}$$

or

$$\frac{a^2\beta+ba(m^2-\alpha)}{(m^2-\alpha)^2}=\text{a square.}$$

We have therefore to solve the equation

$$abm^2+a(a\beta-\alpha b)=y^2,$$

and this form can or cannot be solved by the methods already given according to the nature of the coefficients[1]. Thus it can be solved if $(a\beta-\alpha b)/a$ is a square or if a/b is a square.

Exx. from Diophantus:

$$\left.\begin{aligned}6x^2+4x&=u^2\\6x^2+3x&=w^2\end{aligned}\right\}, \qquad \text{(VI. 12.)}$$

$$\left.\begin{aligned}6x^2-5x&=u^2\\6x^2-3x&=w^2\end{aligned}\right\}. \qquad \text{(VI. 14.)}$$

(*b*) *Indeterminate equations of a degree higher than the second.*

(1) *Single equations.*

These are properly divided by Nesselmann into two classes; the first comprises those problems in which it is required to make a function of x, of a degree higher than the second, a square; the second comprises those in which a rational value of x has to be found which will make any function of x, not a square, but a higher power of some number. The first class of problems requires the solution in rational numbers of

$$Ax^n+Bx^{n-1}+\ldots+Kx+L=y^2,$$

the second the solution of

$$Ax^n+Bx^{n-1}+\ldots+Kx+L=y^3,$$

for Diophantus does not go beyond making a certain function of x a cube. In no instance, however, of the first class does the index n exceed 6, while in the second class n does not (except in a special case or two) exceed 3.

[1] Diophantus apparently did not observe that the above form of double-equation can be reduced to one of the first degree by dividing by x^2 and substituting y for $1/x$, when it becomes

$$\alpha+ay=u'^2,$$
$$\beta+by=w'^2.$$

Adapting Bachet's second condition, we see that the equations can be rationally solved if $(\beta a-\alpha b)/a$ is a square, which is of course the same as one of the conditions under which the above equation $abm^2+a(a\beta-\alpha b)$ can be solved.

First Class. Equation

$$Ax^n + Bx^{n-1} + \dots + Kx + L = y^2.$$

The forms found in Diophantus are as follows:

1. Equation $Ax^3 + Bx^2 + Cx + d^2 = y^2$.

Here, as the absolute term is a square, we might put for y the expression $mx + d$, and determine m so that the coefficient of x in the resulting equation vanishes. In that case

$$2md = C, \text{ and } m = C/2d;$$

and we obtain, in Diophantus' manner, a simple equation for x, giving

$$x = \frac{C^2 - 4d^2B}{4d^2A}.$$

Or we might put for y the expression $m^2x^2 + nx + d$, and determine m, n so that the coefficients of x, x^2 in the resulting equation both vanish, in which case we should again have a simple equation for x. Diophantus, in the only example of this form of equation which occurs (VI. 18), makes the first supposition. The equation is

$$x^3 - 3x^2 + 3x + 1 = y^2,$$

and Diophantus assumes $y = \frac{3}{2}x + 1$, whence $x = \frac{21}{4}$.

2. Equation $Ax^4 + Bx^3 + Cx^2 + Dx + E = y^2$.

In order that this equation may be solved by Diophantus' method, either A or E must be a square. If A is a square and equal to a^2, we may assume $y = ax^2 + \frac{B}{2a}x + n$, determining n so that the term in x^2 vanishes. If E is a square ($= e^2$), we may write $y = mx^2 + \frac{D}{2e}x + e$, determining m so that the term in x^2 in the resulting equation may vanish. We shall then, in either case, obtain a simple equation in x.

The examples of this form in Diophantus are of the kind

$$a^2x^4 + Bx^3 + Cx^2 + Dx + e^2 = y^2,$$

where we can assume $y = \pm ax^2 + kx \pm e$, determining k so that in the resulting equation the coefficient of x^3 or of x may vanish; when we again have a simple equation.

Ex. from Diophantus (IV. 28):

$$9x^4 - 4x^3 + 6x^2 - 12x + 1 = y^2.$$

Diophantus assumes $y = 3x^2 - 6x + 1$, and the equation reduces to

$$32x^3 - 36x^2 = 0, \text{ whence } x = \tfrac{9}{8}.$$

Diophantus is guided in his choice of signs in the expression $\pm ax^2 + kx \pm e$ by the necessity for obtaining a "rational" result.

Far more difficult to solve are those equations in which, the left-hand expression being bi-quadratic, the odd powers of x are wanting, *i.e.* the equations $Ax^4 + Cx^2 + E = y^2$ and $Ax^4 + E = y^2$, even when A or E is a square, or both are so. These cases Diophantus treats more imperfectly.

3. Equation $Ax^4 + Cx^2 + E = y^2$.

Only very special cases of this form occur. The type is

$$a^2x^4 - c^2x^2 + e^2 = y^2,$$

which is written

$$a^2x^2 - c^2 + \frac{e^2}{x^2} = y'^2.$$

Here y' is assumed to be ax or e/x, and in either case we have a rational value for x.

Exx. from Diophantus:

$$25x^2 - 9 + \frac{25}{4x^2} = y^2. \qquad \text{(V. 27.)}$$

This is assumed to be equal to $25x^2$.

$$\frac{25}{4}x^2 - 25 + \frac{25}{4x^2} = y^2, \qquad \text{(V. 28.)}$$

where y^2 is assumed to be equal to $25/4x^2$.

4. Equation $Ax^4 + E = y^2$.

The case occurring in Diophantus is $x^4 + 97 = y^2$ (V. 29). Diophantus tries one assumption, $y = x^2 - 10$, and finds that this gives $x^2 = \frac{3}{20}$, which leads to no rational result. Instead, however, of investigating in what cases this equation can be solved, he simply drops the equation $x^4 + 97 = y^2$ and seeks, by altering his original assumptions, to obtain, in place of it, another equation of the same type which can be solved in rational numbers. In this case, by altering his assumptions, he is able to replace the refractory equation by a new one, $x^4 + 337 = y^2$, and at the same time to find a suitable substitution for y, namely $y = x^2 - 25$, which brings out a rational result, namely $x = \frac{12}{5}$. This is a good example of his characteristic artifice of "Back-reckoning[1]," as Nesselmann calls it.

5. Equation of sixth degree in the special form

$$x^6 - Ax^3 + Bx + c^2 = y^2.$$

[1] "Methode der Zurückrechnung und Nebenaufgabe."

It is only necessary to put $y = x^3 + c$, and we have

$$-Ax^2 + B = 2cx^2,$$

or

$$x^2 = \frac{B}{A + 2c},$$

which gives a rational solution if $B/(A + 2c)$ is a square.

6. If, however, this last condition does not hold, as in the case occurring IV. 18, $x^6 - 16x^3 + x + 64 = y^2$, Diophantus employs his usual artifice of "back-reckoning," which enables him to replace the equation by another, $x^6 - 128x^3 + x + 4096 = y^2$, where the condition is satisfied, and, by assuming $y = x^3 + 64$, x is found to be $\frac{1}{16}$.

Second Class. Equation of the form

$$Ax^n + Bx^{n-1} + \dots + Kx + L = y^3.$$

Except for such simple cases as $Ax^2 = y^3$, $Ax^4 = y^3$, where it is only necessary to assume $y = mx$, the only cases occurring in Diophantus are of the forms

$$Ax^2 + Bx + C = y^3,$$

$$Ax^3 + Bx^2 + Cx + D = y^3.$$

1. Equation $\qquad Ax^2 + Bx + C = y^3.$

There are only two examples of this form. First, in VI. 1 the expression $x^2 - 4x + 4$ is to be made a cube, being already a square. Diophantus naturally assumes $x - 2 =$ a cube number, say 8, and $x = 10$.

Secondly, in VI. 17 a peculiar case occurs. A cube is to be found which exceeds a square by 2. Diophantus assumes $(x - 1)^3$ for the cube and $(x + 1)^2$ for the square, and thus obtains the equation

$$x^3 - 3x^2 + 3x - 1 = x^2 + 2x + 3,$$

or

$$x^3 + x = 4x^2 + 4,$$

previously mentioned (pp. 66–7), which is satisfied by $x = 4$. The question arises whether it was accidentally or not that this cubic took so simple a form. Were $x - 1$, $x + 1$ assumed with knowledge and intention? Since 27 and 25 are, as Fermat observes[1], the only integral numbers which satisfy the conditions, it would seem that Diophantus so chose his assumptions as to lead back to a known result, while apparently making them arbitrarily with no particular reference to the end desired. Had this not

[1] Note on VI. 17, *Oeuvres*, I. pp. 333–4, II. p. 434. The fact was proved by Euler (*Algebra*, Part II. Arts. 188, 193). See note on VI. 17 *infra* for the proof.

been so, we should probably have found him, here as elsewhere in the work, first leading us on a false tack and then showing us how we can correct our assumptions. The fact that he here makes the right assumptions to begin with makes us suspect that the solution is not based on a general principle but is empirical merely.

2. Equation $Ax^3 + Bx^2 + Cx + D = y^3$.

If A or D is a cube number, this equation is easy of solution. For, first, if $A = a^3$, we have only to write $y = ax + \frac{B}{3a^2}$, and we obtain a simple equation in x.

Secondly, if $D = d^3$, we put $y = \frac{C}{3d^2} x + d$.

If the equation is $a^3x^3 + Bx^2 + Cx + d^3 = y^3$, we can use either assumption, or we may put $y = ax + d$, obtaining a simple equation as before.

Apparently Diophantus used the last assumption only; for in IV. 27 he rejects as impossible the equation

$$8x^3 - x^2 + 8x - 1 = y^3,$$

because $y = 2x - 1$ gives a negative value $x = -\frac{2}{11}$, whereas either of the other assumptions gives a rational value[1].

(2) *Double-equations.*

There are a few examples in which, of two functions of x, one is to be made a square, and the other a cube, by one and the same rational value of x. The cases are for the most part very simple; *e.g.* in VI. 19 we have to solve

$$\left.\begin{array}{r} 4x + 2 = y^3 \\ 2x + 1 = z^2 \end{array}\right\};$$

thus $y^3 = 2z^2$, and $z = 2$.

A rather more complicated case is VI. 21, where we have the double-equation

$$\left.\begin{array}{r} 2x^2 + 2x = y^2 \\ x^3 + 2x^2 + x = z^3 \end{array}\right\}.$$

Diophantus assumes $y = mx$, whence $x = 2/(m^2 - 2)$, and we have

$$\left(\frac{2}{m^2-2}\right)^3 + 2\left(\frac{2}{m^2-2}\right)^2 + \frac{2}{m^2-2} = z^3,$$

or

$$\frac{2m^4}{(m^2-2)^3} = z^3.$$

[1] There is a special case in which C and D vanish, $Ax^3 + Bx^2 = y^3$. Here y is put equal to mx, and $x = B/(m^3 - A)$. Cf. IV. 6, 28 (2).

To make $2m^4$ a cube, we need only make $2m$ a cube or put $m=4$. This gives $x=\frac{1}{7}$.

The general case

$$\left.\begin{aligned} Ax^3+Bx^2+Cx &= z^3 \\ bx^2+cx &= y^2 \end{aligned}\right\}$$

would, of course, be much more difficult; for, putting $y=mx$, we have

$$x=c/(m^2-b),$$

and we have to solve

$$A\left(\frac{c}{m^2-b}\right)^3+B\left(\frac{c}{m^2-b}\right)^2+C\left(\frac{c}{m^2-b}\right)=z^3,$$

or $$Ccm^4+c(Bc-2bC)m^2+bc(bC-Bc)+Ac^3=u^3,$$

of which equation the above corresponding equation is a very particular case.

Summary of the preceding investigation.

1. Diophantus solves completely equations of the first degree, but takes pains to secure beforehand that the solution shall be positive. He shows remarkable address in reducing a number of simultaneous equations of the first degree to a single equation in *one* variable.

2. For determinate equations of the second degree he has a general method or rule of solution. He takes, however, in the *Arithmetica*, no account of more than one root, even where both roots are positive rational numbers. But, his object being simply to obtain *some* solution in rational numbers, we need not be surprised at his ignoring one of two roots, even though he knew of its existence.

3. No equations of a degree higher than the second are solved in the book except a particular case of a cubic.

4. Indeterminate equations of the first degree are not treated of in the work. Of indeterminate equations of the second degree, as $Ax^2+Bx+C=y^2$, only those cases are fully dealt with in which A or C vanishes, while the methods employed only enable us to solve equations of the more general forms

$$Ax^2+C=y^2 \text{ and } Ax^2+Bx+C=y^2$$

when A, or C, or $\frac{1}{4}B^2-AC$ is positive and a square number, or (in the case of $Ax^2 \pm C=y^2$) when one solution is already known.

5. For double-equations of the second degree Diophantus has a definite method when the coefficient of x^2 in both expressions vanishes; the applicability of this method is, however, subject to conditions, and it has to be supplemented in one or two cases by another artifice. Of more complicated cases we find only a few examples under conditions favourable for solution by his method.

6. Diophantus' treatment of indeterminate equations of degrees higher than the second depends upon the particular conditions of the problems, and his methods lack generality.

7. More wonderful than his actual treatment of equations are the clever artifices by which he contrives to avoid such equations as he cannot theoretically solve, *e.g.* by his device of "back-reckoning," instances of which would have been out of place in this chapter and can only be studied in the problems themselves.

I shall not attempt to class as "methods" certain headings in Nesselmann's classification of the problems, such as (*a*) "Solution by mere reflection," (*b*) "Solution in general expressions," of which there are few instances definitely so described by Diophantus, or (*c*) "Arbitrary determinations and assumptions." The most that can be done by way of describing these "methods" is to quote a few characteristic instances. This is what Nesselmann has done, and he regrets at the end of his chapter on "Methods of Solution" that it must of necessity be so incomplete. To understand and appreciate the various artifices of Diophantus it is in fact necessary to read the problems themselves in their entirety.

With regard to the "Use of the right-angled triangle," all that can be said of a general character is that only "rational" right-angled triangles (those namely in which the three sides can all be represented by rational numbers) are used in Diophantus, and accordingly the introduction of the "right-angled triangle" is merely a convenient way of indicating the problem of finding two square numbers, the sum of which is also a square number. The general form used by Diophantus (except in one case, VI. 19, *q.v.*) for the sides of a right-angled triangle is (a^2+b^2), (a^2-b^2), $2ab$, which expressions clearly satisfy the condition

$$(a^2+b^2)^2=(a^2-b^2)^2+(2ab)^2.$$

The expression of the sides of a right-angled triangle in this form Diophantus calls "forming a right-angled triangle from the numbers *a* and *b*." His right-angled triangles are of course formed from *particular* numbers. "Forming a right-angled triangle from 7, 2" means taking a right-angled triangle with sides (7^2+2^2), (7^2-2^2), $2.7.2$, or 53, 45, 28.

II. METHOD OF LIMITS.

As Diophantus often has to find a series of numbers in ascending or descending order of magnitude, and as he does not admit negative solutions, it is often necessary for him to reject a solution which he has found by a straightforward method because it does not satisfy the necessary condition; he is then very frequently obliged to find solutions which lie *within certain limits* in place of those rejected.

1. A very simple case is the following: Required to find a value of x such that some power of it, x^n, shall lie between two given numbers. Let the given numbers be a, b. Then Diophantus' method is to multiply both a and b by 2^n, 3^n, and so on, successively, until some nth power is seen which lies between the two products. Thus suppose that c^n lies between ap^n and bp^n; then we can put $x=c/p$, in which case the condition is satisfied, for $(c/p)^n$ lies between a and b.

EXX. In IV. 31 (2) Diophantus has to find a square between $1\frac{1}{4}$ and 2. He multiplies both by a square, 64; this gives 80 and 128, and 100 is clearly a square which lies between them; therefore $(\frac{10}{8})^2$ or $\frac{25}{16}$ satisfies the prescribed condition.

Here, of course, Diophantus might have multiplied by any other square, as 16. In that case the limits would have become 20 and 32, between these lies the square 25, which gives the same square $\frac{25}{16}$ as that before found.

In VI. 21 a sixth power ("cube-cube") is sought which shall lie between 8 and 16. The sixth powers of the first four natural numbers are 1, 64, 729, 4096. Multiply 8 and 16 by 2^6 or 64, and we have as limits 512 and 1024, between which 729 lies. Therefore $\frac{729}{64}$ is a sixth power satisfying the given condition. To multiply by 729 in this case would not give us a solution.

2. Sometimes a value of x has to be found which will give some function of x a value intermediate between the values of two other functions of x.

EX. 1. In IV. 25 it is necessary to find a value of x such that $8/(x^2+x)$ shall lie between x and $x+1$.

The first condition gives $8>x^3+x^2$.

Diophantus accordingly assumes that

$$8 = (x + \tfrac{1}{3})^3 = x^3 + x^2 + \tfrac{1}{3}x + \tfrac{1}{27},$$

which is greater than $x^3 + x^2$.

Thus $x = \frac{5}{3}$ satisfies one condition. It is also seen to satisfy the second condition, or $\dfrac{8}{x^2 + x} < x + 1$. Diophantus, however, says nothing about the second condition being satisfied; his method is, therefore, here imperfect.

Ex. 2. In V. 30 a value of x has to be found which shall make

$$x > \tfrac{1}{8}(x^2 - 60) \text{ but } < \tfrac{1}{5}(x^2 - 60),$$

that is,

$$\left.\begin{matrix} x^2 - 60 > 5x \\ x^2 - 60 < 8x \end{matrix}\right\}.$$

Hence, says Diophantus, x is not less than 11 and not greater than 12. We have already spoken (p. 60 sqq.) of his treatment of such cases.

Next, the problem in question requires that $x^2 - 60$ shall be a square. Assume then that

$$x^2 - 60 = (x - m)^2,$$

and we have

$$x = (m^2 + 60)/2m.$$

Since, says Diophantus, x is greater than 11 and less than 12, it follows that

$$m^2 + 60 > 22m \text{ but } < 24m;$$

and m must therefore lie between 19 and 21 (cf. p. 62 above). He puts $m = 20$, and so finds $x = 11\tfrac{1}{2}$.

III. Method of Approximation to Limits.

We come, lastly, to a very distinctive method called by Diophantus *παρισότης* or *παρισότητος ἀγωγή*. The object of this is to solve such problems as that of finding two, or three, square numbers the sum of which is a given number, while each of them approximates as closely as possible to one and the same number.

This method can be best exhibited by giving Diophantus' two instances, in the first of which *two* such squares, and in the second *three*, are required. In cases like this the principles cannot be so well indicated with general symbols as with concrete numbers, which have the advantage that their properties are immediately obvious, and the separate expression of conditions is rendered unnecessary.

Ex. 1. Divide 13 into two squares each of which >6 (V. 9).

Take half of 13, or $6\frac{1}{2}$, and find what small fraction $1/x^2$ added to it will make it a square: thus

$$6\tfrac{1}{2}+\frac{1}{x^2}, \text{ or } 26+\frac{1}{y^2}, \text{ must be a square.}$$

Diophantus assumes

$$26+\frac{1}{y^2}=\left(5+\frac{1}{y}\right)^2, \text{ or } 26y^2+1=(5y+1)^2,$$

whence $y=10$ and $1/y^2=\frac{1}{100}$, or $1/x^2=\frac{1}{400}$; and

$$6\tfrac{1}{2}+\tfrac{1}{400}=\text{a square, } (\tfrac{51}{20})^2.$$

[The assumption of $(5y+1)^2$ is not arbitrary, for assume $26y^2+1=(py+1)^2$, and y is then $2p/(26-p^2)$; since $1/y$ should be a *small* proper fraction, 5 is the most suitable and the smallest possible value for p, inasmuch as $26-p^2<2p$ or $p^2+2p+1>27$.]

It is now necessary, says Diophantus, to divide 13 into two squares the sides of which are both as near as possible to $\frac{51}{20}$.

Now the sides of the two squares into which 13 is naturally decomposed are 3 and 2, and

$$3 \text{ is } > \tfrac{51}{20} \text{ by } \tfrac{9}{20},$$

$$2 \text{ is } < \tfrac{51}{20} \text{ by } \tfrac{11}{20}.$$

But, if $3-\frac{9}{20}$, $2+\frac{11}{20}$ were taken as the sides of two squares, the sum of the squares would be

$$2\,(\tfrac{51}{20})^2=\frac{2\,.\,2601}{400},$$

which is >13.

Accordingly Diophantus puts $3-9x$, $2+11x$ for the sides of the required squares, where therefore x is not exactly $\frac{1}{20}$ but near it.

Thus $$(3-9x)^2+(2+11x)^2=13,$$

and Diophantus obtains $$x=\tfrac{5}{101}.$$

The sides of the required squares are $\frac{257}{101}$, $\frac{258}{101}$.

[It is of course a necessary condition that the original number, here 13, shall be a number capable of being expressed as the sum of two squares.]

Ex. 2. Divide 10 into three squares such that each of them is > 3 (V. 11).

[The original number, here 10, must of course be expressible as the sum of three squares.]

Take one-third of 10, or $3\frac{1}{3}$, and find what small fraction of the form $1/x^2$ added to $3\frac{1}{3}$ will make a square; *i.e.* we have to make $30 + \frac{9}{x^2}$ a square, or $30y^2 + 1$ a square, where $3/x = 1/y$.

Diophantus assumes

$$30y^2 + 1 = (5y + 1)^2,$$

whence $y = 2$ and therefore $1/x^2 = \frac{1}{36}$; and $3\frac{1}{3} + \frac{1}{36} = \frac{121}{36}$, a square.

[As before, if we assume $30y^2 = (py + 1)^2$, $y = 2p/(30 - p^2)$; and, since $1/y$ must be a small proper fraction, $30 - p^2$ should be $< 2p$, or $p^2 + 2p + 1 > 31$. Accordingly Diophantus chooses 5 for p as being the smallest possible integral value.]

We have now, says Diophantus, to make each of the sides of our required squares as near as may be to $\frac{11}{6}$.

Now $$10 = 9 + 1 = 3^2 + (\tfrac{3}{5})^2 + (\tfrac{4}{5})^2,$$

and 3, $\frac{3}{5}$, $\frac{4}{5}$ are the sides of three squares the sum of which is 10.

Bringing (3, $\frac{3}{5}$, $\frac{4}{5}$) and $\frac{11}{6}$ to a common denominator, we have

$$(\tfrac{90}{30}, \tfrac{18}{30}, \tfrac{24}{30}) \text{ and } \tfrac{55}{30}.$$

And $$3 > \tfrac{55}{30} \text{ by } \tfrac{35}{30},$$
$$\tfrac{3}{5} < \tfrac{55}{30} \text{ by } \tfrac{37}{30},$$
$$\tfrac{4}{5} < \tfrac{55}{30} \text{ by } \tfrac{31}{30}.$$

If now we took $3 - \frac{35}{30}$, $\frac{3}{5} + \frac{37}{30}$, $\frac{4}{5} + \frac{31}{30}$ for sides of squares, the sum of the squares would be $3\,(\frac{11}{6})^2$ or $\frac{363}{36}$, which is > 10.

Accordingly Diophantus assumes as the sides of the three required squares

$$3 - 35x,\ \tfrac{3}{5} + 37x,\ \tfrac{4}{5} + 31x,$$

where x must therefore be not exactly $\frac{1}{30}$ but near it.

Solving $$(3 - 35x)^2 + (\tfrac{3}{5} + 37x)^2 + (\tfrac{4}{5} + 31x)^2 = 10,$$

or $$10 - 116x + 3555x^2 = 10,$$

we find $$x = \tfrac{116}{3555};$$

the required sides are therefore

$$\tfrac{1321}{711},\ \tfrac{1285}{711},\ \tfrac{1288}{711},$$

and the required squares

$$\tfrac{1745041}{505521},\ \tfrac{1651225}{505521},\ \tfrac{1658944}{505521}.$$

Other instances of the application of the method will be found in V. 10, 12, 13, 14, where, however, the squares are not required to be nearly equal, but each of them is subject to limits which may be the same or different; *e.g.* sometimes each square is merely required to be less than a given number (10, say), sometimes the squares lie respectively between different pairs of numbers, sometimes they are respectively greater than different numbers, while they are always subject to the condition that their sum is a given number.

As it only lies within the scope of this Introduction to explain what we actually find in Diophantus, I cannot do more than give a reference to such investigations as those of Poselger in his "Beiträge zur unbestimmten Analysis" published in the *Abhandlungen der Königlichen Akademie der Wissenschaften zu Berlin aus dem Jahre* 1832, Berlin, 1834. One section of this paper Poselger entitles "Annäherungs-methoden nach Diophantus," and obtains in it, on Diophantus' principles, a method of approximation to the value of a surd which will furnish the same results as the method of continued fractions, with the difference that the "Diophantine method" is actually quicker than the method of continued fractions, so that it may serve to expedite the latter.

CHAPTER V

THE PORISMS AND OTHER ASSUMPTIONS IN DIOPHANTUS

I HAVE already mentioned (in Chapter I.) the three explicit references made by Diophantus to "The Porisms" and the possibility that, if these formed a separate work, it may have been from that work that Diophantus took a number of other propositions relating to properties of numbers which he enunciates or tacitly takes for granted in the *Arithmetica*.

I begin with the three propositions for which he expressly refers to "The Porisms."

Porism I. In V. 3 he says, "We have it in the Porisms that, 'If each of two numbers and their product when severally added to the same given number produce squares, the squares with which they are so connected are squares of two consecutive numbers[1].'"

That is to say, if $x+a=m^2$, $y+a=n^2$, and if $xy+a$ is also a square, then $m \sim n = 1$.

The theorem is not correctly enunciated, for it would appear that $m \sim n = 1$ is not the only condition under which the three expressions may be simultaneously squares.

For suppose

$$x+a=m^2,\quad y+a=n^2,\quad xy+a=p^2.$$

By means of the first two equations we have

$$xy+a=m^2n^2-a(m^2+n^2-1)+a^2.$$

In order that

$$m^2n^2-a(m^2+n^2-1)+a^2$$

may be a square certain conditions must be satisfied. One sufficient condition is

$$m^2+n^2-1=2mn,$$

or

$$m \sim n = \pm 1,$$

which is Diophantus' condition.

[1] Literally "(the numbers) arise from two consecutive squares" (γεγόνασιν ἀπὸ δύο τετραγώνων τῶν κατὰ τὸ ἑξῆς).

But we may also regard

$$m^2n^2 - a(m^2 + n^2 - 1) + a^2 = p^2$$

as an indeterminate equation in m of which we know one solution, namely $m = n \pm 1$.

Other solutions are then found by substituting $z + (n \pm 1)$ for m, whence we obtain the equation

$$(n^2 - a)z^2 + 2\{n^2(n \pm 1) - a(n \pm 1)\}z$$
$$+ (n^2 - a)(n \pm 1)^2 - a(n^2 - 1) + a^2 = p^2,$$

or $$(n^2 - a)z^2 + 2(n^2 - a)(n \pm 1)z + \{n(n \pm 1) - a\}^2 = p^2,$$

which is easy to solve in Diophantus' manner, since the absolute term is a square.

But in the problem V. 3 *three* numbers are required, such that each of them, and the product of each pair, when severally added to a given number, produce squares. Thus if the third number be z, three additional conditions have to be satisfied, namely

$$z + a = u^2, \quad zx + a = v^2, \quad zy + a = w^2.$$

The two last conditions are satisfied, if $m + 1 = n$, by putting

$$z = 2(x + y) - 1 = 4m^2 + 4m + 1 - 4a,$$

when $$xz + a = \{m(2m + 1) - 2a\}^2$$

and $$yz + a = \{(m + 1)(2m + 1) - 2a\}^2;$$

and perhaps this means of satisfying the conditions may have affected the formulation of the Porism[1].

The problem V. 4 immediately following assumes the truth of the same Porism with $-a$ substituted for $+a$.

Porism 2. In V. 5 Diophantus says, "Again we have it in the Porisms that, 'Given any two consecutive squares, we can find in addition a third number, namely the number greater by 2 than the double of the sum of the two squares, which makes the greatest of three numbers such that the product of any pair of them added to either the sum of that pair or the remaining number gives a square.'"

That is, the three numbers

$$m^2, \ (m + 1)^2, \ 4(m^2 + m + 1)$$

[1] Euler has a paper describing and illustrating a general method of finding such "porisms" the effect of which is to secure that, when some conditions are satisfied, the rest are simultaneously satisfied ("De problematibus indeterminatis quae videntur plus quam determinata" in *Novi Commentarii Acad. Petropol.* 1756–57, Vol. VI. (1761), p. 85 sqq. = *Commentationes arithmeticae collectae*, I. pp. 245—259). This particular porism of Diophantus appears as a particular case in § 13 of the paper.

have the property that the product of any two *plus* either the sum of those two or the remaining number gives a square. In fact, if X, Y, Z denote the numbers respectively,

$$XY+X+Y=(m^2+m+1)^2,\quad XY+Z=(m^2+m+2)^2,$$
$$YZ+Y+Z=(2m^2+3m+3)^2,\quad YZ+X=(2m^2+3m+2)^2,$$
$$ZX+Z+X=(2m^2+m+2)^2,\quad ZX+Y=(2m^2+m+1)^2.$$

Porism 3 occurs in V. 16. Unfortunately the text is defective and Tannery has had to supply three words[1]; but there can be no doubt that the correct statement of the Porism here in question is "The difference of any two cubes is also the sum of two cubes," *i.e.* can be transformed into the sum of two cubes, or two cubes can be found the sum of which is equal to the difference between any two given cubes. Diophantus contents himself with the enunciation of the proposition and does not show how to prove it or how he effected the transformation in practice. The subject of the transformation of sums and differences of cubes was investigated by Vieta, Bachet and Fermat.

Vieta (*Zetetica*, IV. 18–20) has three problems on the subject.

(1) Given two cubes, to find in rational numbers two other cubes such that their sum is equal to the difference of the given cubes[2].

As a solution of $a^3-b^3=x^3+y^3$, he finds

$$x=\frac{a(a^3-2b^3)}{a^3+b^3},\quad y=\frac{b(2a^3-b^3)}{a^3+b^3}.$$

[1] ἔχομεν δὲ ἐν τοῖς Πορίσμασιν ὅτι "πάντων δύο κύβων ἡ ὑπεροχὴ κύβων <δύο σύνθεμά ἐστιν>."

[2] The solution given by Vieta is obtainable thus. The given cubes being a^3, b^3, where $a>b$, we assume $x-b$, $a-kx$ as the sides of the required cubes.

Thus $$(x-b)^3+(a-kx)^3=a^3-b^3,$$
whence $$x^3(1-k^3)+3x^2(ak^2-b)+3x(b^2-a^2k)=0.$$

This reduces to a simple equation if we assume

$$b^2-a^2k=0,\ \text{or}\ k=b^2/a^2,$$

in which case

$$x=\frac{3(b-ak^2)}{1-k^3}=\frac{3a^3b}{a^3+b^3},$$

and the sides of the cubes are therefore

$$\frac{b(2a^3-b^3)}{a^3+b^3},\quad \frac{a(a^3-2b^3)}{a^3+b^3}.$$

Vieta's second problem is similarly solved by taking $a+x$, $kx-b$ as the sides of the required cubes, and the third problem by taking $x-b$, $kx-a$ as the sides of the required cubes respectively.

(2) Given two cubes, to find in rational numbers two others such that their difference is equal to the sum of the given cubes.

Solving $a^3+b^3=x^3-y^3$, we find that

$$x=\frac{a(a^3+2b^3)}{a^3-b^3}, \quad y=\frac{b(2a^3+b^3)}{a^3-b^3}.$$

(3) Given two cubes, to find in rational numbers two cubes such that their difference is equal to the difference of the given cubes.

For the equation $a^3-b^3=x^3-y^3$, Vieta finds

$$x=\frac{b(2a^3-b^3)}{a^3+b^3}, \quad y=\frac{a(2b^3-a^3)}{a^3+b^3}$$

as a solution[1].

In the solution of (1) x is clearly negative if $2b^3>a^3$; therefore, in order that the result may be "rational," a^3 must be $>2b^3$. But for a "rational" result in (3) we must, on the contrary, have $a^3<2b^3$. Fermat was apparently the first to notice that, in consequence, the processes in (1) and (3) exactly supplement each other, so that by employing them successively we can effect the transformation required in (1) even when a^3 is not $>2b^3$.

The process (2) is always possible; therefore, by a suitable combination of the three processes, the transformation of a sum of two cubes into a difference of two cubes, or of a difference of two cubes into a sum or a difference of two other cubes is always

[1] Vieta's formulae for these transformations give any number of very special solutions (in integers and fractions) of the indeterminate equation $x^3+y^3+z^3=v^3$, including solutions in which one of the first three cubes is negative. These special solutions are based on the assumption that the values of two of the unknowns are given to begin with. Euler observed, however, that the method does not give all the possible values of the other two even in that case. Given the cubes 3^3 and 4^3, the method furnishes the solution $3^3+4^3+\left(\frac{465}{37}\right)^3=\left(\frac{472}{37}\right)^3$, but not the simpler solution $3^3+4^3+5^3=6^3$. Euler accordingly attacked the problem of solving the equation $x^3+y^3+z^3=v^3$ more generally. He began with assuming only one, instead of two, of the cubes to be given, and, on that assumption, found a solution much more general than that of Vieta. Next he gave a more general solution still, on the assumption that *none* of the cubes are given to begin with. Lastly he proceeded to the problem *To find all the sets of three integral cubes the sum of which is a cube* and showed how to obtain a very large number of such sets including sets in which one of the cubes is negative (*Novi Commentarii Acad. Petropol.* 1756–57, Vol. VI. (1761), p. 155 sq. = *Commentationes arithmeticae*, I. pp. 193—207). The problem of solving $x^3+y^3=z^3+v^3$ in integers in any number of ways had occupied Frénicle, who gave a number of solutions (*Oeuvres de Fermat*, III. pp. 420, 535); but the method by which he discovered them does not appear.

practicable[1]. Fermat showed also how, by a repeated use of the several processes as required, we can transform a sum of two cubes into a sum of two other cubes, the latter sum into the sum of two others and so on *ad infinitum*[2].

Besides the "Porisms" there are many other propositions assumed or implied by Diophantus which are not definitely called

[1] Fermat (note on IV. 2) illustrates by the following case:

Given two cubes 125 *and* 64, *to transform their difference into the sum of two other cubes.*

Here $a=5$, $b=4$, and so $2b^3>a^3$; therefore we must first apply the third process by which we obtain

$$5^3-4^3=\left(\frac{248}{63}\right)^3-\left(\frac{5}{63}\right)^3.$$

As $\left(\frac{248}{63}\right)^3>2\left(\frac{5}{63}\right)^3$, we can, by the first process, turn the difference between the cubes $\left(\frac{248}{63}\right)^3$ and $\left(\frac{5}{63}\right)^3$ into the sum of two cubes.

"In fact," says Fermat, "if the three processes are used in turn and continued *ad infinitum*, we shall get a succession *ad infinitum* of two cubes satisfying the same condition; for from the two cubes last found, the sum of which is equal to the difference of the two given cubes, we can, by the second process, find two more cubes the difference of which is equal to the sum of the two cubes last found, that is, to the difference between the two original cubes; from the new difference between two cubes we can obtain a new sum of two cubes, and so on *ad infinitum*."

As a last illustration, to show how a difference between cubes can be transformed into the difference between two other cubes even where the condition for process (3) is not satisfied, Fermat takes the case of $8-1$, *i.e.* the case where

$$a=2,\ b=1 \text{ and } a^3>2b^3.$$

First use process (1) and we have

$$2^3-1^3=\left(\frac{4}{3}\right)^3+\left(\frac{5}{3}\right)^3.$$

Then use process (2), and

$$\left(\frac{5}{3}\right)^3+\left(\frac{4}{3}\right)^3=\left(\frac{1265}{183}\right)^3-\left(\frac{1256}{183}\right)^3.$$

[2] Suppose it required to solve the fourth problem of *transforming the sum of two cubes into the sum of two other cubes.*

Let it be required so to transform 2^3+1^3 or 9.

First transform the sum into a difference of two cubes by process (2). This gives

$$2^3+1^3=\left(\frac{20}{7}\right)^3-\left(\frac{17}{7}\right)^3.$$

The latter two cubes satisfy the condition for process (3) and, applying that process, we get

$$\left(\frac{20}{7}\right)^3-\left(\frac{17}{7}\right)^3=\left(\frac{188479}{90391}\right)^3-\left(\frac{36520}{90391}\right)^3.$$

The cubes last found satisfy the condition for process (1), and accordingly the difference between the said last cubes, and therefore the sum of the original cubes, is at last transformed into the sum of two other cubes.

porisms, though some of them are of the same character as the three porisms above described.

Of these we may distinguish two classes.

1. The first class of theorems or facts assumed without explanation by Diophantus are more or less of the nature of *identical formulae*. Some are quite simple, *e.g.* the facts that the expressions $\{\frac{1}{2}(a+b)\}^2 - ab$ and $a^2(a+1)^2 + a^2 + (a+1)^2$ are respectively squares, that the expression $a(a^2-a) + a + (a^2-a)$ is always a cube, and the like.

Others are more difficult and betoken a certain facility in working with quasi-algebraical expressions. Examples of this kind are the following:

(α) If $X = a^2x + 2a$, $Y = (a+1)^2x + 2(a+1)$, or, in other words, if $xX + 1 = (ax+1)^2$, $xY + 1 = \{(a+1)x+1\}^2$, then $XY + 1$ is a square [IV. 20]. As a matter of fact,

$$XY + 1 = \{a(a+1)x + (2a+1)\}^2.$$

(β) 8 times a triangular number *plus* 1 gives a square [IV. 38]. In fact, $8 \cdot \dfrac{x(x+1)}{2} + 1 = (2x+1)^2$.

(γ) If $X \pm a = m^2$, $Y \pm a = (m+1)^2$, and $Z = 2(X+Y) - 1$, then the expressions $YZ \pm a$, $ZX \pm a$, $XY \pm a$ are all squares. (The upper signs refer to the assumption in V. 3, the lower to that in V. 4.)

In fact,

$$YZ \pm a = \{(m+1)(2m+1) \mp 2a\}^2,$$
$$ZX \pm a = \{m(2m+1) \mp 2a\}^2,$$
$$XY \pm a = \{m(m+1) \mp a\}^2.$$

(δ) If $X = m^2 + 2$, $Y = (m+1)^2 + 2$, $Z = 2\{m^2 + (m+1)^2 + 1\} + 2$, then the six expressions

$$YZ-(Y+Z), \quad ZX-(Z+X), \quad XY-(X+Y)$$
$$YZ-X, \quad ZX-Y, \quad XY-Z$$

are all squares [V. 6].

In fact,

$$YZ - (Y+Z) = (2m^2+3m+3)^2, \quad YZ - X = (2m^2+3m+4)^2, \text{ etc.}$$

2. The second class is much more important, consisting of a number of propositions in the Theory of Numbers which we find

first stated or assumed in the *Arithmetica*. It was, in general, in explanation or extension of these that Fermat's most famous notes were written. How far Diophantus possessed scientific proofs of the propositions which he assumes, as distinct from a merely empirical knowledge of them, must remain to a great extent matter of speculation.

(*a*) *Theorems in Diophantus respecting the composition of numbers as the sum of two squares.*

(1) Any square number can be resolved into two squares in any number of ways, II. 8.

(2) Any number which is the sum of two squares can be resolved into two other squares in any number of ways, II. 9.

N.B. It is implied throughout that the squares may be fractional as well as integral.

(3) *If there are two whole numbers each of which is the sum of two squares, their product can be resolved into the sum of two squares in two ways*, III. 19.

The object of III. 19 is to find four rational right-angled triangles having the same hypotenuse. The method is this. Form two right-angled triangles from (a, b) and (c, d) respectively, *i.e.* let the sides of the triangles be respectively

$$a^2+b^2,\ a^2-b^2,\ 2ab,$$

and

$$c^2+d^2,\ c^2-d^2,\ 2cd.$$

Multiplying all the sides in each by the hypotenuse of the other, we have two triangles with the same hypotenuse, namely

$$(a^2+b^2)(c^2+d^2),\ (a^2-b^2)(c^2+d^2),\ 2ab\,(c^2+d^2),$$

and

$$(a^2+b^2)(c^2+d^2),\ (a^2+b^2)(c^2-d^2),\ 2cd\,(a^2+b^2).$$

Two other triangles having the same hypotenuse are obtained by using the theorem enunciated. In fact,

$$(a^2+b^2)(c^2+d^2)=(ac\pm bd)^2+(ad\mp bc)^2$$

and the triangles are formed from $ac\pm bd$, $ad\mp bc$, being the triangles

$$(a^2+b^2)(c^2+d^2),\ 4abcd+(a^2-b^2)(c^2-d^2),\ 2\,(ac+bd)(ad-bc),$$

$$(a^2+b^2)(c^2+d^2),\ 4abcd-(a^2-b^2)(c^2-d^2),\ 2\,(ac-bd)(ad+bc).$$

In the case taken by Diophantus

$$a^2 + b^2 = 2^2 + 1^2 = 5,$$
$$c^2 + d^2 = 3^2 + 2^2 = 13,$$

and the four triangles are respectively

(65, 52, 39), (65, 60, 25), (65, 63, 16), (65, 56, 33).

(If certain relations[1] hold between *a, b, c, d,* this method fails. Diophantus has provided against them by taking two triangles "in the smallest numbers" (ὑπὸ ἐλαχίστων ἀριθμῶν), namely 3, 4, 5 and 5, 12, 13.)

Upon this problem III. 19 Fermat has a long and important note which begins as follows[2]:

"[1] A prime number of the form $4n+1$ is the hypotenuse of a right-angled triangle in one way only, its square is so in two ways, its cube in three, its biquadrate in four ways, and so on *ad infinitum.*

"[2] The same prime number $4n+1$ and its square are the sum of two squares in one way only, its cube and its biquadrate in two ways, its fifth and sixth powers in three ways, and so on *ad infinitum.*

"[3] If a prime number which is the sum of two squares be multiplied into another prime number which is also the sum of two squares, the product will be the sum of two squares in two ways; if the first prime be multiplied into the square of the second

[1] (1) We must not have $a/b = c/d$ or $a/b = d/c$, for in either case one of the perpendiculars of one of the resulting triangles vanishes, making that triangle illusory. Nor (2) must c/d be equal to $(a+b)/(a-b)$ or to $(a-b)/(a+b)$, for in the first case $ac - bd = ad + bc$, and in the second case $ac + bd = ad - bc$, so that one of the sums of squares equal to $(a^2+b^2)(c^2+d^2)$ is the sum of two *equal* squares, and consequently the triangle formed from the sides of these equal squares is illusory, one of its perpendicular sides vanishing.

[2] G. Vacca (in *Bibliotheca Mathematica*, II_3. 1901, pp. 358–9) points out that Fermat seems to have been anticipated, in the matter of these theorems, by Albert Girard, who has the following note on Diophantus V. 9 (*Oeuvres mathématiques de Simon Stevin par Albert Girard*, 1634, p. 156, col. 1):

"ALB. GIR. *Determinaison d'un nombre qui se peut diviser en deux quarrez entiers.*

I. Tout nombre quarré.
II. Tout nombre premier qui excede un nombre quaternaire de l'unité.
III. Le produict de ceux qui sont tels.
IV. Et le double d'un chacun d'iceux.

Laquelle determinaison n'estant faicte n'y de l'Autheur n'y des interpretes, servira tant en la presente et suivante comme en plusieurs autres."

Now Girard died on 9 December, 1632; and the Theorems of Fermat above quoted are apparently mentioned by him for the first time in his letter to Mersenne of 25 December, 1640 (*Oeuvres de Fermat*, II. p. 213). Was the passage of Girard known to Fermat?

prime, the product will be the sum of two squares in three ways; if the first prime be multiplied into the cube of the second, the product will be the sum of two squares in four ways, and so on *ad infinitum*[1]."

It is not probable that Diophantus was aware that prime numbers of the form $4n+1$ and numbers arising from the multiplication of such numbers are the only classes of numbers which are always the sum of two squares; this was first proved by Euler[2]. But it is remarkable that Diophantus should have selected the first two prime numbers of the form $4n+1$, namely 5 and 13, which are both sums of two squares, as the hypotenuses of his first two right-angled triangles and then made their product, 65, the hypotenuse of other right-angled triangles, that product having precisely the property of being, as in Fermat's [3], the sum of two squares in two ways. Diophantus may therefore have had an inkling, whether obtained empirically or otherwise, of some of the properties enunciated by Fermat.

(4) Still more remarkable is a condition of possibility of solution prefixed to the problem V. 9. The object of this problem is "to divide 1 into two parts such that, if a given number is added to either part, the result will be a square." Unfortunately, the text of the added condition is uncertain. There is no doubt about the first few words, "*The given number must not be odd*," *i.e. No number of the form* $4n+3$ [or $4n-1$] *can be the sum of two squares.*

The text, however, of the latter half of the condition is corrupt. The true condition is given by Fermat thus: "*The given number must not be odd, and the double of it increased by one, when divided by the greatest square which measures it, must not be divisible by a prime number of the form* $4n-1$." (Note upon V. 9; also in a letter to Roberval[3].) There is room for any number of conjectures as to what may have been Diophantus' words[4].

[1] For a fuller account of this note see the Supplement, section I.

[2] *Novi Commentarii Acad. Petropol.* 1752–3, Vol. IV. (1758), pp. 3–40, and 1754–5, Vol. V. (1760), pp. 3–58 = *Commentationes arithmeticae*, I. pp. 155–173 and pp. 210–233; cf. Legendre, *Zahlentheorie*, tr. Maser, I. p. 208; Weber and Wellstein's *Encyclopädie der Elementar-Mathematik*, I_2. pp. 285 sqq.

[3] *Oeuvres de Fermat*, II. pp. 203–4. See the Supplement, section I.

[4] Bachet's text has δεῖ δὴ τὸν διδόμενον μήτε περισσὸν εἶναι, μήτε ὁ διπλασίων αὐτοῦ ϥʹ μ° ᾱ. μείζονα ἔχῃ μέρος δ̄. ἢ μετρεῖται ὑπὸ τοῦ ᾱ^{οῦ}. ς^{οῦ}.

He also says that a Vatican MS. reads μήτε ὁ διπλασίων αὐτοῦ ἀριθμὸν μονάδα α. μείζονα ἔχῃ μέρος τέταρτον, ἢ μετρεῖται ὑπὸ τοῦ πρώτου ἀριθμοῦ.

Neither does Xylander help us much. He frankly tells us that he cannot understand

There would seem to be no doubt that in Diophantus' condition there was something about "double the number" (*i.e.* a number of the form $4n$), also about "greater by unity" and "a prime number." It seems, then, not unlikely that, if Diophantus did not succeed in giving the complete sufficient and necessary condition stated by Fermat, he made an approximation to it; and he certainly knew that no number of the form $4n+3$ could be the sum of two squares[1].

(*b*) *On numbers which are the sum of three squares.*

In the problem V. 11 a condition is stated by Diophantus respecting the form of a number which, added to three parts of unity, makes each of them square. If a be this number, clearly $3a+1$ must be divisible into three squares.

Respecting the number a Diophantus says, "It must not be 2 or any multiple of 8 increased by 2."

That is, *a number of the form* $24n+7$ *cannot be the sum of three squares.* Now the factor 3 of 24 is irrelevant here, for with respect to *three* this number is of the form $3m+1$, and this, so far as 3 is concerned, might be a square or the sum of two or three squares. Hence we may neglect the factor 3 in $24n$.

We must therefore credit Diophantus with the knowledge of

---

the passage. "Imitari statueram bonos grammaticos hoc loco, quorum (ut aiunt) est multa nescire. Ego verò nescio heic non multa, sed paene omnia. Quid enim (ut reliqua taceam) est *μήτε ὁ διπλασίων αὑτοῦ αρ̄ μο̄ α* etc., quae causae huius *προσδιορισμοῦ*, quae processus? immo qui processus, quae operatio, quae solutio?"

Nesselmann discusses an attempt made by Schulz to correct the text, and himself suggests *μήτε τὸν διπλασίονα αὑτοῦ ἀριθμὸν μονάδι μείζονα ἔχειν, ὃς μετρεῖται ὑπό τινος πρώτου ἀριθμοῦ.* But this ignores *μέρος τέταρτον* and is not satisfactory.

Hankel, however (*Gesch. d. Math.* p. 169), says: "Ich zweifele nicht, dass die von den Msscr. arg entstellte Determination so zu lesen ist: *Δεῖ δὴ τὸν διδόμενον μήτε περισσὸν εἶναι, μήτε τὸν διπλασίονα αὑτοῦ ἀριθμὸν μονάδι ᾱ μείζονα μετρεῖσθαι ὑπό του πρώτου ἀριθμοῦ, ὃς ἂν μονάδι ᾱ μείζων ἔχῃ μέρος τέταρτον.*" This correction seems a decidedly probable one. Here the words *μέρος τέταρτον* find a place; and, secondly, the repetition of *μονάδι ᾱ μείζων* might well confuse a copyist. *του* for *τοῦ* is of course natural enough; Nesselmann reads *τινος* for *του*.

Tannery, improving on Hankel, reads *Δεῖ δὴ τὸν διδόμενον μήτε περισσὸν εἶναι, μήτε* †*τὸν διπλάσιον αὑτοῦ καὶ μονάδι μιᾷ μείζονα μετρεῖσθαι ὑπό του πρώτου ἀριθμοῦ* <*οὗ ὁ μονάδι μιᾷ μείζων*> *ἔχῃ μέρος τέταρτον*†, "the given number must not be odd, and twice it *plus* 1 must not be measured by any prime number which, when increased by 1, is divisible by 4."

[1] A discussion of the text and a suggestion as to the considerations which may have led to the formulation of the condition will be found in Jacobi, "Ueber die Kenntnisse des Diophantus von der Zusammensetzung der Zahlen" (*Berliner Monatsberichte*, 1847; *Gesammelte Werke*, VII., 1891, pp. 332–344).

the fact that *no number of the form* $8n+7$ *can be the sum of three squares*[1].

This condition is true, but does not include *all* the numbers which cannot be the sum of three squares, for it is not true that all numbers which are not of the form $8n+7$ are made up of three squares. Even Bachet remarked that the number a might not be of the form $32n+9$, or a number of the form $96n+28$ cannot be the sum of three squares.

Fermat gives the conditions to which a must be subject thus[2].

Write down two geometrical series (common ratio of each 4), the first and second series beginning respectively with 1, 8,

$$\begin{array}{ccccccc} 1 & 4 & 16 & 64 & 256 & 1024 & 4096 \\ 8 & 32 & 128 & 512 & 2048 & 8192 & 32768; \end{array}$$

then a must not be (1) any number obtained by taking twice any term of the upper series and adding all the preceding terms, or (2) the number found by adding to the numbers so obtained any multiple of the corresponding term of the second series.

Thus a must not be

$$\begin{aligned} 8k+2.1 &= 8k+2, \\ 32k+2.4+1 &= 32k+9, \\ 128k+2.16+4+1 &= 128k+37, \\ 512k+2.64+16+4+1 &= 512k+149, \end{aligned}$$

and so on, where $k=0$ or any integer.

That is, since $1+4+4^2+\ldots+4^{n-1}=\frac{1}{3}(4^n-1)$, a cannot be either

$$2.4^n+\tfrac{1}{3}(4^n-1)=\tfrac{1}{3}(7.4^n-1)$$

or $$2k.4^{n+1}+\tfrac{1}{3}(7.4^n-1)=\tfrac{1}{3}(24k.4^n+7.4^n-1);$$

therefore $3a+1$ cannot be of the form $4^n(24k+7)$ or $4^n(8k+7)$.

Again, there are other problems, *e.g.* V. 10 and V. 20, in which, though conditions are necessary for the possibility of solution, none are mentioned; but suitable assumptions are tacitly made, without explanation. It does not follow, from the omission to state the conditions, that Diophantus was ignorant of even the minutest points connected with them; as, however, we have no definite statements, we must be content to remain in doubt.

[1] Legendre proved (*Zahlentheorie*, tr. Maser, I. p. 386), that numbers of this form are the only *odd* numbers which are not divisible into three squares.

[2] Note on Diophantus V. 11.

(*c*) *Composition of numbers as the sum of four squares.*

Every number is either a square or the sum of two, three or four squares. This well-known theorem, enunciated by Fermat[1], and proved by Lagrange[2] (who followed up results obtained by Euler) shows at once that any number can be divided into four squares either integral or fractional, since any square number can be divided into two other squares, integral or fractional. We have now to look for indications in the *Arithmetica* as to how far Diophantus was acquainted with the properties of numbers as the sum of four squares. Unfortunately, it is impossible to decide this question with anything like certainty. There are three problems, IV. 29, 30 and V. 14, in which it is required to divide a number into four squares, and from the absence of mention of any condition to which the number must conform, considering that in both cases where a number is to be divided into *three* or *two* squares, V. 11 and V. 9, he does state a condition, we should probably be right in inferring that Diophantus was aware, at least *empirically*, that *any* number could be divided into four squares. That he was able to prove the theorem scientifically it would be rash to assert. But we may at least be certain that Diophantus came as near to the proof of it as did Bachet, who takes all the natural numbers up to 120 and finds by trial that all of them can actually be expressed as squares, or as the sum of two, three or four squares in whole numbers. So much we may be sure that Diophantus could do, and hence he might have empirically satisfied himself that it is possible to divide any number into four squares, integral or fractional, even if he could not give a rigorous mathematical demonstration of the general theorem.

[1] See note on Diophantus IV. 29; cf. also section I. of the Supplement.

[2] "Démonstration d'un théorème d'arithmétique" in *Nouveaux Mémoires de l'Acad. royale des sciences de Berlin*, année 1770, Berlin 1772, pp. 123–133 = *Oeuvres de Lagrange*, III. pp. 187–201; cf. Wertheim's account of the proof in his Diophantus, pp. 324–330.

CHAPTER VI

THE PLACE OF DIOPHANTUS

IN algebra, as in geometry, the Greeks learnt the beginnings from the Egyptians. Familiarity on the part of the Greeks with Egyptian methods of calculation is well attested. Thus (1) Psellus in the letter published by Tannery[1] speaks of "the method of arithmetical calculations used by the Egyptians, by which problems in analysis are handled" (ἡ κατ' Αἰγυπτίους τῶν ἀριθμῶν μέθοδος, δι' ἧς οἰκονομεῖται τὰ κατὰ τὴν ἀναλυτικὴν προβλήματα); the details which he goes on to give respecting the technical terms for different kinds of numbers, including the powers of the unknown quantity, in use among the Egyptians are doubtless taken from Anatolius. (2) The scholiast to Plato's *Charmides* 165 E may be drawing on the same source when he says that "parts of λογιστική (the science of calculation) are the so-called Greek and Egyptian methods in multiplications and divisions, and the additions and subtractions of fractions....The aim of it all is the service of common life and utility for contracts, though it seems to deal with things of sense as if they were perfect or abstract." (3) Plato himself, in the *Laws*[2], says that free-born boys should, as is the practice in Egypt, learn, side by side with reading, simple mathematical calculations adapted to their age, which should be put into a form such as to give amusement and pleasure as well as instruction; *e.g.* there should be different distributions of such things as apples, garlands, etc., different arrangements of numbers of boys in contests of boxing or wrestling, illustrations by bowls of different metals, gold, copper, silver, etc., and simple problems of calculation of mixtures; all of which are useful in military and civil life and "in any case make men more useful to themselves and more wide-awake."

[1] Dioph. II. pp. 37–42.

[2] *Laws*, VII. 819 A–C.

The Egyptian calculations here in point (apart from their method of writing and calculating in fractions, which differed from that of the Greeks in that the Greeks worked with ordinary fractions, whereas the Egyptians separated fractions into sums of submultiples, with the exception of $\frac{2}{3}$ which was not decomposed) are the *hau*-calculations. *Hau*, meaning a *heap*, is the term used to denote the unknown quantity, and the calculations in terms of it are equivalent to the solutions of simple equations with one unknown quantity[1]. Examples from the Papyrus Rhind[2] correspond to the following equations:

$$\tfrac{1}{7}x + x = 19,$$
$$\tfrac{2}{3}x + \tfrac{1}{2}x + \tfrac{1}{7}x + x = 33,$$
$$(x + \tfrac{2}{3}x) - \tfrac{1}{3}(x + \tfrac{2}{3}x) = 10.$$

Before leaving the Egyptians, it is right to mention their anticipation, though in an elementary form, of a favourite method of Diophantus, that of the "false supposition" or "regula falsi" as it is sometimes called. An arbitrary assumption is made as to the value of the unknown, and the value is afterwards corrected by a comparison of the result of substituting the wrong value in the original expression with the actual fact. Two instances mentioned by Cantor[3] may be given. The first, taken from the Papyrus Rhind, is the problem of dividing 100 loaves among five persons in numbers forming an arithmetical progression and such that one-seventh of the sum of the first three shares is equal to the sum of the other two. If $a + 4d$, $a + 3d$, $a + 2d$, $a + d$, a are the shares, we have

$$3a + 9d = 7(2a + d),$$

or

$$d = 5\tfrac{1}{2}a.$$

Ahmes merely says, without explanation, "make the difference, as it is, $5\frac{1}{2}$," and then, assuming $a = 1$, writes the series 23, $17\frac{1}{2}$, 12, $6\frac{1}{2}$, 1. The addition of these gives 60, and 100 is $1\frac{2}{3}$ times 60. Ahmes says simply "multiply $1\frac{2}{3}$ times" and thus gets the correct values $38\frac{1}{3}$, $29\frac{1}{6}$, 20, $10\frac{2}{3}\,\frac{1}{6}$, $1\frac{2}{3}$. The second instance (taken from the Berlin Papyrus 6619) is the solution of the equations

$$x^2 + y^2 = 100,$$
$$x : y = 1 : \tfrac{3}{4}, \text{ or } y = \tfrac{3}{4}x.$$

[1] For a complete account of the subject the reader is referred to Moritz Cantor's *Geschichte der Mathematik*, I_3. Chapter II., especially pp. 74–81.

[2] Eisenlohr, *Ein mathematisches Handbuch der alten Ägypter* (*Papyrus Rhind des British Museum*), Leipzig, 1877.

[3] *Geschichte der Math.* I_3. pp. 78–9 and p. 95.

x is first assumed to be 1, and x^2+y^2 is then found to be 25/16. In order to make 100, 25/16 has to be multiplied by 64 or 8^2. The true value of x is therefore 8 times 1, or 8.

The simple equations solved in the Papyrus Rhind are just the kind of equations of which we find numerous examples in the arithmetical epigrams included in the Greek Anthology. Most of these appear under the name of Metrodorus, a grammarian, who probably lived about the time of the Emperors Anastasius I. (491–518 A.D.) and Justin I. (518–527 A.D.). They were obviously only collected by Metrodorus, from ancient as well as more recent sources; none of them can with certainty be attributed to Metrodorus himself. Many of the epigrams (46 in number) lead to simple equations, with one unknown, of the type of the *hau*-equations, and several of them are problems of dividing a number of apples or nuts among a certain number of persons, that is to say, the very type of problem alluded to by Plato. For example, a number of apples has to be determined such that, if four persons out of six receive one-third, one-eighth, one-fourth and one-fifth respectively of the total number of apples, while the fifth person receives ten apples, there remains one apple as the share of the sixth person, *i.e.*

$$\tfrac{1}{3}x+\tfrac{1}{8}x+\tfrac{1}{4}x+\tfrac{1}{5}x+10+1=x.$$

We are reminded of Plato's allusion to problems about bowls (φιάλαι) of different metals by two problems (*Anthol. Palat.* XIV. 12 and 50) in which the weights of bowls have to be found. We can now understand the allusions of Proclus[1] and the scholiast on *Charmides* 165 E to μηλῖται and φιαλῖται ἀριθμοί, the adjectives being respectively formed from μῆλον, an apple, and φιάλη, a bowl. It is clear from Plato's allusions that the origin of such simple algebraical problems dates back, at least, to the fifth century B.C.

I have not thought it worth while to reproduce at length the problems contained in the Anthology[2], but the following is a classification of them. (1) Twenty-three are simple equations containing one unknown and of the type shown above; one of these is the epigram on the age of Diophantus and incidents in his life (XIV. 126). (2) Twelve more are easy simultaneous

[1] Proclus, *Comment. on Eucl. I.*, ed. Friedlein, p. 40, 5.

[2] They are printed in Greek, with the scholia, in Tannery's edition of Diophantus (II. pp. 43–72 and x), and they are included in Wertheim's German translation of Diophantus, pp. 331–343.

equations containing two unknowns, and of the same sort as Diophantus I. 1–6; or, of course, they can be reduced to a simple equation with one unknown by means of an easy elimination. One other (XIV. 51) gives simultaneous equations in three unknowns

$$x = y + \frac{z}{3},\ y = z + \frac{x}{3},\ z = 10 + \frac{y}{3},$$

and one (XIV. 49) gives four equations in four unknowns

$$x + y = 40,\ x + z = 45,\ x + u = 36,\ x + y + z + u = 60.$$

With these may be compared Diophantus I. 16–21. (3) Six more are problems of the usual type about the filling of vessels by pipes: *e.g.* (XIV. 130) one pipe fills the vessel in one day, a second in two, and a third in three; how long will all three running together take to fill it? Another about brickmakers (XIV. 136) is of the same sort.

The Anthology contains (4) two *indeterminate* equations of the first degree which can be solved in positive integers in an infinite number of ways (XIV. 48 and 144); the first is a distribution of apples satisfying the equation $x - 3y = y$, where y is not less than 2, and the original number of apples is $3x$; the second leads to the following three equations between four unknown quantities:

$$x + y = x_1 + y_1,$$
$$x = 2y_1,$$
$$x_1 = 3y,$$

the general solution of which is $x = 4k$, $y = k$, $x_1 = 3k$, $y_1 = 2k$. These very equations, made however determinate by assuming that $x + y = x_1 + y_1 = 100$, are solved in Diophantus I. 12.

We mentioned above the problem in the Anthology (XIV. 49) leading to the following four simultaneous linear equations with four unknown quantities,

$$x + y = a,$$
$$x + z = b,$$
$$x + u = c,$$
$$x + y + z + u = d.$$

The general solution of any number of simultaneous linear equations of this type with the same number of unknown quantities was given by Thymaridas, apparently of Paros, and an early Pythagorean. He gave a rule, ἔφοδος, or *method* of attack (as

Iamblichus[1], our informant, calls it) which must have been widely known, inasmuch as it was called by the name of the ἐπάνθημα, "flower" or "bloom," of Thymaridas. The rule is stated in general terms, but, though no symbols are used, the content is pure algebra. Thymaridas, too, distinguishes between what he calls ἀόριστον, the undefined or unknown quantity, and the ὡρισμένον, the definite or known, therein anticipating the very phrase of Diophantus, πλῆθος μονάδων ἀόριστον, "an undefined number of units," by which he describes his ἀριθμός or x. Thymaridas' rule, though obscurely expressed, states in effect that, if there are n equations between n unknown quantities x, x_1, $x_2 \dots x_{n-1}$ of the following form,

$$x + x_1 = a_1,$$
$$x + x_2 = a_2,$$
$$\dots\dots\dots\dots\dots$$
$$x + x_{n-1} = a_{n-1},$$
$$x + x_1 + x_2 + \dots + x_{n-1} = s,$$

then the solution is given by

$$x = \frac{(a_1 + a_2 + \dots + a_{n-1}) - s}{n - 2}.$$

Iamblichus goes on to show that other types of equations can be reduced to this, so that the rule does not leave us in the lurch (οὐ παρέλκει) in those cases either. Thus we can reduce to Thymaridas' form the indeterminate problem represented by the following three linear equations between four unknown quantities:

$$x + y = a(z + u),$$
$$x + z = b(u + y),$$
$$x + u = c(y + z).$$

From the first equation we obtain

$$x + y + z + u = (a + 1)(z + u),$$

from which it follows that, if x, y, z, u are all to be integers, $x + y + z + u$ must contain $a + 1$ as a factor. Similarly it must contain $b + 1$ and $c + 1$ as factors.

Suppose now that $x + y + z + u = (a + 1)(b + 1)(c + 1)$. Therefore, by means of the first equation, we get

$$(x + y)\left(1 + \frac{1}{a}\right) = (a + 1)(b + 1)(c + 1),$$

[1] Iamblichus, *In Nicomachi arithmeticam introductionem* (ed. Pistelli), pp. 62, 18–68, 26.

or $$x+y=a(b+1)(c+1).$$

Similarly $$x+z=b(c+1)(a+1),$$
$$x+u=c(a+1)(b+1),$$

and the equations are in the form to which Thymaridas' rule is applicable.

Hence, by that rule,

$$x=\frac{a(b+1)(c+1)+\ldots-(a+1)(b+1)(c+1)}{2}.$$

In order to ensure that x may always be integral, it is only necessary to assume

$$x+y+z+u=2(a+1)(b+1)(c+1).$$

The factor 2 is of course determined by the number of unknowns. If there are n unknowns, the factor to be put in place of 2 is $n-2$.

Iamblichus has the particular case corresponding to $a=2$, $b=3$, $c=4$. He goes on to apply the method to the equations

$$x+y=\frac{k}{l}(z+u),$$

$$x+z=\frac{m}{n}(u+y),$$

$$x+u=\frac{p}{q}(y+z),$$

for the case where $k/l=\frac{3}{2}$, $m/n=\frac{4}{3}$, $p/q=\frac{5}{4}$.

Enough has been said to show that Diophantus was not the inventor of Algebra. Nor was he the first to solve indeterminate problems of the second degree.

Take, first, the problem of dividing a square number into two squares (Diophantus II. 8), or of finding a right-angled triangle with sides in rational numbers. This problem was, as we learn from Proclus[1], attributed to Pythagoras, who was credited with the discovery of a general formula for finding such triangles which may be shown thus:

$$n^2+\left(\frac{n^2-1}{2}\right)^2=\left(\frac{n^2+1}{2}\right)^2,$$

where n is an odd number. Plato again is credited, according to the same authority, with another formula of the same sort,

$$(2n)^2+(n^2-1)^2=(n^2+1)^2.$$

[1] *Comment. on Euclid, Book I.* pp. 428, 7 sqq.

Both these formulae are readily connected with the geometrical proposition in Eucl. II. 5, the algebraical equivalent of which may be stated as

$$\left(\frac{a+b}{2}\right)^2 - \left(\frac{a-b}{2}\right)^2 = ab.$$

The content of Euclid Book II. is beyond doubt Pythagorean, and this way of stating the proposition quoted could not have escaped the Pythagoreans. If we put 1 for b and the square of any odd number for a, we have the Pythagorean formula; and, if we put $a = 2n^2$, $b = 2$, we obtain Plato's formula. Euclid finds a more general formula in Book X. (Lemma following X. 28). Starting with numbers $u = c + b$ and $v = c - b$, so that

$$uv = c^2 - b^2,$$

Euclid points out that, in order that uv may be a square, u and v must be "similar plane numbers" or numbers of the form mnp^2, mnq^2. Substituting we have

$$m^2n^2p^2q^2 = \left(\frac{mnp^2 + mnq^2}{2}\right)^2 - \left(\frac{mnp^2 - mnq^2}{2}\right)^2.$$

But the problem of finding right-angled triangles in rational numbers was not the only indeterminate problem of the second degree solved by the Pythagoreans. They solved the equation

$$2x^2 - y^2 = \pm 1$$

in such a way as to prove that there are an infinite number of solutions of that equation in integral numbers. The Pythagoreans used for this purpose the system of "side-" and "diagonal-" numbers[1], afterwards fully described by Theon of Smyrna[2]. We begin with unity as both the first "side" and the first "diagonal"; thus

$$a_1 = 1,\ d_1 = 1.$$

We then form $(a_2,\ d_2)$, $(a_3,\ d_3)$, etc., in accordance with the following law,

$$a_2 = a_1 + d_1,\ d_2 = 2a_1 + d_1;$$

$$a_3 = a_2 + d_2,\ d_3 = 2a_2 + d_2;$$

and so on. Theon states, with reference to these numbers, the general proposition that

$$d_n^2 = 2a_n^2 \pm 1,$$

and observes that (1) the signs alternate as successive d's and a's

[1] See Proclus, *In Platonis rempublicam commentarii* (Teubner, Leipzig), Vol. II. c. 27, p. 27, 11–18.

[2] Theon of Smyrna, ed. Hiller, pp. 43, 44.

are taken, $d_1^2 - 2a_1^2$ being equal to -1, $d_2^2 - 2a_2^2$ equal to $+1$, $d_3^2 - 2a_3^2$ equal to -1 and so on, (2) the sum of the squares of *all* the d's will be double of the sum of the squares of *all* the a's. For the purpose of (2) the number of successive terms in each series, if finite, must of course be even. The algebraical proof is easy.

$$\begin{aligned} d_n^2 - 2a_n^2 &= (2a_{n-1} + d_{n-1})^2 - 2(a_{n-1} + d_{n-1})^2 \\ &= 2a_{n-1}^2 - d_{n-1}^2 \\ &= -(d_{n-1}^2 - 2a_{n-1}^2) \\ &= +(d_{n-2}^2 - 2a_{n-2}^2), \end{aligned}$$

and so on, while $d_1^2 - 2a_1^2 = -1$. Proclus tells us that the property was proved by means of the theorems of Eucl. II. 9, 10, which are indeed equivalent to

$$(2x+y)^2 - 2(x+y)^2 = 2x^2 - y^2.$$

Diophantus does not particularly mention the indeterminate equation $2x^2 - 1 = y^2$, still less does he mention "side-" and "diagonal-" numbers. But from the Lemma to VI. 15 (quoted above, p. 69) it is clear that he knew how to find any number of solutions when one is known. Thus, seeing that $x = 1$, $y = 1$ is one solution, he would put

$$\begin{aligned} 2(1+x)^2 - 1 &= \text{a square} \\ &= (px-1)^2 \text{ say,} \end{aligned}$$

whence $$x = (4+2p)/(p^2-2).$$

Take the value $p = 2$, and we have $x = 4$, or $x + 1 = 5$; and $2 . 5^2 - 1 = 49 = 7^2$. Putting $x + 5$ in place of x, we find a still higher value, and so on.

In a recent paper Heiberg has published and translated, and Zeuthen has commented on, still further Greek examples of indeterminate analysis[1]. They come from the Constantinople MS. (probably of 12th c.) from which Schöne edited the *Metrica* of Heron. The first two of the thirteen problems had been published before (though in a less complete form)[2]; the others are new.

The first bids us find two rectangles such that the perimeter of the second is three times that of the first, and the area of the first is three times that of the second (the first of the two conditions is, by some accident, omitted in the text). The number 3

[1] *Bibliotheca Mathematica*, VIII$_3$, 1907–8, pp. 118–134.

[2] Hultsch's Heron, *Geeponica*, 78, 79. The two problems are discussed by Cantor, *Agrimensoren*, p. 62, and Tannery, *Mém. de la soc. des sc. de Bordeaux*, IV$_2$, 1882.

is of course only an illustration, and the problem is equivalent to the solution of the equations

$$\left.\begin{aligned} u+v &= n(x+y) \\ xy &= n\,.\,uv \end{aligned}\right\} \quad \ldots\ldots\ldots\ldots\ldots\ldots\ldots(1);$$

the solution given in the text is equivalent to

$$\left.\begin{aligned} x &= 2n^3-1,\ y=2n^3 \\ u &= n(4n^3-2),\ v=n \end{aligned}\right\} \quad \ldots\ldots\ldots\ldots\ldots\ldots(2).$$

Zeuthen suggests that this solution may have been arrived at thus. As the problem is indeterminate, it would be natural to make trial of some hypothesis, *e.g.* to put $v=n$. It would follow from the first equation in (1) that u is a multiple of n, say nz. We have then

$$x+y=1+z,$$

$$xy=n^3z,$$

whence $$xy=n^3(x+y)-n^3,$$

or $$(x-n^3)(y-n^3)=n^3(n^3-1).$$

An obvious solution of this is

$$x-n^3=n^3-1,\ y-n^3=n^3.$$

The second problem is equivalent to the solution of the equations

$$\left.\begin{aligned} x+y &= u+v \\ xy &= n\,.\,uv \end{aligned}\right\} \quad \ldots\ldots\ldots\ldots\ldots\ldots\ldots\ldots(1);$$

and the solution given in the text is

$$x+y=u+v=n^3-1 \quad \ldots\ldots\ldots\ldots\ldots\ldots\ldots(2),$$

$$\left.\begin{aligned} u &= n-1,\quad v=n(n^2-1) \\ x &= n^2-1,\ y=n^2(n-1) \end{aligned}\right\} \quad \ldots\ldots\ldots\ldots\ldots(3).$$

In this case trial may have been made of the assumption

$$v=nx,\ y=n^2u,$$

when the first equation in (1) would give

$$(n-1)x=(n^2-1)u,$$

a solution of which is $x=n^2-1,\ u=n-1$.

The fifth problem is of interest in one respect. We are asked to find a right-angled triangle (in rational numbers) with area of 5 feet. We are told to multiply 5 by some square *containing* 6 *as a factor*, *e.g.* 36. This makes 180, and this is the area of the triangle (9, 40, 41). Dividing each side by 6, we have the triangle required. The author, then, is aware of the fact that the area of a right-angled triangle with sides in whole numbers is divisible by 6. If we take the Euclidean formula for a right-angled triangle, thus making the sides

$$a \, . \, mn, \quad a \, . \frac{m^2 - n^2}{2}, \quad a \, . \frac{m^2 + n^2}{2},$$

where a is any number, and m, n are numbers which are both odd or both even, the area is

$$a^2 \frac{mn(m-n)(m+n)}{4},$$

and, as a matter of fact, the numerator $mn(m-n)(m+n)$ is divisible by 24, as was proved later (for another purpose) by Leonardo of Pisa[1]. There is no sign that Diophantus was aware of the proposition; this however may be due to the fact that he does not trouble as to whether his solutions are integral, but is satisfied with *rational* results.

The last four problems (numbered 10 to 13) are of great interest. They are different particular cases of one problem, that of finding a rational right-angled triangle such that the numerical sum of its area and all its three sides is a given number. The author's solution depends on the following formulae, where a, b are the perpendiculars, and c the hypotenuse, of a right-angled triangle, S its area, r the radius of its inscribed circle, and $s = \frac{1}{2}(a+b+c)$:

$$S = rs = \tfrac{1}{2}ab, \quad r + s = a + b, \quad c = s - r.$$

(The proof of these formulae by means of the usual figure, that used by Heron to prove his formula for the area of a triangle in terms of its sides, is easy.)

Solving the first two equations, in order to find a and b, we have

$$\left.\begin{matrix} a \\ b \end{matrix}\right\} = \frac{r + s \mp \sqrt{\{(r+s)^2 - 8rs\}}}{2},$$

which formula is actually used by the author for finding a and b. The method employed is to take the sum of the area and the three sides $S + 2s$, separated into its two obvious factors $s(r+2)$, to put $s(r+2) = A$ (the given number), and then to separate A into suitable factors to which s and $r+2$ may be equated. They must obviously be such that sr, the area, is divisible by 6. To take the first example where A is equal to 280: the possible factors are

[1] *Scritti*, ed. B. Boncompagni, II. (1862), p. 264. Cf. Cantor, *Gesch. d. Math.* II_1, p. 40.

2×140, 4×70, 5×56, 7×40, 8×35, 10×28, 14×20. The suitable factors in this case are $r+2=8$, $s=35$, because r is then equal to 6, and rs is a multiple of 6.

The author then says that

$$a=\frac{6+35-\sqrt{\{(6+35)^2-8.6.35\}}}{2}=\frac{41-1}{2}=20,$$

$$b=\frac{41+1}{2}=21,$$

and $$c=35-6=29.$$

The triangle is therefore (20, 21, 29) in this case. The triangles found in the other cases, by the same method, are (9, 40, 41), (8, 15, 17) and (9, 12, 15).

Unfortunately there is no guide to the date of the problems just given. The form, however, cannot be that in which the discoverer or discoverers of the methods indicated originally explained those methods. The probability is that the original formulation of the most important of the problems belongs to the period between Euclid and Diophantus. This supposition best agrees with the fact that the problems include nothing taken from the great collection in the *Arithmetica*. On the other hand, it is strange that none of the seven problems above mentioned is found in Diophantus. The five of them which relate to rational right-angled triangles might well have been included by him; thus he finds rational triangles such that the area *plus* or *minus* one of the perpendiculars is a given number, but not the rational triangle which has a given area; and he finds rational triangles such that the area *plus* or *minus* the sum of two sides is a given number, but not the rational triangle such that the sum of the area and the three sides is a given number. The omitted problems might, it is true, have come in the lost Books; but, on the other hand, Book VI. is the place where we should have expected to find them. Nor do we find in the above problems any trace of Diophantus' peculiar methods.

Lastly, the famous Cattle-Problem attributed to Archimedes[1] has to be added to the indeterminate problems propounded before Diophantus' time. According to the heading prefixed to the epigram, it was communicated by Archimedes to the mathematicians at Alexandria in a letter to Eratosthenes. The scholiast

[1] Archimedes, ed. Heiberg, Vol. II. p. 450 sqq.

on *Charmides* 165 E also refers to the problem "called by Archimedes the Cattle-Problem." Krumbiegel, who discussed the arguments for and against the attribution to Archimedes, concluded apparently that, while the epigram can hardly have been written by Archimedes in its present form, it is possible, nay probable, that the problem was in substance originated by Archimedes[1]. Hultsch[2] has a most attractive suggestion as to the occasion of it. It is known that Apollonius in his ὠκυτόκιον had calculated an approximation to the value of π closer than that of Archimedes, and he must therefore have worked out more difficult multiplications than those contained in the *Measurement of a circle*. Also the other work of Apollonius on the multiplication of large numbers, which is partly preserved in Pappus, was inspired by the *Sand-reckoner* of Archimedes; and, though we need not exactly regard the treatise of Apollonius as polemical, yet it did in fact constitute a criticism of the earlier book. That Archimedes should then reply with a problem involving such a manipulation of immense numbers as would be difficult even for Apollonius is not altogether outside the bounds of possibility. And there is an unmistakable vein of satire in the opening words of the epigram, "Compute the number of the oxen of the Sun, giving thy mind thereto, if thou hast a share of wisdom," in the transition from the first part to the second, where it is said that ability to solve the first part would entitle one to be regarded as "not unknowing nor unskilled in numbers, but still not yet to be counted among the wise," and again in the last lines. Hultsch concludes that in any case the problem is not much later than the time of Archimedes and dates from the beginning of the second century B.C. at the latest.

I have reproduced elsewhere[3], from Amthor, details regarding the solution of the problem, and I need do little more than state here its algebraical equivalent. Eight unknown quantities have to be found, namely, the numbers of bulls and cows respectively of each of four colours (I use large letters for the bulls and small letters for the cows). The first part of the problem connects the eight unknowns by seven simple equations; the second part adds two more conditions.

[1] *Zeitschrift für Math. u. Physik* (Hist. litt. Abtheilung), XXV. (1880), p. 121 sq. Amthor added (p. 153 sq.) a discussion of the problem itself.

[2] Art. Archimedes in Pauly-Wissowa's *Real-Encyclopädie*, II. 1, pp. 534, 535.

[3] *The Works of Archimedes*, pp. 319–326.

First part of Problem.

$$\text{(I)}\quad W=(\tfrac{1}{2}+\tfrac{1}{3})X+Y \quad\text{(1)},$$
$$X=(\tfrac{1}{4}+\tfrac{1}{5})Z+Y \quad\text{(2)},$$
$$Z=(\tfrac{1}{6}+\tfrac{1}{7})W+Y \quad\text{(3)}.$$
$$\text{(II)}\quad w=(\tfrac{1}{3}+\tfrac{1}{4})(X+x) \quad\text{(4)},$$
$$x=(\tfrac{1}{4}+\tfrac{1}{5})(Z+z) \quad\text{(5)},$$
$$z=(\tfrac{1}{5}+\tfrac{1}{6})(Y+y) \quad\text{(6)},$$
$$y=(\tfrac{1}{6}+\tfrac{1}{7})(W+w) \quad\text{(7)}.$$

Second part.

$$W+X=\text{a square} \quad\text{(8)},$$
$$Y+Z=\text{a triangular number} \quad\text{(9)}.$$

The solution of the first part gives

$$W=10366482\,n,\quad w=7206360\,n,$$
$$X=7460514\,n,\quad x=4893246\,n,$$
$$Y=4149387\,n,\quad y=5439213\,n,$$
$$Z=7358060\,n,\quad z=3515820\,n,$$

where n is an integer. The solution given by the scholiast[1] corresponds to $n=80$.

The complete problem would not be unmanageable but for the condition (8). If for this were substituted the requirement that $W+X$ shall be merely a product of two unequal factors ("Wurm's problem"), the solution in the least possible numbers is

$$W=1217263415886,\quad w=846192410280,$$
$$X=876035935422,\quad x=574579625058,$$
$$Y=487233469701,\quad y=638688708099,$$
$$Z=864005479380,\quad z=412838131860.$$

But, if we include condition (8) and first of all find a solution satisfying the conditions (1) to (8), we have then, in order to satisfy condition (9), to solve the equation

$$q(q+1)/2=51285802909803\,.\,\xi^2$$
$$=3\cdot 7\cdot 11\,.\,29\cdot 353\cdot 4657^2\,.\,\xi^2.$$

If we multiply by 8, and put

$$2q+1=t,\quad 2\,.\,4657\,\xi=u,$$

we have the equation

$$t^2-1=2\,.\,3\,.\,7\,.\,11\,.\,29\,.\,353\,.\,u^2,$$

or

$$t^2-4729494\,u^2=1.$$

[1] Archimedes, ed. Heiberg, Vol. II. pp. 454, 455.

The value of W would be a number containing 206545 digits.

Such are the very few and scattered particulars which we possess of problems similar to those of Diophantus solved or propounded before his time. They show indeed that the kind of problem was not invented by him, but on the other hand they show little or no trace of anything like his characteristic algebraical methods. In the circumstances, and in default of discovery of fresh documents, the question how much of his work represents original contributions of his own to the subject must remain a matter of pure speculation. It is pretty obvious that one man could not have been the author of all the problems contained in the six Books. There are also inequalities in the work; some problems are very inferior in interest to the remainder, and some solutions may be assumed to be reproduced from other writers of less calibre, since they reveal none of the mastery of the subject which Diophantus possessed. Again, it seems probable that the problem V. 30, which is exceptionally in epigrammatic form, was taken from someone else. The *Arithmetica* was no doubt a *collection*, much in the same sense as Euclid's *Elements* were. And this may be one reason why so little trace remains of earlier labours in the same field. It is well known that Euclid's *Elements* so entirely superseded the works of the earlier writers of Elements (Hippocrates of Chios, Leon and Theudius) and of the great contributors to the body of the *Elements*, Theaetetus and Eudoxus, that those works have disappeared almost entirely. So no doubt would Diophantus' work supersede, and have the effect of consigning to oblivion, any earlier collections of problems of the same kind. But, if it was a compilation, we cannot doubt that it was a compilation in the best sense, therein resembling Euclid's *Elements*; it was a compilation by one who was a master of the subject, who took account of and assimilated all the best that had been written upon it, arranged the whole of the available material in due and progressive order, but also added much of his own, not only in the form of new problems but also (and even more) in the mode of treatment, the development of more general methods, and so on.

It is perhaps desirable to add a few words on the previous history of the theory of polygonal numbers. The theory certainly goes back to Pythagoras and the earliest Pythagoreans. The triangle came first, being obtained by first taking 1, then adding

2 to it, then 3 to the sum; each successive number would be represented by the proper number of dots, and, when each number was represented by that number of dots arranged symmetrically under the row representing the preceding number, the triangular form would be apparent to the eye, thus:

Next came the Pythagorean discovery of the fact that a similar successive addition of *odd* numbers produced successive square numbers, the odd numbers being on that account called *gnomons*, and again the process was shown by dots arranged to represent squares. The accompanying figure shows the successive squares and gnomons.

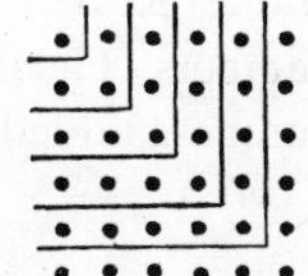

Following triangles and squares came the figured numbers in which the "gnomons," or the numbers added to make one number of a given form into the next larger of the same form, were numbers in arithmetical progression starting from 1, but with common difference 3, 4, 5, etc., instead of 1, 2. Thus, if the common difference is 3, so that the successive numbers added to 1 are 4, 7, 10, etc., the number is a pentagonal number, if the common difference is 4 and the gnomons 5, 9, 13, etc., the number is a hexagonal number, and so on. Hence the law that the common difference of the gnomons in the case of a n-gon is $n-2$.

Perhaps these facts had already been arrived at by Philippus of Opus (4th c. B.C.), who is said to have written a work on polygonal numbers[1]. Next Speusippus, nephew and successor of Plato, wrote on Pythagorean Numbers, and a fragment of his book survives[2], in which linear numbers, polygonal numbers, triangles and pyramids are spoken of: a fact which leaves no room for doubt as to the Pythagorean origin of all these conceptions[3].

Hypsicles, who wrote about 170 B.C., is twice mentioned by Diophantus as the author of a "definition" of a polygonal number,

[1] Βιογράφοι, *Vitarum scriptores Graeci minores*, ed. Westermann, 1845, p. 448.

[2] *Theologumena arithmeticae* (ed. Ast), 1817, pp. 61, 62; the passage is translated with notes by Tannery, *Pour l'histoire de la science hellène*, pp. 386–390.

[3] Cantor, *Geschichte der Mathematik*, I_3, p. 249.

which is even quoted verbatim[1]. The definition does not mention any polygonal number beyond the pentagonal; but indeed this was unnecessary: the facts about the triangle, the square and the pentagon were sufficient to enable Hypsicles to pass to a general conclusion. The definition amounts to saying that the nth a-gon (1 counting as the first) is

$$\tfrac{1}{2}n\{2+(n-1)(a-2)\}.$$

Theon of Smyrna[2], Nicomachus[3] and Iamblichus[4] all devote some space to polygonal numbers. The first two, who flourished about 100 A.D., were earlier than Diophantus, and are accordingly of interest here. Besides a description of the successive polygonal numbers, Theon gives the theorem that two successive triangular numbers added together give a square. That is,

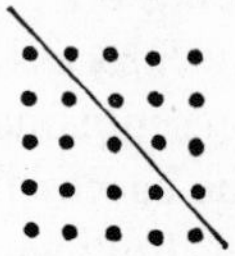

$$\frac{(n-1)n}{2}+\frac{n(n+1)}{2}=n^2.$$

The fact is of course clear if we divide a square into two triangles as in the figure.

Nicomachus gave various rules for transforming triangles into squares, squares into pentagons, etc.

1. If we put two consecutive triangles together we get a square (as in Theon's theorem).

2. A pentagon is obtained from a square by adding to it a triangle the side of which is 1 less than that of the square; similarly a hexagon from a pentagon by adding a triangle the side of which is 1 less than that of the pentagon; and so on.

In fact,

$$\tfrac{1}{2}n\{2+(n-1)(a-2)\}+\tfrac{1}{2}(n-1)n=\tfrac{1}{2}n[2+(n-1)\{(a+1)-2\}].$$

Next Nicomachus sets out the first triangles, squares, pentagons, hexagons and heptagons in a diagram thus:

Triangles ...	1	3	6	10	15	21	28	36	45	55
Squares ...	1	4	9	16	25	36	49	64	81	100
Pentagons ...	1	5	12	22	35	51	70	92	117	145
Hexagons ...	1	6	15	28	45	66	91	120	153	190
Heptagons ...	1	7	18	34	55	81	112	148	189	235

and observes that

[1] Dioph. I. pp. 470–472.

[2] *Expositio rerum mathematicarum ad legendum Platonem utilium*, ed. Hiller, pp. 31–40.

[3] *Introductio arithmetica*, ed. Hoche, II. 8–12, pp. 87–99.

[4] *In Nicomachi arithmeticam introd.*, ed. Pistelli, pp. 58–61, 68–72.

3. Each polygon is equal to the polygon immediately above it in the diagram *plus* the triangle with 1 less in its side, *i.e.* the triangle in the preceding column.

4. The vertical columns are arithmetical progressions, the common difference of which is the triangle in the preceding column.

But Plutarch, a contemporary of Nicomachus, mentioned another method of transforming triangles into squares: *Every triangular number taken eight times and then increased by* 1 *gives a square*[1]. That is,

$$8 \cdot \frac{n(n+1)}{2} + 1 = (2n+1)^2.$$

Diophantus generalised this proposition into his theorem for transforming *any* polygonal number into a square.

If P be a polygonal number, a the number of angles,

$$8P(a-2) + (a-4)^2 = \text{a square}.$$

He deduces rules for finding a polygonal number when the side and the number of angles are given, and for finding the side when the number and the number of its angles are given. These fine results and the fragment of the difficult problem of *finding the number of ways in which any given number can be a polygonal number* no doubt represent part of the original contributions by Diophantus to the theory of that class of numbers.

1 *Plat. quaest.* V. 2, 4, 1003 F.

THE ARITHMETICA

BOOK I

PRELIMINARY

Dedication.

"Knowing, my most esteemed friend Dionysius, that you are anxious to learn how to investigate problems in numbers, I have tried, beginning from the foundations on which the science is built up, to set forth to you the nature and power subsisting in numbers.

"Perhaps the subject will appear rather difficult, inasmuch as it is not yet familiar (beginners are, as a rule, too ready to despair of success); but you, with the impulse of your enthusiasm and the benefit of my teaching, will find it easy to master; for eagerness to learn, when seconded by instruction, ensures rapid progress."

After the remark that "all numbers are made up of some multitude of units, so that it is manifest that their formation is subject to no limit," Diophantus proceeds to define what he calls the different "species" of numbers, and to describe the abbreviative signs used to denote them. These "species" are, in the first place, the various powers of the unknown quantity from the second to the sixth inclusive, the unknown quantity itself, and units.

Definitions.

A *square* ($=x^2$) is δύναμις ("power"), and its sign is a Δ with Y superposed, thus Δ^Y.

A *cube* ($=x^3$) is κύβος, and its sign K^Y.

A *square-square* ($=x^4$) is δυναμοδύναμις[1], and its sign is $\Delta^Y\Delta$.

A *square-cube* ($=x^5$) is δυναμόκυβος, and its sign ΔK^Y.

A *cube-cube* ($=x^6$) is κυβόκυβος, and its sign $K^Y K$.

[1] The term δυναμοδύναμις was already used by Heron (*Metrica*, ed. Schöne, p. 48, 11, 19) for the fourth power of a side of a triangle.

"It is," Diophantus observes, "from the addition, subtraction or multiplication of these numbers or from the ratios which they bear to one another or to their own sides respectively that most arithmetical problems are formed"; and "each of these numbers... is recognised as an element in arithmetical inquiry."

"But the number which has none of these characteristics, but *merely has in it an indeterminate multitude of units* (πλῆθος μονάδων ἀόριστον) *is called* ἀριθμός; '*number*,' *and its sign is* ς [$=x$]."

"And there is also another sign denoting that which is invariable in determinate numbers, namely the unit, the sign being M with o superposed, thus $\overset{o}{M}$."

Next follow the definitions of the reciprocals, the names of which are derived from the names of the corresponding species themselves.

Thus

from ἀριθμός [x] we derive the term ἀριθμοστόν [$= 1/x$]
,, δύναμις [x^2] ,, ,, δυναμοστόν [$= 1/x^2$]
,, κύβος [x^3] ,, ,, κυβοστόν [$= 1/x^3$]
,, δυναμοδύναμις [x^4] ,, ,, δυναμοδυναμοστόν [$= 1/x^4$]
,, δυναμόκυβος [x^5] ,, ,, δυναμοκυβοστόν [$= 1/x^5$]
,, κυβόκυβος [x^6] ,, ,, κυβοκυβοστόν [$= 1/x^6$],

and each of these has the same sign as the corresponding original species, but with a distinguishing mark which Tannery writes in the form $^{\times}$ above the line to the right.

Thus $\Delta^{Y\times} = 1/x^2$, just as $\gamma^{\times} = \frac{1}{3}$.

Sign of Subtraction (*minus*).

"*A minus multiplied by a minus makes a plus*[1]; *a minus multiplied by a plus makes a minus; and the sign of a minus is a truncated* Ψ *turned upside down, thus* ⋔."

Diophantus proceeds: "It is well that one who is beginning this study should have acquired practice in the addition, subtraction and multiplication of the various species. He should know how to add positive and negative terms with different coefficients to

[1] The literal rendering would be "A wanting multiplied by a wanting makes a forthcoming." The word corresponding to *minus* is λεῖψις ("wanting"): when it is used exactly as our *minus* is, it is in the dative λείψει, but there is some doubt whether Diophantus himself used this form (cf. p. 44 above). For the probable explanation of the sign, see pp. 42–44. The word for "forthcoming" is ὕπαρξις, from ὑπάρχω, to exist. Negative terms are λείποντα εἴδη, and positive ὑπάρχοντα.

other terms[1], themselves either positive or likewise partly positive and partly negative, and how to subtract from a combination of positive and negative terms other terms either positive or likewise partly positive and partly negative.

"Next, if a problem leads to an equation in which certain terms are equal to terms of the same species but with different coefficients, it will be necessary to subtract like from like on both sides, until one term is found equal to one term. If by chance there are on either side or on both sides any negative terms, it will be necessary to add the negative terms on both sides, until the terms on both sides are positive, and then again to subtract like from like until one term only is left on each side.

"This should be the object aimed at in framing the hypotheses of propositions, that is to say, to reduce the equations, if possible, until one term is left equal to one term; *but I will show you later how, in the case also where two terms are left equal to one term, such a problem is solved.*"

Diophantus concludes by explaining that, in arranging the mass of material at his disposal, he tried to distinguish, so far as possible, the different types of problems, and, especially in the elementary portion at the beginning, to make the more simple lead up to the more complex, in due order, such an arrangement being calculated to make the beginner's course easier and to fix what he learns in his memory. The treatise, he adds, has been divided into thirteen Books.

PROBLEMS

1. To divide a given number into two having a given difference.

Given number 100, given difference 40.

Lesser number required x. Therefore

$$2x + 40 = 100,$$

$$x = 30.$$

The required numbers are **70, 30.**

2. To divide a given number into two having a given ratio.

Given number 60, given ratio 3 : 1.

Two numbers x, $3x$. Therefore $x = 15$.

The numbers are **45, 15.**

[1] εἶδος, "species," is the word used by Diophantus throughout.

3. To divide a given number into two numbers such that one is a given ratio of the other *plus* a given difference[1].

Given number 80, ratio 3 : 1, difference 4.

Lesser number x. Therefore the larger is $3x + 4$, and $4x + 4 = 80$, so that $x = 19$.

The numbers are **61, 19.**

4. To find two numbers in a given ratio and such that their difference is also given.

Given ratio 5 : 1, given difference 20.

Numbers $5x$, x. Therefore $4x = 20$, $x = 5$, and the numbers are **25, 5.**

5. To divide a given number into two numbers such that given fractions (not the same) of each number when added together produce a given number.

Necessary condition. The latter given number must be such that it lies between the numbers arising when the given fractions respectively are taken of the first given number.

First given number 100, given fractions $\frac{1}{3}$ and $\frac{1}{5}$, given sum of fractions 30.

Second part $5x$. Therefore first part $= 3(30 - x)$.

Hence $90 + 2x = 100$, and $x = 5$.

The required parts are **75, 25.**

6. To divide a given number into two numbers such that a given fraction of the first exceeds a given fraction of the other by a given number.

Necessary condition. The latter number must be less than that which arises when that fraction of the first number is taken which exceeds the other fraction.

Given number 100, given fractions $\frac{1}{4}$ and $\frac{1}{6}$ respectively, given excess 20.

Second part $6x$. Therefore the first part is $4(x + 20)$.

Hence $10x + 80 = 100$, $x = 2$, and the parts are **88, 12.**

[1] Literally "to divide an assigned number into two in a given ratio and difference (ἐν λόγῳ καὶ ὑπεροχῇ τῇ δοθείσῃ)." The phrase means the same, though it is not so clear, as Euclid's expression (*Data*, Def. 11 and *passim*) δοθέντι μείζων ἢ ἐν λόγῳ. According to Euclid's definition a magnitude is greater than a magnitude "by a given amount (more) than in a (certain) ratio" when the remainder of the first magnitude, after subtracting the given amount, has the said ratio to the second magnitude. This means that, if x, y are the magnitudes, d the given amount, and k the ratio, $x - d = ky$ or $x = ky + d$.

7. From the same (required) number to subtract two given numbers so as to make the remainders have to one another a given ratio.

Given numbers 100, 20, given ratio 3 : 1.

Required number x. Therefore $x - 20 = 3(x - 100)$, and $x = 140$.

8. To two given numbers to add the same (required) number so as to make the resulting numbers have to one another a given ratio.

Necessary condition. The given ratio must be less than the ratio which the greater of the given numbers has to the lesser.

Given numbers 100, 20, given ratio 3 : 1.

Required number x. Therefore $3x + 60 = x + 100$, and $x = 20$.

9. From two given numbers to subtract the same (required) number so as to make the remainders have to one another a given ratio.

Necessary condition. The given ratio must be greater than the ratio which the greater of the given numbers has to the lesser.

Given numbers 20, 100, given ratio 6 : 1.

Required number x. Therefore $120 - 6x = 100 - x$, and $x = 4$.

10. Given two numbers, to add to the lesser and to subtract from the greater the same (required) number so as to make the sum in the first case have to the difference in the second case a given ratio.

Given numbers 20, 100, given ratio 4 : 1.

Required number x. Therefore $(20 + x) = 4(100 - x)$, and $x = 76$.

11. Given two numbers, to add the first to, and subtract the second from, the same (required) number, so as to make the resulting numbers have to one another a given ratio.

Given numbers 20, 100, given ratio 3 : 1.

Required number x. Therefore $3x - 300 = x + 20$, and $x = 160$.

12. To divide a given number twice into two numbers such that the first of the first pair may have to the first of the second pair a given ratio, and also the second of the second pair to the second of the first pair another given ratio.

Given number 100, ratio of greater of first parts to lesser of second 2 : 1, and ratio of greater of second parts to lesser of first parts 3 : 1.

x lesser of second parts.

The parts then are

$$\left.\begin{matrix} 2x \\ 100-2x \end{matrix}\right\} \text{ and } \left.\begin{matrix} 300-6x \\ x \end{matrix}\right\}.$$

Therefore $300 - 5x = 100$, $x = 40$, and

the parts are (**80**, **20**), (**60**, **40**).

13. To divide a given number thrice into two numbers such that one of the first pair has to one of the second pair a given ratio, the second of the second pair to one of the third pair another given ratio, and the second of the third pair to the second of the first pair another given ratio.

Given number 100, ratio of greater of first parts to lesser of second 3 : 1, of greater of second to lesser of third 2 : 1, and of greater of third to lesser of first 4 : 1.

x lesser of third parts.

Therefore greater of second parts $= 2x$, lesser of second $= 100 - 2x$, greater of first $= 300 - 6x$.

Hence lesser of first $= 6x - 200$, so that greater of third $= 24x - 800$.

Therefore $25x - 800 = 100$, $x = 36$, and

the respective divisions are (**84**, **16**), (**72**, **28**), (**64**, **36**).

14. To find two numbers such that their product has to their sum a given ratio. [One is arbitrarily assumed.]

Necessary condition. The assumed value of one of the two must be greater than the number representing the ratio[1].

Ratio 3 : 1, x one of the numbers, 12 the other (> 3).

Therefore $12x = 3x + 36$, $x = 4$, and

the numbers are **4**, **12**.

15. To find two numbers such that each after receiving from the other a given number may bear to the remainder a given ratio.

Let the first receive 30 from the second, the ratio being then 2 : 1, and the second 50 from the first, the ratio being then 3 : 1; take $x + 30$ for the second.

[1] Literally "the number homonymous with the given ratio."

Therefore the first $= 2x - 30$, and

$$(x + 80) = 3(2x - 80).$$

Thus $x = 64$, and

the numbers are **98, 94**.

16. To find three numbers such that the sums of pairs are given numbers.

Necessary condition. Half the sum of the three given numbers must be greater than any one of them singly.

Let $(1) + (2) = 20$, $(2) + (3) = 30$, $(3) + (1) = 40$.

x the sum of the three. Therefore the numbers are

$$x - 30, \quad x - 40, \quad x - 20.$$

The sum $x = 3x - 90$, and $x = 45$.

The numbers are **15, 5, 25**.

17. To find four numbers such that the sums of all sets of three are given numbers.

Necessary condition. One-third of the sum of the four must be greater than any one singly.

Sums of threes 22, 24, 27, 20 respectively.

x the sum of all four. Therefore the numbers are

$$x - 22, \quad x - 24, \quad x - 27, \quad x - 20.$$

Therefore $4x - 93 = x$, $x = 31$, and

the numbers are **9, 7, 4, 11**.

18. To find three numbers such that the sum of any pair exceeds the third by a given number.

Given excesses 20, 30, 40.

$2x$ the sum of all three.

We have $(1) + (2) = (3) + 20$.

Adding (3) to each side, we have: twice $(3) + 20 = 2x$, and $(3) = x - 10$.

Similarly the numbers (1) and (2) are $x - 15$, $x - 20$ respectively.

Therefore $3x - 45 = 2x$, $x = 45$, and

the numbers are **30, 25, 35**.

[*Otherwise thus*[1]. As before, if the third number (3) is x,

$$(1) + (2) = x + 20.$$

Next, if we add the equations

$$\left.\begin{array}{l}(1) + (2) - (3) = 20 \\ (2) + (3) - (1) = 30\end{array}\right\},$$

[1] Tannery attributes the alternative solution of I. 18 (as of I. 19) to an old scholiast.

we have $(2) = \frac{1}{2}(20 + 30) = 25$.
Hence $(1) = x - 5$.
Lastly $(3) + (1) - (2) = 40$,
or $2x - 5 - 25 = 40$.
Therefore $x = 35$.
The numbers are **30, 25, 35**.]

19. To find four numbers such that the sum of any three exceeds the fourth by a given number.

Necessary condition. Half the sum of the four given differences must be greater than any one of them.

Given differences 20, 30, 40, 50.

$2x$ the sum of the required numbers. Therefore the numbers are

$$x - 15,\ x - 20,\ x - 25,\ x - 10.$$

Therefore $4x - 70 = 2x$, and $x = 35$.

The numbers are **20, 15, 10, 25**.

[*Otherwise thus*[1]. If the fourth number (4) is x,

$$(1) + (2) + (3) = x + 20.$$

Put $(2) + (3)$ equal to half the sum of the two excesses 20 and 30, *i.e.* 25 [this is equivalent to adding the two equations

$$(1) + (2) + (3) - (4) = 20,$$
$$(2) + (3) + (4) - (1) = 30].$$

It follows by subtraction that $(1) = x - 5$.

Next we add the equations beginning with (2) and (3) respectively, and we obtain

$$(3) + (4) = \tfrac{1}{2}(30 + 40) = 35,$$

so that $(3) = 35 - x$.

It follows that $(2) = x - 10$.

Lastly, since $(4) + (1) + (2) - (3) = 50$,

$$3x - 15 - (35 - x) = 50, \text{ and } x = 25.$$

The numbers are accordingly **20, 15, 10, 25**.]

20. To divide a given number into three numbers such that the sum of each extreme and the mean has to the other extreme a given ratio.

Given number 100; and let $(1) + (2) = 3 \cdot (3)$ and $(2) + (3) = 4 \cdot (1)$.

[1] Tannery attributes the alternative solution of I. 19 (as of I. 18) to an old scholiast.

x the third number. Thus the sum of the first and second $= 3x$, and the sum of the three $= 4x = 100$.

Hence $x = 25$, and the sum of the first two $= 75$.

Let y be the first[1]. Therefore sum of second and third $= 4y$, $5y = 100$ and $y = 20$.

The required parts are **20, 55, 25.**

21. To find three numbers such that the greatest exceeds the middle number by a given fraction of the least, the middle exceeds the least by a given fraction of the greatest, but the least exceeds a given fraction of the middle number by a given number.

Necessary condition. The middle number must exceed the least by such a fraction of the greatest that, if its denominator[2] be multiplied into the excess of the middle number over the least, the coefficient of x in the product is greater than the coefficient of x in the expression for the middle number resulting from the assumptions made[3].

Suppose greatest exceeds middle by $\frac{1}{3}$ of least, middle exceeds least by $\frac{1}{3}$ of greatest, and least exceeds $\frac{1}{3}$ of middle by 10. [Diophantus assumes the three given fractions or submultiples to be one and the same.]

$x + 10$ the least. Therefore middle $= 3x$, and greatest $= 6x - 30$.

Hence, lastly, $6x - 30 - 3x = \frac{1}{3}(x + 10)$,

or $\quad x + 10 = 9x - 90$, and $x = 12\frac{1}{2}$.

The numbers are **45, 37½, 22½.**

[1] As already remarked (p. 52), Diophantus does not use a second symbol for the second unknown, but makes ἀριθμός do duty for the second as well as for the first.

[2] "Denominator," literally the "number homonymous with the fraction," *i.e.* the denominator on the assumption that the fraction is, or is expressed as, a submultiple.

[3] Wertheim points out that this condition has reference, not to the general solution of the problem, but to the general applicability of the particular procedure which Diophantus adopts in his solution. Suppose X, Y, Z required such that $X - Y = Z/m$, $Y - Z = X/n$, $Z - a = Y/p$. Diophantus assumes $Z = x + a$, whence $Y = px$, $X = n(px - x - a)$. The condition states that $np - n > p$. If we solve for x by substituting the values of X, Y, Z in the first equation, we in fact obtain

$$m\{(np - n - p)x - na\} = x + a,$$

or

$$x(mnp - mn - mp - 1) = a(mn + 1).$$

In order that the value of x may be positive, we must have $mnp > mn + mp + 1$, that is,

$$np > n + p + \frac{1}{m}$$

or (if m, n, p are positive *integers*) $np > n + p$.

[Another solution[1].

Necessary condition. The given fraction of the greatest must be such that, when it is added to the least, the coefficient of x in the sum is less than the coefficient of x in the expression for the middle number resulting from the assumptions made[2].

Let the least number be $x + 10$, as before, and the given fraction $\frac{1}{3}$; the middle number is therefore $3x$.

Next, greatest = middle + $\frac{1}{3}$ (least) = $3\frac{1}{3}x + 3\frac{1}{3}$.

Lastly, $3x = x + 10 + \frac{1}{3}(3\frac{1}{3}x + 3\frac{1}{3})$

$= 2\frac{1}{9}x + 11\frac{1}{9}$.

Therefore $x = 12\frac{1}{2}$, and

the numbers are, as before, **45, $37\frac{1}{2}$, $22\frac{1}{2}$**.]

22. To find three numbers such that, if each give to the next following a given fraction of itself, in order, the results after each has given and taken may be equal.

Let first give $\frac{1}{3}$ of itself to second, second $\frac{1}{4}$ of itself to third, third $\frac{1}{5}$ of itself to first.

Assume first to be a number of x's divisible by 3, say $3x$, and second to be a number of *units* divisible by 4, say 4.

Therefore second after giving and taking becomes $x + 3$.

Hence the first also after giving and taking must become $x + 3$; it must therefore have taken $x + 3 - 2x$, or $3 - x$; $3 - x$ must therefore be $\frac{1}{5}$ of third, or third $= 15 - 5x$.

Lastly, $15 - 5x - (3 - x) + 1 = x + 3$,

or $13 - 4x = x + 3$, and $x = 2$.

The numbers are **6, 4, 5**.

23. To find four numbers such that, if each give to the next following a given fraction of itself, the results may all be equal.

Let first give $\frac{1}{3}$ of itself to second, second $\frac{1}{4}$ of itself to third, third $\frac{1}{5}$ of itself to fourth, and fourth $\frac{1}{6}$ of itself to first.

Assume first to be a number of x's divisible by 3, say $3x$, and second to be a number of *units* divisible by 4, say 4.

[1] Tannery attributes this alternative solution, like the others of the same kind, to an ancient scholiast.

[2] Wertheim observes that the scholiast's necessary condition comes to the same thing as Diophantus' own.

The second after giving and taking becomes $x+3$.

Therefore first after giving x to second and receiving $\frac{1}{6}$ of fourth $=x+3$; therefore fourth
$$=6(x+3-2x)=18-6x.$$

But fourth after giving $3-x$ to first and receiving $\frac{1}{5}$ of third $=x+3$; therefore third $=30x-60$.

Lastly, third after giving $6x-12$ to fourth and receiving 1 from second $=x+3$.

That is, $24x-47=x+3$, and $x=\frac{50}{23}$.

The numbers are therefore $\frac{150}{23}$, 4, $\frac{120}{23}$, $\frac{114}{23}$; or, after multiplying by the common denominator, **150, 92, 120, 114.**

24. To find three numbers such that, if each receives a given fraction of the sum of the other two, the results are all equal.

Let first receive $\frac{1}{3}$ of (second + third), second $\frac{1}{4}$ of (third + first), and third $\frac{1}{5}$ of (first + second).

Assume first $=x$, and for convenience' sake (**τοῦ προχείρου ἕνεκεν**) take for sum of second and third a number of *units* divisible by 3, say 3.

Then sum of the three $=x+3$,

and first $+\frac{1}{3}$ (second + third) $=x+1$.

Therefore second $+\frac{1}{4}$ (third + first) $=x+1$;

hence 3 times second + sum of all $=4x+4$,

and therefore second $=x+\frac{1}{3}$.

Lastly, third $+\frac{1}{5}$ (first + second) $=x+1$,

or 4 times third + sum of all $=5x+5$,

and third $=x+\frac{1}{2}$.

Therefore $x+(x+\frac{1}{3})+(x+\frac{1}{2})=x+3$,

and $x=\frac{13}{12}$.

The numbers, after multiplying by the common denominator, are **13, 17, 19.**

25. To find four numbers such that, if each receives a given fraction of the sum of the remaining three, the four results are equal.

Let first receive $\frac{1}{3}$ of the rest, second $\frac{1}{4}$ of the rest, third $\frac{1}{5}$ of rest, and fourth $\frac{1}{6}$ of rest.

Assume first to be x and sum of rest a number of units divisible by 3, say 3.

Then sum of all $=x+3$.

Now first $+\frac{1}{3}$ (second + third + fourth) $=x+1$.

Therefore second + $\frac{1}{4}$ (third + fourth + first) $= x + 1$,
whence 3 times second + sum of all $= 4x + 4$,
and therefore second $= x + \frac{1}{3}$.
Similarly third $= x + \frac{1}{2}$,
and fourth $= x + \frac{3}{5}$.
Adding, we have $4x + \frac{43}{30} = x + 3$,
and $x = \frac{47}{90}$.

The numbers, after multiplying by a common denominator, are **47, 77, 92, 101**.

26. Given two numbers, to find a third number which, when multiplied into the given numbers respectively, makes one product a square and the other the side of that square.

Given numbers 200, 5; required number x.
Therefore $200x = (5x)^2$, and
$x = \mathbf{8}$.

27. To find two numbers such that their sum and product are given numbers.

Necessary condition. The square of half the sum must exceed the product by a square number. ἔστι δὲ τοῦτο πλασματικόν[1].

Given sum 20, given product 96.
$2x$ the difference of the required numbers.
Therefore the numbers are $10 + x$, $10 - x$.
Hence $100 - x^2 = 96$.
Therefore $x = 2$, and
the required numbers are **12, 8**.

28. To find two numbers such that their sum and the sum of their squares are given numbers.

Necessary condition. Double the sum of their squares must exceed the square of their sum by a square. ἔστι δὲ καὶ τοῦτο πλασματικόν[1].

[1] There has been controversy as to the meaning of this difficult phrase. Xylander, Bachet, Cossali, Schulz, Nesselmann, all discuss it. Xylander translated it by "effictum aliunde." Bachet of course rejects this, and, while leaving the word untranslated, maintains that it has an active rather than a passive signification; it is, he says, not something "made up" (effictum) but something "a quo aliud quippiam effingi et plasmari potest," "from which something else can be made up," and this he interprets as meaning that from the conditions to which the term is applied, combined with the solutions of the respective problems in which it occurs, the rules for solving mixed quadratics can be evolved. Of the two views I think Xylander's is nearer the mark. πλασματικόν should apparently mean "of the nature of a πλάσμα," just as δραματικόν means something connected with or suitable for a drama; and πλάσμα means something

Given sum 20, given sum of squares 208.
Difference $2x$.
Therefore the numbers are $10+x$, $10-x$.
Thus $200+2x^2=208$, and $x=2$.

The required numbers are **12, 8.**

29. To find two numbers such that their sum and the difference of their squares are given numbers.

Given sum 20, given difference of squares 80.
Difference $2x$.
The numbers are therefore $10+x$, $10-x$.
Hence $(10+x)^2-(10-x)^2=80$,
or $40x=80$, and $x=2$.

The required numbers are **12, 8.**

30. To find two numbers such that their difference and product are given numbers.

Necessary condition. Four times the product together with the square of the difference must give a square. *ἔστι δὲ καὶ τοῦτο πλασματικόν.*

Given difference 4, given product 96.
$2x$ the sum of the required numbers.
Therefore the numbers are $x+2$, $x-2$; accordingly $x^2-4=96$, and $x=10$.

The required numbers are **12, 8.**

31. To find two numbers in a given ratio and such that the sum of their squares also has to their sum a given ratio.

Given ratios $3:1$ and $5:1$ respectively.
Lesser number x.
Therefore $10x^2=5.4x$, whence $x=2$, and
the numbers are **2, 6.**

32. To find two numbers in a given ratio and such that the sum of their squares also has to their difference a given ratio.

Given ratios $3:1$ and $10:1$.
Lesser number x, which is then found from the equation $10x^2=10.2x$.
Hence $x=2$, and
the numbers are **2, 6.**

"formed" or "moulded." Hence the expression would seem to mean "this is of the nature of a formula," with the implication that the formula is not difficult to make up or discover. Nesselmann, like Xylander, gives it much this meaning, translating it "das lässt sich aber bewerkstelligen." Tannery translates πλασματικόν by "formativum."

33. To find two numbers in a given ratio and such that the difference of their squares also has to their sum a given ratio.

Given ratios 3 : 1 and 6 : 1.

Lesser number x, which is found to be 3.

The numbers are **3, 9.**

34. To find two numbers in a given ratio and such that the difference of their squares also has to their difference a given ratio.

Given ratios 3 : 1 and 12 : 1.

Lesser number x, which is found to be 3.

The numbers are **3, 9.**

Similarly by the same method can be found two numbers in a given ratio and (1) such that their product is to their sum in a given ratio, or (2) such that their product is to their difference in a given ratio.

35. To find two numbers in a given ratio and such that the square of the lesser also has to the greater a given ratio.

Given ratios 3 : 1 and 6 : 1 respectively.

Lesser number x, which is found to be 18.

The numbers are **18, 54.**

36. To find two numbers in a given ratio and such that the square of the lesser also has to the lesser itself a given ratio.

Given ratios 3 : 1 and 6 : 1.

Lesser number x, which is found to be 6.

The numbers are **6, 18.**

37. To find two numbers in a given ratio and such that the square of the lesser also has to the sum of both a given ratio.

Given ratios 3 : 1 and 2 : 1.

Lesser number x, which is found to be 8.

The numbers are **8, 24.**

38. To find two numbers in a given ratio and such that the square of the lesser also has to the difference between them a given ratio.

Given ratios 3 : 1 and 6 : 1.

Lesser number x, which is found to be 12.

The numbers are **12, 36.**

Similarly can be found two numbers in a given ratio and

(1) such that the square of the greater also has to the lesser a given ratio, or

(2) such that the square of the greater also has to the greater itself a given ratio, or

(3) such that the square of the greater also has to the sum or difference of the two a given ratio.

39. Given two numbers, to find a third such that the sums of the several pairs multiplied by the corresponding third number give three numbers in arithmetical progression.

Given numbers 3, 5.

Required number x.

The three products are therefore $3x+15$, $5x+15$, $8x$.

Now $3x+15$ must be either the middle or the least of the three, and $5x+15$ either the greatest or the middle.

(1) $5x+15$ greatest, $3x+15$ least.

Therefore $5x+15+3x+15=2.8x$, and

$$x=\frac{15}{4}.$$

(2) $5x+15$ greatest, $3x+15$ middle.

Therefore $(5x+15)-(3x+15)=3x+15-8x$, and

$$x=\frac{15}{7}.$$

(3) $8x$ greatest, $3x+15$ least.

Therefore $8x+3x+15=2(5x+15)$, and

$$x=15.$$

BOOK II

[The first five problems of this Book are mere repetitions of problems in Book I. They probably found their way into the text from some ancient commentary. In each case the ratio of one required number to the other is assumed to be 2 : 1. The enunciations only are here given.]

1. To find two numbers such that their sum is to the sum of their squares in a given ratio [cf. I. 31].

2. To find two numbers such that their difference is to the difference of their squares in a given ratio [cf. I. 34].

3. To find two numbers such that their product is to their sum or their difference in a given ratio [cf. I. 34].

4. To find two numbers such that the sum of their squares is to their difference in a given ratio [cf. I. 32].

5. To find two numbers such that the difference of their squares is to their sum in a given ratio [cf. I. 33].

6[1]. To find two numbers having a given difference and such that the difference of their squares exceeds their difference by a given number.

Necessary condition. The square of their difference must be less than the sum of the said difference and the given excess of the difference of the squares over the difference of the numbers.

Difference of numbers 2, the other given number 20.

Lesser number x. Therefore $x+2$ is the greater, and

$$4x+4=22.$$

Therefore $x=4\frac{1}{2}$, and

the numbers are $4\frac{1}{2}$, $6\frac{1}{2}$.

7[1]. To find two numbers such that the difference of their squares is greater by a given number than a given ratio of their difference[2]. [*Difference assumed.*]

Necessary condition. The given ratio being $3:1$, the square of the difference of the numbers must be less than the sum of three times that difference and the given number.

Given number 10, difference of required numbers 2.

Lesser number x. Therefore the greater is $x+2$, and

$$4x+4=3\cdot 2+10.$$

Therefore $x=3$, and

the numbers are 3, 5.

8. To divide a given square number into two squares[3].

[1] The problems II. 6, 7 also are considered by Tannery to be interpolated from some ancient commentary.

[2] Here we have the identical phrase used in Euclid's *Data* (cf. note on p. 132 above): the difference of the squares is τῆς ὑπεροχῆς αὐτῶν δοθέντι ἀριθμῷ μείζων ἢ ἐν λόγῳ, literally "greater than their difference by a given number (more) than in a (given) ratio," by which is meant "greater by a given number than a given proportion or fraction of their difference."

[3] It is to this proposition that Fermat appended his famous note in which he enunciates what is known as the "great theorem" of Fermat. The text of the note is as follows:

"On the other hand it is impossible to separate a cube into two cubes, or a

Given square number 16.

x^2 one of the required squares. Therefore $16-x^2$ must be equal to a square.

Take a square of the form[1] $(mx-4)^2$, m being any integer and 4 the number which is the square root of 16, *e.g.* take $(2x-4)^2$, and equate it to $16-x^2$.

Therefore $4x^2-16x+16=16-x^2$,

or $5x^2=16x$, and $x=\frac{16}{5}$.

The required squares are therefore $\frac{256}{25}$, $\frac{144}{25}$.

9. To divide a given number which is the sum of two squares into two other squares[2].

---

biquadrate into two biquadrates, or generally *any power except a square into two powers with the same exponent*. I have discovered a truly marvellous proof of this, which however the margin is not large enough to contain."

Did Fermat really possess a proof of the general proposition that $x^m+y^m=z^m$ cannot be solved in rational numbers where m is any number >2? As Wertheim says, one is tempted to doubt this, seeing that, in spite of the labours of Euler, Lejeune-Dirichlet, Kummer and others, a general proof has not even yet been discovered. Euler proved the theorem for $m=3$ and $m=4$, Dirichlet for $m=5$, and Kummer, by means of the higher theory of numbers, produced a proof which only excludes certain particular values of m, which values are rare, at all events among the smaller values of m; thus there is no value of m below 100 for which Kummer's proof does not serve. (I take these facts from Weber and Wellstein's *Encyclopädie der Elementar-Mathematik*, I_2, p. 284, where a proof of the formula for $m=4$ is given.)

It appears that the Göttingen Academy of Sciences has recently awarded a prize to Dr A. Wieferich, of Münster, for a proof that the equation $x^p+y^p=z^p$ cannot be solved in terms of positive integers not multiples of p, if 2^p-2 is not divisible by p^2. "This surprisingly simple result represents the first advance, since the time of Kummer, in the proof of the last Fermat theorem" (*Bulletin of the American Mathematical Society*, February 1910).

Fermat says ("Relation des nouvelles découvertes en la science des nombres," August 1659, *Oeuvres*, II. p. 433) that he proved that *no cube is divisible into two cubes* by a variety of his method of *infinite diminution* (*descente infinie* or *indéfinie*) different from that which he employed for other negative or positive theorems; as to the other cases, see Supplement, sections I., II.

[1] Diophantus' words are: "I form the square from any number of ἀριθμοί *minus* as many units as there are in the side of 16." It is implied throughout that m must be so chosen that the result may be *rational* in Diophantus' sense, *i.e.* rational and positive.

[2] Diophantus' solution is substantially the same as Euler's (*Algebra*, tr. Hewlett, Part II. Art. 219), though the latter is expressed more generally.

Required to find x, y such that

$$x^2+y^2=f^2+g^2.$$

If $x \gtrless f$, then $y \lesseqgtr g$.

Put therefore $$x=f+pz, \quad y=g-qz:$$

Given number $13 = 2^2 + 3^2$.

As the roots of these squares are 2, 3, take $(x+2)^2$ as the first square and $(mx-3)^2$ as the second (where m is an integer), say $(2x-3)^2$.

Therefore $(x^2+4x+4)+(4x^2+9-12x)=13$,

or $5x^2+13-8x=13$.

Therefore $x=\frac{8}{5}$, and

the required squares are $\frac{324}{25}, \frac{1}{25}$.

10. To find two square numbers having a given difference.

Given difference 60.

Side of one number x, side of the other x *plus* any number the square of which is not greater than 60, say 3.

Therefore $(x+3)^2 - x^2 = 60$;

$x = 8\frac{1}{2}$, and

the required squares are $72\frac{1}{4}$, $132\frac{1}{4}$.

11. To add the same (required) number to two given numbers so as to make each of them a square.

(1) Given numbers 2, 3; required number x.

Therefore $\left.\begin{matrix} x+2 \\ x+3 \end{matrix}\right\}$ must both be squares.

This is called a double-equation (διπλοϊσότης).

To solve it, *take the difference between the two expressions and resolve it into two factors*[1]; in this case let us say 4, $\frac{1}{4}$.

Then *take either*

(*a*) *the square of half the difference between these factors and equate it to the lesser expression,*

or (*b*) *the square of half the sum and equate it to the greater.*

---

hence $$2fpz + p^2z^2 - 2gqz + q^2z^2 = 0,$$

and $$z = \frac{2gq - 2fp}{p^2+q^2},$$

so that $$x = \frac{2gpq + f(q^2-p^2)}{p^2+q^2}, \quad y = \frac{2fpq + g(p^2-q^2)}{p^2+q^2},$$

in which we may substitute all possible numbers for p, q.

[1] Here, as always, the factors chosen must be suitable factors, *i.e.* such as will lead to a "rational" result, in Diophantus' sense.

In this case (a) the square of half the difference is $\frac{225}{64}$.

Therefore $x+2=\frac{225}{64}$, and $x=\frac{97}{64}$, the squares being $\frac{225}{64}$, $\frac{289}{64}$.

Taking (b) the square of half the sum, we have $x+3=\frac{289}{64}$, which gives the same result.

(2) To avoid a double-equation[1],

first find a number which when added to 2, or to 3, gives a square.

Take *e.g.* the number x^2-2, which when added to 2 gives a square.

Therefore, since this same number added to 3 gives a square,

$$x^2+1=\text{a square}=(x-4)^2, \text{ say},$$

the number of units in the expression (in this case 4) being so taken that the solution may give $x^2>2$.

Therefore $x=\frac{15}{8}$, and

the required number is $\frac{97}{64}$, as before.

12. To subtract the same (required) number from two given numbers so as to make both remainders squares.

Given numbers 9, 21.

Assuming $9-x^2$ as the required number, we satisfy one condition, and the other requires that $12+x^2$ shall be a square.

Assume as the side of this square x *minus* some number the square of which >12, say 4.

Therefore $(x-4)^2=12+x^2$,

and $x=\frac{1}{2}$.

The required number is then $8\frac{3}{4}$.

[Diophantus does not reduce to lowest terms, but says $x=\frac{4}{8}$ and then subtracts $\frac{16}{64}$ from 9 or $\frac{576}{64}$.]

[1] This is the same procedure as that of Euler, who does not use double-equations. Euler (*Algebra*, tr. Hewlett, Part II. Art. 214) solves the problem

$$\left.\begin{array}{l} x+4=u^2 \\ x+7=v^2 \end{array}\right\}$$

Suppose $x+4=p^2$;

therefore $x=p^2-4$, and $x+7=p^2+3$.

Suppose that $p^2+3=(p+q)^2$;

therefore $p=(3-q^2)/2q$.

Thus $x=(9-22q^2+q^4)/4q^2$,

or, if we take a fraction r/s instead of q,

$$x=(9s^4-22r^2s^2+r^4)/4r^2s^2.$$

13. From the same (required) number to subtract two given numbers so as to make both remainders squares.

Given numbers 6, 7.

(1) Let x be the required number.

Therefore $\left.\begin{matrix} x-6 \\ x-7 \end{matrix}\right\}$ are both squares.

The difference is 1, which is the product of, say, 2 and $\frac{1}{2}$; and, by the rule for solving a double equation,

$$x-7=\frac{9}{16}, \text{ and } x=\frac{121}{16}.$$

(2) To avoid a double-equation, seek a number which exceeds a square by 6, say x^2+6.

Therefore x^2-1 must also be a square $=(x-2)^2$, say.

Therefore $x=\frac{5}{4}$, and

the required number is $\frac{121}{16}$.

14. To divide a given number into two parts and to find a square which when added to each of the two parts gives a square number.

Given number 20.

Take two numbers[1] such that the sum of their squares < 20, say 2, 3.

[1] Diophantus implies here that the two numbers chosen *must* be such that the sum of their squares <20. Tannery pointed out (*Bibliotheca Mathematica*, 1887, p. 103) that this is not so and that the condition actually necessary to ensure a real solution in Diophantus' sense is something different. We have to solve the equations

$$x+y=a, \quad z^2+x=u^2, \quad z^2+y=v^2.$$

We assume $u=z+m$, $v=z+n$, and, eliminating x, y, we obtain

$$z=\frac{a-(m^2+n^2)}{2(m+n)}.$$

In order that z may be positive, we must have $m^2+n^2<a$; but z need not be positive in order to satisfy the above equations. What is really required is that x, y shall both be positive.

Now from the above we derive

$$x-y=(u^2-v^2)=2z(m-n)+m^2-n^2$$
$$=\frac{(m-n)(a+2mn)}{m+n}.$$

Solving for x, y, we have

$$x=\frac{m(a+mn-n^2)}{m+n}, \quad y=\frac{n(a+mn-m^2)}{m+n}.$$

If, of the two assumed numbers, $m>n$, the condition necessary to secure that x, y shall both be positive is $a+mn>m^2$.

Add x to each and square.

We then have

$$\left.\begin{matrix} x^2+4x+4 \\ x^2+6x+9 \end{matrix}\right\},$$

and, if $\left.\begin{matrix} 4x+4 \\ 6x+9 \end{matrix}\right\}$ are respectively subtracted, the remainders are the same square.

Let then x^2 be the required square, and we have only to make $\left.\begin{matrix} 4x+4 \\ 6x+9 \end{matrix}\right\}$ the required parts of 20.

Thus $$10x+13=20,$$

and $$x=\tfrac{7}{10}.$$

The required parts are then $\left(\frac{68}{10}, \frac{132}{10}\right)$, and the required square is $\frac{49}{100}$.

15. To divide a given number into two parts and to find a square which, when each part is respectively subtracted from it, gives a square.

Given number 20.

Take $(x+m)^2$ for the required square[1], where m^2 is not greater than 20,

e.g. take $(x+2)^2$.

This leaves a square if either $\left.\begin{matrix} 4x+4 \\ \text{or} \quad 2x+3 \end{matrix}\right\}$ is subtracted.

Let these then be the parts of 20.

[1] Here again the implied condition, namely that m^2 is not greater than 20, is not necessary; the condition necessary for a real solution is something different.

The equations to be solved are $x+y=a$, $z^2-x=u^2$, $z^2-y=v^2$.

Diophantus here puts $(\xi+m)^2$ for z^2, so that, if $x=2m\xi+m^2$, the second equation is satisfied. Now $(\xi+m)^2-y$ must also be a square, and if this square is equal to $(\xi+m-n)^2$, say, we must have

$$y=2n\xi+2mn-n^2.$$

Therefore, since $x+y=a$,

$$2(m+n)\xi+m^2+2mn-n^2=a,$$

whence $$\xi=\frac{a-m^2+n^2-2mn}{2(m+n)},$$

and it follows that

$$x=\frac{m(a-mn+n^2)}{m+n}, \quad y=\frac{n(a-mn+m^2)}{m+n}.$$

If $m>n$, it is necessary, in order that x, y may both be positive, that $a+n^2>mn$, which is the true condition for a real solution.

Therefore $6x + 7 = 20$, and $x = \frac{13}{6}$.

The required parts are therefore $\left(\frac{76}{6}, \frac{44}{6}\right)$, and the required square is $\frac{625}{36}$.

16. To find two numbers in a given ratio and such that each when added to an assigned square gives a square.

Given square 9, given ratio $3 : 1$.

If we take a square of side $(mx + 3)$ and subtract 9 from it, the remainder may be taken as one of the numbers required.

Take, *e.g.*, $(x + 3)^2 - 9$, or $x^2 + 6x$, for the lesser number.

Therefore $3x^2 + 18x$ is the greater number, and $3x^2 + 18x + 9$ must be made a square $= (2x - 3)^2$, say.

Therefore $x = 30$, and

the required numbers are 1080, 3240.

17. To find three numbers such that, if each give to the next following a given fraction of itself and a given number besides, the results after each has given and taken may be equal[1].

First gives to second $\frac{1}{5}$ of itself $+ 6$, second to third $\frac{1}{6}$ of itself $+ 7$, third to first $\frac{1}{7}$ of itself $+ 8$.

Let first and second be $5x$, $6x$ respectively.

When second has taken $x + 6$ from first it becomes $7x + 6$, and when it has given $x + 7$ to third it becomes $6x - 1$.

But first when it has given $x + 6$ to second becomes $4x - 6$; and this too when it has taken $\frac{1}{7}$ of third $+ 8$ must become $6x - 1$.

Therefore $\frac{1}{7}$ of third $+ 8 = 2x + 5$, and

third $= 14x - 21$.

Next, third after receiving $\frac{1}{6}$ of second $+ 7$ and giving $\frac{1}{7}$ of itself $+ 8$ must become $6x - 1$.

Therefore $13x - 19 = 6x - 1$, and $x = \frac{18}{7}$.

The required numbers are $\frac{90}{7}, \frac{108}{7}, \frac{105}{7}$.

[1] Tannery is of opinion that the problems II. 17 and 18 have crept into the text from an ancient commentary to Book I. to which they would more appropriately belong. Cf. I. 22, 23.

18. To divide a given number into three parts satisfying the conditions of the preceding problem[1].

Given number 80.

Let first give to second $\frac{1}{5}$ of itself + 6, second to third $\frac{1}{6}$ of itself + 7, and third to first $\frac{1}{7}$ of itself + 8.

[What follows in the text is not a solution of the problem but an alternative solution of the preceding. The first two numbers are assumed to be $5x$ and 12, and the numbers found are $\frac{170}{19}, \frac{228}{19}, \frac{217}{19}$.]

19. To find three squares such that the difference between the greatest and the middle has to the difference between the middle and the least a given ratio.

Given ratio 3 : 1.

Assume the least square $= x^2$, the middle $= x^2 + 2x + 1$.

Therefore the greatest $= x^2 + 8x + 4 =$ square $= (x + 3)^2$, say.

Thus $x = 2\frac{1}{2}$, and

the squares are $30\frac{1}{4}, 12\frac{1}{4}, 6\frac{1}{4}$.

20. To find two numbers such that the square of either added to the other gives a square[2].

[1] Though the solution is not given in the text, it is easily obtained from the *general* solution of the preceding problem, which again, at least with our notation, is easy.

Let us assume, with Wertheim, that the numbers required in II. 17 are $5x$, $6y$, $7z$. Then by the conditions of the problem

$$4x - 6 + z + 8 = 5y - 7 + x + 6 = 6z - 8 + y + 7,$$

from which two equations we can find x, z in terms of y.

In fact $x = (26y - 18)/19$ and $z = (17y - 3)/19$,

and the general solution is

$$5(26y - 18)/19, \quad 6y, \quad 7(17y - 3)/19.$$

$\left[\text{In his solution Diophantus assumes } x = y, \text{ whence } y = \frac{18}{7}\right]$.

Now, to solve II. 18, we have only to equate the sum of the three expressions to 80, and so find y.

We have

$$y(5 \cdot 26 + 6 \cdot 19 + 7 \cdot 17) - 5 \cdot 18 - 7 \cdot 3 = 80 \cdot 19, \quad y = \frac{1631}{363};$$

and the required numbers are

$$\frac{9440}{363}, \quad \frac{9786}{363}, \quad \frac{9814}{363}.$$

[2] Euler (*Algebra*, Part II. Art. 239) solves this problem more generally thus.

Required to find x, y such that $x^2 + y$ and $y^2 + x$ are squares.

If we begin by supposing $x^2 + y = p^2$, so that $y = p^2 - x^2$, and then substitute the value of y in terms of x in the second expression, we must have

$$p^4 - 2p^2x^2 + x^4 + x = \text{square}.$$

But, as this is difficult to solve, let us suppose instead that

$$x^2 + y = (p - x)^2 = p^2 - 2px + x^2,$$

Assume for the numbers x, $2x+1$, which by their form satisfy one condition.

The other condition gives

$$4x^2+5x+1=\text{square}=(2x-2)^2, \text{ say.}$$

Therefore $x=\frac{3}{13}$, and

the numbers are $\frac{3}{13}, \frac{19}{13}$.

21. To find two numbers such that the square of either *minus* the other number gives a square.

$x+1$, $2x+1$ are assumed, satisfying one condition.

The other condition gives

$$4x^2+3x=\text{square}=9x^2, \text{ say.}$$

Therefore $x=\frac{3}{5}$, and

the numbers are $\frac{8}{5}, \frac{11}{5}$.

22. To find two numbers such that the square of either added to the sum of both gives a square.

Assume x, $x+1$ for the numbers. Thus one condition is satisfied.

It remains that

$$x^2+4x+2=\text{square}=(x-2)^2, \text{ say.}$$

Therefore $x=\frac{1}{4}$, and

the numbers are $\frac{1}{4}, \frac{5}{4}$.

[Diophantus has $\frac{2}{8}$, $\frac{10}{8}$.]

23. To find two numbers such that the square of either *minus* the sum of both gives a square.

Assume x, $x+1$ for the numbers, thus satisfying one condition.

Then $x^2-2x-1=\text{square}=(x-3)^2$, say.

Therefore $x=2\frac{1}{2}$, and

the numbers are $2\frac{1}{2}$, $3\frac{1}{2}$.

---

and that $$y^2+x=(q-y)^2=q^2-2qy+y^2.$$

It follows that $$y+2px=p^2,$$

$$x+2qy=q^2,$$

whence $$x=\frac{2qp^2-q^2}{4pq-1}, \quad y=\frac{2pq^2-p^2}{4pq-1}.$$

Suppose, for example, $p=2$, $q=3$, and we have $x=\frac{15}{23}$, $y=\frac{32}{23}$; and so on. We must of course choose p, q such that x, y are both positive. Diophantus' solution is obtained by putting $p=-1$, $q=3$.

24. To find two numbers such that either added to the square of their sum gives a square.

Since $x^2 + 3x^2$, $x^2 + 8x^2$ are both squares, let the numbers be $3x^2$, $8x^2$ and their sum x.

Therefore $121x^4 = x^2$, whence $11x^2 = x$, and $x = \frac{1}{11}$.

The numbers are therefore $\frac{3}{121}$, $\frac{8}{121}$.

25. To find two numbers such that the square of their sum *minus* either number gives a square.

If we subtract 7 or 12 from 16, we get a square.

Assume then $12x^2$, $7x^2$ for the numbers, and $16x^2$ for the square of their sum.

Hence $19x^2 = 4x$, and $x = \frac{4}{19}$.

The numbers are $\frac{192}{361}$, $\frac{112}{361}$.

26. To find two numbers such that their product added to either gives a square, and the sides of the two squares added together produce a given number.

Let the given number be 6.

Since $x(4x - 1) + x$ is a square, let x, $4x - 1$ be the numbers.

Therefore $4x^2 + 3x - 1$ is a square, and the side of this square must be $6 - 2x$ [since $2x$ is the side of the first square and the sum of the sides of the square is 6].

Since $$4x^2 + 3x - 1 = (6 - 2x)^2,$$
we have $x = \frac{37}{27}$, and

the numbers are $\frac{37}{27}$, $\frac{121}{27}$.

27. To find two numbers such that their product *minus* either gives a square, and the sides of the two squares so arising when added together produce a given number.

Let the given number be 5.

Assume $4x + 1$, x for the numbers, so that one condition is satisfied.

Also $$4x^2 - 3x - 1 = (5 - 2x)^2.$$

Therefore $x = \frac{26}{17}$, and

the numbers are $\frac{26}{17}$, $\frac{121}{17}$.

28. To find two square numbers such that their product added to either gives a square.

Let the numbers[1] be x^2, y^2.

Therefore $\left.\begin{matrix} x^2y^2 + y^2 \\ x^2y^2 + x^2 \end{matrix}\right\}$ are both squares.

To make the first expression a square we make $x^2 + 1$ a square, putting

$$x^2 + 1 = (x - 2)^2, \text{ say.}$$

Therefore $x = \frac{3}{4}$, and $x^2 = \frac{9}{16}$.

We have now to make $\frac{9}{16}(y^2 + 1)$ a square [and y must be different from x].

Put $9y^2 + 9 = (3y - 4)^2$, say,

and $y = \frac{7}{24}$.

Therefore the numbers are $\frac{9}{16}, \frac{49}{576}$.

29. To find two square numbers such that their product *minus* either gives a square.

Let x^2, y^2 be the numbers.

Then $\left.\begin{matrix} x^2y^2 - y^2 \\ x^2y^2 - x^2 \end{matrix}\right\}$ are both squares.

A solution of $x^2 - 1 = (\text{a square})$ is $x^2 = \frac{25}{16}$.

We have now to solve

$$\tfrac{25}{16}y^2 - \tfrac{25}{16} = \text{a square.}$$

Put $y^2 - 1 = (y - 4)^2$, say.

Therefore $y = \frac{17}{8}$, and

the numbers are $\frac{289}{64}, \frac{100}{64}$.

30. To find two numbers such that their product $\pm$ their sum gives a square.

Now $m^2 + n^2 \pm 2mn$ is a square.

Put 2, 3, say, for m, n respectively, and of course

$$2^2 + 3^2 \pm 2 . 2 . 3 \text{ is a square.}$$

Assume then product of numbers $= (2^2 + 3^2)x^2$ or $13x^2$, and sum $= 2 . 2 . 3x^2$ or $12x^2$.

The product being $13x^2$, let $x, 13x$ be the numbers.

Therefore their sum $14x = 12x^2$, and $x = \frac{7}{6}$.

The numbers are therefore $\frac{7}{6}, \frac{91}{6}$.

[1] Diophantus does not use two unknowns, but assumes the numbers to be x^2 and 1 until he has found x. Then he uses the same unknown (x) to find what he had first taken to be unity, as explained above, p. 52. The same remark applies to the next problem.

31. To find two numbers such that their sum is a square and their product $\pm$ their sum gives a square.

$2 \cdot 2m \cdot m =$ a square, and $(2m)^2 + m^2 \pm 2 \cdot 2m \cdot m =$ a square.

If $m = 2$, $4^2 + 2^2 \pm 2 \cdot 4 \cdot 2 = 36$ or 4.

Let then the product of the numbers be $(4^2 + 2^2)x^2$ or $20x^2$, and their sum $2 \cdot 4 \cdot 2x^2$ or $16x^2$, and take $2x$, $10x$ for the numbers.

Then $12x = 16x^2$, and $x = \frac{3}{4}$.

The numbers are $\frac{6}{4}, \frac{30}{4}$.

32. To find three numbers such that the square of any one of them added to the next following gives a square.

Let the first be x, the second $2x + 1$, and the third $2(2x + 1) + 1$ or $4x + 3$, so that two conditions are satisfied.

The last condition gives $(4x + 3)^2 + x =$ square $= (4x - 4)^2$, say.

Therefore $x = \frac{7}{57}$, and

the numbers are $\frac{7}{57}, \frac{71}{57}, \frac{199}{57}$.

33. To find three numbers such that the square of any one of them *minus* the next following gives a square.

Assume $x + 1$, $2x + 1$, $4x + 1$ for the numbers, so that two conditions are satisfied.

Lastly, $16x^2 + 7x =$ square $= 25x^2$, say,

and $x = \frac{7}{9}$.

The numbers are $\frac{16}{9}, \frac{23}{9}, \frac{37}{9}$.

34. To find three numbers such that the square of any one added to the sum of all three gives a square.

$\{\frac{1}{2}(m - n)\}^2 + mn$ is a square. Take a number separable into two factors (m, n) in three ways, say 12, which is the product of (1, 12), (2, 6) and (3, 4).

The values then of $\frac{1}{2}(m - n)$ are $5\frac{1}{2}$, 2, $\frac{1}{2}$.

Take $5\frac{1}{2}x$, $2x$, $\frac{1}{2}x$ for the numbers, and for their sum $12x^2$.

Therefore $8x = 12x^2$, and $x = \frac{2}{3}$.

The numbers are $\frac{11}{3}, \frac{4}{3}, \frac{1}{3}$.

[Diophantus says $\frac{4}{6}$, and $\frac{22}{6}, \frac{8}{6}, \frac{2}{6}$.]

35. To find three numbers such that the square of any one *minus* the sum of all three gives a square.

$\{\frac{1}{2}(m+n)\}^2 - mn$ is a square. Take, as before, a number divisible into factors in three ways, as 12.

Let then $6\frac{1}{2}x$, $4x$, $3\frac{1}{2}x$ be the numbers, and their sum $12x^2$.

Therefore $14x = 12x^2$, and $x = \frac{7}{6}$.

The numbers are $\frac{45\frac{1}{2}}{6}$, $\frac{28}{6}$, $\frac{24\frac{1}{2}}{6}$.

BOOK III

1. To find three numbers such that, if the square of any one of them be subtracted from the sum of all three, the remainder is a square[1].

Take two squares x^2, $4x^2$; the sum is $5x^2$.

If then we take $5x^2$ as the sum of the three numbers, and x, $2x$ as two of them, we satisfy two conditions.

Next divide 5, which is the sum of two squares, into two other squares $\frac{4}{25}$, $\frac{121}{25}$ [II. 9], and assume $\frac{2}{5}x$ for the third number.

Therefore $x + 2x + \frac{2}{5}x = 5x^2$, and $x = \frac{17}{25}$.

The numbers are $\frac{17}{25}$, $\frac{34}{25}$, $\frac{34}{125}$.

[Diophantus writes $\frac{85}{125}$ for x and $\frac{85}{125}$, $\frac{170}{125}$, $\frac{34}{125}$ for the numbers.]

2. To find three numbers such that the square of the sum of all three added to any one of them gives a square.

Let the square of the sum of all three be x^2, and the numbers $3x^2$, $8x^2$, $15x^2$.

Hence $26x^2 = x$, $x = \frac{1}{26}$, and

the numbers are $\frac{3}{676}$, $\frac{8}{676}$, $\frac{15}{676}$.

3. To find three numbers such that the square of the sum of all three *minus* any one of them gives a square.

Sum of all three $4x$, its square $16x^2$, the numbers $7x^2$, $12x^2$, $15x^2$.

Then $34x^2 = 4x$, $x = \frac{2}{17}$, and

the numbers are $\frac{28}{289}$, $\frac{48}{289}$, $\frac{60}{289}$.

[1] The fact that the problems III. 1–4 are very like II. 34, 35 makes Tannery suspect that they have found their way into the text from some ancient commentary.

4. To find three numbers such that, if the square of their sum be subtracted from any one of them, the remainder is a square.

Sum x, numbers $2x^2$, $5x^2$, $10x^2$.

Then $17x^2 = x$, $x = \frac{1}{17}$, and

the numbers are $\frac{2}{289}$, $\frac{5}{289}$, $\frac{10}{289}$.

5. To find three numbers such that their sum is a square and the sum of any pair exceeds the third by a square.

Let the sum of the three be $(x+1)^2$; let first + second = third + 1, so that third $= \frac{1}{2}x^2 + x$; let second + third = first + x^2, so that first $= x + \frac{1}{2}$.

Therefore second $= \frac{1}{2}x^2 + \frac{1}{2}$.

It remains that first + third = second + a square.

Therefore $2x$ = square = 16, say, and $x = 8$.

The numbers are $8\frac{1}{2}$, $32\frac{1}{2}$, 40.

Otherwise thus[1].

First find three squares such that their sum is a square.

Find *e.g.* what square number $+4+9$ gives a square, that is, 36;

4, 36, 9 are therefore squares with the required property.

Next find three numbers such that the sum of each pair = the third + a given number; in this case suppose

first + second − third = 4,

second + third − first = 9,

third + first − second = 36.

This problem has already been solved [I. 18].

The numbers are respectively 20, $6\frac{1}{2}$, $22\frac{1}{2}$.

[1] We should naturally suppose that this alternative solution, like others, was interpolated. But we are reluctant to think so because the solution is so elegant that it can hardly be attributed to a scholiast. If the solution is not genuine, we have here an illustration of the truth that, however ingenious they are, Diophantus' solutions are not always the best imaginable (Loria, *Le scienze esatte nell' antica Grecia*, Libro v. pp. 138–9). In this case the more elegant solution is the alternative one. Generalised, it is as follows. We have to find x, y, z so that

$$\left.\begin{aligned} -x+y+z &= \text{a square} \\ x-y+z &= \text{a square} \\ x+y-z &= \text{a square} \end{aligned}\right\},$$

and also

$$x+y+z = \text{a square}.$$

We have only to equate the first three expressions to squares a^2, b^2, c^2 such that $a^2+b^2+c^2$ = a square, k^2 say, since the sum of the first three expressions is itself $x+y+z$.

The solution is then

$$x = \frac{1}{2}(b^2+c^2),\quad y = \frac{1}{2}(c^2+a^2),\quad z = \frac{1}{2}(a^2+b^2).$$

6. To find three numbers such that their sum is a square and the sum of any pair is a square.

Let the sum of all three be x^2+2x+1, sum of first and second x^2, and therefore the third $2x+1$; let sum of second and third be $(x-1)^2$.

Therefore the first $=4x$, and the second $=x^2-4x$.

But first + third = square,

that is, $6x+1=\text{square}=121$, say.

Therefore $x=20$, and

the numbers are **80, 320, 41.**

[An alternative solution, obviously interpolated, is practically identical with the above except that it takes the square 36 as the value of $6x+1$, so that $x=\frac{35}{6}$, and the numbers are $\frac{140}{6}=\frac{840}{36}, \frac{385}{36}, \frac{456}{36}$.]

7. To find three numbers in A.P. such that the sum of any pair gives a square.

First find three square numbers in A.P. and such that half their sum is greater than any one of them. Let x^2, $(x+1)^2$ be the first and second of these; therefore the third is $x^2+4x+2=(x-8)^2$, say.

Therefore $x=\frac{62}{20}$ or $\frac{31}{10}$;

and we may take as the numbers 961, 1681, 2401.

We have now to find three numbers such that the sums of pairs are the numbers just found.

The sum of the three $=\frac{5043}{2}=2521\frac{1}{2}$, and

the three numbers are **$120\frac{1}{2}$, $840\frac{1}{2}$, $1560\frac{1}{2}$.**

8. Given one number, to find three others such that the sum of any pair of them added to the given number gives a square, and also the sum of the three added to the given number gives a square.

Given number 3.

Suppose first required number + second $=x^2+4x+1$,

second + third $=x^2+6x+6$,

sum of all three $=x^2+8x+13$.

Therefore third $=4x+12$, second $=x^2+2x-6$, first $=2x+7$.

Also first + third + 3 = a square,

that is, $6x+22=\text{square}=100$, suppose.

Hence $x=13$, and

the numbers are **33, 189, 64.**

9. Given one number, to find three others such that the sum of any pair of them *minus* the given number gives a square, and also the sum of the three *minus* the given number gives a square.

Given number 3.

Suppose first of required numbers + second $= x^2 + 3$,

second + third $= x^2 + 2x + 4$,

sum of the three $= x^2 + 4x + 7$.

Therefore third $= 4x + 4$, second $= x^2 - 2x$, first $= 2x + 3$.

Lastly, first + third $- 3 = 6x + 4 =$ a square $= 64$, say.

Therefore $x = 10$, and

(23, 80, 44) is a solution.

10. To find three numbers such that the product of any pair of them added to a given number gives a square.

Let the given number be 12. Take a square (say 25) and subtract 12. Take the difference (13) for the product of the first and second numbers, and let these numbers be $13x$, $1/x$ respectively.

Again subtract 12 from another square, say 16, and let the difference (4) be the product of the second and third numbers.

Therefore the third number $= 4x$.

The third condition gives $52x^2 + 12 =$ a square; now $52 = 4 . 13$, and 13 is not a square; but, if it were a square, the equation could easily be solved[1].

Thus we must find two numbers to replace 13 and 4 such that their product is a square, while either + 12 is also a square.

Now the product is a square if both are squares; hence we must find two squares such that either $+ 12 =$ a square.

"This is easy[2] and, as we said, it makes the equation easy to solve."

The squares 4, $\frac{1}{4}$ satisfy the condition.

[1] The equation $52x^2 + 12 = u^2$ can in reality be solved as it stands, by virtue of the fact that it has one obvious solution, namely $x = 1$. Another solution is found by substituting $y + 1$ for x, and so on. Cf. pp. 69, 70 above. The value $x = 1$ itself gives (13, 1, 4) as a solution of the problem.

[2] The method is indicated in II. 34. We have to find two pairs of squares differing by 12. (*a*) If we put $12 = 6 . 2$, we have

$$\left\{\frac{1}{2}(6-2)\right\}^2 + 12 = \left\{\frac{1}{2}(6+2)\right\}^2,$$

and 16, 4 are squares differing by 12, or 4 is a square which when added to 12 gives a square. (*b*) If we put $12 = 4 . 3$, we find $\left\{\frac{1}{2}(4-3)\right\}^2$ or $\frac{1}{4}$ to be a square which when added to 12 gives a square.

Retracing our steps, we now put $4x$, $1/x$ and $x/4$ for the numbers, and we have to solve the equation

$$x^2 + 12 = \text{square} = (x+3)^2, \text{ say}.$$

Therefore $x = \frac{1}{2}$, and

$$\left(2, 2, \frac{1}{8}\right) \text{ is a solution}[1].$$

11. To find three numbers such that the product of any pair *minus* a given number gives a square.

Given number 10.

Put product of first and second = a square + 10 = 4 + 10, say, and let first = $14x$, second = $1/x$.

Let product of second and third = a square + 10 = 19, say; therefore third = $19x$.

By the third condition, $266x^2 - 10$ must be a square; but 266 is not a square[2].

Therefore, as in the preceding problem, we must find two squares each of which exceeds a square by 10.

The squares $30\frac{1}{4}$, $12\frac{1}{4}$ satisfy these conditions[3].

Putting now $30\frac{1}{4}x$, $1/x$, $12\frac{1}{4}x$ for the numbers, we have, by the third condition, $370\frac{9}{16}x^2 - 10 = \text{square}$ [for $370\frac{9}{16}$ Diophantus writes $370\frac{1}{2}\,\frac{1}{16}$];

therefore $5929x^2 - 160 = \text{square} = (77x - 2)^2$, say.

Therefore $x = \frac{41}{77}$, and

the numbers are $\dfrac{1240\frac{1}{4}}{77}, \dfrac{77}{41}, \dfrac{502\frac{1}{4}}{77}$.

[1] Euler (*Algebra*, Part II. Art. 232) has an elegant solution of this problem in whole numbers. Let it be required to find x, y, z such that $xy+a$, $yz+a$, $zx+a$ are all squares. Suppose $xy+a=p^2$, and make $z=x+y+q$;

therefore $$xz+a=x^2+xy+qx+a=x^2+qx+p^2,$$

and $$yz+a=xy+y^2+qy+a=y^2+qy+p^2;$$

and the right hand expressions are both squares if $q=\pm 2p$, so that $z=x+y\pm 2p$.

We can therefore take any value for p such that $p^2>a$, split p^2-a into factors, take those factors respectively for the values of x and y, and so find z.

E.g. suppose $a=12$ and $p^2=25$, so that $xy=13$; let $x=1$, $y=13$, and we have $z=14\pm 10=24$ or 4, and (1, 13, 4), (1, 13, 24) are solutions.

[2] As a matter of fact, the equation $266x^2-10=u^2$ can be solved as it stands, since it has one obvious solution, namely $x=1$. (Cf. pp. 69, 70 above and note on preceding problem, p. 159.) The value $x=1$ gives (14, 1, 19) as a solution of the problem.

[3] Tannery brackets the passage in the text in which these squares are found, on the ground that, as the solution was not given in the corresponding place of III. 10, there was no necessity to give it here. 10 and 1 being factors of 10,

$$\left\{\frac{1}{2}(10-1)\right\}^2+10=\left\{\frac{1}{2}(10+1)\right\}^2;$$

thus $30\frac{1}{4}$ is a square which exceeds a square by 10. Similarly $\left\{\frac{1}{2}(5+2)\right\}^2$ or $12\frac{1}{4}$ is such a square. The latter is found in the text by putting $m^2-10=\text{square}=(m-2)^2$, whence $m=3\frac{1}{2}$, and $m^2=12\frac{1}{4}$.

12. To find three numbers such that the product of any two added to the third gives a square.

Take a square and subtract part of it for the third number; let x^2+6x+9 be one of the sums, and 9 the third number.

Therefore product of first and second $=x^2+6x$; let first $=x$, so that second $=x+6$.

By the two remaining conditions

$$\left.\begin{array}{l}10x+54\\10x+\ \ 6\end{array}\right\}\text{ are both squares.}$$

Therefore we have to find two squares differing by 48; "this is easy and can be done in an infinite number of ways."

The squares 16, 64 satisfy the condition. Equating these squares to the respective expressions, we obtain $x=1$, and

the numbers are 1, 7, 9.

13. To find three numbers such that the product of any two *minus* the third gives a square.

First x, second $x+4$; therefore product $=x^2+4x$, and we assume third $=4x$.

Therefore, by the other conditions,

$$\left.\begin{array}{l}4x^2+15x\\4x^2-x-4\end{array}\right\}\text{ are both squares.}$$

The difference $=16x+4=4(4x+1)$, and we put

$$\{\tfrac{1}{2}(4x+5)\}^2=4x^2+15x.$$

Therefore $x=\frac{25}{20}$, and

the numbers are $\frac{25}{20}$, $\frac{105}{20}$, $\frac{100}{20}$.

14. To find three numbers such that the product of any two added to the square of the third gives a square[1].

[1] Wertheim gives a more general solution, as follows. If we take as the required numbers $X=\frac{1}{4}ax$, $Y=ax+b^2$, $Z=\frac{1}{4}b^2$, two conditions are already satisfied, namely $XY+Z^2=$a square, and $YZ+X^2=$a square.

It only remains to satisfy the condition $ZX+Y^2=$a square, or

$$a^2x^2+\frac{33}{16}ab^2x+b^4=\text{a square.}$$

Put

$$a^2x^2+\frac{33}{16}ab^2x+b^4=(ax+kb^2)^2,$$

and

$$x=\frac{16b^2(k^2-1)}{a(33-32k)},$$

where k remains undetermined.

First x, second $4x+4$, third 1. Two conditions are thus satisfied.

The third condition gives

$$x+(4x+4)^2 = \text{a square} = (4x-5)^2, \text{ say.}$$

Therefore $x = \frac{9}{73}$, and the numbers (omitting the common denominator) are 9, 328, 73.

15. To find three numbers such that the product of any two added to the sum of those two gives a square[1].

[*Lemma.*] The product of the squares of any two consecutive numbers added to the sum of the said squares gives a square[2].

Let 4, 9 be two of the required numbers, x the third.

Therefore $\left.\begin{matrix}10x+9\\5x+4\end{matrix}\right\}$ are both squares.

The difference $= 5x+5 = 5(x+1)$.

Equating the square of half the sum of the factors to $10x+9$, we have

$$\{\tfrac{1}{2}(x+6)\}^2 = 10x+9.$$

Therefore $x = 28$, and (4, 9, 28) is a solution.

---

[1] The problem can of course be solved more elegantly, with our notation, thus. (The same remark applies to the next problem, III. 16.)

If x, y, z are the required numbers, $xy+x+y$, etc. are to be squares. We may therefore write the conditions in the form

$$(y+1)(z+1) = \text{a square} + 1,$$
$$(z+1)(x+1) = \text{a square} + 1,$$
$$(x+1)(y+1) = \text{a square} + 1.$$

Assuming a^2, b^2, c^2 for the respective squares, and putting $\xi = x+1$, $\eta = y+1$, $\zeta = z+1$, we have to solve

$$\eta\zeta = a^2+1,$$
$$\zeta\xi = b^2+1,$$
$$\xi\eta = c^2+1.$$

[This is practically the same problem as that in the Lemma to Dioph. V. 8.]

Multiplying the second and third equations and dividing by the first, we have

$$\xi = \sqrt{\{(b^2+1)(c^2+1)/(a^2+1)\}},$$

with similar expressions for η, ζ.

x, y, z are these expressions *minus* 1 respectively. a^2, b^2, c^2 must of course be so chosen that the resulting values of ξ, η, ζ may be rational. Cf. Euler, *Commentationes arithmeticae*, II. p. 577.

[2] In fact, $a^2(a+1)^2 + a^2 + (a+1)^2 = \{a(a+1)+1\}^2$.

Otherwise thus[1].

Assume first number to be x, second 3.

Therefore $4x+3=\text{square}=25$ say, whence $x=5\frac{1}{2}$, and $5\frac{1}{2}$, 3 satisfy one condition.

[1] This alternative solution would appear to be undoubtedly genuine.

Diophantus has solved the equations

$$\left.\begin{aligned} yz+y+z&=u^2\\ zx+z+x&=v^2\\ xy+x+y&=w^2\end{aligned}\right\}.$$

Fermat shows how to solve the corresponding problem with *four* numbers instead of three. He uses for this purpose Diophantus' solution of V. 5, namely the problem of finding x^2, y^2, z^2, such that

$$\left.\begin{aligned} &y^2z^2+x^2=r^2, && z^2x^2+y^2=s^2, && x^2y^2+z^2=t^2\\ &y^2z^2+y^2+z^2=u^2, && z^2x^2+z^2+x^2=v^2, && x^2y^2+x^2+y^2=w^2\end{aligned}\right\}.$$

Diophantus finds $\left(\frac{25}{9}, \frac{64}{9}, \frac{196}{9}\right)$ as a solution of the latter problem. Fermat takes these as the first three of the four numbers which are to satisfy the condition that the product of any two plus the sum of those two gives a square, and assumes x for the fourth. Three relations out of six are already satisfied, and the other three require

$$\left.\begin{aligned} &\frac{25}{9}x+x+\frac{25}{9}, \text{ or } \frac{34x}{9}+\frac{25}{9}\\ &\frac{64}{9}x+x+\frac{64}{9}, \text{ or } \frac{73x}{9}+\frac{64}{9}\\ &\frac{196}{9}x+x+\frac{196}{9}, \text{ or } \frac{205x}{9}+\frac{196}{9}\end{aligned}\right\}$$

to be made squares: a "triple-equation" to be solved by Fermat's method. (See the Supplement, section V.)

Fermat does not give the solution, but I had the curiosity to work it out in order to verify to what enormous numbers the method of the triple-equation leads, even in such comparatively simple cases.

We may of course neglect the denominator 9 and solve the equations

$$\begin{aligned} 34x+25&=u^2,\\ 73x+64&=v^2,\\ 205x+196&=w^2.\end{aligned}$$

The method gives

$$x=-\frac{459818598496844787200}{631629004828419699201},$$

the denominator being equal to $(25132230399)^2$.

Verifying the correctness of the solution, we find that, in fact,

$$\frac{34}{25}x+1=\left(\frac{2505136897}{25132230399}\right)^2,$$

$$\frac{73}{64}x+1=\left(\frac{10351251901}{25132230399}\right)^2,$$

$$\frac{205}{196}x+1=\left(\frac{12275841601}{25132230399}\right)^2.$$

Strictly speaking, as the value found for x is negative, we ought to substitute $y-A$ for it (where $-A$ is the value found) in the three equations and start afresh. The portentous numbers which would thus arise must be left to the imagination.

Let the third be x, while $5\frac{1}{2}$, 3 are the first two.

Therefore $\left.\begin{matrix} 4x+3 \\ 6\frac{1}{2}x+5\frac{1}{2} \end{matrix}\right\}$ must both be squares;

but, since the coefficients in one expression are respectively greater than those in the other, but neither of the ratios of corresponding coefficients is that of a square to a square, our suppositions will not serve the purpose; we cannot solve by our method.

Hence (to replace $5\frac{1}{2}$, 3) we must find two numbers such that their product + their sum = a square, and the ratio of the numbers increased by 1 respectively is the ratio of a square to a square.

Let these be y and $4y+3$, which satisfy the latter condition; and, in order that the other may be satisfied, we must have

$$4y^2+8y+3 = \text{square} = (2y-3)^2, \text{ say.}$$

Therefore $y = \frac{3}{10}$.

Assume now $\frac{3}{10}$, $4\frac{1}{5}$, x for the three numbers.

Therefore $\left.\begin{matrix} 5\frac{1}{5}x+4\frac{1}{5} \\ \frac{13}{10}x+\frac{3}{10} \end{matrix}\right\}$ are both squares,

or, if we multiply by 25 and 100 respectively,

$$\left.\begin{matrix} 130x+105 \\ 130x+\ \ 30 \end{matrix}\right\} \text{ are both squares.}$$

The difference is $75 = 3 \cdot 25$, and the usual method of solution gives $x = \frac{7}{10}$.

The numbers are $\frac{3}{10}, \frac{42}{10}, \frac{7}{10}$.

16. To find three numbers such that the product of any two *minus* the sum of those two gives a square.

Put x for the first, and any number for the second; we then fall into the same difficulty as in the last problem.

We have to find two numbers such that

(*a*) their product *minus* their sum = a square, and

(*b*) when each is diminished by 1, the remainders have the ratio of squares.

Now $4y+1$, $y+1$ satisfy the latter condition.

The former (*a*) requires that

$$4y^2-1 = \text{square} = (2y-2)^2, \text{ say,}$$

which gives $y = \frac{5}{8}$.

Assume then $\frac{13}{8}$, $\frac{28}{8}$, x for the numbers.

Therefore $\left.\begin{matrix} 2\frac{1}{2}x - 3\frac{1}{2} \\ \frac{5}{8}x - \frac{13}{8} \end{matrix}\right\}$ are both squares,

or, if we multiply by 4, 16 respectively,

$$\left.\begin{matrix} 10x - 14 \\ 10x - 26 \end{matrix}\right\} \text{ are both squares.}$$

The difference is $12 = 2 . 6$, and the usual method gives $x = 3$.

The numbers are $\frac{13}{8}$, $3\frac{1}{2} = \frac{28}{8}$, $3 = \frac{24}{8}$.

17. To find two numbers such that their product added to both or to either gives a square.

Assume x, $4x - 1$ for the numbers, since

$$x(4x - 1) + x = 4x^2, \text{ a square.}$$

Therefore also $\left.\begin{matrix} 4x^2 + 3x - 1 \\ 4x^2 + 4x - 1 \end{matrix}\right\}$ are both squares.

The difference is $x = 4x . \frac{1}{4}$, and we find

$$x = \frac{65}{224}.$$

The numbers are $\frac{65}{224}$, $\frac{36}{224}$.

18. To find two numbers such that their product *minus* either, or *minus* the sum of both, gives a square[1].

[1] With this problem should be compared that in paragraph 42 of Part I. of the *Inventum Novum* of Jacobus de Billy (*Oeuvres de Fermat*, III. pp. 351–2), where three conditions correspond to those of the above problem, and there is a fourth in addition. The problem is to find ξ, η $(\xi > \eta)$ such that

$$\left.\begin{matrix} \xi - \xi\eta \\ \eta - \xi\eta \\ \xi + \eta - \xi\eta \\ \xi - \eta - \xi\eta \end{matrix}\right\} \text{ are all squares.}$$

Suppose $\eta = x$, $\xi = 1 - x$; the first two conditions are thus satisfied. The other two give

$$x^2 - x + 1 = u^2,$$
$$x^2 - 3x + 1 = v^2.$$

Separating the difference $2x$ into the factors $2x$, 1, we put, as usual,

$$\left(x + \frac{1}{2}\right)^2 = x^2 - x + 1,$$

whence $x = \frac{3}{8}$, and the numbers are $\frac{5}{8}$, $\frac{3}{8}$.

To find another value of x by means of the value thus found, we put $y + \frac{3}{8}$ in place of x in the double-equation, whence

$$y^2 - \frac{1}{4}y + \frac{49}{64} = u^2,$$

$$y^2 - \frac{9}{4}y + \frac{1}{64} = v^2.$$

Multiplying the lower expression by 49, we can solve in the usual way. Our expressions

Assume $x+1$, $4x$ for the numbers, since

$$4x(x+1)-4x = \text{a square}.$$

Therefore also $\left.\begin{array}{l}4x^2+3x-1\\4x^2-\ \ x-1\end{array}\right\}$ are both squares.

The difference is $4x=4x \cdot 1$, and we find

$$x=1\tfrac{1}{4}.$$

The numbers are $2\frac{1}{4}$, 5.

19. To find four numbers such that the square of their sum *plus* or *minus* any one singly gives a square.

Since, in any right-angled triangle,

(sq. on hypotenuse) $\pm$ (twice product of perps.) = a square,

we must seek four right-angled triangles [in rational numbers] having the same hypotenuse,

or we must find a square which is divisible into two squares in four different ways; and "we saw how to divide a square into two squares in an infinite number of ways." [II. 8.]

Take right-angled triangles in the smallest numbers, (3, 4, 5) and (5, 12, 13); and multiply the sides of

---

are now $y^2-\frac{1}{4}y+\frac{49}{64}$ and $49y^2-\frac{441}{4}y+\frac{49}{64}$, and the difference between them is $48y^2-110y$. The solution next mentioned by De Billy was clearly obtained by separating this difference into factors such that, when the square of half their difference is equated to $y^2-\frac{1}{4}y+\frac{49}{64}$, the absolute terms cancel out. The factors are $\frac{440}{7}y$, $\frac{42}{55}y-\frac{7}{4}$, and we put

$$\left\{\left(\frac{220}{7}-\frac{21}{55}\right)y+\frac{7}{8}\right\}^2=y^2-\frac{1}{4}y+\frac{49}{64}.$$

This gives $y=-\frac{4045195}{71362992}$, whence $x=\frac{22715927}{71362992}$, and the numbers are

$$\frac{48647065}{71362992},\ \frac{22715927}{71362992}.$$

A solution in smaller numbers is obtained by separating $48y^2-110y$ into factors such that the terms in x^2 in the resulting equation cancel out. The factors are $6y$, $8y-\frac{55}{3}$, and we put

$$\left(y-\frac{55}{6}\right)^2=y^2-\frac{1}{4}y+\frac{49}{64},$$

whence $y=\frac{47959}{10416}$, and $x=\frac{47959}{10416}+\frac{3}{8}=\frac{51865}{10416}$.

This would give a negative value for $1-x$; but, owing to the symmetry of the original double-equation in x, since $x=\frac{51865}{10416}$ satisfies it, so does $x=\frac{10416}{51865}$; hence the numbers are $\frac{10416}{51865}$ and $\frac{41449}{51865}$: a solution also mentioned by De Billy.

Cf. note on IV. 23.

the first by the hypotenuse of the second and *vice versa.*

This gives the triangles (39, 52, 65) and (25, 60, 65); thus 65^2 is split up into two squares in *two* ways.

Again, 65 is "naturally" divided into two squares in two ways, namely into 7^2+4^2 and 8^2+1^2, "which is due to the fact that 65 is the product of 13 and 5, each of which numbers is the sum of two squares."

Form now a right-angled triangle[1] from 7, 4. The sides are $(7^2-4^2, 2.7.4, 7^2+4^2)$ or (33, 56, 65).

Similarly, forming a right-angled triangle from 8, 1, we obtain $(2.8.1, 8^2-1^2, 8^2+1^2)$ or 16, 63, 65.

Thus 65^2 is split into two squares in *four* ways.

Assume now as the sum of the numbers $65x$ and

as first number $2.39.52x^2=4056x^2$,
" second " $2.25.60x^2=3000x^2$,
" third " $2.33.56x^2=3696x^2$,
" fourth " $2.16.63x^2=2016x^2$,

the coefficients of x^2 being four times the areas of the four right-angled triangles respectively.

The sum $12768x^2=65x$, and $x=\frac{65}{12768}$.

The numbers are

$$\frac{17136600}{163021824}, \frac{12675000}{163021824}, \frac{15615600}{163021824}, \frac{8517600}{163021824}.$$

20. To divide a given number into two parts and to find a square which, when either of the parts is subtracted from it, gives a square[2].

Given number 10, required square x^2+2x+1.

Put for one of the parts $2x+1$, and for the other $4x$.

The conditions are therefore satisfied if

$$6x+1=10.$$

Therefore $x=1\frac{1}{2}$;

the parts are (4, 6) and the square $6\frac{1}{4}$.

[1] If there are two numbers p, q, to "form a right-angled triangle" from them means to take the numbers p^2+q^2, p^2-q^2, $2pq$. These are the sides of a right-angled triangle, since

$$(p^2+q^2)^2=(p^2-q^2)^2+(2pq)^2.$$

[2] This problem and the next are the same as II. 15, 14 respectively. It may therefore be doubted whether the solutions here given are genuine, especially as interpolations from ancient commentaries occur most at the beginning and end of Books.

21. To divide a given number into two parts and to find a square which, when added to either of the parts, gives a square.

Given number 20, required square $x^2 + 2x + 1$.

If to the square there be added either $2x + 3$ or $4x + 8$, the result is a square.

Take $2x + 3$, $4x + 8$ as the parts of 20, and $6x + 11 = 20$, whence $x = 1\frac{1}{2}$.

Therefore the parts are (6, 14) and the square $6\frac{1}{4}$.

BOOK IV

1. To divide a given number into two cubes such that the sum of their sides is a given number[1].

Given number 370, given sum of sides 10.

Sides of cubes $5 + x$, $5 - x$, satisfying one condition.

Therefore $30x^2 + 250 = 370$, $x = 2$,

and the cubes are 7^3, 3^3, or **343**, **27**.

2. To find two numbers such that their difference is a given number, and also the difference of their cubes is a given number.

Difference 6, difference of cubes 504.

Numbers $x + 3$, $x - 3$.

Therefore $18x^2 + 54 = 504$, $x^2 = 25$, and $x = 5$.

The sides of the cubes are **8**, **2** and the cubes **512**, **8**.

3. To multiply one and the same number into a square and its side respectively so as to make the latter product a cube and the former product the side of the cube.

Let the square be x^2. Its side being x, let the number be $8/x$.

Hence the products are $8x$, 8, and

$$(8x)^3 = 8.$$

Therefore $2 = 8x$, $x = \frac{1}{4}$, and the number to be multiplied is **32**.

The square is $\frac{1}{16}$ and its side $\frac{1}{4}$.

[1] It will be observed that Diophantus chooses, as his given numbers, numbers such as will make the resulting "pure" quadratic equation give a "rational" value for x. If the given numbers are $2a$, $2b$, respectively, we assume $b+x$, $b-x$ as the sides of the cubes, and we have

$$2b^3 + 6bx^2 = 2a,$$

so that $x^2 = (a - b^3)/3b$; x is therefore "irrational" unless $(a - b^3)/3b$ is a square. In Diophantus' hypothesis a is taken as 185, and b as 5, and the condition is satisfied. He shows therefore incidentally that he knew how to find two numbers a, b such that $(a - b^3)/3b$ is a square (Loria, *Le scienze esatte nell' antica Grecia*, Libro v. pp. 129–30).

A similar remark applies to the next problem, IV. 2.

4. To add the same number to a square and its side respectively and make them the same[1] [*i.e.* make the first product a square of which the second product is the side].

Square x^2, with side x.

Let the number added to x^2 be such as to make a square say $3x^2$.

Therefore $3x^2 + x =$ side of $4x^2 = 2x$, and $x = \frac{1}{3}$.

The square is $\frac{1}{9}$, its side $\frac{1}{3}$, and the number $\frac{1}{3}$.

5. To add the same number to a square and its side and make them the opposite[2].

Square x^2, the number a square number of times x^2 *minus* x, say $4x^2 - x$.

Hence $5x^2 - x =$ side of $4x^2 = 2x$, and $x = \frac{3}{5}$.

The square is $\frac{9}{25}$, its side $\frac{3}{5}$, and the number $\frac{21}{25}$.

6. To add the same square number to a cube and a square and make them the same.

Let the cube be x^3 and the square any square number of times x^2, say $9x^2$.

We want now a square which when added to $9x^2$ makes a square. Take two factors of 9, say 9 and 1, subtract 1 from 9, take half the difference and square. This gives 16.

Therefore $16x^2$ is the square to be added.

Next, $x^3 + 16x^2 =$ a cube $= 8x^3$, say; and $x = \frac{16}{7}$.

The cube is therefore $\frac{4096}{343}$, the square $\frac{2304}{49}$, and the added square number $\frac{4096}{49}$.

[1] In this and the following enunciations I have kept closely to the Greek partly for the purpose of showing Diophantus' mode of expression and partly for the brevity gained thereby.

In Prop. 4 to "make them the same" means what I have put in brackets; to "make them the opposite" in Prop. 5 means to make the first product a side of which the second product is the square.

[2] Nesselmann solves the problem generally, thus (Notes in *Zeitschrift für Math. u. Physik*, XXXVII. (1892), Hist. litt. Abt. p. 162).

$x^2 + y = \sqrt{(x+y)}$; therefore $x^4 + 2x^2y + y^2 = x + y$, or $y^2 - (1 - 2x^2)y = x - x^4$.

Solving for y, we obtain, as one of the solutions,

$$y = \frac{1}{2} - x^2 + \sqrt{\left(\frac{1}{4} + x - x^2\right)}.$$

To make the expression under the radical a square we put $\frac{1}{4} + x - x^2 = \left(mx - \frac{1}{2}\right)^2$, whence $x = \frac{m+1}{m^2+1}$, $y = \frac{m^4 + m^3 - m - 1}{(m^2+1)^2}$. Diophantus' solution corresponds to $m = 2$.

7. To add the same square number to a cube and a square respectively and make them the opposite.

For brevity call the cube (1), the second square (2) and the added square (3).

Now, since (2) + (3) = a cube, suppose (2) + (3) = (1).

Since $a^2 + b^2 \pm 2ab$ is a square, suppose $(1) = (a^2 + b^2)$, $(3) = 2ab$, so that the condition that (1) + (3) = square is satisfied.

But (3) is a square, and, in order that $2ab$ may be a square, we put $a = x$, $b = 2x$.

Suppose then $(1) = x^2 + (2x)^2 = 5x^2$, $(3) = 2 . x . 2x = 4x^2$; therefore $(2) = x^2$, by subtraction.

But $5x^2$ is a cube; therefore $x = 5$, and the cube (1) = 125, the square (2) = 25, the square (3) = 100.

Otherwise thus.

Let (2) + (3) = (1).

Then, since (1) + (3) = a square, we have to find two squares such that their sum + one of them = a square.

Let the first of these squares be x^2, the second 4.

Therefore $2x^2 + 4 = \text{square} = (2x - 2)^2$, say; thus $x = 4$, and the squares are 16, 4.

Assume now $(2) = 4x^2$, $(3) = 16x^2$.

Therefore $20x^2$ is a cube, so that $x = 20$; the cube (1) is 8000, the square (2) is 1600, and the added square (3) is 6400.

8. To add the same number to a cube and its side and make them the same[1].

Added number x, cube $8x^3$, say. Therefore second sum $= 3x$, and this must be the side of $8x^3 + x$.

That is, $8x^3 + x = 27x^3$, and $19x^3 = x$, or $19x^2 = 1$.

[1] Nesselmann (*op. cit.* p. 163) gives a more general solution.
We have $x^3 + y = (x+y)^3$, whence $1 = 3x^2 + 3xy + y^2$.
Solving for y, we find

$$y = -\frac{3}{2}x \pm \sqrt{\left(1 - \frac{3}{4}x^2\right)} = \frac{1}{2}\{-3x \pm \sqrt{(4 - 3x^2)}\}.$$

Lastly, putting $4 - 3x^2 = \left(2 - \frac{m}{n}x\right)^2$, we find $x = \frac{4mn}{3n^2 + m^2}$, $\sqrt{(4 - 3x^2)} = \pm \frac{2m^2 - 6n^2}{3n^2 + m^2}$, and $y = \frac{-6mn \pm (m^2 - 3n^2)}{3n^2 + m^2}$. If the positive sign be taken, then, in order that y may always be positive, m/n must be $> 3 + \sqrt{12}$; Diophantus' solution corresponds to $m = 7$, $n = 1$.

But 19 *is not a square.* Hence we must find, to replace it, some square number. Now $19x^3$ arises from $27x^3 - 8x^3$, where 27 is the cube of 3, and 8 the cube of 2. And the $3x$ comes from the assumed side $2x$, by increasing the coefficient by unity.

Thus we must find *two consecutive numbers such that their cubes differ by a square.*

Let them be $y, y+1$.

Therefore $3y^2 + 3y + 1 = \text{square} = (1 - 2y)^2$, say, and $y = 7$.

Going back to the beginning, we assume added number $= x$, side of cube $= 7x$.

The side of the new cube is then $8x$, and

$$343x^3 + x = 512x^3.$$

Therefore $x^2 = \frac{1}{169}$, and $x = \frac{1}{13}$.

The cube is $\frac{343}{2197}$, its side $\frac{7}{13}$, and the added number $\frac{1}{13}$.

9. To add the same number to a cube and its side and make them the opposite[1].

Suppose the cube is $8x^3$, its side being $2x$, and the added number is $27x^3 - 2x$. (The coefficients 8, 27 are chosen as cube numbers.)

Therefore $35x^3 - 2x = \text{side of cube } 27x^3 = 3x$, or $35x^2 = 5$.

This gives no rational value.

But $35 = 27 + 8$, and $5 = 3 + 2$.

Therefore we have to find two cubes such that their sum has to the sum of their sides the ratio of a square to a square[2].

Let sum of sides = any number, 2 say, and side of first cube $= z$, so that the side of the other cube is $2 - z$.

[1] Nesselmann (*op. cit.* p. 163) solves as follows. The equation being $x + y = (x^3 + y)^3$, put $y = z - x^3$, and the equation becomes $x + z - x^3 = z^3$, or $x^3 + z^3 = x + z$.

Dividing by $x + z$, we have $x^2 - xz + z^2 = 1$.

Solving for x, we obtain $x = \frac{1}{2}\{z \pm \sqrt{(4 - 3z^2)}\}$.

To make $4 - 3z^2$ a square, equate it to $\left(\frac{m}{n}z - 2\right)^2$; therefore $z = \frac{4mn}{m^2 + 3n^2}$, so that $x = \frac{2mn \pm (m^2 - 3n^2)}{m^2 + 3n^2}$, and $y = z - x^3$. If the positive sign be taken, Diophantus' solution corresponds to $m = 2$, $n = 1$.

[2] It will be observed that here and in the next problem Diophantus makes no use of the fact that

$$(x^3 + y^3)/(x + y) = x^2 - xy + y^2.$$

Cf. note on IV. 11 below.

Therefore $8-12z+6z^2$ must be twice a square.

That is, $4-6z+3z^2=\text{square}=(2-4z)^2$, say; $z=\frac{10}{13}$, and the sides are $\frac{10}{13}, \frac{16}{13}$.

Neglecting the denominator and the factor 2 in the numerators, we take 5, 8 for the sides.

Starting afresh, we put for the cube $125x^3$ and for the number to be added $512x^3-5x$; we thus get

$$637x^3-5x=8x, \text{ and } x=\tfrac{1}{7}.$$

The cube is $\frac{125}{343}$, its side $\frac{5}{7}$, and the added number $\frac{267}{343}$.

10. To find two cubes the sum of which is equal to the sum of their sides.

Let the sides be $2x$, $3x$.

This gives $35x^3=5x$; but *this equation gives an irrational result.*

We have therefore, as in the last problem, to find two cubes the sum of which has to the sum of their sides the ratio of a square to a square[1].

These are found, as before, to be 5^3, 8^3.

Assuming then $5x$, $8x$ as the sides of the required cubes, we obtain the equation $637x^3=13x$, and $x=\frac{1}{7}$.

The cubes are $\frac{125}{343}, \frac{512}{343}$.

[1] Here, as in the last problem, Diophantus could have solved his auxiliary problem of making $(x^3+y^3)/(x+y)$ a square by making x^2-xy+y^2 a square in the same way as in Lemma I. to V. 7 he makes x^2+xy+y^2 a square.

The original problem, however, of solving

$$x^3+y^3=x+y$$

can be more directly and generally solved thus. Dividing out by $(x+y)$, we must have

$$x^2-xy+y^2=1.$$

This can be solved by the method shown in the note to the preceding problem.

Alternatively, we may (with Wertheim) put $x^2-xy+y^2=(x+ky)^2$, and at the same time $1=\pm(x+ky)$.

Thus we have to solve the equations

$$\left.\begin{aligned} x(1+2k)&=y(1-k^2)\\ x+ky&=\pm 1\end{aligned}\right\},$$

which give
$$x=\pm\frac{1-k^2}{1+k+k^2}, \qquad y=\pm\frac{1+2k}{1+k+k^2},$$

where k remains undetermined.

Diophantus' solution is obtained by taking the positive sign and putting $k=\frac{1}{4}$ or by taking the negative sign and putting $k=-\frac{3}{2}$.

11. To find two cubes such that their difference is equal to the difference of their sides.

Assume $2x$, $3x$ as the sides.

This gives $19x^3 = x$, and x is irrational.

We have therefore to find two cubes such that their difference has to the difference of their sides the ratio of a square to a square[1]. Let them be $(z+1)^3$, z^3, so that the difference of the sides may be a square, namely 1.

Therefore $3z^2 + 3z + 1 = \text{square} = (1 - 2z)^2$, say, and $z = 7$.

Starting afresh, assume $7x$, $8x$ as the sides; therefore $169x^3 = x$, and $x = \frac{1}{13}$.

The sides of the two cubes are therefore $\frac{7}{13}, \frac{8}{13}$.

[1] Nesselmann (*Die Algebra der Griechen*, pp. 447–8) comments on the fact that Diophantus makes no use here of the formula $(x^3 - y^3)/(x - y) = x^2 + xy + y^2$, although he must of course have known it (it is indeed included in Euclid's much more general summation of a geometrical progression, IX. 35). To solve the auxiliary problem in IV. 11 he had only to solve the equation

$$x^2 + xy + y^2 = \text{a square},$$

which equation he does actually solve in his Lemma I. to V. 7.

The whole problem can be more simply and generally solved thus. We are to have

$$x^3 - y^3 = x - y,$$

or

$$x^2 + xy + y^2 = 1.$$

Nesselmann's method of solution (cf. note on IV. 9) gives $x = \frac{1}{2}\{-y \pm \sqrt{(4 - 3y^2)}\}$, and hence $y = \frac{4mn}{m^2 + 3n^2}$, $x = \frac{-2mn \pm (m^2 - 3n^2)}{m^2 + 3n^2}$. Diophantus' solution is obtained by putting $m = 1$, $n = 2$ and taking the lower sign.

Wertheim's method (see note on preceding problem) gives in this case

$$x = \pm \frac{1 - k^2}{1 - k + k^2}, \quad y = \pm \frac{2k - 1}{1 - k + k^2},$$

where k is undetermined.

If we take the negative sign and put $k = -3$, we obtain Diophantus' solution.

Bachet in his notes to IV. 10, 11 solves the problems represented by

$$x^3 \pm y^3 = m(x \pm y)$$

subject to the condition that m is either a square or the third part of a square. His method corresponds to that of Diophantus. He does not divide out by $x \pm y$, and he reduces the problem to the subsidiary one of finding ξ, η such that the ratio of $\xi^3 \pm \eta^3$ to $\xi \pm \eta$ is the ratio of a square to a square. His assumptions for the "sides," ξ, η, are of the same kind as those made by Diophantus; in the first problem he assumes x, $6 - x$ and in the second x, $x + 2$. In fact, it being given that $(x^3 \pm y^3)/(x \pm y) = a$, Bachet assumes $x \pm y = z$ and thus obtains

$$3x^2 - 3xz + z^2 = a,$$

which equation can easily be solved by Diophantus' method if a is a square or triple of a square.

Fermat observes that the διορισμός of Bachet is incorrect because not general. It should be added that the number (m) may also be the product of a square number into a prime number of the form $3n + 1$, as 7, 13, 19, 37 etc. or into any number which has no factors except 3 and prime numbers of the form $3n + 1$, as 21, 91 etc. "The proof and the solution are to be obtained by my method."

12. To find two numbers such that the cube of the greater + the less = the cube of the less + the greater[1].

Assume $2x$, $3x$ for the numbers.

Therefore $27x^3 + 2x = 8x^3 + 3x$, or $19x^3 = x$, and x is irrational.

But 19 is the difference of two cubes, and 1 the difference of their sides. Therefore, as in the last problem, we have to find two cubes such that their difference has to the difference of their sides the ratio of a square to a square[2].

The sides of these cubes are found, as before, to be 7, 8.

Starting afresh, we assume $7x$, $8x$ for the numbers; then $343x^3 + 8x = 512x^3 + 7x$, and $x = \frac{1}{13}$.

The numbers are $\frac{7}{13}$, $\frac{8}{13}$.

13. To find two numbers such that either, or their sum, or their difference added to unity gives a square.

Take for the first number any square less 1; let it be, say, $9x^2 + 6x$. But the second + 1 = a square; and first + second + 1 also = a square. Therefore we must find a square such that the sum of that square and $9x^2 + 6x$ = a square.

Take factors of the difference $9x^2 + 6x$, say $9x + 6$, x; the square of half the difference between these factors $= 16x^2 + 24x + 9$.

Therefore, if we put for the second number this expression *minus* 1, or $16x^2 + 24x + 8$, three conditions are satisfied.

The remaining condition gives difference + 1 = square, or $7x^2 + 18x + 9 = \text{square} = (3 - 3x)^2$, say.

Therefore $x = 18$, and (3024, 5624) is a solution.

14. To find three square numbers such that their sum is equal to the sum of their differences.

Sum of differences = (greatest) – (middle) + (middle) – (least) + (greatest) – least = twice difference of greatest and least.

This is equal to the sum of all three, by hypothesis.

Let the least square be 1, the greatest $x^2 + 2x + 1$;

[1] This problem will be seen to be identical with the preceding problem.

[2] See note, p. 173.

therefore twice difference of greatest and least = sum of the three $= 2x^2 + 4x$.

But least + greatest $= x^2 + 2x + 2$, so that

middle $= x^2 + 2x - 2$.

Hence $x^2 + 2x - 2 = \text{square} = (x-4)^2$, say, and $x = \frac{9}{5}$.

The squares are $\left(\frac{196}{25}, \frac{121}{25}, 1\right)$ or $(196, 121, 25)$.

15. To find three numbers such that the sum of any two multiplied into the third is a given number.

Let (first + second) × third = 35, (second + third) × first = 27 and (third + first) × second = 32.

Let the third be x.

Therefore (first + second) $= 35/x$.

Assume first $= 10/x$, second $= 25/x$; then

$$\left.\begin{aligned} \frac{250}{x^2} + 10 &= 27 \\ \frac{250}{x^2} + 25 &= 32 \end{aligned}\right\}.$$

These equations are inconsistent; but they would not be if $25 - 10$ *were equal to* $32 - 27$ *or* 5.

Therefore we have to divide 35 into two parts (to replace 25 and 10) such that their difference is 5. The parts are 15, 20. [Cf. I. 1.]

We take therefore $15/x$ for the first number, $20/x$ for the second, and we have

$$\left.\begin{aligned} \frac{300}{x^2} + 15 &= 27 \\ \frac{300}{x^2} + 20 &= 32 \end{aligned}\right\}.$$

Therefore $x = 5$, and $(3, 4, 5)$ is a solution[1].

[1] As Loria says (*Le scienze esatte nell' antica Grecia*, Libro V. p. 131), this method of the "false hypothesis," though somewhat indirect, would not be undeserving of a place in a modern textbook.

Here again, as in IV. 1, 2, Diophantus tacitly chooses, for his given numbers, numbers which will make the resulting "pure" quadratic equation give a rational value for x.

We may put the solution more generally thus. We have to solve the equations

$$(y+z)\,x = a, \quad (z+x)\,y = b, \quad (x+y)\,z = c.$$

Diophantus takes z for his principal unknown and, writing the third equation in the form $x+y=c/z$, he assumes $x=\alpha/z$, $y=\beta/z$, where α, β have to be determined. One equation connecting α, β is $\alpha+\beta=c$. Next, substituting the values of x, y in the first two equations, we have

$$\frac{\alpha\beta}{z^2} + \alpha = a, \qquad \frac{\alpha\beta}{z^2} + \beta = b,$$

16. To find three numbers such that their sum is a square, while the sum of the square of each added to the next following number gives a square.

Let the middle number be any number of x's, say $4x$; we have therefore to find what square $+4x$ gives a square. Split $4x$ into two factors, say $2x$, 2, and take the square of half their difference, $(x-1)^2$. This is the square required.

Thus the first number is $x-1$.

Again, $16x^2+$ third number $=$ a square. Therefore, if we subtract $16x^2$ from a square, we shall have the third number. Take as the side of this square the side of $16x^2$, or $4x$, *plus* 1.

Therefore third number $=(4x+1)^2-16x^2=8x+1$.

Now the sum of the three numbers $=$ a square; therefore $13x=$ a square $=169y^2$, say[1].

The numbers are then $13y^2-1$, $52y^2$, $104y^2+1$.

Lastly, $(\text{third})^2+\text{first}=$ a square.

Therefore $\qquad 10816y^4+221y^2=$ a square,

or $10816y^2+221=$ a square $=(104y+1)^2$, say.

Therefore $y=\frac{220}{208}=\frac{55}{52}$,

and $\left(\frac{36621}{2704}, \frac{157300}{2704}, \frac{317304}{2704}\right)$ is a solution.

17. To find three numbers such that their sum is a square, while the square on any one *minus* the next following also gives a square.

The solution is precisely similar to the last.

---

whence it follows that $\alpha-\beta=a-b$. From this condition and $\alpha+\beta=c$, we obtain

$$\alpha=\frac{1}{2}(a-b+c),\quad \beta=\frac{1}{2}(-a+b+c).$$

Thus
$$z=\sqrt{\left(\frac{\alpha\beta}{a-\alpha}\right)}=\sqrt{\left\{\frac{(a-b+c)(-a+b+c)}{2(a+b-c)}\right\}},$$

$$x=\frac{\alpha}{z}=\sqrt{\left\{\frac{(a-b+c)(a+b-c)}{2(-a+b+c)}\right\}},\quad y=\frac{\beta}{z}=\sqrt{\left\{\frac{(-a+b+c)(a+b-c)}{2(a-b+c)}\right\}}.$$

Now x, y, z must all be rational, and this is the case if

$$-a+b+c=2qr,\quad a-b+c=2rp,\quad a+b-c=2pq,$$

where p, q, r are any integers.

This gives $\qquad a=p(q+r),\quad b=q(r+p),\quad c=r(p+q);$

a fact which can hardly have been unknown to Diophantus, since his values $a=27$, $b=32$, $c=35$ correspond to the values $p=3$, $q=4$, $r=5$ (Loria, *loc. cit.*).

[1] Diophantus uses the same unknown ς for y as for x, writing actually καὶ γίνεται ὁ ς Δ^Y $\overline{\iota\gamma}$, literally "and x becomes $13x^2$."

The middle number is assumed to be $4x$. The square which exceeds this by a square is $(x+1)^2$, and we therefore take $x+1$ for the first number.

For the third number we take $16x^2-(4x-1)^2$ or $8x-1$.

The sum of the numbers being a square,

$$13x = \text{a square} = 169y^2, \text{ say.}$$

The numbers are then $13y^2+1$, $52y^2$, $104y^2-1$.

Lastly, since $(\text{third})^2 - \text{first} = \text{a square}$,

$$10816y^4 - 221y^2 = \text{a square},$$

or $10816y^2 - 221 = \text{a square} = (104y-1)^2$, say.

Thus $y = \frac{111}{104}$,

and $\left(\frac{170989}{10816}, \frac{640692}{10816}, \frac{1270568}{10816}\right)$ is a solution.

18. To find two numbers such that the cube of the first added to the second gives a cube, and the square of the second added to the first gives a square.

First number x. Therefore second is a cube number *minus* x^3, say $8-x^3$.

Therefore $x^6-16x^3+64+x = \text{a square} = (x^3+8)^2$, say, whence $32x^3 = x$, or $32x^2 = 1$.

This gives an irrational result; x would however be rational if 32 were a square.

But 32 comes from 4 times 8. We must therefore substitute for 8 in our assumptions a cube which when multiplied by 4 gives a square. If y^3 is the cube, $4y^3 = \text{a square} = 16y^2$ say; whence $y = 4$.

Thus we must assume x, $64-x^3$ for the numbers.

Therefore $x^6-128x^3+4096+x = \text{a square} = (x^3+64)^2$, say; whence $256x^3 = x$, and $x = \frac{1}{16}$.

The numbers are $\frac{1}{16}$, $\frac{262143}{4096}$.

19. To find three numbers indeterminately[1] such that the product of any two increased by 1 is a square.

Take for the product of first and second some square *minus* 1, say x^2+2x; this satisfies one condition.

Let second $= x$, so that first $= x+2$.

Now product of second and third $+1 = $ a square; let the

[1] The expression is ἐν τῷ ἀορίστῳ, which is defined at the end of the problem to mean in terms of one unknown (and units), so that the conditions of the problem are satisfied whatever value is given to the unknown.

square be $(3x+1)^2$, so that product of second and third $= 9x^2+6x$;

therefore third $= 9x+6$.

Also product of third and first $+1 =$ a square; therefore $9x^2+24x+13 =$ a square.

Now, if 13 were a square, and the coefficient of x were twice the product of the side of this square and the side of the coefficient of x^2, the problem would be solved indeterminately.

But 13 comes from $2.6+1$, the 2 in this from twice 1, and the 6 from twice 3. Therefore we want two coefficients (to replace 1, 3) such that the product of their doubles $+1 =$ a square, or four times their product $+1 =$ a square.

Now four times the product of any two numbers *plus* the square of their difference gives a square. Thus the requirement is satisfied by taking as coefficients any two consecutive numbers, since the square of their difference is 1. [The assumption of two consecutive numbers for the coefficients simultaneously satisfies the second of the two requirements indicated in the italicised sentence above.]

Beginning again, we take $(x+1)^2-1$ for the product of first and second and $(2x+1)^2-1$ for the product of second and third.

Let the second be x, so that first $= x+2$, third $= 4x+4$.

[Then product of first and third $+1 = 4x^2+12x+9$, and the third condition is satisfied.]

Thus the required indeterminate solution[1] is

$$(x+2,\ x,\ 4x+4).$$

[1] The result obtained by Diophantus really amounts to the more general solution

$$a^2x+2a,\quad x,\quad (a+1)^2x+2(a+1).$$

With this solution should be compared that of Euler (*Algebra*, Part II. Art. 231).

I. To determine x, y, z so that

$$xy+1,\ yz+1,\ zx+1 \text{ are all squares.}$$

Suppose $zx+1=p^2,\quad yz+1=q^2,$

so that $x=(p^2-1)/z,\quad y=(q^2-1)/z.$

Therefore $$xy+1=\frac{(p^2-1)(q^2-1)}{z^2}+1=\text{a square},$$

or $$(p^2-1)(q^2-1)+z^2=\text{a square}$$
$$=(z-r)^2, \text{ say;} \qquad \text{[Euler has } (z+r)^2\text{]}$$

whence $$z=\frac{r^2-(p^2-1)(q^2-1)}{2r},$$

where any numbers may be substituted for p, q, r.

20. To find four numbers such that the product of any two increased by unity is a square.

For the product of first and second take a square *minus* 1, say $(x+1)^2 - 1 = x^2 + 2x$.

Let first $= x$, so that second $= x + 2$.

For example, if $r = pq + 1$, we shall have

$$z = \frac{(p+q)^2}{2(pq+1)} \text{ and } x = \frac{2(pq+1)(p^2-1)}{(p+q)^2}, \quad y = \frac{2(pq+1)(q^2-1)}{(p+q)^2}.$$

II. But, *if whole numbers are required*, we put $xy + 1 = p^2$, and assume $z = x + y + q$.

We then have $$xz + 1 = x^2 + xy + qx + 1 = x^2 + qx + p^2,$$

and $$yz + 1 = xy + y^2 + qy + 1 = y^2 + qy + p^2.$$

These expressions are both squares if $q = \pm 2p$.

Thus a solution is obtained from $xy = p^2 - 1$ combined with either

$$z = x + y + 2p, \text{ or } z = x + y - 2p.$$

We take a certain value for p^2, split $p^2 - 1$ into two factors, take these factors for the values of x, y respectively, and so find z.

For example, let $p = 3$, so that $p^2 - 1 = 8$; if we make $x = 2$, $y = 4$, we find $z =$ either 12 or 0; and in this case $x = 2$, $y = 4$, $z = 12$ is the solution.

If we put $p^2 = (\xi + 1)^2$, we have $xy = \xi^2 + 2\xi$; and if we put $x = \xi + 2$, $y = \xi$, we have

$$z = \xi + 2 + \xi \pm 2(\xi + 1) = 4\xi + 4 \text{ or } 0.$$

The solution is then $(\xi + 2, \xi, 4\xi + 4)$, as in Diophantus.

Fermat in his note on this problem shows how to find three numbers satisfying not only the conditions of the problem but three more also, namely that each of the numbers shall itself when increased by 1 give a square, *i.e.* to solve the equations

$$\left.\begin{array}{l} \eta\zeta + 1 = r^2, \quad \zeta\xi + 1 = s^2, \quad \xi\eta + 1 = t^2, \\ \xi + 1 = u^2, \quad \eta + 1 = v^2, \quad \zeta + 1 = w^2. \end{array}\right\}$$

Solve, he says, the present problem of Diophantus in such a way that the terms independent of x in the first and third of the numbers obtained by his method shall be such as when increased by 1 give a square. It is easy to find a value for a such that $2a + 1$ and $2(a + 1) + 1$ are both squares. Fermat takes the value $2a = \frac{13}{36}$, which satisfies the conditions, and the general expressions for the three numbers sought are therefore

$$\frac{169}{5184}x + \frac{13}{36}, \quad x, \quad \frac{7225}{5184}x + \frac{85}{36}.$$

Each of these has, when increased by 1, to become a square, that is, we have to solve the triple-equation

$$\left.\begin{array}{r} \frac{169}{5184}x + \frac{49}{36} = u^2 \\ x + 1 = v^2 \\ \frac{7225}{5184}x + \frac{121}{36} = w^2 \end{array}\right\}.$$

Fermat does not give the solution; but it is effected as follows.

Multiplying the third expression by 36 and the first by $\frac{121}{49} \cdot 36$ (in order that the absolute terms in the two may be equal), we have to solve

For the product of first and third take $(2x+1)^2-1$, or $4x^2+4x$, the coefficient of x being the number next following the coefficient (1) taken in the first case, for the reason shown in the last problem;

thus third number $= 4x+4$.

Similarly take $(3x+1)^2-1$, or $9x^2+6x$, for the product of first and fourth; therefore fourth $= 9x+6$.

And product of third and fourth + 1

$$= (4x+4)(9x+6)+1 = 36x^2+60x+25,$$

which is a square[1].

$$\left.\begin{aligned} x+1 &= v^2 \\ \left(\frac{143}{7\cdot 12}\right)^2 x+121 &= u'^2 \\ \left(\frac{85}{12}\right)^2 x+121 &= w'^2 \end{aligned}\right\}.$$

In order to solve by the method of the triple-equation, we make $x+1$ a square by putting $x=y^2+2y$.

Substitute this value in the other two expressions, and for convenience multiply each by 144; this gives

$$\left.\begin{aligned} \left(\frac{143}{7}\right)^2 (y^2+2y)+(132)^2 &= \text{a square} \\ (85)^2 (y^2+2y)+(132)^2 &= \text{a square} \end{aligned}\right\}.$$

The difference $= (y^2+2y)\left(85+\frac{143}{7}\right)\left(85-\frac{143}{7}\right)$

$$=\frac{738}{7}y\left(\frac{452}{7}y+\frac{2\cdot 452}{7}\right).$$

The square of half the difference of the factors equated to the smaller expression gives

$$\left(\frac{143}{7}y-\frac{452}{7}\right)^2=\left(\frac{143}{7}\right)^2(y^2+2y)+(132)^2;$$

whence $y=-\frac{324736}{85085}$; and we find that

$$x=y^2+2y=\frac{50193144576}{7239457225}.$$

It is easily verified that

$$\left(\frac{13}{12}\right)^2 x+7^2=\left(\frac{643149}{85085}\right)^2 \text{ and } \left(\frac{85}{12}\right)^2 x+11^2=\left(\frac{1842375}{85085}\right)^2,$$

so that the value of x satisfies the three equations.

The numbers satisfying Fermat's six conditions are then

$$\frac{169}{5184}x+\frac{13}{36}=\frac{100604981}{171348100},\quad x=\frac{50193144576}{7239457225},\ \text{and}\ \frac{7225}{5184}x+\frac{85}{36}=\frac{48192621}{4008004}.$$

[1] This results from the fact that, if we have three numbers x, y, z such that

$$xy+1=(mx+1)^2 \text{ and } xz+1=\{(m+1)x+1\}^2,$$

then

$$yz+1=\{m(m+1)x+(2m+1)\}^2.$$

Lastly, product of second and fourth $+1 = 9x^2 + 24x + 13$;
therefore $9x^2 + 24x + 13 = \text{square} = (3x - 4)^2$, say;
which gives $x = \frac{1}{16}$.

All the conditions are now satisfied[1],

and $\frac{1}{16}, \frac{33}{16}, \frac{68}{16}, \frac{105}{16}$ is the solution[2].

[1] The remaining condition was: product of second and third $+1 =$ a square. That this is satisfied also follows from the general property stated in the last note. In fact

$$(x+2)(4x+4)+1=4x^2+12x+9,$$

which is a square.

[2] With this solution should be compared Euler's solution (*Algebra*, Part II. Art. 233) of the problem of finding x, y, z, v such that the six expressions

$$xy+a, \quad yz+a, \quad zx+a, \quad xv+a, \quad yv+a, \quad zv+a$$

are all squares. The solution follows the method adopted to solve the corresponding problem with three unknowns x, y, z only. See note on III. 10 above.

If we begin by supposing $xy+a=p^2$, and take $z=x+y+2p$, the second and third expressions become squares (*vide* note on III. 10, p. 160).

If we further suppose $v=x+y-2p$, the fourth and fifth expressions also become squares (*vide* the same note).

Consequently we have only to secure that the sixth expression $zv+a$ shall be a square; that is,

$$x^2+2xy+y^2-4p^2+a=\text{a square},$$

or (since $xy+a=p^2$)

$$x^2-2xy+y^2-3a=\text{a square}.$$

Suppose that

$$(x-y)^2-3a=(x-y-q)^2;$$

therefore

$$x-y=(q^2+3a)/2q,$$

or

$$x=y+\frac{q^2+3a}{2q}.$$

Consequently

$$p^2=xy+a=y^2+\frac{q^2+3a}{2q}y+a.$$

If we put $p=y+r$, we have

$$2ry+r^2=\frac{q^2+3a}{2q}y+a,$$

and

$$y=\frac{2qr^2-2aq}{q^2-4qr+3a},$$

from which p, x, and therefore z, v also, are found in terms of q, r, where q, r may have any values provided that x, y, z, v are all positive.

Euler observed that this method is not suited for finding integral solutions, and, pursuing the matter further, he gave the following very elegant solution of Diophantus' actual problem (the case where $a=1$) in integers ("Miscellanea analytica" in *Commentationes arithmeticae*, II. pp. 45–6).

Six conditions have to be satisfied. If x, y, z, v are the required numbers, let $x=m$, $y=n$, where m, n are any integers such that $mn+1=l^2$.

Then put $z=m+n+2l$, and three conditions are already satisfied, for

$$xy+1=mn+1=l^2, \text{ by hypothesis},$$
$$xz+1=m(m+n+2l)+1=(l+m)^2,$$
$$yz+1=n(m+n+2l)+1=(l+n)^2.$$

The three conditions remaining to be satisfied are

$$xv+1=mv+1=\text{a square},$$
$$yv+1=nv+1=\text{a square},$$
$$zv+1=(m+n+2l)v+1=\text{a square}.$$

Let us make the continued product of these expressions a square.

21. To find three numbers in proportion and such that the difference of any two is a square.

Assume x for the least, $x+4$ for the middle (in order that the difference of middle and least may be a square), $x+13$ for the greatest (in order that difference of greatest and middle may be a square).

This product will be found to be

$$1+2(m+n+l)v+\{(m+n+l)^2-1\}v^2+mn(m+n+2l)v^3.$$

Let us equate this to $\left\{1+(m+n+l)v-\frac{1}{2}v^2\right\}^2$, in order that the terms in v, v^2 as well as the absolute term may vanish; therefore

$$mn(m+n+2l)=-(m+n+l)+\frac{1}{4}v,$$

whence
$$\frac{1}{4}v=(m+n+l)+mn(m+n+2l)$$
$$=(mn+1)(m+n+l)+lmn$$
$$=l^2(m+n+l)+lmn$$
$$=l(l+m)(l+n),$$

and therefore
$$v=4l(l+m)(l+n).$$

It is true that we have only made the product of the three expressions $mv+1$, $nv+1$, $(m+n+2l)v+1$ a square; but, as the value of v has turned out to be an integral number, so that all three formulae are prime to one another, we may conclude that each of the expressions is a square.

The solution is therefore

$$x=m,\quad y=n,\quad z=m+n+2l,\quad v=4l(l+m)(l+n),$$

where $mn+1=l^2$.

In fact, while three of the conditions have been above shown to be satisfied, we find, as regards the other three, that

$$xv+1=4lm(l+m)(l+n)+1=(2l^2+2lm-1)^2,$$
$$yv+1=4ln(l+m)(l+n)+1=(2l^2+2ln-1)^2,$$
$$zv+1=4l(m+n+2l)(l+m)(l+n)+1=(4l^2+2lm+2ln-1)^2.$$

It is to be observed that l may be either positive or negative.

Ex. Let $m=3$, $n=8$, so that $l=\pm 5$.

If $l=+5$, the solution is 3, 8, 21, 2080; if $l=-5$, the solution is 3, 8, 1, 120.

Fermat shows how to solve this problem, alternatively, by means of the "triple-equation."

Take *three* numbers with the required property, *e.g.* 3, 1, 8. Let x be the fourth, and we have then to satisfy the conditions

$$3x+1=u^2,\quad x+1=v^2,\quad 8x+1=w^2.$$

Put $x=y^2+2y$, so as to make the second expression a square, and then substitute the value of x in the other two. We have then the double-equation

$$3(y^2+2y)+1=u^2,$$
$$8(y^2+2y)+1=w^2.$$

The difference $=5(y^2+2y)=5y(y+2)$.

We put then
$$(3y+1)^2=8(y^2+2y)+1,$$

whence $y=10$, and $x=y^2+2y=120$, which value satisfies the triple-equation.

The four numbers are then 3, 1, 8, 120, which solution is identical with one of those obtained by Euler as above.

If now 13 were a square, we should have an indeterminate solution satisfying three of the conditions.

We must therefore replace 13 by a square which is the sum of two squares. Any rational right-angled triangle will furnish what is wanted, say 3, 4, 5;

we therefore put for the numbers x, $x+9$, $x+25$.

The fourth condition gives

$$x(x+25)=(x+9)^2, \text{ and } x=\tfrac{81}{7}.$$

Thus $\frac{81}{7}, \frac{144}{7}, \frac{256}{7}$ is a solution.

22. To find three numbers such that their solid content[1] added to any one of them gives a square.

Assume continued product x^2+2x, first number 1, second number $4x+9$, so that two conditions are satisfied.

The third number is then $(x^2+2x)/(4x+9)$.

This cannot be divided out unless $x^2 : 4x = 2x : 9$ or, alternately, $x^2 : 2x = 4x : 9$; but it could be done if 4 were half of 9.

Now $4x$ comes from $6x-2x$, and the $6x$ in this from twice $3x$; the 9 comes from 3^2.

Therefore we have to find a number m to replace 3 such that $2m-2=\frac{1}{2}m^2$: thus $m^2=4m-4$, whence[2] $m=2$.

We put therefore for the second number $(x+2)^2-(x^2+2x)$, or $2x+4$; the third number is then

$$(x^2+2x)/(2x+4) \text{ or } \tfrac{1}{2}x.$$

Lastly, the third condition requires

$$x^2+2x+\tfrac{1}{2}x=\text{a square}=4x^2, \text{ say.}$$

Therefore $x=\frac{5}{6}$,

and $\left(1, \frac{34}{6}, \frac{2\frac{1}{2}}{6}\right)$ is a solution[3].

[1] ὁ ἐξ αὐτῶν στερεός, "the solid (number formed) from them" = the continued product of the three numbers.

[2] Observe the solution of a mixed quadratic.

[3] Fermat gives a solution which avoids the necessity for the auxiliary problem.

Let the solid content be x^2-2x, the first number 1, and the second number $2x$; two conditions are thus satisfied.

The third number is now x^2-2x divided by $2x \cdot 1$, or $\frac{1}{2}x-1$; and the third condition gives

$$x^2-\frac{3}{2}x-1=\text{a square.}$$

Now x must be greater than 2; we therefore put

$$x^2-\frac{3}{2}x-1=(x-m)^2,$$

where m is greater than 2.

23. To find three numbers such that their solid content *minus* any one gives a square[1].

First number x, solid content x^2+x; therefore product of second and third $=x+1$.

Let the second be 1, so that the third is $x+1$.

The two remaining conditions require that

$$\left.\begin{array}{r} x^2+x-1 \\ x^2-1 \end{array}\right\} \text{shall both be squares. [Double-equation.]}$$

The difference $=x=\frac{1}{2}\cdot 2x$, say;

thus $(x+\frac{1}{4})^2=x^2+x-1$, and $x=\frac{17}{8}$.

The numbers are $\left(\frac{17}{8}, 1, \frac{25}{8}\right)$.

24. To divide a given number into two parts such that their product is a cube *minus* its side.

Given number 6. First part x; therefore second $=6-x$, and $6x-x^2=$ a cube *minus* its side.

Form a cube from a side of the form $mx-1$, say $2x-1$, and equate $6x-x^2$ to this cube *minus* its side.

Therefore $8x^3-12x^2+4x=6x-x^2$.

1 A remarkable problem of this kind (in respect of the apparent number of conditions satisfied) is given by De Billy in the *Inventum Novum*, Part I. paragraph 43 (*Oeuvres de Fermat*, III. p. 352): To find three numbers ξ, η, ζ (ξ, ζ, η being in ascending order of magnitude) such that the following nine expressions may become squares:

(1) $\xi-\xi\eta\zeta$, (4) $\eta-\xi-\xi\eta\zeta$, (7) $\xi\eta-\xi\eta\zeta$,

(2) $\eta-\xi\eta\zeta$, (5) $\zeta-\xi-\xi\eta\zeta$, (8) $\eta\zeta-\xi\eta\zeta$,

(3) $\zeta-\xi\eta\zeta$, (6) $\eta-\zeta-\xi\eta\zeta$, (9) $\eta^2-\xi\eta\zeta$.

Take x, 1, $1-x$ as the values of ξ, η, ζ respectively. Then *six conditions*, namely, (1), (3), (4), (6), (7), (8), are all automatically satisfied.

By conditions (2) and (9) alike,

$$1-x+x^2=\text{a square}.$$

And, by (5),

$$1-3x+x^2=\text{a square}.$$

Solving this double-equation in the usual way, we get $x=\frac{3}{8}$, and the numbers are $\frac{3}{8}, 1, \frac{5}{8}$.

Another solution can be obtained by putting $y+\frac{3}{8}$ in place of x in the two expressions, and so on. Cf. note on III. 18 above.

It would appear from a letter from Fermat to De Billy of 26 Aug. 1659 (*Oeuvres*, II. pp. 436–8) that this problem and the above single solution were De Billy's own. De Billy had supposed that this was the only solution, but Fermat observed that there were any number, as the above double-equation has any number of solutions. Fermat gave $\left(\frac{10416}{51865}, 1, \frac{41449}{51865}\right)$ as another solution.

Now, if the coefficient of x were the same on both sides, this would reduce to a simple equation, and x would be rational.

In order that this may be the case, we must put m for 2 in our assumption, where $3m - m = 6$ (the 6 being the given number in the original hypothesis). Thus $m = 3$.

We therefore assume

$$(3x-1)^3 - (3x-1) = 6x - x^2,$$

or

$$27x^3 - 27x^2 + 6x = 6x - x^2,$$

and

$$x = \tfrac{26}{27}.$$

The parts are $\frac{26}{27}$, $\frac{136}{27}$.

25. To divide a given number into three parts such that their continued product gives a cube the side of which is equal to the sum of the differences of the parts.

Given number 4.

Since the product is a cube, let it be $8x^3$, the side of which is $2x$.

Now (second part) – (first) + (third) – (second) + (third) – (first) = twice difference between third and first.

Therefore difference between third and first = half sum of differences $= x$.

Let the first be any multiple of x, say $2x$; therefore the third $= 3x$.

Hence second $= 8x^3/6x^2 = \frac{4}{3}x$; and, *if the second had lain between the first and third, the problem would have been solved.*

Now the second came from dividing 8 by 2 . 3, and the 2 and 3 are not two numbers at random but consecutive numbers.

Therefore we have to find two consecutive numbers such that, when 8 is divided by their product, the quotient lies between the numbers.

Assume m, $m+1$; therefore $8/(m^2+m)$ lies between m and $m+1$.

Therefore

$$\frac{8}{m^2+m} + 1 > m + 1,$$

so that

$$m^2 + m + 8 > m^3 + 2m^2 + m,$$

or

$$8 > m^3 + m^2.$$

I form a cube such that it has m^3, m^2 as terms, that is, the cube $(m+\frac{1}{3})^3$, which is greater than m^3+m^2, and I put

$$(m+\tfrac{1}{3})^3 = 8;$$

therefore $m+\frac{1}{3}=2$, and $m=\frac{5}{3}$.

Assume now for first number $\frac{5}{3}x$; the third is $\frac{8}{3}x$, and the second is $\frac{9}{5}x$.

Multiplying throughout by 15, we take $25x$, $27x$, $40x$, and the product of these numbers is a cube the side of which is the sum of their differences.

The sum $= 92x = 4$, by hypothesis.

Therefore $x = \frac{1}{23}$,

$$\text{and } \left(\frac{25}{23}, \frac{27}{23}, \frac{40}{23}\right) \text{ are the parts required.}$$

[N.B. The condition $8/(m^2+m) < m+1$ is ignored in the work, and is *incidentally* satisfied.]

26. To find two numbers such that their product added to either gives a cube.

Let the first number be of the form m^3x, say $8x$.

Second x^2-1. Therefore one condition is satisfied, since

$$8x^3 - 8x + 8x = \text{a cube}.$$

Also $8x^3 - 8x + x^2 - 1 = \text{a cube} = (2x-1)^3$, say.

Therefore $13x^2 = 14x$, and $x = \frac{14}{13}$.

The numbers are $\frac{112}{13}$, $\frac{27}{169}$.

27. To find two numbers such that their product *minus* either gives a cube.

Let the first be of the form m^3x, say $8x$, and the second x^2+1 (since $8x^3+8x-8x = \text{a cube}$).

Also $8x^3+8x-x^2-1$ must be a cube, "which is impossible[1]."

[1] Diophantus means that, if we are to get rid of the third power and the absolute term, we can only put the expression equal to $(2x-1)^3$, which gives a negative and therefore "impossible" value for x. But the equation is not really impossible, for we can get rid of the terms in x^3 and x^2 by putting

$$8x^3+8x-x^2-1 = \left(2x-\frac{1}{12}\right)^3, \text{ whence } x = \frac{1727}{13752},$$

or we can make the term in x and the absolute term disappear by putting

$$8x^3+8x-x^2-1 = \left(\frac{8}{3}x-1\right)^3, \text{ whence } x = \frac{549}{296}.$$

Diophantus has actually shown us how to do the former in IV. 25 just preceding.

Accordingly we assume for the first number an expression of the form m^3x+1, say $8x+1$, and for the second number x^2 (since $8x^3+x^2-x^2=$ a cube).

Also $8x^3+x^2-8x-1=$ a cube $=(2x-1)^3$, say.

Therefore $x=\frac{14}{13}$,

and the numbers are $\frac{125}{13}, \frac{196}{169}$.

28. To find two numbers such that their product $\pm$ their sum gives a cube.

Assume the first cube (product + sum) to be 64, and the second (product − sum) to be 8.

Therefore twice sum of numbers $=64-8=56$, and the sum $=28$, while the product + the sum $=64$; therefore the product $=36$.

Therefore we have to find two numbers such that their sum is 28 and their product 36. If $14+x$, $14-x$ are the numbers[1], we have $196-x^2=36$, or $x^2=160$; and, if 160 were a square, we should have a rational solution.

Now 160 arises from 14^2-36, and $14=\frac{1}{2}.28=\frac{1}{4}.56$ $=\frac{1}{4}$ (difference of two cubes); also $36=\frac{1}{2}$ (sum of the cubes).

Therefore we have to find two cubes such that

$$(\tfrac{1}{4}\text{ of their difference})^2-\tfrac{1}{2}\text{ their sum}=\text{a square}.$$

Let the sides of the cubes be $(z+1)$, $(z-1)$;

therefore $\frac{1}{4}$ of difference $=1\frac{1}{2}z^2+\frac{1}{2}$, and the square of this is $2\frac{1}{4}z^4+1\frac{1}{2}z^2+\frac{1}{4}$;

$\frac{1}{2}$ the sum of the cubes is z^3+3z;

therefore $2\frac{1}{4}z^4+1\frac{1}{2}z^2+\frac{1}{4}-z^3-3z=$ a square,

or $9z^4+6z^2+1-4z^3-12z=$ a square $=(3z^2+1-6z)^2$, say;

whence $32z^3=36z^2$, and $z=\frac{9}{8}$.

The sides of the cubes are therefore $\frac{17}{8}, \frac{1}{8}$, and the cubes $\frac{4913}{512}, \frac{1}{512}$.

Put now product of numbers + their sum $=\frac{4913}{512}$, and product − sum $=\frac{1}{512}$.

Therefore their sum $=\frac{2456}{512}$, and their product $=\frac{2457}{512}$.

Now let the first number $=x+$ half sum $=x+\frac{1228}{512}$,

and the second $=$ half sum $-x=\frac{1228}{512}-x$;

therefore $\frac{1507984}{262144}-x^2=\frac{2457}{512}$,

and $262144x^2=250000$.

[1] Cf. I. 27.

Therefore $x = \frac{500}{512}$,

and $\left(\frac{1728}{512}, \frac{728}{512}\right)$ is a solution.

Otherwise thus.

If any square number is divided into two parts one of which is its side, the product of the parts added to their sum gives a cube.

[That is, $x(x^2 - x) + x^2 - x + x =$ a cube.]

Let the square be x^2, and be divided into the parts $x, x^2 - x$.

Then, by the second condition of the problem,

$x^3 - x^2 - x^2 = x^3 - 2x^2 =$ a cube (less than x^3) $= (\frac{1}{2}x)^3$, say.

Therefore $8x^3 - 16x^2 = x^3$, so that $x = \frac{16}{7}$,

and $\left(\frac{16}{7}, \frac{144}{49}\right)$ is a solution.

29. To find four square numbers such that their sum added to the sum of their sides makes a given number[1].

Given number 12.

Now $x^2 + x + \frac{1}{4} =$ a square.

Therefore the sum of four squares + the sum of their sides + 1 = the sum of four other squares = 13, by hypothesis.

Therefore we have to divide 13 into four squares; then, if we subtract $\frac{1}{2}$ from each of their sides, we shall have the sides of the required squares.

[1] On this problem Bachet observes that Diophantus appears to assume, here and in some problems of Book V., that any number not itself a square is the sum of two or three or four squares. He adds that he has verified this statement for all numbers up to 325, but would like to see a scientific proof of the theorem. These remarks of Bachet's are the occasion for another of Fermat's famous notes: "I have been the first to discover a most beautiful theorem of the greatest generality, namely this: Every number is either a triangular number or the sum of two or three triangular numbers; every number is a square or the sum of two, three, or four squares; every number is a pentagonal number or the sum of two, three, four or five pentagonal numbers; and so on *ad infinitum*, for hexagons, heptagons and any polygons whatever, the enunciation of this general and wonderful theorem being varied according to the number of the angles. The proof of it, which depends on many various and abstruse mysteries of numbers, I cannot give here; for I have decided to devote a separate and complete work to this matter and thereby to advance arithmetic in this region of inquiry to an extraordinary extent beyond its ancient and known limits."

Unfortunately the promised separate work did not appear. The theorem so far as it relates to squares was first proved by Lagrange (*Nouv. Mémoires de l'Acad. de Berlin*, année 1770, Berlin 1772, pp. 123–133; *Oeuvres*, III. pp. 189–201), who followed up results obtained by Euler. Cf. also Legendre, *Zahlentheorie*, tr. Maser, I. pp. 212 sqq. Lagrange's proof is set out as shortly as possible in Wertheim's Diophantus, pp. 324–330. The theorem of Fermat in all its generality was proved by Cauchy (*Oeuvres*, IIe série, Vol. VI. pp. 320–353); cf. Legendre, *Zahlentheorie*, tr. Maser, II. pp. 332 sqq.

Now $13 = 4 + 9 = (\frac{64}{25} + \frac{36}{25}) + (\frac{144}{25} + \frac{81}{25})$,

and the sides of the required squares are $\frac{11}{10}, \frac{7}{10}, \frac{19}{10}, \frac{13}{10}$,

the squares themselves being $\frac{121}{100}, \frac{49}{100}, \frac{361}{100}, \frac{169}{100}$.

30. To find four squares such that their sum *minus* the sum of their sides is a given number.

Given number 4.

Now $x^2 - x + \frac{1}{4} =$ a square.

Therefore (the sum of four squares) − (sum of their sides) + 1 = the sum of four other squares = 5, by hypothesis.

Divide 5 into four squares, as $\frac{9}{25}, \frac{16}{25}, \frac{64}{25}, \frac{36}{25}$.

The sides of these squares *plus* $\frac{1}{2}$ in each case are the sides of the required squares.

Therefore sides of required squares are $\frac{11}{10}, \frac{13}{10}, \frac{21}{10}, \frac{17}{10}$,

and the squares themselves $\frac{121}{100}, \frac{169}{100}, \frac{441}{100}, \frac{289}{100}$.

31. To divide unity into two parts such that, if given numbers are added to them respectively, the product of the two sums gives a square.

Let 3, 5 be the numbers to be added; x, $1 - x$ the parts of 1.

Therefore $(x + 3)(6 - x) = 18 + 3x - x^2 =$ a square $= 4x^2$, say;

thus $18 + 3x = 5x^2$, *which does not give a rational result.*

Now 5 comes from a square + 1; and, in order that the equation may have a rational solution, we must substitute for the square taken (4) a square such that

(the square + 1) . $18 + (\frac{3}{2})^2 =$ a square.

Put $(m^2 + 1)18 + 2\frac{1}{4} =$ a square,

or $72m^2 + 81 =$ a square $= (8m + 9)^2$, say,

and $m = 18$, $m^2 = 324$.

Hence we must put

$$(x + 3)(6 - x) = 18 + 3x - x^2 = 324x^2.$$

Therefore[1] $325x^2 - 3x - 18 = 0$,

$$x = \frac{78}{325} = \frac{6}{25},$$

and $\left(\frac{6}{25}, \frac{19}{25}\right)$ is a solution.

Otherwise thus.

The numbers to be added being 3, 5, assume the first of the two parts to be $x - 3$; the second is then $4 - x$.

Therefore $x(9 - x) =$ a square $= 4x^2$, say,

and $x = \frac{9}{5}$.

But I cannot take 3 *from* $\frac{9}{5}$, and x must be > 3 and < 4.

[1] Observe the solution of a mixed quadratic equation.

Now the value of x comes from $9/(\text{a square}+1)$, and, since $x>3$, this square + 1 should be <3, so that the square must be less than 2; but, since $x<4$, the square + 1 must be $>\frac{9}{4}$, so that the square must be $>\frac{5}{4}$.

Therefore I must find a square lying between $\frac{5}{4}$ and 2, or between $\frac{80}{64}$ and $\frac{128}{64}$.

$\frac{100}{64}$ or $\frac{25}{16}$ satisfies the condition.

Put now $$x(9-x)=\tfrac{25}{16}x^2;$$

therefore $$x=\tfrac{144}{41},$$

and $\left(\frac{21}{41}, \frac{20}{41}\right)$ is a solution.

32. To divide a given number into three parts such that the product of the first and second $\pm$ the third gives a square.

Given number 6.

Suppose third part $=x$, second = any number less than 6, say 2; therefore first part $=4-x$.

The two remaining conditions require that $8-2x\pm x=$ a square,

or $\left.\begin{matrix}8-x\\8-3x\end{matrix}\right\}$ are both squares. [Double-equation.]

This *does not give a rational result* ("is not rational"), *since the ratio of the coefficients of x is not a ratio of a square to a square.*

But the coefficients of x are $2-1$ and $2+1$; therefore we must find a number y to replace 2 such that

$(y+1)/(y-1)=$ ratio of square to square $=\frac{4}{1}$, say.

Therefore $y+1=4y-4$, and $y=\frac{5}{3}$.

Put now second part $=\frac{5}{3}$; therefore first $=\frac{13}{3}-x$.

Therefore $$\tfrac{65}{9}-\tfrac{5}{3}x\pm x=\text{a square}.$$

That is, $\left.\begin{matrix}65-6x\\65-24x\end{matrix}\right\}$ are both squares,

or $\left.\begin{matrix}260-24x\\65-24x\end{matrix}\right\}$ are both squares.

The difference $=195=15\cdot13$;

we put therefore $\frac{1}{4}(15-13)^2=65-24x$, and $x=\frac{8}{3}$.

Therefore the required parts are $\left(\frac{5}{3}, \frac{5}{3}, \frac{8}{3}\right)$[1].

1 Fermat observes: "The following is an easier method of solution. Divide the number 6 into two in any manner, *e.g.* into 5 and 1. Divide their product less 1, that is 4, by 6, the given number: the result is $\frac{2}{3}$. Subtracting this first from 5 and then from 1,

33. To find two numbers such that the first with a fraction of the second is to the remainder of the second in a given ratio, and also the second with the same fraction of the first is to the remainder of the first in a given ratio.

Let the first with the fraction of the second = 3 times the remainder of the second, and the second with the same fraction of the first = 5 times the remainder of the first.

[The fraction may be either an aliquot part or not, τὸ αὐτὸ μέρος or τὰ αὐτὰ μέρη as Diophantus says, following the ordinary definition of those terms ("the same *part*" or "the same *parts*"): cf. Euclid VII. Deff. 3, 4.]

Let the second $= x + 1$, and let the part of it received by the first $= 1$;

therefore the first $= 3x - 1$ (since $3x - 1 + 1 = 3x$).

Since the second *plus* the fraction of the first = 5 times the remainder of the first,

the second + the first = 6 times the remainder of the first.

And first + second $= 4x$; therefore remainder of first $= \frac{2}{3}x$, and hence the second receives from the first $3x - 1 - \frac{2}{3}x$ or $\frac{7}{3}x - 1$.

We have therefore to secure that $\frac{7}{3}x - 1$ is the same fraction of $3x - 1$ that 1 is of $x + 1$.

This requires that $(\frac{7}{3}x - 1)(x + 1) = (3x - 1) . 1$;

therefore $\frac{7}{3}x^2 + \frac{4}{3}x - 1 = 3x - 1$, and $x = \frac{5}{7}$.

Accordingly the numbers are $\frac{8}{7}$, $\frac{12}{7}$; and 1 is $\frac{7}{12}$ of the second.

---

we have as remainders $\frac{13}{3}$ and $\frac{1}{3}$, which are the first two parts of the number to be divided; the third is therefore $\frac{4}{3}$."

That is, if ξ, η, ζ be the required parts of the number a, Fermat divides a into two parts x, $a - x$ and then puts

$$\xi = x - \frac{x(a-x) - 1}{a} = \frac{x^2 + 1}{a},$$

$$\eta = a - x - \frac{x(a-x) - 1}{a} = \frac{(a-x)^2 + 1}{a};$$

whence $$\zeta = a - (\xi + \eta) = \frac{2(ax - x^2 - 1)}{a} = \frac{2\{x(a-x) - 1\}}{a}.$$

The three general expressions in x satisfy the conditions, and x may be given any value $< a$.

Multiply by 7 and the numbers are 8, 12, and the fraction is $\frac{7}{12}$; but 8 is not divisible by 12: so multiply by 3, and (24, 36) is a solution.

Lemma to the next problem.

To find two numbers indeterminately such that their product together with their sum is a given number.

Given number 8.

Assume the first number to be x, the second 3.

Therefore $3x + x + 3 = \text{given number} = 8$; $x = \frac{5}{4}$, and the numbers are $\frac{5}{4}$, 3.

Now $\frac{5}{4}$ arises from $(8 - 3)/(3 + 1)$, where 3 is the assumed second number.

We may accordingly put for the second number (instead of 3) any (undetermined) number whatever[1]; then, substituting this for 3 in the above expression, we have the corresponding first number.

For example, we may take $x - 1$ for the second number; the first is then $9 - x$ divided by x, or $\frac{9}{x} - 1$.

34. To find three numbers such that the product of any two together with the sum of those two makes a given number[2].

[1] The Greek phrase is ἐὰν ἄρα τάξωμεν τὸν β^{ον} ς^{οῦ} οἱουδήποτε (οἱουδήποτε ς in Lemma to IV. 36), "If we make the second" (literally "*put* the second *at*") "any ς whatever." But the ς is not here, as it is in the Lemma to IV. 36, the actual x of the problem, for Diophantus goes on to say "E.g. let the second be $x - 1$." In the Lemma to IV. 34 the corresponding expression is "any quantity whatever" (ὁσουδήποτε without ς). The present Lemma amounts to saying that, if $xy + x + y = a$, then $x = (a - y)/(y + 1)$.

[2] This determinate set of equations can of course be solved, with our notation, by a simple substitution.

The equations

$$\left.\begin{aligned} yz + y + z &= a \\ zx + z + x &= b \\ xy + x + y &= c \end{aligned}\right\}$$

are equivalent to

$$\left\{\begin{aligned} (y+1)(z+1) &= a+1, \\ (z+1)(x+1) &= b+1, \\ (x+1)(y+1) &= c+1, \end{aligned}\right. \quad \text{or} \quad \left\{\begin{aligned} \eta\zeta &= a+1, \\ \zeta\xi &= b+1, \\ \xi\eta &= c+1, \end{aligned}\right.$$

where

$$\xi = x + 1, \quad \eta = y + 1, \quad \zeta = z + 1.$$

The solution is

$$\xi = x + 1 = \sqrt{\left\{\frac{(b+1)(c+1)}{a+1}\right\}} \text{ etc.}$$

In order that the result may be rational, it is only necessary that $(a+1)(b+1)(c+1)$ should be a square; it is not necessary that *each* of the expressions $a+1$, $b+1$, $c+1$ should be a square, as Diophantus says.

Necessary condition. Each number must be 1 less than some square[1].

Let (product + sum) of first and second = 8.
" " " second and third = 15.
" " " third and first = 24.

By the first equation, if we divide (8 − second) by (second + 1), we have the first number.

Let the second number be $x - 1$.

Therefore the first $= \frac{9-x}{x} = \frac{9}{x} - 1$.

Similarly the third number $= \frac{16}{x} - 1$.

The third equation remains, which gives

$$\frac{144}{x^2} - 1 = 24, \text{ and } x = \tfrac{12}{5}.$$

The numbers are $\frac{33}{12}, \frac{7}{5}, \frac{68}{12}$,

or, when reduced to a common denominator, $\frac{165}{60}, \frac{84}{60}, \frac{340}{60}$.

Lemma to the following problem.

To find two numbers indeterminately such that their product *minus* their sum is a given number.

Given number 8.

First number x, second 3, suppose; therefore (product) − (sum) $= 3x - x - 3 = 2x - 3 = 8$, and $x = 5\frac{1}{2}$.

The first number is therefore $5\frac{1}{2}$, the second 3.

But $5\frac{1}{2}$ comes from $(8 + 3)/(3 - 1)$, and we may put for 3 any number whatever.

E.g. put the second number $= x + 1$; the first is then $x + 9$ divided by x, or $1 + \frac{9}{x}$.

35. To find three numbers such that the product of any two *minus* the sum of those two is a given number[2].

Necessary condition. Each of the given numbers must be 1 less than some square[2].

Let (product − sum) of first and second = 8.
" " " second and third = 15.
" " " third and first = 24.

[1] See last paragraph of preceding note.

[2] The notes to IV. 34 above apply, *mutatis mutandis*, to this problem as well.

By the first equation, if we divide (8 + second) by (second − 1), we have the first number.

Assuming $x + 1$ for the second number, we have $1 + \frac{9}{x}$ for the first.

Similarly $1 + \frac{16}{x}$ is the third number, and two conditions are satisfied.

The third gives $\frac{144}{x^2} - 1 = 24$, and $x = \frac{12}{5}$.

The numbers are $\frac{57}{12}, \frac{17}{5}, \frac{92}{12}$,

or, with a common denominator, $\frac{285}{60}, \frac{204}{60}, \frac{460}{60}$.

Lemma to the following problem.

To find two numbers indeterminately such that their product has to their sum a given ratio.

Let the given ratio be $3 : 1$, the first number x, the second 5.

Therefore $5x = 3(5 + x)$, $x = 7\frac{1}{2}$; and the numbers are $7\frac{1}{2}$, 5.

But $7\frac{1}{2}$ arises from 15 divided by 2, while the 15 is the second number multiplied by the given ratio, and the 2 is the excess of the second number over the ratio.

Putting therefore x (instead of 5) for the second number, we have, for the first number, $3x$ divided by $x - 3$.

The numbers are therefore $3x/(x - 3)$, x.

36. To find three numbers such that the product of any two bears to the sum of those two a given ratio.

Let product of first and second be 3 times their sum.
" " second and third be 4 times their sum.
" " third and first be 5 times their sum.

Let second number be x; the first is therefore $3x/(x - 3)$, by the Lemma, and similarly the third is $4x/(x - 4)$.

Lastly $$\frac{3x}{x-3} \cdot \frac{4x}{x-4} = 5\left(\frac{3x}{x-3} + \frac{4x}{x-4}\right),$$

or $$12x^2 = 35x^2 - 120x.$$

Therefore $x = \frac{120}{23}$,

and the numbers are $\frac{360}{51}, \frac{120}{23}, \frac{480}{28}$.

37. To find three numbers such that the product of any two has to the sum of the three a given ratio[1].

Let product of first and second = 3 times sum of the three,
" " of second and third = 4 " "
" " of third and first = 5 " "

First seek three numbers such that the product of any two has to an *arbitrary* number (say 5) the given ratio.

Then product of first and second = 15; and, if x be the second, the first is $15/x$.

The product of second and third = 20; therefore third $= 20/x$.

It follows that $20 . 15/x^2 = 25$.

And, if the ratio of 20 . 15 to 25 were that of a square to a square, the problem would be solved.

Now 15 = 3 . 5, and 20 is 4 . 5, the 3 and 4 being fixed by the original hypothesis, but 5 being an *arbitrary* number.

We must therefore find a number m (to replace 5) such that $12m^2/5m$ = ratio of a square to a square.

Thus $12m^2 . 5m = 60m^3$ = a square $= 900m^2$, say; and $m = 15$.

Let then the sum of the three numbers be 15.

Product of first and second is therefore 45, and first $= 45/x$.

Similarly third $= 60/x$.

Therefore $45 . 60/x^2 = 75$, and $x = 6$.

Therefore the numbers are $7\frac{1}{2}$, 6, 10, and the sum of these $= 23\frac{1}{2}$.

Now, *if this sum were* 15 *instead, the problem would be solved.*

[1] Loria (*op. cit.* p. 130) quotes this problem as an instance of Diophantus' ingenious choice of unknowns. Here the equations are, with our notation,

$$yz = a(x+y+z),$$
$$zx = b(x+y+z),$$
$$xy = c(x+y+z),$$

and Diophantus chooses as his principal unknown the sum of the three numbers, $x+y+z=w$, say.

We may then write $x = cw/y$, $z = aw/y$, so that $zx = acw^2/y^2 = bw$, and $y^2 = \frac{ac}{b} w$.

Putting $w = \frac{ac}{b} \xi^2$, we have

$$x+y+z = \frac{ac}{b} \xi^2, \quad y = \frac{ac}{b} \xi, \quad z = a\xi, \quad x = c\xi,$$

from which, by eliminating x, y, z, we obtain $\xi = (bc+ca+ab)/ac$.

Hence $x = (bc+ca+ab)/a, \quad y = (bc+ca+ab)/b, \quad z = (bc+ca+ab)/c.$

Put therefore for the sum of the three numbers $15x^2$, and for the numbers themselves $7\frac{1}{2}x$, $6x$, $10x$.

Therefore $23\frac{1}{2}x = 15x^2$, so that $x = \frac{47}{30}$,

and $\frac{352\frac{1}{2}}{30}, \frac{282}{30}, \frac{470}{30}$ is a solution.

38. To find three numbers such that their sum multiplied into the first gives a triangular number, their sum multiplied into the second a square, and their sum multiplied into the third a cube.

Let the sum be x^2, and let the numbers be m/x^2, n/x^2, p/x^2, where m, n, p are a triangular number, a square and a cube respectively;

say first number $= 6/x^2$, second $4/x^2$, third $8/x^2$.

But the sum is x^2; therefore $18/x^2 = x^2$, or $18 = x^4$.

Therefore *we must replace* 18 *by some fourth power.*

But $18 =$ sum of a triangular number, a square and a cube.

Let x^4 be the required fourth power, which must therefore be the sum of a triangular number, a square and a cube.

Let the square be $x^4 - 2x^2 + 1$;

therefore the triangular number + the cube $= 2x^2 - 1$.

Let the cube be 8; therefore the triangular number is $2x^2 - 9$.

But 8 *times a triangular number* + 1 = *a square*; therefore $16x^2 - 71 =$ a square $= (4x - 1)^2$, say; thus $x = 9$, the triangular number is 153, the square 6400 and the cube 8.

Assume then as the numbers $153/x^2$, $6400/x^2$, $8/x^2$.

Therefore $6561/x^2 = x^2$, or $x^4 = 6561$, and $x = 9$.

Thus $\left(\frac{153}{81}, \frac{6400}{81}, \frac{8}{81}\right)$ is a solution[1].

[1] The procedure may be shown more generally thus.

Let ξ, η, ζ be the required numbers; suppose

$$\xi + \eta + \zeta = x^2,$$

and

$$\xi = \frac{\alpha(\alpha+1)}{2x^2}, \quad \eta = \frac{\beta^2}{x^2}, \quad \zeta = \frac{\gamma^3}{x^2}.$$

It follows that

$$x^4 = \frac{\alpha(\alpha+1)}{2} + \beta^2 + \gamma^3.$$

Suppose now that $\beta = x^2 - z^2$ [Diophantus and Bachet assume $z = 1$].

Then

$$\frac{\alpha(\alpha+1)}{2} = 2z^2x^2 - z^4 - \gamma^3.$$

Eight times the left hand side plus 1 gives a square (by the property of triangular numbers); that is,

$$(2\alpha+1)^2 = 16z^2x^2 - 8z^4 - 8\gamma^3 + 1 = \text{a square}$$
$$= (4zx - k)^2, \text{ say,}$$

39. To find three numbers such that the difference of the greatest and the middle has to the difference of the middle and the least a given ratio, and also the sum of any two is a square.

Ratio 3 : 1. Since middle number + least = square, let the square be 4.

Therefore middle > 2; let it be $x+2$, so that least $= 2-x$.

Therefore difference of greatest and middle $= 6x$, whence the greatest $= 7x+2$.

Therefore $\left.\begin{matrix} 8x+4 \\ 6x+4 \end{matrix}\right\}$ are both squares. [*Double-equation.*]

Take the difference $2x$, split it into factors, say $\frac{1}{2}x$, 4, and proceed by the rule; therefore $x = 112$.

But I cannot take 112 *from* 2; therefore x must be found to be < 2, so that $6x+4 < 16$.

Thus there are to be three squares $8x+4$, $6x+4$ and 4 (the 4 arising from 2 . 2), and the difference of the greatest and middle is $\frac{1}{3}$ of the difference of the middle and least.

We have therefore to find three squares having this property and such that the least = 4 and the middle < 16.

Let side of middle square be $z+2$; therefore excess of middle over least $= z^2 + 4z$, whence excess of greatest over middle $= \frac{1}{3}z^2 + 1\frac{1}{3}z$, and therefore the greatest $= 1\frac{1}{3}z^2 + 5\frac{1}{3}z + 4$.

This must be a square; therefore, multiplying by 9, we have

$$12z^2 + 48z + 36 = \text{a square},$$

---

whence $$x = \frac{8z^4 + 8y^3 + k^2 - 1}{8kz}.$$

But $\frac{a(a+1)}{2}$ must be integral, and therefore a integral, so that $\frac{1}{2}(4zx - k - 1)$ must be integral; that is, $\frac{8z^4 + 8y^3 - (k+1)^2}{4k}$ must be integral.

Bachet assumes that it is necessary, with Diophantus, to take $k=1$, observing that trial will show that the problem can hardly be solved otherwise. On this Fermat remarks that Bachet's trial had not been carried far enough. We may, he says, put for y^3 any cube, for instance, with side of the form $3n+1$. Suppose, for example, we take 7^3. Then [z being 1] we have to make

$$2x^2 - 344 \text{ a triangle},$$

and therefore $16x^2 - 2751$ a square, and we may take, if we please, $4x-3$ as the side of this square [so that k is in this case 3].

By varying the cubes we may use an unlimited variety of odd numbers, besides 3, as values for k which will satisfy the required condition.

Loria (*op. cit.* p. 138) points out that the problem could have been more simply solved by substituting x for x^2 and z for z^2 in the above assumptions. The ultimate expression to be made a square would then have been $16zx - 8z^2 - 8y^3 + 1$, and we could have equated this to λ^2, thus finding x.

or $3z^2 + 12z + 9 = \text{a square} = (mz - 3)^2$, say.

It follows that $z = (6m + 12)/(m^2 - 3)$, which must be < 2.

Therefore $6m + 12 < 2m^2 - 6$, or $2m^2 > 6m + 18$.

"When we solve such an equation[1], we multiply half the coefficient of x into itself—this gives 9—then multiply the coefficient of x^2 into the units—$2 . 18 = 36$—add this last number to the 9, making 45, and take the side [square root] of 45, which is not less than 7; add half the coefficient of x—making a number not less than 10—and divide the result by the coefficient of x^2; the result is not less than 5."

[$3^2 + 18 . 2 = 45$, and $\frac{1}{2}\sqrt{45} + \frac{3}{2}$ is not less than $\frac{3}{2} + \frac{7}{2}$.]

We may therefore put $m = \frac{3}{2} + \frac{7}{2}$, or 5, and we thus have

$$3z^2 + 12z + 9 = (3 - 5z)^2.$$

Therefore $z = \frac{21}{11}$, and the side of the middle square is $\frac{43}{11}$, the square itself being $\frac{1849}{121}$.

Turning to the original problem, we put $6x + 4 = \frac{1849}{121}$, and $x = \frac{1365}{726}$, which *is* less than 2.

The greatest of the required numbers $= 7x + 2 = \dfrac{11007}{726}$,

$$\text{the middle} = x + 2 = \frac{2817}{726},$$

$$\text{and the least} = 2 - x = \frac{87}{726}.$$

The denominator not being a square, we can make it a square by dividing out by 6; the result is

$$\frac{1834\frac{1}{2}}{121}, \quad \frac{469\frac{1}{2}}{121}, \quad \frac{14\frac{1}{2}}{121},$$

or again, to avoid the $\frac{1}{2}$ in the numerators, we may multiply numerators, and denominators, by 4; thus

$$\frac{7338}{484}, \quad \frac{1878}{484}, \quad \frac{58}{484} \text{ is a solution}$$[2].

[1] I have quoted Diophantus' exact words here, with the few added by Tannery, "making a number not less than 10...coefficient of x^2," in order to show the precise rule by which Diophantus solved a complete quadratic.

When he says $\sqrt{45}$ is not less than 7, Diophantus is not seeking exact limits. Since $\sqrt{45}$ is between 6 and 7 we cannot take a smaller integral value than 7 in order to satisfy the conditions of the problem (cf. p. 65 above).

[2] A note in the *Inventum Novum* (Part II, paragraph 26) remarks upon the prolix and involved character of Diophantus' solution and gives a shorter alternative. The problem is to solve

$$\xi - \eta = m(\eta - \zeta), \qquad (\xi > \eta > \zeta, \text{ and } m = 3, \text{ say})$$

$$\eta + \zeta = u^2,$$

$$\zeta + \xi = v^2,$$

$$\xi + \eta = w^2.$$

40. To find three numbers such that the difference of the squares of the greatest and the middle numbers has to the difference of the middle and the least a given ratio, and also the sum of each pair is a square.

Ratio $3:1$.

Let greatest + middle number = the square $16x^2$; therefore greatest $> 8x^2$: let it be $8x^2+2$; hence middle $= 8x^2-2$.

And, since greatest + middle > greatest + least,

$$16x^2 > (\text{greatest} + \text{least}) > 8x^2;$$

let greatest + least $= 9x^2$, say; therefore least $= x^2-2$.

Now difference of squares of greatest and middle $= 64x^2$, and difference of middle and least $= 7x^2$.

But 64 is not equal to $3 \cdot 7$ or 21.

Now 64 comes from $32 \cdot 2$; therefore we must find a number m (in place of 2) such that $32m = 21$.

Therefore $m = \frac{21}{32}$.

Assume now greatest number $= 8x^2 + \frac{21}{32}$, middle $= 8x^2 - \frac{21}{32}$, least $= x^2 - \frac{21}{32}$.

[And difference of squares of greatest and middle

$$= 21x^2 = 3 \cdot 7x^2.]$$

The only condition left is: middle + least = square; that is,

$$9x^2 - \tfrac{42}{32} = \text{a square} = (3x-6)^2, \text{ say}.$$

Therefore $x = \frac{597}{576}$,

and $\left(\frac{3069000}{331776}, \frac{2633544}{331776}, \frac{138681}{331776}\right)$ is a solution.

Take an arbitrary square number, say 4, for the sum of η, ζ; suppose $2+x=\eta$, $2-x=\zeta$, so that $\eta-\zeta=2x$; therefore $\xi-\eta=3(\eta-\zeta)=6x$, whence $\xi=2+7x$.

The last two conditions require that

$$\left.\begin{matrix}4+8x\\4+6x\end{matrix}\right\} \text{ shall be squares.}$$

Replace x by $\frac{1}{6}y^2+\frac{2}{3}y$. This will make $4+6x$ a square. It remains that

$$4+\frac{16}{3}y+\frac{4}{3}y^2 = \text{a square}$$

$$= \left(2+\frac{5}{4}y\right)^2, \text{ say.}$$

Thus

$$y\left(\frac{25}{16}-\frac{4}{3}\right) = \left(\frac{16}{3}-5\right),$$

and $y=\frac{16}{11}$, so that $x=\frac{1}{6}y^2+\frac{2}{3}y=\frac{160}{121}$.

The numbers are therefore $\frac{1362}{121}, \frac{402}{121}, \frac{82}{121}$.

BOOK V

1. To find three numbers in geometrical progression such that each of them *minus* a given number gives a square.

Given number 12.

Find a *square* which exceeds 12 by a square. "This is easy [II. 10]; $42\frac{1}{4}$ is such a number."

Let the first number be $42\frac{1}{4}$, the third x^2; therefore the middle number $= 6\frac{1}{2}x$.

Therefore $\left.\begin{array}{r} x^2 - 12 \\ 6\frac{1}{2}x - 12 \end{array}\right\}$ are both squares;

their difference $= x^2 - 6\frac{1}{2}x = x(x - 6\frac{1}{2})$; half the difference of the factors multiplied into itself $= \frac{169}{16}$; therefore, putting $6\frac{1}{2}x - 12 = \frac{169}{16}$, we have $x = \frac{361}{104}$,

and $\left(42\frac{1}{4}, \frac{2346\frac{1}{2}}{104}, \frac{130321}{10816}\right)$ is a solution.

2. To find three numbers in geometrical progression such that each of them when added to a given number gives a square.

Given number 20.

Take a square which when added to 20 gives a square, say 16.

Put for one of the extremes 16, and for the other x^2, so that the middle term $= 4x$.

Therefore $\left.\begin{array}{r} x^2 + 20 \\ 4x + 20 \end{array}\right\}$ are both squares.

Their difference is $x^2 - 4x = x(x - 4)$, and the usual method gives $4x + 20 = 4$, *which is absurd*, because the 4 ought to be some number greater than 20.

But the $4 = \frac{1}{4}(16)$, while the 16 is a square which when added to 20 makes a square; therefore, to replace 16, we must find some square greater than $4 . 20$ and such that when increased by 20 it makes a square.

Now $81 > 80$; therefore, putting $(m + 9)^2$ for the required square, we have

$$(m + 9)^2 + 20 = \text{square} = (m - 11)^2, \text{ say};$$

therefore $m = \frac{1}{2}$, and the square $= (9\frac{1}{2})^2 = 90\frac{1}{4}$.

Assume now for the numbers $90\frac{1}{4}$, $9\frac{1}{2}x$, x^2, and we have

$$\left.\begin{array}{r} x^2+20 \\ 9\frac{1}{2}x+20 \end{array}\right\} \text{both squares.}$$

The difference $= x(x - 9\frac{1}{2})$, and we put $9\frac{1}{2}x + 20 = \frac{361}{16}$.
Therefore $x = \frac{41}{152}$, and

$$\left(90\tfrac{1}{4},\ \frac{389\frac{1}{2}}{152},\ \frac{1681}{23104}\right) \text{ is a solution.}$$

3. Given one number, to find three others such that any one of them, or the product of any two of them, when added to the given number, gives a square.

Given number 5.

"*We have it in the Porisms* that if, of two numbers, each, as well as their product, when added to one and the same given number, severally make squares, the two numbers are obtained from the squares of consecutive numbers[1]."

Take then the squares $(x+3)^2$, $(x+4)^2$, and, subtracting the given number 5 from each, put for the first number x^2+6x+4, and for the second $x^2+8x+11$, and let the third[2] be twice their sum *minus* 1, or

$$4x^2+28x+29.$$

[1] On this Porism, see pp. 99, 100 *ante*.

[2] The Porism states that, if a be the given number, the numbers x^2-a, $(x+1)^2-a$ satisfy the conditions.

In fact, their product $+a = \{x(x+1)\}^2 - a(2x^2+2x+1)+a^2+a$

$$= \{x(x+1)\}^2 - 2ax(x+1)+a^2 = \{x(x+1)-a\}^2.$$

Diophantus here adds, without explanation, that, if X, Y denote the above two numbers, we should assume for the third required number $Z=2(X+Y)-1$. We want *three* numbers such that *any two* satisfy the same conditions as X, Y. Diophantus takes for the third $Z=2(X+Y)-1$ because, as is easily seen, with this assumption two out of the three additional conditions are thereby satisfied.

For
$$Z = 2(X+Y)-1 = 2(2x^2+2x+1)-4a-1$$
$$=(2x+1)^2-4a;$$

therefore
$$XZ+a = x^2(2x+1)^2 - a\{(2x+1)^2+4x^2\}+4a^2+a$$
$$=x^2(2x+1)^2 - a\cdot 4x(2x+1)+4a^2$$
$$=\{x(2x+1)-2a\}^2,$$

while
$$YZ+a = (x+1)^2(2x+1)^2 - a\{(2x+1)^2+4(x+1)^2\}+4a^2+a$$
$$=(x+1)^2(2x+1)^2 - a(8x^2+12x+4)+4a^2$$
$$=\{(x+1)(2x+1)-2a\}^2.$$

The only condition remaining is then

$$Z+a = \text{a square},$$

or
$$(2x+1)^2-3a = \text{a square} = (2x-k)^2, \text{ say,}$$

and x is found.

Cf. pp. 100, 104 above.

Therefore $4x^2 + 28x + 34 =$ a square $= (2x - 6)^2$, say.

Hence $x = \frac{1}{26}$, and $\left(\frac{2861}{676}, \frac{7645}{676}, \frac{20336}{676}\right)$ is a solution[1].

4. Given one number, to find three others such that any one of them, or the product of any two, *minus* the given number gives a square.

Given number 6.

Take two consecutive squares x^2, $x^2 + 2x + 1$.

Adding 6 to each, we assume for the first number $x^2 + 6$, and for the second $x^2 + 2x + 7$.

For the third[2] we take twice the sum of the first and second *minus* 1, or $4x^2 + 4x + 25$.

Therefore third *minus* $6 = 4x^2 + 4x + 19 =$ square $= (2x - 6)^2$, say.

Therefore $x = \frac{17}{28}$,

and $\left(\frac{4993}{784}, \frac{6729}{784}, \frac{22660}{784}\right)$ is a solution.

[The same Porism is assumed as in the preceding problem but with a *minus* instead of a *plus*. Cf. p. 99 above.]

5. To find three squares such that the product of any two added to the sum of those two, or to the remaining square, gives a square.

"*We have it in the Porisms*" that, if the squares on any two consecutive numbers be taken, and a third number be also taken which exceeds twice the sum of the squares by 2, we have three numbers such that the product of any two added to those two or to the remaining number gives a square[3].

[1] Diophantus having solved the problem of finding three numbers ξ, η, ζ satisfying the six equations

$$\xi + a = r^2, \quad \eta\zeta + a = u^2,$$
$$\eta + a = s^2, \quad \zeta\xi + a = v^2,$$
$$\zeta + a = t^2, \quad \xi\eta + a = w^2,$$

Fermat observes that we can deduce the solution of the problem

To find four numbers such that the product of any pair added to a given number produces a square.

Taking three numbers, as found by Diophantus, satisfying the above six conditions, we take $x + 1$ as the fourth number. We then have three conditions which remain to be satisfied. These give a "triple-equation" to be solved by Fermat's method.

[2] Diophantus makes this assumption for the same reason as in the last problem, v. 3. The second note on p. 201 covers this case if we substitute $-a$ for a throughout.

[3] On this Porism, see pp. 100–1 *ante*.

Assume as the first square x^2+2x+1, and as the second x^2+4x+4, so that third number $=4x^2+12x+12$.

Therefore $x^2+3x+3=$ a square $=(x-3)^2$, say, and $x=\frac{2}{3}$.

Therefore $\left(\frac{25}{9}, \frac{64}{9}, \frac{196}{9}\right)$ is a solution.

6. To find three numbers such that each *minus* 2 gives a square, and the product of any two *minus* the sum of those two, or *minus* the remaining number, gives a square.

Add 2 to each of three numbers found as in the Porism quoted in the preceding problem.

Let the numbers so obtained be x^2+2, x^2+2x+3, $4x^2+4x+6$.

All the conditions are now satisfied[1], except one, which gives

$$4x^2+4x+6-2=\text{a square.}$$

Divide by 4, and $x^2+x+1=$ a square $=(x-2)^2$, say.

Therefore $x=\frac{3}{5}$,

and $\left(\frac{59}{25}, \frac{114}{25}, \frac{246}{25}\right)$ is a solution.

Lemma I to the following problem.

To find two numbers such that their product added to the squares of both gives a square.

Suppose first number x, second any number (m), say 1.

Therefore $x.1+x^2+1=x^2+x+1=$ a square $=(x-2)^2$, say.

Thus $x=\frac{3}{5}$, and

$\left(\frac{3}{5}, 1\right)$ is a solution, or (3, 5).

Lemma II to the following problem.

To find three right-angled triangles (*i.e.* three right-angled triangles *in rational numbers*[2]) which have equal areas.

We must first find two numbers such that their product + the sum of their squares = a square, *e.g.* 3, 5, as in the preceding problem.

[1] The numbers are x^2+2, $(x+1)^2+2$, $2\{x^2+(x+1)^2+1\}+2$; and if X, Y, Z denote these numbers respectively, it is easily verified that

$$XY-(X+Y)=(x^2+x+1)^2, \quad XY-Z=(x^2+x)^2,$$
$$XZ-(X+Z)=(2x^2+x+2)^2, \quad XZ-Y=(2x^2+x+3)^2,$$

and

$$YZ-(Y+Z)=(2x^2+3x+3)^2, \quad YZ-X=(2x^2+3x+4)^2.$$

[2] All Diophantus' right-angled triangles must be understood to be right-angled triangles with sides expressible in rational numbers. In future I shall say "right-angled triangle" simply, for brevity.

Now form right-angled triangles from the pairs of numbers[1]

$$(7, 3),\ (7, 5),\ (7, 3+5)$$

[*i.e.* the right-angled triangles $(7^2+3^2, 7^2-3^2, 2.7.3)$, etc.].

The triangles are $(40, 42, 58)$, $(24, 70, 74)$, $(15, 112, 113)$, the area of each being 840.

[1] Diophantus here tacitly assumes that, if $ab+a^2+b^2=c^2$, and right-angled triangles be formed from (c, a), (c, b) and $(c, a+b)$ respectively, their areas are equal. The areas are of course $(c^2-a^2)\,ca$, $(c^2-b^2)\,cb$ and $\{(a+b)^2-c^2\}\,(a+b)\,c$, and it is easy to see that each $=abc\,(a+b)$.

Nesselmann suggests that Diophantus discovered the property as follows. Let the triangles formed from (n, m), (q, m), (r, m) have their areas equal; therefore

$$n\,(m^2-n^2)=q\,(m^2-q^2)=r\,(r^2-m^2).$$

It follows, first, since $m^2n-n^3=m^2q-q^3$,

that $m^2=(n^3-q^3)/(n-q)=n^2+nq+q^2$.

Again, given (q, m, n), to find r.

We have $q\,(m^2-q^2)=r\,(r^2-m^2)$,

and $m^2-q^2=n^2+nq$, from above;

therefore $q\,(n^2+nq)=r\,(r^2-n^2-nq-q^2)$,

or $q\,(n^2+nr)+q^2\,(n+r)=r\,(r^2-n^2)$.

Dividing by $r+n$, we have $qn+q^2=r^2-rn$;

therefore $(q+r)\,n=r^2-q^2$,

and $r=q+n$.

Fermat observes that, given any rational right-angled triangle, say z, b, d, where z is the hypotenuse, it is possible to find an infinite number of other rational right-angled triangles having the same area. Form a right-angled triangle from z^2, $2bd$; this gives the triangle $z^4+4b^2d^2$, $z^4-4b^2d^2$, $4z^2bd$. Divide each of these sides by $2z\,(b^2-d^2)$, b being $>d$; and we have a triangle with the same area $\left(\frac{1}{2}bd\right)$ as the original triangle. Trying this method with Diophantus' first triangle $(40, 42, 58)$, we obtain as the new triangle

$$\frac{1412881}{1189},\ \frac{1412880}{1189},\ \frac{1681}{1189}.$$

The method gives $\left(\frac{7}{10}, \frac{120}{7}, \frac{1201}{70}\right)$ as a right-angled triangle with area equal to that of $(3, 4, 5)$.

Another method of finding other rational right-angled triangles having the same area as a given right-angled triangle is explained in the *Inventum Novum*, Part I, paragraph 38 (*Œuvres de Fermat*, III. p. 348).

Let the given triangle be 3, 4, 5, so that it is required to find a new rational right-angled triangle with area 6.

Let 3, $x+4$ be the perpendicular sides; therefore

the square of the hypotenuse $=x^2+8x+25=$ a square.

Again, the area is $\frac{3}{2}x+6$; and, as this is to be 6, it must be six times a certain square; that is, $\frac{3}{2}x+6$ divided by 6 must be a square, and this again multiplied by 36 must be a square; therefore

$$9x+36=\text{a square}.$$

Accordingly we have to solve the double-equation

$$\left.\begin{aligned} x^2+8x+25&=u^2\\ 9x+36&=v^2 \end{aligned}\right\}.$$

7. To find three numbers such that the square of any one $\pm$ the sum of the three gives a square.

Since, in a right-angled triangle,

(hypotenuse)^2 $\pm$ twice product of perps. = a square,

we make the three required numbers hypotenuses and the sum of the three four times the area.

Therefore we must find three right-angled triangles having the same area, *e.g.*, as in the preceding problem,

(40, 42, 58), (24, 70, 74), (15, 112, 113).

Reverting to the substantive problem, we put for the numbers $58x$, $74x$, $113x$; their sum $245x$ = four times the area of any one of the triangles $= 3360x^2$.

Therefore $x = \frac{7}{96}$,

and $\left(\frac{406}{96}, \frac{518}{96}, \frac{791}{96}\right)$ is a solution.

Lemma to the following problem.

Given three squares, it is possible to find three numbers such that the products of the three pairs shall be respectively equal to those squares.

This gives $$x = -\frac{6725600}{2405601},$$

whence $$x+4 = \frac{2896804}{2405601}.$$

The triangle is thus found to be

$$3, \frac{2896804}{2405601}, \frac{7776485}{2405601}.$$

The area is 6 times a certain square, namely $\frac{724201}{2405601}$, the root of which is $\frac{851}{1551}$.

Dividing each of the above sides by $\frac{851}{1551}$, we obtain a triangle with area 6, namely

$$\frac{4653}{851}, \frac{3404}{1551}, \frac{7776485}{1319901}.$$

Another solution of the double-equation, $x = -\frac{13959}{3600}$, giving $x+4 = \frac{49}{400}$, leads to the same triangle $\left(\frac{7}{10}, \frac{120}{7}, \frac{1201}{70}\right)$ as that obtained by Fermat's rule (see above).

The method of the *Inventum Novum* has a feature in common with the procedure in the ancient Greek problem reproduced and commented on by Heiberg and Zeuthen (*Bibliotheca Mathematica*, VIII$_3$, 1907/8, p. 122), where it is required to find a rational right-angled triangle, having given the area, 5 feet, and where the 5 is multiplied by a square number containing 6 as a factor and such that the product "can form the area of a right-angled triangle." 36 is taken and the area becomes 180, which is the area of (9, 40, 41). The sides of the latter triangle are then divided by 6, and we have the required triangle (cf. p. 119, *ante*).

Squares 4, 9, 16.

First number x, so that the others are $4/x$, $9/x$; and $36/x^2=16$.

Therefore $x=\frac{6}{4}$, and the numbers are $(1\frac{1}{2}, 2\frac{2}{3}, 6)$.

We observe that $x=\frac{6}{4}$, where 6 is the product of 2 and 3, and 4 is the side of 16.

Hence the following *rule*. Take the product of two sides (2, 3), divide by the side of the third square 4 [the result is the first number]; divide 4, 9 respectively by the result, and we have the second and third numbers.

8. To find three numbers such that the product of any two $\pm$ the sum of the three gives a square.

As in Lemma II to the 7th problem, we find three right-angled triangles with equal areas; the squares of their hypotenuses are 3364, 5476, 12769.

Now find, as in the last Lemma, three numbers such that the products of the three pairs are equal to these squares respectively, which we take because each $\pm 4\cdot$(area) or 3360 gives a square; the three numbers then are

$\frac{4292}{113}x$, $\frac{3277}{37}x$ [$\frac{380132}{4292}x$ Tannery],
$\frac{4181}{29}x$ [$\frac{618788}{4292}x$ Tannery].

It remains that the sum of the three $= 3360x^2$.

Therefore $\frac{32824806}{121249}x$ [$\frac{131299224}{484996}x$ Tannery] $= 3360x^2$.

Therefore $x=\frac{32824806}{407396640}$ [$\frac{131299224}{1629586560}$ or $\frac{781543}{9699920}$ Tannery],

[and the numbers are $\frac{781543}{255380}$, $\frac{781543}{109520}$, $\frac{781543}{67280}$].

9. To divide unity into two parts such that, if the same given number be added to either part, the result will be a square.

Necessary condition. The given number must not be odd and the double of it + 1 must not be divisible by any prime number which, when increased by 1, is divisible by 4 [*i.e.* any prime number of the form $4n-1$][1].

Given number 6. Therefore 13 must be divided into two squares each of which >6. If then we divide 13 into two squares the difference of which <1, we solve the problem.

[1] For a discussion of the text of this condition see pp. 107–8, *ante*.

Take half of 13 or $6\frac{1}{2}$, and we have to add to $6\frac{1}{2}$ a small fraction which will make it a square,

or, multiplying by 4, we have to make $\frac{1}{x^2} + 26$ a square,

i.e. $26x^2 + 1 =$ a square $= (5x + 1)^2$, say, whence $x = 10$.

That is, in order to make 26 a square, we must add $\frac{1}{100}$, or, to make $6\frac{1}{2}$ a square, we must add $\frac{1}{400}$, and

$$\tfrac{1}{400} + 6\tfrac{1}{2} = (\tfrac{51}{20})^2.$$

Therefore we must divide 13 *into two squares such that their sides may be as nearly as possible equal to* $\frac{51}{20}$. [This is the παρισότητος ἀγωγή described above, pp. 95–8.]

Now $13 = 2^2 + 3^2$. Therefore we seek two numbers such that 3 *minus* the first $= \frac{51}{20}$, so that the first $= \frac{9}{20}$, and 2 *plus* the second $= \frac{51}{20}$, so that the second $= \frac{11}{20}$.

We write accordingly $(11x + 2)^2$, $(3 - 9x)^2$ for the required squares [substituting x for $\frac{1}{20}$].

The sum $= 202x^2 - 10x + 13 = 13$.

Therefore $x = \frac{5}{101}$, and the sides are $\frac{257}{101}$, $\frac{258}{101}$.

Subtracting 6 from the squares of each, we have, as the parts of unity,

$$\frac{4843}{10201}, \frac{5358}{10201}.$$

10. To divide unity into two parts such that, if we add different given numbers to each, the results will be squares.

Let the numbers[1] be 2, 6 and let them and the unit be represented in the figure, where $DA = 2$, $AB = 1$, $BE = 6$, and G is a point in AB so chosen that DG, GE are both squares.

D A G B E

Now $DE = 9$. *Therefore we have to divide* 9 *into two squares such that one of them lies between* 2 *and* 3.

Let the latter square be x^2, so that the other is $9 - x^2$, where $3 > x^2 > 2$.

Take two squares, one > 2, the other < 3 [the former being the smaller], say $\frac{289}{144}$, $\frac{361}{144}$.

[1] Loria (*op. cit.* p. 150 *n.*), as well as Nesselmann, observes that Diophantus omits to state the necessary condition, namely that the sum of the two given numbers *plus* 1 must be the sum of two squares.

Therefore, if we can make x^2 lie between these, we shall solve the problem.

We must have $x > \frac{17}{12}$ and $< \frac{19}{12}$.

Hence, in making $9 - x^2$ a square, we must find

$$x > \tfrac{17}{12} \text{ and } < \tfrac{19}{12}.$$

Put $9 - x^2 = (3 - mx)^2$, say, whence $x = 6m/(m^2 + 1)$.

Therefore $$\frac{17}{12} < \frac{6m}{m^2+1} < \frac{19}{12}.$$

The first inequality gives $72m > 17m^2 + 17$; and

$$36^2 - 17 \cdot 17 = 1007,$$

the square root of which[1] is not greater than 31;

therefore $m \not> \dfrac{31 + 36}{17}$, *i.e.* $m \not> \dfrac{67}{17}$.

Similarly from the inequality $19m^2 + 19 > 72m$ we find[2]

$$m \not< \tfrac{66}{19}.$$

Let $m = 3\frac{1}{2}$. Therefore $9 - x^2 = (3 - 3\frac{1}{2}x)^2$, and $x = \frac{84}{53}$.

Therefore $x^2 = \frac{7056}{2809}$,

and the segments of 1 are $\left(\dfrac{1438}{2809}, \dfrac{1371}{2809}\right)$.

11. To divide unity into three parts such that, if we add the same number to each of the parts, the results are all squares.

Necessary condition[3]. The given number must not be 2 or any multiple of 8 increased by 2.

Given number 3. Thus 10 is to be divided into three squares such that each > 3.

Take $\frac{1}{3}$ of 10, or $3\frac{1}{3}$, and find x so that $\dfrac{1}{9x^2} + 3\frac{1}{3}$ may be a square, or $30x^2 + 1 = $ a square $= (5x + 1)^2$, say.

Therefore $x = 2$, $x^2 = 4$, $1/x^2 = \frac{1}{4}$, and

$$\tfrac{1}{36} + 3\tfrac{1}{3} = \tfrac{121}{36} = \text{a square}.$$

Therefore we have to divide 10 into three squares each of which is as near as possible to $\frac{121}{36}$. [παρισότητος ἀγωγή.]

Now $10 = 3^2 + 1^2 =$ the sum of the three squares $9, \frac{16}{25}, \frac{9}{25}$.

Comparing the sides $3, \frac{4}{5}, \frac{3}{5}$ with $\frac{11}{6}$,

or (multiplying by 30) 90, 24, 18 with 55, we must make each side approach 55.

[1] *I.e.* the *integral* part of the root is $\not> 31$. The limits taken in each case are *a fortiori* limits as explained above, pp. 61–3.

[2] See p. 61, *ante*.

[3] See pp. 108–9, *ante*.

[Since then $\frac{55}{30} = 3 - \frac{35}{30} = \frac{4}{5} + \frac{31}{30} = \frac{3}{5} + \frac{37}{30}$], we put for the sides of the required numbers

$$3 - 35x,\quad 31x + \tfrac{4}{5},\quad 37x + \tfrac{3}{5}.$$

The sum of the squares $= 3555x^2 - 116x + 10 = 10$.

Therefore $x = \frac{116}{3555}$,

and this solves the problem.

12. To divide unity into three parts such that, if three different given numbers be added to the parts respectively, the results are all squares.

Given numbers 2, 3, 4. Then I have to divide 10 into three squares such that the first > 2, the second > 3, and the third > 4.

Let us add $\frac{1}{2}$ of unity to each, and we have to find three squares such that their sum is 10, while the first lies between 2, $2\frac{1}{2}$, the second between 3, $3\frac{1}{2}$, and the third between 4, $4\frac{1}{2}$.

It is necessary, first, to divide 10 (the sum of two squares) into two squares one of which lies between 2, $2\frac{1}{2}$; then, if we subtract 2 from the latter square, we have one of the required parts of unity.

Next divide the other square into two squares, one of which lies between 3, $3\frac{1}{2}$;

subtracting 3 from the latter square, we have the second of the required parts of unity.

Similarly we can find the third part[1].

[1] Diophantus only thus briefly indicates the course of the solution. Wertheim solves the problem in detail after Diophantus' manner; and, as this is by no means too easy, I think it well to reproduce his solution.

I. It is first necessary to divide 10 into two squares one of which lies between 2 and 3. We use the παρισότητος ἀγωγή.

The first square must be in the neighbourhood of $2\frac{1}{2}$; and we seek a small fraction $\frac{1}{x^2}$ which when added to $2\frac{1}{2}$ gives a square: in other words, we must make $4\left(2\frac{1}{2} + \frac{1}{x^2}\right)$ a square. This expression may be written $10 + \left(\frac{1}{y}\right)^2$, and, to make this a square, we put

$$10y^2 + 1 = (3y + 1)^2, \text{ say,}$$

whence $y = 6$, $y^2 = 36$, $x^2 = 144$, so that $2\frac{1}{2} + \frac{1}{x^2} = \frac{361}{144} = \left(\frac{19}{12}\right)^2$, which is an approximation to the first of the two squares the sum of which is 10.

The second of these squares approximates to $7\frac{1}{2}$, and we seek a small fraction $\frac{1}{x^2}$ such that $7\frac{1}{2} + \frac{1}{x^2}$ is a square, or $30 + \left(\frac{2}{x}\right)^2 = 30 + \left(\frac{1}{y}\right)^2$, say $=$ a square.

13. To divide a given number into three parts such that the sum of any two of the parts gives a square.

Given number 10.

Put $$30y^2+1=(5y+1)^2, \text{ say};$$

therefore $y=2$, $y^2=4$, $x^2=16$, so that $7\frac{1}{2}+\frac{1}{x^2}=\frac{121}{16}=\left(\frac{11}{4}\right)^2=\left(\frac{33}{12}\right)^2$.

Now, since $10=1^2+3^2$, and $\frac{19}{12}=1+\frac{7}{12}$, while $\frac{33}{12}=3-\frac{3}{12}$,

we put $$(1+7x)^2+(3-3x)^2=10, \qquad \text{[Cf. v. 9]}$$

so that $$x=\frac{2}{29},$$

$$(1+7x)^2=\left(1+\frac{14}{29}\right)^2=\left(\frac{43}{29}\right)^2=\frac{1849}{841},$$

$$(3-3x)^2=\left(3-\frac{6}{29}\right)^2=\left(\frac{81}{29}\right)^2=\frac{6561}{841}.$$

Therefore the two squares into which 10 is divided are $\frac{1849}{841}$ and $\frac{6561}{841}$, and the first of these lies in fact between 2 and $2\frac{1}{2}$.

II. We have next to divide the square $\frac{6561}{841}$ into two squares, one of which, which we will call x^2, lies between 3 and 4. [The method of v. 10 is here applicable.]

Instead of 3, 4 take $\frac{49}{16}, \frac{64}{16}$ as the limits.

Therefore $$\frac{49}{16}<x^2<\frac{64}{16},$$

or $$\frac{7}{4}<x<\frac{8}{4}.$$

And $\frac{6561}{841}-x^2$ must be a square $=\left(\frac{81}{29}-kx\right)^2$, say,

which gives $$x=\frac{162k}{29(1+k^2)};$$

k has now to be chosen such that

(1) $$\frac{162k}{29(1+k^2)}>\frac{7}{4},$$

from which it follows that $$k<2{\cdot}8\ldots,$$

and (2) $$\frac{162k}{29(1+k^2)}<\frac{8}{4},$$

whence $$k>2{\cdot}3\ldots.$$

We may therefore put $$k=2{\cdot}5.$$

Therefore $$x=\frac{1620}{841}, \quad x^2=\frac{2624400}{707281},$$

and $$\frac{6561}{841}-x^2=\frac{2893401}{707281}.$$

The three required squares into which 10 is divided are therefore

$$\frac{1849}{841}, \quad \frac{2624400}{707281}, \quad \frac{2893401}{707281}.$$

And if we subtract 2 from the first, 3 from the second and 4 from the third, we obtain as the required parts of unity

$$\frac{140447}{707281}, \quad \frac{502557}{707281}, \quad \frac{64277}{707281}.$$

Since the sum of each pair of parts is a square less than 10, while the sum of the three pairs is twice the sum of the three parts or 20,

we have to divide 20 *into three squares each of which is* < 10.

But 20 is the sum of two squares, 16 and 4;

and, if we put 4 for one of the required squares, we have to divide 16 into two squares, each of which is < 10, or, in other words, into two squares, one of which lies between 6 and 10. This we learnt how to do[1] [V. 10].

We have, when this is done, three squares such that each is < 10, while their sum is 20;

and by subtracting each of these squares from 10 we obtain the parts of 10 required.

14. To divide a given number into four parts such that the sum of any three gives a square.

Given number 10.

Three times the sum of the parts = the sum of four squares.

Therefore 30 has to be divided into four squares, each of which is < 10.

(1) If we use the method of approximation (παρισότης), we have to make each square approximate to $7\frac{1}{2}$;

[1] Wertheim gives a solution in full, thus.

Let the squares be x^2, $16 - x^2$, of which one, x^2, lies between 6 and 10.

Put instead of 6 and 10 the limits $\frac{25}{4}$ and 9, so that

$$\frac{5}{2} < x < 3.$$

To make $16 - x^2$ a square, we put

$$16 - x^2 = (4 - kx)^2,$$

whence

$$x = \frac{8k}{1 + k^2}.$$

Now (1) $\frac{8k}{1+k^2} > \frac{5}{2}$, and (2) $\frac{8k}{1+k^2} < 3$.

These conditions give, as limits for k, 2·84... and 2·21... .

We may therefore *e.g.* put $k = 2\frac{1}{2}$.

Then

$$x = \frac{80}{29}, \quad x^2 = \frac{6400}{841}, \quad 16 - x^2 = \frac{7056}{841}.$$

The required three squares making up 20 are $4, \frac{6400}{841}, \frac{7056}{841}$.

Subtracting these respectively from 10, we have the required parts of the given number 10, namely

$$6, \quad \frac{2010}{841}, \quad \frac{1354}{841}.$$

then, when the squares are found, we subtract each from 10, and so find the required parts.

(2) *Or*, observing that $30 = 16 + 9 + 4 + 1$, we take 4, 9 for two of the squares, and then divide 17 into two squares, each of which < 10.

If then we divide 17 into two squares, one of which lies between $8\frac{1}{2}$ and 10, as we have learnt how to do[1] [cf. v. 10], the squares will satisfy the conditions.

We shall then have divided 30 into four squares, each of which is less than 10, two of them being 4, 9 and the other two the parts of 17 just found.

Subtracting each of the four squares from 10, we have the required parts of 10, two of which are 1 and 6.

15. To find three numbers such that the cube of their sum added to any one of them gives a cube.

Let the sum be x and the numbers $7x^3$, $26x^3$, $63x^3$.

Therefore $96x^3 = x$, or $96x^2 = 1$.

But 96 is not a square; we must therefore replace it by a square in order to solve the problem.

[1] Wertheim gives a solution of this part of the problem.

As usual, we make $8\frac{1}{2} + \frac{1}{x^2}$, or $34 + \left(\frac{2}{x}\right)^2$, a square.

Putting $\frac{2}{x} = \frac{1}{y}$, we must make $34 + \left(\frac{1}{y}\right)^2$ a square.

Let $$34y^2 + 1 = \text{a square} = (6y - 1)^2,$$

and we obtain $$y = 6,\ y^2 = 36,\ x^2 = 144.$$

Thus $$8\tfrac{1}{2} + \frac{1}{144} = \frac{1225}{144} = \left(\frac{35}{12}\right)^2,$$

and $\frac{35}{12}$ is an approximation to the side of each of the required squares.

Next, since $17 = 1^2 + 4^2$, and $\frac{35}{12} = 1 + \frac{23}{12} = 4 - \frac{13}{12}$,

we put $$17 = (1 + 23x)^2 + (4 - 13x)^2,$$

and we obtain $$x = \frac{29}{349}.$$

The squares are then $$(1 + 23x)^2 = \left(\frac{1016}{349}\right)^2 = \frac{1032256}{121801},$$

and $$(4 - 13x)^2 = \left(\frac{1019}{349}\right)^2 = \frac{1038361}{121801}.$$

Subtracting each of these from 10, we have the third and fourth of the required parts of 10, namely

$$\frac{185754}{121801},\ \frac{179649}{121801}.$$

Now 96 is the sum of three numbers, each of which is 1 less than a cube;

therefore we have to find three numbers such that each of them is a cube less 1, and the sum of the three is a square.

Let the sides of the cubes[1] be $m+1$, $2-m$, 2, whence the numbers are m^3+3m^2+3m, $7-12m+6m^2-m^3$, 7; their sum $=9m^2-9m+14=$ a square $=(3m-4)^2$, say;

therefore $m=\frac{2}{15}$,

and the numbers are $\frac{1538}{3375}$, $\frac{18577}{3375}$, 7.

Reverting to the original problem, we put x for the sum of the numbers, and for the numbers respectively

$$\tfrac{1538}{3375}x^3,\ \tfrac{18577}{3375}x^3,\ 7x^3,$$

whence $\frac{43740}{3375}x^3=x$,

that is (if we divide out by 15 and by x),

$$2916x^2=225, \text{ and } x=\tfrac{15}{54}.$$

The numbers are therefore found.

16. To find three numbers such that the cube of their sum *minus* any one of them gives a cube.

Let the sum be x, and the numbers $\frac{7}{8}x^3$, $\frac{26}{27}x^3$, $\frac{63}{64}x^3$.

Therefore $\frac{4877}{1728}x^3=x$,

and, if $\frac{4877}{1728}$ were the ratio of a square to a square, the problem would be solved.

But $\frac{4877}{1728}=3-$(the sum of three cubes).

Therefore we must find three cubes, each of which <1, and such that $(3-\text{their sum})=$ a square.

If, *a fortiori*, the sum of the three cubes is made <1, the square will be >2. Let[2] it be $2\frac{1}{4}$.

[1] If a^3, b^3, c^3 are the three cubes, so that $a^3+b^3+c^3-3$ has to be a square, Diophantus chooses c^3 arbitrarily (8) and then makes such assumptions for the sides of a^3, b^3, being linear expressions in m, that, in the expression to be turned into a square, the coefficient of m^3 vanishes, and that of m^2 is a square. If $a=m$, the condition is satisfied by putting $b=3k^2-m$, where k is any number.

[2] Bachet, finding no way of hitting upon $2\frac{1}{4}$ as the particular square to be taken in order that the difference between it and 3 may be separable into three cubes, and observing that he could not solve the problem if he took another arbitrary square between 2 and 3, *e.g.* $2\frac{7}{9}$, instead of $2\frac{1}{4}$, concluded that Diophantus must have hit upon $2\frac{1}{4}$, which does enable the problem to be solved, by accident.

Fermat would not admit this and considered that the method used by Diophantus for finding $2\frac{1}{4}$ as the square to be taken should not be difficult to discover. Fermat accordingly suggested a method as follows.

Let $x-1$ be the side of the required square lying between 2 and 3. Then $3-(x-1)^2=2+2x-x^2$, and this has to be separated into three cubes. Fermat assumes for the sides

We have therefore to find three cubes the sum of which $= \frac{3}{4}$ or $\frac{162}{216}$;

that is, we have to divide 162 into three cubes.

But $162 = 125 + 64 - 27$;

and "we have it in the Porisms" that *the difference of two cubes can be transformed into the sum of two cubes*[1].

Having thus found the three cubes[2], we start again, and $x = 2\frac{1}{4}x^3$, so that $x = \frac{2}{3}$.

The three numbers are thus determined.

---

of two of the required cubes two linear expressions in x such that, when the sum of their cubes is subtracted from $2 + 2x - x^2$, the result only contains terms in x^2 and x^3 or in x and units.

The first alternative is secured if the sides of the first and second cubes are $1 - \frac{1}{3}x$ and $1 + x$ respectively; for

$$2 + 2x - x^2 - \left(1 - \frac{1}{3}x\right)^3 - (1 + x)^3 = -4\frac{1}{3}x^2 - \frac{26}{27}x^3.$$

This latter expression has to be made a cube, for which purpose we put

$$-4\frac{1}{3}x^2 - \frac{26}{27}x^3 = -\frac{m^3x^3}{27}, \text{ say,}$$

which gives a value for x. We have only to see that this value makes $\frac{1}{3}x$ less than 1, and we can easily choose m so as to fulfil this condition.

[*E.g.* suppose $m = 5$, and we find $x = \frac{13}{11}$, so that

$$\frac{1}{3}x = \frac{13}{33}, \quad 1 - \frac{1}{3}x = \frac{20}{33}, \quad 1 + x = \frac{72}{33},$$

and the side of the third cube is $-\frac{65}{33}$.

The square $(x-1)^2 = \left(\frac{2}{11}\right)^2$, and in fact $3 - \left\{\left(\frac{20}{33}\right)^3 + \left(\frac{72}{33}\right)^3 - \left(\frac{65}{33}\right)^3\right\} = \left(\frac{2}{11}\right)^2$.]

We then have three cubes which make up the excess of 3 over a certain square; but, while the first of these cubes is < 1, the second is > 1 and the third is negative. Hence we must, like Diophantus, proceed to transform the difference between the two latter cubes into the sum of two other cubes.

It will, however, be seen by trial that even Fermat's method is not quite general, for it will not, as a matter of fact, give the particular solution obtained by Diophantus in which the square is $2\frac{1}{4}$.

[1] On the transformation of the difference of two cubes into the sum of two cubes, see pp. 101–3, *ante*.

[2] Vieta's rule gives $4^3 - 3^3 = \left(\frac{303}{91}\right)^3 + \left(\frac{40}{91}\right)^3$. It follows that

$$\frac{3}{4} = \frac{162}{216} = \left(\frac{5}{6}\right)^3 + \left(\frac{101}{182}\right)^3 + \left(\frac{20}{273}\right)^3;$$

and, since $x^3 = \frac{8}{27}$, the required numbers are

$$\frac{91}{216} \cdot \frac{8}{27}, \quad \frac{4998267}{6028568} \cdot \frac{8}{27}, \quad \frac{20338417}{20346417} \cdot \frac{8}{27}.$$

17. To find three numbers such that each of them *minus* the cube of their sum gives a cube.

Let the sum be x and the numbers $2x^3$, $9x^3$, $28x^3$.

Therefore $39x^2 = 1$;

and we must replace 39 by a square which is the sum of three cubes + 3;

therefore we must find three cubes such that their sum + 3 is a square.

Let their sides[1] be m, $3 - m$, and any number, say 1.

Therefore $9m^2 + 31 - 27m =$ a square $= (3m - 7)^2$, say, so that $m = \frac{6}{5}$, and the sides of the cubes are $\frac{6}{5}$, $\frac{9}{5}$, 1.

Starting again, we put x for the sum, and for the numbers $\frac{341}{125}x^3$, $\frac{854}{125}x^3$, $\frac{250}{125}x^3$,

whence $1445x^2 = 125$, $x^2 = \frac{25}{289}$, and $x = \frac{5}{17}$.

The required numbers are thus found.

18. To find three numbers such that their sum is a square and the cube of their sum added to any one of them gives a square.

Let the sum be x^2 and the numbers $3x^6$, $8x^6$, $15x^6$.

It follows that $26x^4 = 1$; and, if 26 were a fourth power, the problem would be solved.

To replace it by a fourth power, we have to find three numbers such that each increased by 1 gives a square, while the sum of the three gives a fourth power.

Let these numbers be $m^4 - 2m^2$, $m^2 + 2m$, $m^2 - 2m$ [the sum being m^4]; these are indeterminate numbers satisfying the conditions.

Putting any number, say 3, for m, we have as the required auxiliary numbers 63, 15, 3.

Starting again, we put x^2 for the sum and $3x^6$, $15x^6$, $63x^6$ for the required numbers,

and we have $81x^6 = x^2$, so that $x = \frac{1}{3}$.

The numbers are thus found $\left(\frac{3}{729}, \frac{15}{729}, \frac{63}{729}\right)$.

19. To find three numbers such that their sum is a square and the cube of their sum *minus* any one of them gives a square.

[There is obviously a lacuna in the text after this enunciation; for the next words are "And we have *again* to divide 2 *as before*,"

[1] Cf. note on V. 15. In this case, if one of the cubes is chosen arbitrarily and m^3 is another, we have only to put $(3k^2 - m)$ for the side of the third cube in order that, in the expression to be made a square, the term in m^3 may vanish, and the term in m^2 may be a square.

whereas there is nothing in our text to which they can refer, and the lines which follow are clearly no part of the solution of V. 19.

Bachet first noticed the probability that three problems intervened between V. 19 and V. 20, and he gave solutions of them. But he seems to have failed to observe that the eight lines or so in the text between the enunciation of V. 19 and the enunciation of V. 20 belonged to the solution of the last of the three missing problems. The first of the missing problems is connected with V. 18 and 19, making a natural trio with them, while the second and third similarly make with V. 20 a set of three. The enunciations were doubtless somewhat as follows.

19 *a*. To find three numbers such that their sum is a square and any one of them *minus* the cube of their sum gives a square.

19 *b*. To find three numbers such that their sum is a given number and the cube of their sum *plus* any one of them gives a square.

19 *c*. To find three numbers such that their sum is a given number and the cube of their sum *minus* any one of them gives a square.

The words then in the text after the enunciation of V. 19 evidently belong to this last problem.]

The given sum is 2, the cube of which is 8.

We have to subtract each of the numbers from 8 and thereby make a square.

Therefore we have to divide 22 into three squares, each of which is greater than 6;

after which, by subtracting each of the squares from 8, we find the required numbers.

But we have already shown [cf. V. 11] how to divide 22 into three squares, each of which is greater than 6— and less than 8, Diophantus should have added.

[The above is explained by the fact that, by addition, three times the cube of the sum *minus* the sum itself is the sum of three squares, and three times the cube of the sum *minus* the sum $= 3 . 8 - 2 = 22$.][1]

[1] Wertheim adds a solution in Diophantus' manner. We have to find what small fraction of the form $\frac{1}{x^2}$ we have to add to $\frac{22}{3}$ or $\frac{66}{9}$, and therefore to 66, in order to make a square. In order that $66 + \frac{1}{x^2}$ may be a square, we put

$$66x^2 + 1 = \text{square} = (1 + 8x)^2, \text{ say,}$$

which gives

$$x = 8 \text{ and } x^2 = 64.$$

20. To divide a given fraction into three parts such that any one of them *minus* the cube of their sum gives a square.

Given fraction $\frac{1}{4}$.

Therefore each part $= \frac{1}{64} +$ a square.

Therefore the sum of the three $= \frac{1}{4} =$ the sum of three squares $+ \frac{3}{64}$.

Hence we have to divide $\frac{13}{64}$ into three squares, "which is easy[1]."

21. To find three squares such that their continued product added to any one of them gives a square.

Let the "solid content" $= x^2$.

We want now three squares, each of which increased by 1 gives a square.

They can be got from right-angled triangles[2] by dividing the square of one of the sides about the right angle by the square of the other.

Let the squares then be

$$\frac{9}{16}x^2,\ \frac{25}{144}x^2,\ \frac{64}{225}x^2.$$

The continued product $= \frac{14400}{518400}x^6 = x^2$, by hypothesis.

Therefore $\frac{120}{720}x^2 = 1$; and, if $\frac{120}{720}$ were a square, the problem would be solved.

We have therefore to increase 66 by $\frac{1}{64}$, and therefore $7\frac{1}{3}$ by $\frac{1}{576}$, in order to make a square. And in fact $7\frac{1}{3} + \frac{1}{576} = \left(\frac{65}{24}\right)^2$.

Next, since $22 = 3^2 + 3^2 + 2^2$, and $65 - 48 = 17$, while $72 - 65 = 7$, we put

$$22 = (3 - 7x)^2 + (3 - 7x)^2 + (2 + 17x)^2,$$

and

$$x = \frac{16}{387}.$$

Therefore the sides of the squares are $\frac{1049}{387}, \frac{1049}{387}, \frac{1046}{387}$,

the squares themselves $\frac{1100401}{149769}, \frac{1100401}{149769}, \frac{1094116}{149769}$,

and the required parts of 2 are $\frac{97751}{149769}, \frac{97751}{149769}, \frac{104036}{149769}$.

[1] As Wertheim observes, $\frac{13}{64} = \frac{9}{64} + \frac{1}{25} + \frac{9}{400}$, and the required fractions into which $\frac{1}{4}$ is divided are $\frac{250}{1600}, \frac{89}{1600}, \frac{61}{1600}$.

[2] If a, b be the perpendiculars, c the hypotenuse in a right-angled triangle,

$$\frac{a^2}{b^2} + 1 = \frac{c^2}{b^2} = \text{a square}.$$

Diophantus uses the triangles (3, 4, 5), (5, 12, 13), (8, 15, 17).

As it is not, we must find three right-angled triangles such that, if b's are their bases, and p's are their perpendiculars, $p_1 p_2 p_3 b_1 b_2 b_3 =$ a square;

and, if we assume one triangle arbitrarily (3, 4, 5), we have to make $12 p_1 p_2 b_1 b_2$ a square, or $3 p_1 b_1 / p_2 b_2$ a square.

"This is easy[1]," and the three triangles are (3, 4, 5), (9, 40, 41), (8, 15, 17) or similar to them.

[1] Diophantus does not give the work here, but only the result. Bachet obtains it in this way. Suppose it required to find three rational right-angled triangles (h_1, p_1, b_1), (h_2, p_2, b_2) and (h_3, p_3, b_3) such that $p_1 p_2 p_3 / b_1 b_2 b_3$ is the ratio of a square to a square. One triangle (h_1, p_1, b_1) being chosen arbitrarily, form two others by putting

$$h_2 = h_1^2 + p_1^2, \quad p_2 = h_1^2 - p_1^2 = b_1^2, \quad b_2 = 2 h_1 p_1,$$
$$h_3 = h_1^2 + b_1^2, \quad p_3 = h_1^2 - b_1^2 = p_1^2, \quad b_3 = 2 h_1 b_1,$$

and we have

$$\frac{p_1 p_2 p_3}{b_1 b_2 b_3} = \left(\frac{p_1}{2h_1}\right)^2 = \text{a square}.$$

If now $h_1 = 5$, $p_1 = 4$, $b_1 = 3$, the triangles (h_2, p_2, b_2) and (h_3, p_3, b_3) are (41, 9, 40) and (34, 16, 30) respectively. Dividing the sides of the latter throughout by 2 (which does not alter the ratio), we have Diophantus' second and third triangles (9, 40, 41) and (8, 15, 17).

Fermat, in his note on the problem, gives the following general rule for finding two right-angled triangles the areas of which are in the ratio $m : n$ $(m > n)$.

Form (1) the greater triangle from $2m + n$, $m - n$, and the lesser from $m + 2n$, $m - n$,
or (2) the greater from $2m - n$, $m + n$, the lesser from $2n - m$, $m + n$,
or (3) the greater from $6m$, $2m - n$, the lesser from $4m + n$, $4m - 2n$,
or (4) the greater from $m + 4n$, $2m - 4n$, the lesser from $6n$, $m - 2n$.

The alternative (2) gives Diophantus' solution if we put $m = 3$, $n = 1$ and substitute $m - 2n$ for $2n - m$.

Fermat continues as follows: We can deduce a method of finding *three* right-angled triangles the areas of which are in the ratio of three given numbers, provided that the sum of two of these numbers is equal to four times the third. Suppose *e.g.* that m, n, q are three numbers such that $m + q = 4n$ $(m > q)$. Now form the following triangles:

(1) from $m + 4n$, $2m - 4n$,
(2) from $6n$, $m - 2n$,
(3) from $4n + q$, $4n - 2q$.

[If A_1, A_2, A_3 be the areas, we have, as a matter of fact,

$$A_1/m = A_2/n = A_3/q = -6m^3 + 36m^2 n + 144mn^2 - 384n^3.]$$

We can derive, says Fermat, a method of *finding three right-angled triangles the areas of which themselves form a right-angled triangle.* For we have only to find a triangle such that the sum of the base and hypotenuse is four times the perpendicular. This is easy, and the triangle will be similar to (17, 15, 8); the three triangles will then be formed

(1) from $17 + 4 \cdot 8$, $2 \cdot 17 - 4 \cdot 8$ or 49, 2,
(2) from $6 \cdot 8$, $17 - 2 \cdot 8$ or 48, 1,
(3) from $4 \cdot 8 + 15$, $4 \cdot 8 - 2 \cdot 15$ or 47, 2.

[The areas of the three right-angled triangles are in fact 234906, 110544 and 207270, and these numbers form the sides of a right-angled triangle.]

Hence also we can derive a method of *finding three right-angled triangles the areas of which are in the ratio of three given squares such that the sum of two of them is equal to*

Starting again, we put for the squares

$$\frac{9}{16}x^2, \ \frac{225}{64}x^2, \ \frac{81}{1600}x^2.$$

Equating the product of these to x^2, we find x to be rational [$x = \frac{16}{9}$, and the squares are $\frac{16}{9}, \frac{100}{9}, \frac{4}{25}$].

22. To find three squares such that their continued product *minus* any one of them gives a square.

Let the solid content be x^2, and let the numbers be obtained from right-angled triangles, being

$$\frac{16}{25}x^2, \ \frac{25}{169}x^2, \ \frac{64}{289}x^2.$$

Therefore the continued product $\left(\frac{4 \cdot 5 \cdot 8}{5 \cdot 13 \cdot 17}\right)^2 x^6 = x^2$,

or
$$\left(\frac{4 \cdot 5 \cdot 8}{5 \cdot 13 \cdot 17}\right)^2 x^4 = \frac{25600}{1221025} x^4 = 1.$$

If then $\frac{25600}{1221025}$ were a fourth power, *i.e.* if $\frac{4 \cdot 5 \cdot 8}{5 \cdot 13 \cdot 17}$ were a square, the problem would be solved.

We have therefore to find three right-angled triangles with hypotenuses h_1, h_2, h_3 respectively, and with p_1, p_2, p_3 as one of the perpendiculars in each respectively, such that

$$h_1 h_2 h_3 p_1 p_2 p_3 = \text{a square}.$$

Assuming one of the triangles to be (3, 4, 5), so that *e.g.* $h_3 p_3 = 5 \cdot 4 = 20$, we must have

$$5 h_1 p_1 h_2 p_2 = \text{a square}.$$

This is satisfied if $h_1 p_1 = 5 h_2 p_2$.

With a view to this we have first (cf. the last proposition) to find two right-angled triangles such that, if x_1, y_1 are the two *perpendiculars* in one and x_2, y_2 the two *perpendiculars* in the other, $x_1 y_1 = 5 x_2 y_2$. From such a pair of triangles we can form two more right-angled triangles such that the product of the *hypotenuse* and *one perpendicular* in one is five times the product of the *hypotenuse* and *one perpendicular* in the other[1].

---

four times the third, and we can also in the same way *find three right-angled triangles of the same area*; we can also *construct*, in an infinite number of ways, *two right-angled triangles the areas of which are in a given ratio*, by multiplying one of the terms of the ratio or the two terms by given squares, etc.

[1] Diophantus' procedure is only obscurely indicated in the Greek text. It was explained by Schulz in his edition (cf. Tannery in *Oeuvres de Fermat*, I. p. 323, note).

Since the triangles found satisfying the relation $x_1 y_1 = 5x_2 y_2$ are (5, 12, 13) and (3, 4, 5) respectively[1], we have in fact to find two new right-angled triangles from them, namely the triangles (h_1, p_1, b_1) and (h_2, p_2, b_2), such that

$$h_1 p_1 = 30 \text{ and } h_2 p_2 = 6,$$

the numbers 30 and 6 being the areas of the two triangles mentioned.

These triangles are $(6\frac{1}{2}, \frac{60}{13}, [\frac{119}{26}])$ and $(2\frac{1}{2}, \frac{12}{5}, [\frac{7}{10}])$ respectively.

Starting again, we take for the numbers

$$\frac{16}{25}x^2, \frac{576}{625}x^2, \frac{14400}{28561}x^2.$$

[$\frac{12}{5}$ divided by $2\frac{1}{2}$ gives $\frac{24}{25}$, and $\frac{60}{13}$ divided by $6\frac{1}{2}$ gives $\frac{120}{169}$.]

The product $= x^2$:

therefore, taking the square root, we have

$$\frac{4 \cdot 24 \cdot 120}{5 \cdot 25 \cdot 169} x^2 = 1,$$

so that $x = \frac{65}{48}$, and the required squares are found.

23. To find three squares such that each *minus* the product of the three gives a square.

Having given a rational right-angled triangle (z, x, y), Diophantus knows how to find a rational right-angled triangle (h, p, b) such that $hp = \frac{1}{2} xy$. We have in fact to put

$$h = \frac{1}{2} z, \; p = \frac{xy}{z}, \text{ whence } b^2 = h^2 - p^2 = \frac{1}{4}\left(\frac{z^4 - 4x^2y^2}{z^2}\right) = \left(\frac{x^2 - y^2}{2z}\right)^2.$$

Thus, having found two triangles (5, 12, 13) and (3, 4, 5) with areas in the ratio of 5 to 1 (see next paragraph of text with note thereon), Diophantus takes

$$h_1 = \frac{1}{2} \cdot 13 = 6\tfrac{1}{2}, \; p_1 = \frac{5 \cdot 12}{13} = \frac{60}{13}; \text{ and similarly } h_2 = \frac{1}{2} \cdot 5 = 2\tfrac{1}{2}, \; p_2 = \frac{3 \cdot 4}{5} = \frac{12}{5}.$$

Cossali (after Bachet) gives a formula for three right-angled triangles such that the solid content of the three hypotenuses has to the solid content of three perpendiculars (one in each triangle) the ratio of a square to a square; his triangles are

$$(1)\; i, b, p \; [i = \text{ipotenusa}], \qquad (2)\; \frac{4p^2 + b^2}{b}, \frac{4p^2 - b^2}{b}, \frac{4bp}{b} = 4p,$$

$$(3)\; \frac{ib^2 + 4ip^2}{b}, \frac{b \cdot 4bp + p(4p^2 - b^2)}{b}, \frac{p \cdot 4bp - b(4p^2 - b^2)}{b} = b^2,$$

and, in fact,

$$\frac{i(b^2 + 4p^2)(ib^2 + 4ip^2)}{b^2} : p \cdot 4p \cdot b^2 = \frac{i^2(b^2 + 4p^2)^2}{b^2} : 4p^2b^2.$$

If $i = 5$, $b = 4$, $p = 3$, we can get from this triangle the triangles (13, 5, 12) and (65, 63, 16), and our equation is $\frac{3 \cdot 12 \cdot 16}{5 \cdot 13 \cdot 65} x^2 = 1$.

[1] These triangles can be obtained by putting $m = 5$, $n = 1$ in Fermat's *fourth* formula (note on last proposition). By that formula the triangles are formed from (9, 6) and (6, 3) respectively; and, dividing out by 3, we form the triangles from (3, 2) and (2, 1) respectively.

Let the "solid content" be x^2, and let the squares be formed from right-angled triangles, as before.

If we take the same triangles as those found in the last problem and put for the three squares

$$\frac{25}{16}x^2,\ \frac{625}{576}x^2,\ \frac{28561}{14400}x^2,$$

each of these *minus* the continued product (x^2) gives a square.

It remains that their product $=x^2$;

this gives $x=\frac{48}{65}$, and the problem is solved.

24. To find three squares such that the product of any two increased by 1 gives a square.

Product of first and second $+1=$ a square, and the third is a square; therefore "solid content" $+$ each $=$ a square.

The problem therefore reduces to V. 21 above[1].

[1] De Billy in the *Inventum Novum*, Part II. paragraph 28 (*Oeuvres de Fermat*, III. pp. 373–4), extends this problem, showing how to find *four* numbers, three of which (only) are squares, having the given property, *i.e.* to solve the equations

$$x_2^2x_3^2+1=r^2,\quad x_1^2x_4+1=u^2,$$
$$x_3^2x_1^2+1=s^2,\quad x_2^2x_4+1=v^2,$$
$$x_1^2x_2^2+1=t^2,\quad x_3^2x_4+1=w^2.$$

First seek three square numbers satisfying the conditions of Diophantus' problem V. 24, say $\left(\frac{9}{16},\ \frac{25}{4},\ \frac{256}{81}\right)$, the solution of V. 21 given in Bachet's edition. We have then to find a fourth number (x, say) such that

$$\left.\begin{array}{l}\frac{9}{16}x+1\\ \frac{25}{4}x+1\\ \frac{256}{81}x+1\end{array}\right\}\text{ are all squares.}$$

Substitute $\frac{16}{9}y^2+\frac{32}{9}y$ for x, so as to make the first expression a square. We have then to solve the double-equation

$$\left.\begin{array}{l}\frac{100}{9}y^2+\frac{200}{9}y+1=u^2\\ \frac{4096}{729}y^2+\frac{8192}{729}y+1=v^2\end{array}\right\},$$

which can be solved by the ordinary method.

De Billy does not give the solution, but it may be easily supplied thus.

The difference $$=\left(\frac{10}{3}+\frac{64}{27}\right)\left(\frac{10}{3}-\frac{64}{27}\right)(y^2+2y)$$
$$=\frac{154}{27}y\left(\frac{26}{27}y+\frac{2\cdot 26}{27}\right).$$

25. To find three squares such that the product of any two *minus* 1 gives a square.

This reduces, similarly, to V. 22 above.

26. To find three squares such that, if we subtract the product of any two of them from unity, the result is a square.

This again reduces to an earlier problem, V. 23.

27. Given a number, to find three squares such that the sum of any two added to the given number makes a square.

Given number 15.

Let one of the required squares be 9;

I have then to find two other squares such that each $+24=$ a square, and their sum $+15=$ a square.

To find two squares, each of which $+24=$ a square, take two pairs of numbers which have 24 for their product[1].

Let one pair of factors be $4/x$, $6x$, and let the side of one square be half their difference or $\frac{2}{x}-3x$.

Let the other pair of factors be $3/x$, $8x$, and let the side of the other square be half their difference or $\frac{1\frac{1}{2}}{x}-4x$.

Therefore each of the squares $+24$ gives a square.

It remains that their sum $+15=$ a square;

therefore $\left(\frac{1\frac{1}{2}}{x}-4x\right)^2+\left(\frac{2}{x}-3x\right)^2+15=$ a square,

---

Equating the square of half the sum of the factors to the larger expression, we have

$$\left(\frac{10}{3}y+\frac{26}{27}\right)^2=\frac{100}{9}y^2+\frac{200}{9}y+1,$$

whence $$y=-\frac{53}{11520}, \text{ and } y^2+2y=-\frac{1218311}{(11520)^2}.$$

Therefore $x=\frac{16}{9}(y^2+2y)=-\frac{1218311}{74649600}$, which satisfies the equations. In fact $\frac{9}{16}x+1=\left(\frac{11467}{11520}\right)^2$, $\frac{25}{4}x+1=\left(\frac{3275}{3456}\right)^2$, and $\frac{256}{81}x+1=\left(\frac{4733}{4860}\right)^2$.

But even here, as the value of x which we have found is negative, we ought, strictly speaking, to deduce a further value by substituting $y-\frac{1218311}{74649600}$ for x in the equations and solving again, which would of course lead to very large numbers.

[1] The text adds the words "and [let us take] sides about the right angle in a right-angled triangle." I think these words must be a careless interpolation: they are not wanted and give no sense; nor do they occur in the corresponding place in the next problem.

or $$\frac{6\frac{1}{4}}{x^2}+25x^2-9=\text{a square}=25x^2,\text{ say.}$$

Therefore $x=\frac{5}{6}$, and the problem is solved[1].

28. Given a number, to find three squares such that the sum of any two *minus* the given number makes a square.

Given number 13.

Let one of the squares be 25;

I have then to find two other squares such that each $+12=$ a square, and (sum of both) $-13=$ a square.

Divide 12 into factors in two ways, and let the factors be $(3x, 4/x)$ and $(4x, 3/x)$.

Take as the sides of the squares half the differences of the factors, *i.e.* let the squares be

$$\left(1\tfrac{1}{2}x-\frac{2}{x}\right)^2,\ \left(2x-\frac{1\frac{1}{2}}{x}\right)^2.$$

Each of these $+12$ gives a square.

It remains that the sum of the squares $-13=$ a square,

or $\frac{6\frac{1}{4}}{x^2}+6\frac{1}{4}x^2-25=\text{a square}=\frac{6\frac{1}{4}}{x^2}$, say.

Therefore $x=2$, and the problem is solved[2].

[1] Diophantus has found values of ξ, η, ζ satisfying the equations

$$\left.\begin{aligned}\eta^2+\zeta^2+a&=u^2\\ \zeta^2+\xi^2+a&=v^2\\ \xi^2+\eta^2+a&=w^2\end{aligned}\right\}.$$

Fermat shows how to find *four* numbers (not squares) satisfying the corresponding conditions, namely that the sum of any two added to a shall give a square. Suppose $a=15$.

Take three numbers satisfying the conditions of Diophantus' problem, say 9, $\frac{1}{100}$, $\frac{529}{225}$.

Assume x^2-15 as the first of the four required numbers; and let the second be $6x+9$ (because 9 is one of the square numbers taken and 6 is twice its side); for the same reason let the third number be $\frac{1}{5}x+\frac{1}{100}$ and the fourth $\frac{46}{15}x+\frac{529}{225}$.

Three of the conditions are now fulfilled since each of the last three numbers added to the first (x^2-15) *plus* 15 gives a square. The three remaining conditions give the triple-equation

$$6\tfrac{1}{5}x+\ \ 9+\frac{1}{100}+15=6\tfrac{1}{5}x+\left(\frac{49}{10}\right)^2=u^2,$$
$$\frac{136}{15}x+\ \ 9+\frac{529}{225}+15=\frac{136}{15}x+\left(\frac{77}{15}\right)^2=v^2,$$
$$\frac{49}{15}x+\frac{1}{100}+\frac{529}{225}+15=\frac{49}{15}x+\left(\frac{25}{6}\right)^2=w^2.$$

[2] Fermat observes that *four* numbers (not squares) with the property indicated can be found by the same procedure as that shown in the note to the preceding problem.

If a is the given number, put x^2+a for the first of the four required numbers.

29. To find three squares such that the sum of their squares is a square.

Let the squares be x^2, 4, 9 respectively[1].

Therefore $x^4 + 97$ = a square $= (x^2 - 10)^2$, say;

whence $x^2 = \frac{3}{20}$.

If the ratio of 3 to 20 were the ratio of a square to a square, the problem would be solved; but it is not.

Therefore *I have to find two squares* (p^2, q^2, *say*) *and a number* (m, *say*) *such that* $m^2 - p^4 - q^4$ *has to* $2m$ *the ratio of a square to a square.*

Let $p^2 = z^2$, $q^2 = 4$ and $m = z^2 + 4$.

Therefore $m^2 - p^4 - q^4 = (z^2 + 4)^2 - z^4 - 16 = 8z^2$.

Hence $8z^2/(2z^2 + 8)$, or $4z^2/(z^2 + 4)$, must be the ratio of a square to a square.

Put $$z^2 + 4 = (z + 1)^2, \text{ say};$$

therefore $z = 1\frac{1}{2}$, and the squares are $p^2 = 2\frac{1}{4}$, $q^2 = 4$, while $m = 6\frac{1}{4}$;

or, if we take 4 times each, $p^2 = 9$, $q^2 = 16$, $m = 25$.

Starting again, we put for the squares x^2, 9, 16;

then the sum of the squares $= x^4 + 337 = (x^2 - 25)^2$, and $x = \frac{12}{5}$.

The required squares are $\frac{144}{25}$, 9, 16.

30. [The enunciation of this problem is in the form of an epigram, the meaning of which is as follows.]

A man buys a certain number of measures (χόες) of wine, some at 8 drachmas, some at 5 drachmas each. He pays for them a *square* number of drachmas; and if we add 60 to this number, the result is a square, the side of which is equal to the whole number of measures. Find how many he bought at each price.

Let x = the whole number of measures; therefore $x^2 - 60$ was the price paid, which is a square $= (x - m)^2$, say.

If now k^2, l^2, m^2 represent three numbers satisfying the conditions of the present problem of Diophantus, put for the second of the required numbers $2kx + k^2$, for the third $2lx + l^2$, and for the fourth $2mx + m^2$. These satisfy three conditions, since each of the last three numbers added to the first $(x^2 + a)$ less the number a gives a square. The remaining three conditions give a triple-equation.

1 "Why," says Fermat, "does not Diophantus seek *two* fourth powers such that their sum is a square? This problem is in fact impossible, as by my method I am in a position to prove with all rigour." It is probable that Diophantus knew the fact without being able to prove it generally. That neither the sum nor the difference of two fourth powers can be a square was proved by Euler (*Commentationes arithmeticae*, I. pp. 24 sqq., and *Algebra*, Part II. c. XIII.).

Now $\frac{1}{5}$ of the price of the five-drachma measures $+ \frac{1}{8}$ of the price of the eight-drachma measures $= x$;

so that $x^2 - 60$, the total price, has to be divided into two parts such that $\frac{1}{5}$ of one $+ \frac{1}{8}$ of the other $= x$.

We cannot have a real solution of this unless

$$x > \tfrac{1}{8}(x^2 - 60) \text{ and } < \tfrac{1}{5}(x^2 - 60).$$

Therefore $\qquad 5x < x^2 - 60 < 8x.$

(1) Since $\qquad x^2 > 5x + 60,$

$x^2 = 5x +$ a number greater than 60,

whence x is[1] *not less than* 11.

(2) $\qquad x^2 < 8x + 60$

or $\qquad x^2 = 8x +$ some number less than 60,

whence x is[1] *not greater than* 12.

Therefore $\qquad 11 < x < 12.$

Now (from above) $x = (m^2 + 60)/2m$;

therefore $22m < m^2 + 60 < 24m$.

Thus (1) $\quad 22m = m^2 +$ (some number less than 60),

and therefore m is[2] *not less than* 19.

(2) $\quad 24m = m^2 +$ (some number greater than 60),

and therefore m is[2] *less than* 21.

Hence we put $m = 20$, and

$$x^2 - 60 = (x - 20)^2,$$

so that $x = 11\frac{1}{2}$, $x^2 = 132\frac{1}{4}$, and $x^2 - 60 = 72\frac{1}{4}$.

Thus we have to divide $72\frac{1}{4}$ into two parts such that $\frac{1}{5}$ of one part *plus* $\frac{1}{8}$ of the other $= 11\frac{1}{2}$.

Let the first part be $5z$.

Therefore $\frac{1}{8}$ (second part) $= 11\frac{1}{2} - z$,

or second part $= 92 - 8z$;

therefore $5z + 92 - 8z = 72\frac{1}{4}$,

and $z = \dfrac{79}{12}$.

Therefore the number of five-drachma χόες $= \dfrac{79}{12}$.

" " " " eight-drachma " $= \dfrac{59}{12}$.

[1] For an explanation of these limits see p. 60, *ante*.

[2] See p. 62, *ante*.

BOOK VI

1. To find a (rational) right-angled triangle such that the hypotenuse *minus* each of the sides gives a cube[1].

Let the required triangle be formed from x, 3.

Therefore hypotenuse $= x^2 + 9$, perpendicular $= 6x$, base $= x^2 - 9$.

Thus $x^2 + 9 - (x^2 - 9) = 18$ should be a cube, but it is not.

Now $18 = 2 . 3^2$; therefore we must replace 3 by m, where $2 . m^2$ is a cube; and $m = 2$.

We form, therefore, a right-angled triangle from x, 2, namely $(x^2 + 4, 4x, x^2 - 4)$; and one condition is satisfied.

The other gives $x^2 - 4x + 4 =$ a cube;

therefore $(x - 2)^2$ is a cube, or $x - 2$ is a cube $= 8$, say.

Thus $x = 10$,

and the triangle is (40, 96, 104).

2. To find a right-angled triangle such that the hypotenuse added to each side gives a cube.

Form a triangle, as before, from two numbers; and, as before, one of them must be such that twice its square is a cube, *i.e.* must be 2.

We form a triangle from x, 2, namely $x^2 + 4, 4x, 4 - x^2$; therefore $x^2 + 4x + 4$ must be a cube, while x^2 must be less than 4, or $x < 2$.

Thus $x + 2 =$ a cube which must be < 4 and $> 2 = \frac{27}{8}$, say.

Therefore $x = \frac{11}{8}$,

and the triangle is $\left(\frac{135}{64}, 5\frac{1}{2}, \frac{377}{64}\right)$,

or, if we multiply by the common denominator, (135, 352, 377).

3. To find a right-angled triangle such that its area added to a given number makes a square.

Let 5 be the given number, $(3x, 4x, 5x)$ the required triangle.

[1] Diophantus' expressions are ὁ ἐν τῇ ὑποτεινούσῃ, "the (*number*) in (or representing) the hypotenuse," ὁ ἐν ἑκατέρᾳ τῶν ὀρθῶν, "the (*number*) in (or representing) each of the perpendicular sides," ὁ ἐν τῷ ἐμβαδῷ, "the (*number*) in (or representing) the area," etc. It will be convenient to say "the hypotenuse," etc. simply. It will be observed that, as between the numbers representing sides and area, all idea of dimension is ignored.

Therefore $6x^2 + 5 = \text{a square} = 9x^2$, say,

or $3x^2 = 5$.

But 3 should have to 5 the ratio of a square to a square.

Therefore we must find a right-angled triangle and a number such that the difference between the square of the number and the area of the triangle has to 5 the ratio of a square to a square, *i.e.* $= \frac{1}{5}$ of a square.

Form a right-angled triangle from $\left(m, \frac{1}{m}\right)$;

thus the area is $m^2 - \frac{1}{m^2}$.

Let the number be $m + \frac{2 \cdot 5}{m}$, so that we must have

$$4 \cdot 5 + \frac{101}{m^2} = \tfrac{1}{5} \text{ of a square};$$

therefore $4 \cdot 25 + \frac{505}{m^2} = \text{a square}$,

or $100m^2 + 505 = \text{a square} = (10m + 5)^2$, say,

and $m = \frac{24}{5}$.

The auxiliary triangle must therefore be formed from $\frac{24}{5}$, $\frac{5}{24}$, and the auxiliary number sought is $\frac{413}{60}$.

Put now for the original triangle (hx, px, bx), where (h, p, b) is the right-angled triangle formed from $\frac{24}{5}, \frac{5}{24}$;

this gives $\frac{1}{2}pbx^2 + 5 = \frac{170569}{3600}x^2$,

and we have the solution.

[The perpendicular sides of the right-angled triangle are

$$\left(\frac{24^2}{5^2} - \frac{5^2}{24^2}\right)x = \frac{331151}{14400}x \text{ and } 2x,$$

whence $\frac{331151}{14400}x^2 + 5 = \frac{170569}{3600}x^2$,

$$x = \frac{24}{53},$$

and the triangle is

$$\left(\frac{331151}{31800}, \frac{48}{53}, \frac{332401}{31800}\right).]$$

4. To find a right-angled triangle such that its area *minus* a given number makes a square.

Given number 6, triangle $(3x, 4x, 5x)$, say.

Therefore $6x^2 - 6 = \text{square} = 4x^2$, say.

Thus, in this case, we must find a right-angled triangle and a number such that

$$(\text{area of triangle}) - (\text{number})^2 = \tfrac{1}{6} \text{ of a square}.$$

Form a triangle from $m, \frac{1}{m}$.

Its area is $m^2 - \frac{1}{m^2}$, and let the number be $m - \frac{6}{2} . \frac{1}{m}$.

Therefore $6 - \frac{10}{m^2} = \frac{1}{6}$ (a square),

or $36m^2 - 60 =$ a square $= (6m-2)^2$, say.

Therefore $m = \frac{8}{3}$, and the auxiliary triangle is formed from $(\frac{8}{3}, \frac{3}{8})$, the auxiliary number being $\frac{37}{24}$.

We start again, substituting for 3, 4, 5 in the original hypothesis the sides of the auxiliary triangle just found, and putting $(\frac{37}{24})^2 x^2$ in place of $4x^2$; and the solution is obvious.

[The auxiliary triangle is $(\frac{4015}{576}, 2, \frac{4177}{576})$, whence

$$\frac{4015}{576}x^2 - 6 = (\frac{37}{24})^2 x^2, \text{ and } x = \frac{8}{7},$$

so that the required triangle is $(\frac{4015}{504}, \frac{16}{7}, \frac{4177}{504})$.]

5. To find a right-angled triangle such that, if its area be subtracted from a given number, the remainder is a square.

Given number 10, triangle $(3x, 4x, 5x)$, say.

Thus $10 - 6x^2 =$ a square; and we have to find a right-angled triangle and a number such that

$$\text{(area of triangle)} + (\text{number})^2 = \tfrac{1}{10} \text{ of a square.}$$

Form a triangle from $m, \frac{1}{m}$, the area being $m^2 - \frac{1}{m^2}$, and let the number be $\frac{1}{m} + 5m$.

Therefore $26m^2 + 10 = \frac{1}{10}$ of a square,

or $260m^2 + 100 =$ a square,

or again $65m^2 + 25 =$ a square $= (8m+5)^2$, say,

whence $m = 80$.

The rest is obvious.

[The required triangle is $\frac{40959999}{825600}, \frac{2}{129}, \frac{40960001}{825600}$.]

6. To find a right-angled triangle such that the area added to one of the perpendiculars makes a given number.

Given number 7, triangle $(3x, 4x, 5x)$.

Therefore $6x^2 + 3x = 7$.

In order that this might be solved, it would be necessary that (half coefficient of x)^2 + product of coefficient of x^2 and absolute term should be a square;

but $(1\frac{1}{2})^2 + 6 . 7$ is not a square.

Hence we must find, to replace (3, 4, 5), a right-angled triangle such that

$$(\tfrac{1}{2} \text{ one perpendicular})^2 + 7 \text{ times area} = \text{a square.}$$

Let one perpendicular be m, the other 1.

Therefore $3\frac{1}{2}m + \frac{1}{4} =$ a square, or $14m + 1 =$ a square.
Also, since the triangle is rational, $m^2 + 1 =$ a square.

The difference $m^2 - 14m = m(m - 14)$;
and putting, as usual, $7^2 = 14m + 1$,
we have $m = \frac{24}{7}$.
The auxiliary triangle is therefore $(\frac{24}{7}, 1, \frac{25}{7})$ or $(24, 7, 25)$.
Starting afresh, we take as the triangle $(24x, 7x, 25x)$.
Therefore $84x^2 + 7x = 7$,
and $x = \frac{1}{4}$.

We have then $\left(6, \frac{7}{4}, \frac{25}{4}\right)$ as the solution[1].

7. To find a right-angled triangle such that its area *minus* one of the perpendiculars is a given number.

Given number 7.
As before, we have to find a right-angled triangle such that

$$(\tfrac{1}{2} \text{ one perpendicular})^2 + 7 \text{ times area} = \text{a square};$$

this triangle is $(7, 24, 25)$.
Let then the triangle of the problem be $(7x, 24x, 25x)$.
Therefore $84x^2 - 7x = 7$,

$$x = \tfrac{1}{3},$$

and the problem is solved[2].

[1] Fermat observes that this problem and the next can be solved by another method. "Form in this case," he says, "a triangle from the given number and 1, and divide the sides by the sum of the given number and 1; the quotients will give the required triangle."

In fact, if we take as the sides of the required triangle

$$(a^2+1)\,x,\ (a^2-1)\,x,\ 2ax,$$

where a is the given number, we have

$$(a^2-1)\,ax^2 + 2ax = a,$$

one root of which is
$$x = -\frac{1}{a^2-1} + \frac{a}{a^2-1} = \frac{1}{a+1},$$

and the sides of the required triangle are therefore

$$\frac{a^2+1}{a+1},\ \frac{a^2-1}{a+1},\ \frac{2a}{a+1}.$$

The solution is really the same as that of Diophantus.

[2] Similarly in this case we may, with Fermat, form the triangle from the given number and 1, and divide the sides by the difference between the given number and 1, and we shall have the required triangle.

In VI. 6, 7, Diophantus has found triangles ζ, ξ, η (ζ being the hypotenuse), such that

$$(1)\quad \frac{1}{2}\xi\eta + \xi = a,$$

and
$$(2)\quad \frac{1}{2}\xi\eta - \xi = a.$$

Fermat enunciates the third case

$$(3)\quad \xi - \frac{1}{2}\xi\eta = a,$$

8. To find a right-angled triangle such that the area added to the sum of the perpendiculars makes a given number.

Given number 6.

Again I have to find a right-angled triangle such that

$$(\tfrac{1}{2}\text{ sum of perpendiculars})^2 + 6 \text{ times area} = \text{a square}.$$

Let m, 1 be the perpendicular sides of this triangle;

therefore $\frac{1}{4}(m+1)^2 + 3m = \frac{1}{4}m^2 + 3\frac{1}{2}m + \frac{1}{4} = $ a square,

while $m^2 + 1$ must also be a square.

Therefore $\left.\begin{matrix} m^2 + 14m + 1 \\ m^2 + 1 \end{matrix}\right\}$ are both squares.

The difference is $2m.7$, and we put

$$m^2 - 7m + 12\tfrac{1}{4} = m^2 + 1,$$

whence $m = \frac{45}{28}$,

and the auxiliary triangle is $(\frac{45}{28}, 1, \frac{53}{28})$, or $(45, 28, 53)$.

Assume now for the triangle of the problem

$$(45x, 28x, 53x).$$

Therefore $$630x^2 + 73x = 6;$$

x is rational $[=\frac{1}{18}]$, and the solution follows.

9. To find a right-angled triangle such that the area *minus* the sum of the perpendiculars is a given number.

Given number 6.

As before, we find a subsidiary right-angled triangle such that $(\frac{1}{2}\text{sum of perpendiculars})^2 + 6 \text{ times area} = \text{a square}$.

This is found to be $(28, 45, 53)$ as before.

Taking $(28x, 45x, 53x)$ for the required triangle,

$$630x^2 - 73x = 6;$$

$x = \frac{6}{35}$, and the problem is solved[1].

10. To find a right-angled triangle such that the sum of its area, the hypotenuse, and one of the perpendiculars is a given number.

---

observing that Diophantus and Bachet appear not to have known the solution, but that it can be solved "by our method." He does not actually give the solution; but we may compare his solutions of similar problems in the *Inventum Novum*, *e.g.* those given in the notes to VI. 11 and VI. 15 below and in the Supplement. The essence of the method is that, if the first value of x found in the ordinary course is such as to give a negative value for one of the sides, we can derive from it a fresh value which will make all the sides positive.

[1] Here likewise, Diophantus having solved the problem

$$\frac{1}{2}\xi\eta - (\xi + \eta) = a,$$

Fermat enunciates, as to be solved by his method, the corresponding problem

$$\xi + \eta - \frac{1}{2}\xi\eta = a.$$

Given number 4.

If we assumed as the triangle (hx, px, bx), we should have
$$\tfrac{1}{2}pbx^2 + hx + bx = 4;$$
and, in order that the solution may be rational, we must find a right-angled triangle such that
$$\tfrac{1}{4}\,(\text{hyp.} + \text{one perp.})^2 + 4 \text{ times area} = \text{a square}.$$

Form a right-angled triangle from 1, $m + 1$.

Then $\tfrac{1}{4}\,(\text{hyp.} + \text{one perp.})^2 = \tfrac{1}{4}\,(m^2 + 2m + 2 + m^2 + 2m)^2$
$$= m^4 + 4m^3 + 6m^2 + 4m + 1,$$
and 4 times area $= 4\,(m + 1)\,(m^2 + 2m)$
$$= 4m^3 + 12m^2 + 8m.$$

Therefore

$m^4 + 8m^3 + 18m^2 + 12m + 1 = \text{a square} = (6m + 1 - m^2)^2$, say,
whence $m = \frac{4}{5}$, and the auxiliary triangle is formed from $(1, \frac{9}{5})$ or $(5, 9)$. This triangle is $(56, 90, 106)$ or $(28, 45, 53)$.

We assume therefore $28x, 45x, 53x$ for the original triangle, and we have $630x^2 + 81x = 4$.

Therefore $x = \frac{4}{105}$, and the problem is solved.

11. To find a right-angled triangle such that its area *minus* the sum of the hypotenuse and one of the perpendiculars is a given number.

Given number 4.

We have then to find an auxiliary triangle with the same property as in the last problem;

therefore $(28, 45, 53)$ will serve the purpose.

We put for the triangle of the problem $(28x, 45x, 53x)$, and we have $630x^2 - 81x = 4$;

$x = \frac{1}{6}$, and the problem is solved[1].

[1] Diophantus has in VI. 10, 11 shown us how to find a rational right-angled triangle ζ, ξ, η (ζ being the hypotenuse) such that
$$(1)\quad \frac{1}{2}\xi\eta + \zeta + \xi = a,$$
$$(2)\quad \frac{1}{2}\xi\eta - (\zeta + \xi) = a.$$

Fermat, in the *Inventum Novum*, Part III. paragraph 33 (*Oeuvres de Fermat*, III. p. 389), propounds and solves the corresponding problem
$$(3)\quad \zeta + \xi - \frac{1}{2}\xi\eta = a.$$

In the particular case taken by Fermat $a = 4$. He proceeds thus:
First find a rational right-angled triangle in which (since $a = 4$)
$$\left\{\frac{1}{2}(\zeta + \xi)\right\}^2 - 4 \cdot \frac{1}{2}\xi\eta = \text{a square}.$$

Lemma I to the following problem.

To find a right-angled triangle such that the difference of the perpendiculars is a square, the greater alone is a square, and further the area added to the lesser perpendicular gives a square.

Let the triangle be formed from two numbers, the greater perpendicular being twice their product.

Hence I must find two numbers such that (1) twice their product is a square and (2) twice their product exceeds the difference of their squares by a square.

This is true of any two numbers the greater of which = twice the lesser.

Form then the triangle from x, $2x$, and two conditions are satisfied.

The third gives $6x^4 + 3x^2 =$ a square, or $6x^2 + 3 =$ a square.

I have therefore to find a number such that 6 times its square + 3 = a square;

one such number is 1, and there are an infinite number of others[1].

If $x = 1$, the triangle is formed from 1, 2.

Suppose it formed from $x+1$, x; the sides then are

$$\zeta = 2x^2+2x+1, \quad \xi = 2x+1, \quad \eta = 2x^2+2x.$$

Thus $$\left\{\frac{1}{2}(\zeta+\xi)\right\}^2 - 4\cdot\frac{1}{2}\xi\eta = x^4+4x^3+6x^2+4x+1-4(2x^3+3x^2+x)$$
$$= x^4-4x^3-6x^2+1$$
$$= \text{a square}$$
$$= (x^2-2x+1)^2, \text{ say.}$$

Therefore $-6x^2 = 6x^2 - 4x$, $x = \frac{1}{3}$, and $x+1 = \frac{4}{3}$.

The triangle formed from $\frac{4}{3}$, $\frac{1}{3}$ is $\left(\frac{17}{9}, \frac{15}{9}, \frac{8}{9}\right)$. Thus we may take as the auxiliary triangle (17, 15, 8).

Take now $17x$, $15x$, $8x$ for the sides of the triangle originally required to be found. We have then

$$\zeta+\xi-\frac{1}{2}\xi\eta = 32x-60x^2 = 4;$$

whence $x = \frac{1}{3}$, and the required triangle is $\left(\frac{17}{3}, \frac{15}{3}, \frac{8}{3}\right)$.

[The auxiliary right-angled triangle was of course necessary to be found in order to make the final quadratic give a rational result.]

Bachet adds after VI. 11 a solution of the problem represented by

$$\frac{1}{2}\xi\eta - \zeta = a,$$

to which Fermat adds the enunciation of the corresponding problem

$$\zeta - \frac{1}{2}\xi\eta = a.$$

[1] Though there are an infinite number of values of x for which $6x^2+3$ becomes a square, the resulting triangles are all similar. For, if x be any one of the values, the triangle is

Lemma II to the following problem.

Given two numbers the sum of which is a square, an infinite number of squares can be found such that, when the square is multiplied by one of the given numbers and the product is added to the other, the result is a square.

Given numbers 3, 6.

Let x^2+2x+1 be the required square which, say, when multiplied by 3 and then increased by 6, gives a square.

We have $3x^2+6x+9=$ a square;

and, since the absolute term is a square, an infinite number of solutions can be found.

Suppose, *e.g.* $3x^2+6x+9=(3-3x)^2$,

and $x=4$.

The side of the required square is 5, and an infinite number of other solutions can be found.

12. To find a right-angled triangle such that the area added to either of the perpendiculars gives a square.

Let the triangle be $(5x, 12x, 13x)$.

Therefore (1) $30x^2+12x=$ a square $=36x^2$, say,

and $x=2$.

But (2) we must also have

$$30x^2+5x=\text{a square}.$$

This is however not a square when $x=2$.

Therefore I must find a square m^2x^2, to replace $36x^2$, such that $12/(m^2-30)$, the value of x obtained from the first equation, is real and satisfies the condition

$$30x^2+5x=\text{a square}.$$

This gives, by substitution,

$$(60m^2+2520)/(m^4-60m+900)=\text{a square},$$

or $60m^2+2520=$ a square.

This could be solved [by the preceding Lemma II] *if* $60+2520$ *were equal to a square.*

Now 60 arises from 5.12, *i.e.* from the product of the perpendicular sides of (5, 12, 13);

2520 is $30.12.(12-5)$, *i.e.* the continued product of the area, the greater perpendicular, and the difference between the perpendiculars.

---

formed from x, $2x$, and its sides are therefore $3x^2$, $4x^2$, $5x^2$; that is, the triangles are all similar to (3, 4, 5). Fermat shows in his note on the following problem, VI. 12, how to find any number of triangles satisfying the conditions of this Lemma and *not* similar to (3, 4, 5). See p. 235, note.

Hence we must find an auxiliary triangle such that (product of perps.) + (continued product of area, greater perp. and difference of perps.) = a square.

Or, *if we make the greater perpendicular a square* and divide out by it, we must have
(lesser perp.) + (product of area and diff. of perps.)
= a square.

Then, assuming that we have found two numbers, (1) the product of the area and the difference of the perpendiculars and (2) the lesser perpendicular, satisfying these conditions, we have to find a square (m^2) such that the product of this square into the second of the numbers, when added to the first number, gives a square[1].

[1] The text of this sentence is unsatisfactory. Bachet altered the reading of the MSS. So did Tannery, but more by way of filling out. The version above follows Tannery's text, which is as follows: *ἀπάγεται εἰς τὸ δύο ἀριθμοὺς εὑρόντας* [for *ὄντας* of MSS.] <*τόν τε ὑπὸ*> *τοῦ ἐμβαδοῦ καὶ τῆς ὑπεροχῆς τῶν ὀρθῶν*, <*καὶ τὸν ἐν τῇ ἐλάσσονι τῶν ὀρθῶν*>, *αὖθις* [for *αὐτῆς* of MSS.] *ζητεῖν* □*όν τινα, ὃς πολλαπλασιασθεὶς ἐπὶ ἕνα τὸν δοθέντα*, <*καὶ προσλαβὼν τὸν ἕτερον*>, *ποιεῖ τετράγωνον*.

The argument would then be this. If (h, p, b) be the triangle $(b > p)$, we have to make

$$bp + \frac{1}{2}bp(b-p)b \text{ a square,}$$

or, if b is a square, $\quad p + \frac{1}{2}bp(b-p)$ must be a square.

The ultimate equation to be solved (corresponding to $60m^2 + 2520 = \text{a square}$) is

$$bpm^2 + \frac{1}{2}bp(b-p)b = \text{a square,}$$

or, if b is a square, $\quad pm^2 + \frac{1}{2}bp(b-p) = \text{a square}$;

and therefore, according to Tannery's text, "the problem is reduced to this: Having found two numbers $\frac{1}{2}bp(b-p)$ and p [satisfying the conditions, namely that their sum is a square, while b is also a square], to find after that a square such that the product of it and the latter number added to the former number gives a square."

The difficulty is that, with the above readings, there is nothing to correspond exactly to the phraseology of the enunciation of Lemma I, which speaks, not of making $p + \frac{1}{2}bp(b-p)$ a square when b is a square, but of making $b-p$, b and $p + \frac{1}{2}bp$ all simultaneously squares. But the *particular solution* of the Lemma is really equivalent to making b and $p + \frac{1}{2}bp(b-p)$ simultaneously squares. For the triangle is formed from a, $2a$; this method of making b a square $(= 4a^2)$ incidentally makes $b-p$ a square $(= a^2)$, and $p + \frac{1}{2}bp$ becomes $3a^2 + 6a^4$, while $p + \frac{1}{2}bp(b-p)$ becomes $3a^2 + 6a^6$. Since the solution actually used is $a = 1$, the effect is the same whichever way the problem is stated. And in any case, whether the expression to be made a square is $3a^2m^2 + 6a^4$ or $3a^2m^2 + 6a^6$, the problem equally reduces to that of making $3m'^2 + 6$ a square.

How to solve these problems is shown in the Lemmas.

The auxiliary triangle is (3, 4, 5). [Lemma I.]

Accordingly, putting for the original triangle $(3x, 4x, 5x)$,

we have $\left.\begin{matrix}6x^2+4x\\6x^2+3x\end{matrix}\right\}$ both squares.

Let $x = \dfrac{4}{m^2-6}$ be the solution of the first equation;

then $$x^2 = \frac{16}{m^4 - 12m^2 + 36}.$$

The second equation therefore gives

$$\frac{96}{m^4 - 12m^2 + 36} + \frac{12}{m^2 - 6} = \text{a square},$$

whence $12m^2 + 24 = \text{a square}$,

and we have therefore to find a square (m^2) such that twelve times it $+24$ is a square; this is possible, since $12+24$ is a square [Lemma II].

A solution is $m^2 = 25$,

whence $x = \frac{4}{19}$,

and $\left(\frac{12}{19}, \frac{16}{19}, \frac{20}{19}\right)$ is the required triangle[1].

13. To find a right-angled triangle such that its area *minus* either perpendicular gives a square.

We have to find an auxiliary triangle exactly as in the last problem;

Bachet's reading is ἀπάγεται εἰς τὸ δύο ἀριθμῶν δοθέντων τοῦ τε ἐμβαδοῦ, καὶ τῆς ἐλάσσονος τῶν περὶ τὴν ὀρθήν, αὐτοῖς ζητεῖν τετράγωνόν τινα, ὃς πολλαπλασιασθεὶς ἐπὶ ἕνα τῶν δοθέντων, καὶ προσλαβὼν τὸν ἕτερον, ποιῇ τετράγωνον.

[1] Fermat observes that Diophantus gives only one species of triangle satisfying the condition, namely triangles similar to (3, 4, 5), but that by his (Fermat's) method an infinite number of triangles of different species can be found to satisfy the conditions, the first being derived from Diophantus' triangle, the second from the new triangle, and so on.

Suppose that the triangle (3, 4, 5) has been found satisfying the condition that

$$\xi\eta + \xi(\xi - \eta) \cdot \frac{1}{2}\xi\eta = \text{a square},$$

where ξ, η are the perpendicular sides and $\xi > \eta$.

To derive a second such triangle from the first (3, 4, 5), assume the greater of the two perpendicular sides to be 4 and the lesser $3+x$.

Then $$\xi\eta + \xi(\xi-\eta) \cdot \frac{1}{2}\xi\eta = 36 - 12x - 8x^2 = \text{a square}.$$

Also $$\zeta^2 = \xi^2 + \eta^2 = 25 + 6x + x^2 = \text{a square}.$$

We have therefore simply to solve the double-equation

$$\left.\begin{matrix}36 - 12x - 8x^2 = u^2\\ 25 + 6x + x^2 = v^2\end{matrix}\right\},$$

which is a matter of no difficulty. As a matter of fact, the usual method gives

$$x + 3 = \frac{20667}{5932289}, \text{ and the triangle is } \left(\frac{20667}{5932289}, 4, \frac{23729165}{5932289}\right).$$

this triangle is (3, 4, 5), and accordingly we assume for the triangle of the problem $(3x, 4x, 5x)$.

One condition then gives $6x^2-4x=$ a square $=m^2x^2$, say $(m^2<6)$,

and $$x=\frac{4}{6-m^2}.$$

The second condition gives $6x^2-3x=$ a square; and, by substitution,

$$\frac{96}{m^4-12m^2+36}-\frac{12}{6-m^2}=\text{a square},$$

or $$24+12m^2=\text{a square}.$$

This is satisfied by $m=1$,

whence $x=\frac{4}{5}$, and the required triangle is $\left(\frac{12}{5}, \frac{16}{5}, 4\right)$.

Or, if we do not wish to use the value 1 for m,

let $m=z+1$, and (dividing by 4) we have

$$3m^2+6=3z^2+6z+9=\text{a square};$$

z must be found to be not greater than $\frac{13}{9}$ (in order that m^2 may be less than 6), and m will not be greater than $\frac{22}{9}$. The solution is then rational[1].

14. To find a right-angled triangle such that its area *minus* the hypotenuse or *minus* one of the perpendiculars gives a square.

Let the triangle be $(3x, 4x, 5x)$.

Therefore $\left.\begin{matrix}6x^2-5x\\6x^2-3x\end{matrix}\right\}$ are both squares.

Making the latter a square $(=m^2x^2)$, we have

$$x=\frac{3}{6-m^2}\quad(m^2<6).$$

[1] Diophantus having solved the problem of finding a right-angled triangle ζ, η, ξ (ζ being the hypotenuse) such that

$$\left.\begin{matrix}\frac{1}{2}\xi\eta-\xi\\\frac{1}{2}\xi\eta-\eta\end{matrix}\right\}\text{ are both squares,}$$

Fermat enunciates, as susceptible of solution by his method, but otherwise very difficult, the corresponding problem of making

$$\left.\begin{matrix}\xi-\frac{1}{2}\xi\eta\\\eta-\frac{1}{2}\xi\eta\end{matrix}\right\}\text{ both squares.}$$

This problem was solved by Euler (*Novi Commentarii Acad. Petropol.* 1749, II. (1751), pp. 49 sqq. = *Commentationes arithmeticae*, I. pp. 62–72).

The first equation then gives

$$\frac{54}{m^4 - 12m^2 + 36} - \frac{15}{6 - m^2} = \text{a square},$$

or $$15m^2 - 36 = \text{a square}.$$

This equation we cannot solve because 15 *is not the sum of two squares*[1]. Therefore we must change the assumed triangle.

Now (with reference to the triangle 3, 4, 5) $15m^2$ = the continued product of a square less than the area, the hypotenuse, and one perpendicular;

while 36 = the continued product of the area, the perpendicular, and the difference between the hypotenuse and the perpendicular.

Therefore we have to find a right-angled triangle (h, p, b, say) and a square (m^2) less than 6 such that

$$m^2hp - \tfrac{1}{2}pb \,.\, p(h-p) \text{ is a square.}$$

If we form the triangle from two numbers X_1, X_2 and suppose that $p = 2X_1X_2$, and if we then divide throughout by $(X_1 - X_2)^2$ which is equal to $h - p$, we must find a square $z^2 \,[= m^2/(X_1 - X_2)^2]$ such that

$$z^2hp - \tfrac{1}{2}pb \,.\, p \text{ is a square.}$$

The problem can be solved if X_1, X_2 *are "similar plane numbers*[2]*."*

Form the auxiliary triangle from similar plane numbers accordingly, say 4, 1. [The conditions are then satisfied[3].]

[The equation for m then becomes

$$8 \,.\, 17m^2 - 4 \,.\, 15 \,.\, 8 \,.\, 9 = \text{a square},$$

or $$136m^2 - 4320 = \text{a square}.]$$

Let[4] $m^2 = 36$. [This satisfies the equation, and 36 < area of triangle.]

[1] See p. 70 above.

[2] Diophantus states this without proof. [A "plane number" being of the form $a \,.\, b$, a plane number similar to it is of the form $\frac{m}{n} a \,.\, \frac{m}{n} b$ or $\frac{m^2}{n^2} ab$.]

The fact stated may be verified thus. We have

$$z^2 (X_1^2 + X_2^2)\, 2X_1X_2 - X_1X_2 (X_1^2 - X_2^2)\, 2X_1X_2 = \text{a square}.$$

The condition is satisfied if $z^2 = X_1X_2$, for the expression then reduces to $4X_1^2X_2^2 \,.\, X_2^2$. In that case X_1X_2 is a square, or X_1/X_2 is a square.

[3] Since $X_1 = 4$, $X_2 = 1$, we have $h = 17$, $p = 8$, $b = 15$, $z^2 = X_1X_2 = 4$, and

$$z^2hp - \frac{1}{2}pb \,.\, p = 4 \,.\, 17 \,.\, 8 - 4 \,.\, 15 \,.\, 8 = 2 \,.\, 32 = 64, \text{ a square.}$$

[4] The reason for this assumption is that, by hypothesis, $z^2 = m^2/(X_1 - X_2)^2$, or $4 = m^2/3^2$, and $m^2 = 36$.

The triangle formed from 4, 1 being (8, 15, 17), we assume $8x$, $15x$, $17x$ for the original triangle.

We now put $$60x^2 - 8x = 36x^2,$$
and $$x = \tfrac{1}{3}.$$

The required triangle is therefore $\left(\frac{8}{3}, 5, \frac{17}{3}\right)$.

Lemma to the following problem.

Given two numbers, if, when some square is multiplied into one of the numbers and the other number is subtracted from the product, the result is a square, another square larger than the aforesaid square can always be found which has the same property.

Given numbers 3, 11, side of square 5, say, so that $3 \cdot 25 - 11 = 64$, a square.

Let the required square be $(x+5)^2$.

Therefore
$$3(x+5)^2 - 11 = 3x^2 + 30x + 64 = \text{a square}$$
$$= (8-2x)^2, \text{ say,}$$
and $$x = 62.$$

The side of the new square is 67, and the square itself 4489.

15. To find a right-angled triangle such that the area added to either the hypotenuse or one of the perpendiculars gives a square.

In order to guide us to a proper assumption for the required triangle, we have, in this case, to seek a triangle (h, p, b, say) and a square (m^2) such that $m^2 > \frac{1}{2}pb$, the area, and
$$m^2hp - \tfrac{1}{2}pb \cdot p(h-p) \text{ is a square.}$$

Let the triangle be formed from 4, 1, the square (m^2) being 36, as before;

but, the triangle being (8, 15, 17), *the square is not greater than the area.*

We must therefore, as in the preceding Lemma, replace 36 by a greater square.

Now $hp = 136$, and $\frac{1}{2}pb \cdot p(h-p) = 60 \cdot 8 \cdot 9 = 4320$,

so that $$136m^2 - 4320 = \text{a square},$$

which is satisfied by $m^2 = 36$; and we have to find a larger square (z^2) such that
$$136z^2 - 4320 = \text{a square}.$$

Put $z = m + 6$, and we have
$$(m^2 + 12m + 36)\,136 - 4320 = \text{a square},$$
or $136m^2 + 1632m + 576 = \text{a square} = (km - 24)^2$, say.
This equation has any number of solutions; *e.g.*, putting $k = 16$, we have
$$m = 20,\quad z = 26,\ \text{and}\ z^2 = 676.$$
We therefore put $(8x, 15x, 17x)$ for the original triangle, and then assume
$$60x^2 + 8x = 676x^2,$$
whence $x = \frac{1}{77}$, and the problem is solved[1].

[1] In VI. 14, 15 Diophantus has shown how to find a rational right-angled triangle ζ, η, ξ (where ζ is the hypotenuse) such that
$$(1)\quad \left.\begin{array}{l}\frac{1}{2}\xi\eta - \zeta \\ \frac{1}{2}\xi\eta - \xi\end{array}\right\}\ \text{are both squares,}$$
or
$$(2)\quad \left.\begin{array}{l}\frac{1}{2}\xi\eta + \zeta \\ \frac{1}{2}\xi\eta + \xi\end{array}\right\}\ \text{are both squares.}$$

In the *Inventum Novum*, Part I. paragraphs 26, 40 (*Oeuvres de Fermat*, III. pp. 341–2, 349–50) is given Fermat's solution of a third case in which
$$\left.\begin{array}{l}\zeta - \frac{1}{2}\xi\eta \\ \xi - \frac{1}{2}\xi\eta\end{array}\right\}\ \text{are both squares.}$$

This depends on the *Lemma*: To find a rational right-angled triangle in which
$$\zeta\left(\xi + \frac{1}{2}\eta\right) - \frac{1}{2}\xi\eta = \text{a square.}$$

Form a right-angled triangle from $x + 1$, 1; the sides are then
$$x^2 + 2x + 2,\quad x^2 + 2x,\quad 2x + 2.$$

We must therefore have
$$(x^2 + 2x + 2)(x^2 + 3x + 1) - (x + 1)(x^2 + 2x) = \text{a square},$$
or
$$x^4 + 4x^3 + 6x^2 + 6x + 2 = \text{a square}$$
$$= (x^2 + 2x + 1)^2, \text{ say.}$$

Therefore $x = -\frac{1}{2}$, and the triangle has one of its sides $x^2 + 2x$ negative. Instead therefore of forming the triangle from $\frac{1}{2}$, 1 or from 1, 2, we form it from $x + 1$, 2 and repeat the operation. The sides are then
$$x^2 + 2x + 5,\quad x^2 + 2x - 3,\quad 4x + 4,$$
and we have
$$(x^2 + 2x + 5)(x^2 + 4x - 1) - (2x + 2)(x^2 + 2x - 3) = \text{a square},$$
or
$$x^4 + 4x^3 + 6x^2 + 20x + 1 = \text{a square}$$
$$= (1 + 10x - x^2)^2, \text{ say,}$$

16. To find a right-angled triangle such that the number representing the (portion intercepted within the triangle of the) bisector of an acute angle is rational[1].

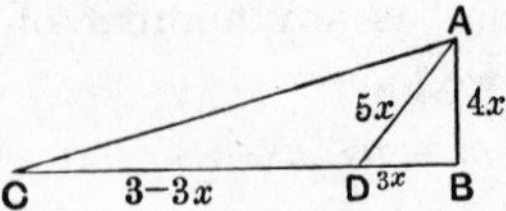

Suppose the bisector $AD = 5x$, and one segment of the base $(DB) = 3x$; therefore the perpendicular $= 4x$.

Let the whole base CB be some multiple of 3, say 3; then

$$CD = 3 - 3x.$$

But, since AD bisects the angle CAB,

$$AC : CD = AB : BD;$$

therefore the hypotenuse $AC = \frac{4}{3}(3 - 3x) = 4 - 4x$.

---

whence $x = \frac{23}{6}$, and the required auxiliary triangle is formed from $\frac{29}{6}$, 2 or from 29, 12, the sides being accordingly 985, 697, 696.

(Fermat observes that the same result is obtained by putting $y - \frac{1}{2}$ for x in the expression $x^4 + 4x^3 + 6x^2 + 6x + 2$; for we must have

$$y^4 + 2y^3 + \frac{3}{2}y^2 + \frac{5}{2}y + \frac{1}{16} = \text{a square} = \left(\frac{1}{4} + 5y - y^2\right)^2, \text{ say,}$$

whence $y = \frac{23}{12}$, so that $x = y - \frac{1}{2} = \frac{17}{12}$, and the triangle is formed from $\frac{29}{12}$, 1 or from 29, 12, as before.)

We now return to the original problem of solving

$$\left.\begin{aligned} \zeta - \tfrac{1}{2}\,\xi\eta &= u^2 \\ \xi - \tfrac{1}{2}\,\xi\eta &= v^2 \end{aligned}\right\}.$$

We assume for the required triangle $(985x, 697x, 696x)$ and we have $\frac{1}{2}\xi\eta = 242556x^2$, so that

$$\left.\begin{aligned} 985x - 242556x^2 \\ 697x - 242556x^2 \end{aligned}\right\} \text{ must both be squares.}$$

Assume that $\quad 697x - 242556x^2 = (697x)^2,$

and we have $\quad x - 348x^2 = 697x^2,$

whence $x = \frac{1}{1045}$, and the required triangle is $\left(\frac{985}{1045}, \frac{697}{1045}, \frac{696}{1045}\right)$.

[The $985x - 242556x^2$ is a square by virtue of the sides 985, 697, 696 satisfying the conditions of the Lemma; for $985x - 242556x^2 = \frac{985}{1045} - \frac{1}{2}\cdot\frac{697 \cdot 696}{(1045)^2}$, which is a square if $985 \cdot 1045 - \frac{1}{2} \cdot 697 \cdot 696$ is a square, and $1045 = 697 + \frac{1}{2} \cdot 696$.]

[1] Why did not Diophantus propound the analogous problem "To find a right-angled triangle such that the sides are rational and the bisector of the right angle is also rational"? Evidently because he knew it to be impossible, as is clear when (a, c being the perpendiculars) the bisector is expressed as $\frac{ac}{a+c}\sqrt{2}$. (Loria, *op. cit.* p. 148 *n.*)

Therefore [by Eucl. I. 47]

$$16x^2 - 32x + 16 = 16x^2 + 9,$$

and $$x = \frac{7}{32}.$$

If we multiply throughout by 32, the perpendicular = **28**, the base = **96**, the hypotenuse = **100**, and the bisector = **35**.

17. To find a right-angled triangle such that the area added to the hypotenuse gives a square, while the perimeter is a cube.

Let the area be x and the hypotenuse some square *minus* x, say $16 - x$.

The product of the perpendiculars $= 2x$;

therefore, if one of them be 2, the other is x, and the perimeter = 18, *which is not a cube.*

Therefore we must find some square which, when 2 is added to it, becomes a cube[1].

[1] "Did Diophantus know that the equation $u^2 + 2 = v^3$ only admits of *one* solution $u = 5$, $v = 3$? Probably not" (Loria, *op. cit.* p. 155). The fact was noted by Fermat (on the present proposition) and proved by Euler.

Euler's proof (*Algebra*, Part II. Arts. 188, 193) is, I think, not too long to be given here. Art. 188 shows how to find x, y such that $ax^2 + cy^2$ may be a cube. Separate $ax^2 + cy^2$ into its factors $x\sqrt{a} + y\sqrt{(-c)}$, $x\sqrt{a} - y\sqrt{(-c)}$, and assume

$$x\sqrt{a} + y\sqrt{(-c)} = \{p\sqrt{a} + q\sqrt{(-c)}\}^3,$$
$$x\sqrt{a} - y\sqrt{(-c)} = \{p\sqrt{a} - q\sqrt{(-c)}\}^3,$$

the product $(ap^2 + cq^2)^3$ being a cube and equal to $ax^2 + cy^2$.

To find values for x and y, we write out the expansions of the cubes in full, and

$$x\sqrt{a} + y\sqrt{(-c)} = ap^3\sqrt{a} + 3ap^2q\sqrt{(-c)} - 3cpq^2\sqrt{a} - cq^3\sqrt{(-c)},$$
$$x\sqrt{a} - y\sqrt{(-c)} = ap^3\sqrt{a} - 3ap^2q\sqrt{(-c)} - 3cpq^2\sqrt{a} + cq^3\sqrt{(-c)},$$

whence $$x = ap^3 - 3cpq^2,$$
$$y = 3ap^2q - cq^3.$$

For example, suppose it is required to make $x^2 + y^2$ a cube. Here $a = 1$ and $c = 1$, so that

$$x = p^3 - 3pq^2,$$
$$y = 3p^2q - q^3,$$

while $x^2 + y^2 = (p^2 + q^2)^3$. If now $p = 2$ and $q = 1$, we find $x = 2$ and $y = 11$, whence

$$x^2 + y^2 = 125 = 5^3.$$

Now (Art. 193) let it be required to find, if possible, in integral numbers, other squares besides 25 which, when added to 2, give cubes.

Since $x^2 + 2$ has to be made a cube, and 2 is double of a square, let us first determine the cases in which $x^2 + 2y^2$ becomes a cube. Here $a = 1$, $c = 2$, so that

$$x = p^3 - 6pq^2, \quad y = 3p^2q - 2q^3;$$

therefore, since $y = \pm 1$, we must have

$$3p^2q - 2q^3 \text{ or } q(3p^2 - 2q^2) = \pm 1;$$

consequently q must be a divisor of 1.

Let, then, $q = 1$, and we shall have $3p^2 - 2 = \pm 1$.

With the upper sign we have $3p^2 = 3$ and, taking $p = -1$, we find $x = 5$; with the lower sign we get an irrational value of p which is of no use.

Let the side of the square be $m+1$, and that of the cube $m-1$.

Therefore $m^3-3m^2+3m-1=m^2+2m+3$, from which m is found[1] to be 4.

Hence the side of the square $=5$, and that of the cube $=3$.

Assuming now x for the area of the original triangle, $25-x$ for its hypotenuse, and 2, x for the perpendiculars, we find that the perimeter is a cube.

But (hypotenuse)^2 = sum of squares of perpendiculars; therefore $x^2-50x+625=x^2+4$;

$x=\frac{621}{50}$, and the problem is solved.

18. To find a right-angled triangle such that the area added to the hypotenuse gives a cube, while the perimeter is a square.

Area x, hypotenuse some cube *minus* x, perpendiculars x, 2.

Therefore we have to find a cube which, when 2 is added to it, becomes a square.

Let the side of the cube be $m-1$.

Therefore $m^3-3m^2+3m+1=$ a square $=(1\frac{1}{2}m+1)^2$, say.

Thus $m=\frac{21}{4}$, and the cube $=(\frac{17}{4})^3=\frac{4913}{64}$.

Put now x for the area, x, 2 for the perpendiculars, and $\frac{4913}{64}-x$ for the hypotenuse;

and x is found from the equation $(\frac{4913}{64}-x)^2=x^2+4$.

[$x=\frac{24121185}{628864}$, and the triangle is $(2, \frac{24121185}{628864}, \frac{24153953}{628864})$.]

19. To find a right-angled triangle such that its area added to one of the perpendiculars gives a square, while the perimeter is a cube.

Make a right-angled triangle from some indeterminate odd number[2], say $2x+1$;

then the altitude $=2x+1$, the base $=2x^2+2x$, and the hypotenuse $=2x^2+2x+1$.

It follows that there is no square except 25 which has the required property.

Fermat says ("Relation des nouvelles découvertes en la science des nombres," *Oeuvres*, II. pp. 433–4) that it was by a special application of his method of *descente*, such as that by which he proved that *a cube cannot be the sum of two cubes*, that he proved (1) that *there is only one integral square which when increased by 2 gives a cube*, and (2) that *there are only two squares in integers which, when added to 4, give cubes*. The latter squares are 4, 121 (as proved by Euler, *Algebra*, Part II. Art. 192).

[1] See pp. 66, 67 above.

[2] This is the method of formation of right-angled triangles attributed to Pythagoras. If m is any odd number, the sides of the right-angled triangle formed therefrom are m, $\frac{1}{2}(m^2-1)$, $\frac{1}{2}(m^2+1)$, for $m^2+\left\{\frac{1}{2}(m^2-1)\right\}^2=\left\{\frac{1}{2}(m^2+1)\right\}^2$. Cf. Proclus, *Comment. on Eucl.* I. (ed. Friedlein), p. 428, 7 sqq., etc. etc.

Since the perimeter = a cube,

$$4x^2+6x+2=(4x+2)(x+1)=\text{a cube};$$

and, if we divide all the sides by $x+1$, we have to make $4x+2$ a cube.

Again, the area + one perpendicular = a square.

Therefore $\dfrac{2x^3+3x^2+x}{(x+1)^2}+\dfrac{2x+1}{x+1}=\text{a square};$

that is, $\dfrac{2x^3+5x^2+4x+1}{x^2+2x+1}=2x+1=\text{a square}.$

But $4x+2=\text{a cube};$

therefore we must find a cube which is double of a square; this is of course 8.

Therefore $4x+2=8$, and $x=1\frac{1}{2}$.

The required triangle is $\left(\frac{8}{5}, \frac{15}{5}, \frac{17}{5}\right)$.

20. To find a right-angled triangle such that the sum of its area and one perpendicular is a cube, while its perimeter is a square.

Proceeding as in the last problem, we have to make

$$\left.\begin{array}{l}4x+2 \text{ a square}\\ 2x+1 \text{ a cube}\end{array}\right\}.$$

We have therefore to seek a square which is double of a cube; this is 16, which is double of 8.

Therefore $4x+2=16$, and $x=3\frac{1}{2}$.

The triangle is $\left(\frac{16}{9}, \frac{63}{9}, \frac{65}{9}\right)$.

21. To find a right-angled triangle such that its perimeter is a square, while its perimeter added to its area gives a cube.

Form a right-angled triangle from x, 1.

The perpendiculars are then $2x$, x^2-1, and the hypotenuse x^2+1.

Hence $2x^2+2x$ should be a square,

and x^3+2x^2+x a cube.

It is easy to make $2x^2+2x$ a square; let $2x^2+2x=m^2x^2$; therefore $x=2/(m^2-2)$.

By the second condition,

$$\frac{8}{(m^2-2)^3}+\frac{8}{(m^2-2)^2}+\frac{2}{m^2-2} \text{ must be a cube,}$$

i.e. $\dfrac{2m^4}{(m^2-2)^3}=\text{a cube}.$

Therefore $2m^4 =$ a cube, or $2m =$ a cube $= 8$, say.

Thus $m = 4$, $x = \frac{2}{14} = \frac{1}{7}$, $x^2 = \frac{1}{49}$.

But one of the perpendiculars of the triangle is $x^2 - 1$, and we cannot subtract 1 from $\frac{1}{49}$.

Therefore we must find another value for x greater than 1; hence $2 < m^2 < 4$.

And we have therefore to find a cube such that $\frac{1}{4}$ of the square of it is greater than 2, but less than 4.

If z^3 be this cube,

$$2 < \tfrac{1}{4}z^6 < 4,$$

or

$$8 < z^6 < 16.$$

This is satisfied by $z^6 = \frac{729}{64}$, or $z^3 = \frac{27}{8}$.

Therefore $m = \frac{27}{16}$, $m^2 = \frac{729}{256}$, and $x = \frac{512}{217}$, the square of which is > 1.

Thus the triangle is known $\left[\frac{1024}{217}, \frac{215055}{47089}, \frac{309233}{47089}\right]$.

22. To find a right-angled triangle such that its perimeter is a cube, while the perimeter added to the area gives a square.

(1) We must first see how, given two numbers, a triangle may be formed such that its perimeter = one of the numbers and its area = the other.

Let 12, 7 be the numbers, 12 being the perimeter, 7 the area.

Therefore the product of the two perpendiculars

$$= 14 = \frac{1}{x} \cdot 14x.$$

If then $\frac{1}{x}$, $14x$ are the perpendiculars,

hypotenuse = perimeter − sum of perps. $= 12 - \frac{1}{x} - 14x$.

Therefore [by Eucl. I. 47]

$$\frac{1}{x^2} + 196x^2 + 172 - \frac{24}{x} - 336x = \frac{1}{x^2} + 196x^2;$$

that is,

$$172 = 336x + \frac{24}{x},$$

or

$$172x = 336x^2 + 24.$$

This equation gives no rational solution, because $86^2 - 24 \cdot 336$ *is not a square.*

Now $172 = (\text{perimeter})^2 + 4$ times area,

$24 \cdot 336 = 8$ times area multiplied by $(\text{perimeter})^2$.

(2) Let now the area $= m$, and the perimeter = any number which is both a square and a cube, say 64.

Therefore $\{\frac{1}{2}(64^2+4m)\}^2 - 8 . 64^2 . m$ must be a square,

or $4m^2 - 24576m + 4194304 =$ a square.

Therefore $m^2 - 6144m + 1048576 =$ a square
Also $m + 64 =$ a square.

To solve this double-equation, multiply the second by such a number as will make the absolute term the same as the absolute term in the first.

Then, if we take the difference and the factors as usual, the equations are solved.

[After the second equation is multiplied by 16384, the double-equation becomes

$$\left.\begin{aligned} m^2 - 6144m + 1048576 &= \text{a square} \\ 16384m + 1048576 &= \text{a square} \end{aligned}\right\}.$$

The difference is $m^2 - 22528m$.

If m, $m - 22528$ are taken as the factors, we find $m = 7680$, which is an impossible value for the area of a right-angled triangle of perimeter 64.

We therefore take as the factors $11m$, $\frac{1}{11}m - 2048$; then, when the square of half the difference is equated to the smaller of the two expressions to be made squares, we have

$$(\tfrac{60}{11}m + 1024)^2 = 16384m + 1048576,$$

and $m = \frac{39424}{225}$.

Returning now to the original problem, we put $\frac{1}{x}$, $2mx$ for the perpendicular sides of the required triangle, and we have

$$\left(64 - \frac{1}{x} - 2mx\right)^2 = \frac{1}{x^2} + 4m^2x^2,$$

which leads, when the value of m is substituted, to the equation

$$78848x^2 - 8432x + 225 = 0.$$

The solution of this equation is rational, namely

$$x = \frac{527 \pm 23}{9856} = \frac{25}{448} \text{ or } \frac{9}{176}.$$

Diophantus would of course use the first value, which would give $(\frac{448}{25}, \frac{176}{9}, \frac{5968}{225})$ as the required right-angled triangle. The second value of x clearly gives the same triangle.]

23. To find a right-angled triangle such that the square of its hypotenuse is also the sum of a different square and the side of that square, while the quotient obtained by dividing the square of the hypotenuse by one of the perpendiculars of the triangle is the sum of a cube and the side of the cube.

Let one of the perpendiculars be x, the other x^2.

Therefore $(\text{hypotenuse})^2 =$ the sum of a square and its side; also $\dfrac{x^4+x^2}{x} = x^3 + x =$ the sum of a cube and its side.

It remains that $x^4 + x^2$ must be a square.

Therefore $x^2 + 1 =$ a square $= (x-2)^2$, say.

Therefore $x = \frac{3}{4}$, and the triangle is found $[\frac{3}{4}, \frac{9}{16}, \frac{15}{16}]$.

24. To find a right-angled triangle such that one perpendicular is a cube, the other is the difference between a cube and its side, and the hypotenuse is the sum of a cube and its side.

Let the hypotenuse be $x^3 + x$, and one perpendicular $x^3 - x$.

Therefore the other perpendicular $= 2x^2 =$ a cube $= x^3$, say.

Thus $x = 2$, and the triangle is (6, 8, 10).

It is on Bachet's note to VI. 22 that Fermat explains his method of solving *triple-equations*, as to which see the Supplement, Section V.

[No. 20 of the problems on right-angled triangles which Bachet appended to Book VI. ("To find a right-angled triangle such that its area is equal to a given number") is the occasion of Fermat's remarkable note upon the theorem discovered by him to the effect that *The area of a right-angled triangle the sides of which are rational numbers cannot be a square number.*

This note will be given in full, with other information on the same subject, in the Supplement.]

ON POLYGONAL NUMBERS

All numbers from 3 upwards in order are polygonal, containing as many angles as they have units, *e.g.* 3, 4, 5, etc.

"As with regard to squares it is obvious that they are such because they arise from the multiplication of a number into itself, so it was found that any polygonal multiplied into a certain number depending on the number of its angles, with the addition to the product of a certain square also depending on the number of the angles, turned out to be a square. This I shall prove, first showing how any assigned polygonal number may be found from a given side, and the side from a given polygonal number. I shall begin by proving the preliminary propositions which are required for the purpose."

1. If there are three numbers with a common difference, then 8 times the product of the greatest and middle + the square of the least = a square, the side of which is the sum of the greatest and twice the middle number.

Let the numbers be AB, BC, BD in the figure, and we have to prove $8AB.BC+BD^2=(AB+2BC)^2$.

E A C D B

By hypothesis $AC=CD$, $AB=BC+CD$, $BD=BC-CD$.

Now $8AB.BC=4AB.BC+(4BC^2+4BC.CD)$.

Therefore $8AB.BC+BD^2$

$$=4AB.BC+4BC^2+(4BC.CD+BD^2)$$

$$=4AB.BC+4BC^2+AB^2, \qquad \text{[Eucl. II. 8]}$$

and we have to see how $AB^2+4AB.BC+4BC^2$ can be made a square.

[Diophantus does this by producing BA to E, so that $AE=BC$, and then proving that

$$AB^2+4AB.BC+4BC^2=(BE+EA)^2.]$$

It is indeed obvious that

$$AB^2+4AB.BC+4BC^2=(AB+2BC)^2.$$

2. If there are any numbers, as many as we please, in A.P., the difference between the greatest and the least is equal to the common difference multiplied by the number of terms less one.

[That is, if in an A.P. the first term is a, the common difference b and the greatest term l, n being the number of terms, then

$$l - a = (n - 1)\,b.]$$

Let AB, BC, BD, BE have a common difference.

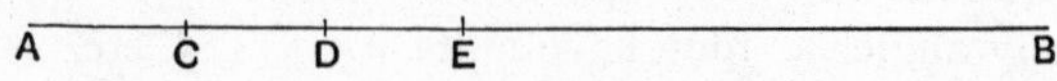

Now AC, CD, DE are all equal.

Therefore $EA = AC \times$ (number of terms AC, CD, DE)
$= AC \times$ (number of terms in series $-$ 1).

3. If there are as many numbers as we please in A.P., then (greatest + least) × number of terms = double the sum of the terms.

[That is, with the usual notation, $2s = n\,(l + a)$.]

(1) Let the numbers be A, B, C, D, E, F, the number of them being *even*.

Let GH contain as many units as there are numbers, and let GH, being even, be bisected at K. Divide GK into units at L, M.

Since $\qquad F - D = C - A,$

$\qquad F + A = C + D.$

But $\qquad F + A = (F + A) \,.\, GL;$

therefore $\qquad C + D = (F + A) \,.\, LM.$

Similarly $\qquad E + B = (F + A) \,.\, MK.$

Therefore, by addition,

$$A + B + C + D + E + F = (F + A) \,.\, GK.$$

Therefore $\qquad 2\,(A + B + \ldots) = 2\,(F + A) \,.\, GK$
$= (F + A) \,.\, GH.$

(2) Let the number of terms be *odd*, the terms being A, B, C, D, E.

Let there be as many units in FG as there are terms, so that there is an odd number of units.

Let FH be one of them; bisect HG at K, and divide HK into units, at L.

Since $$E - C = C - A,$$
$$E + A = 2C = 2C \,.\, LK.$$
Similarly $$B + D = 2C \,.\, LH.$$
Therefore $$A + E + B + D = 2C \,.\, HK$$
$$= C \,.\, HG.$$
Also $$C = C \,.\, HF;$$
therefore, by addition,
$$A + B + C + D + E = C \,.\, FG;$$
and, since $$2C = A + E,$$
$$2(A + B + C + D + E) = (A + E) \,.\, FG.$$

4. If there are as many numbers as we please beginning with 1 and increasing by a common difference, then the sum of all × 8 times the common difference + the square of (common difference − 2) = a square, the side of which diminished by 2 = the common difference multiplied by a number which when increased by 1 is double of the number of terms.

[The A.P. being $1,\ 1 + b, \ldots\ 1 + (n - 1)\, b$, and s the sum, we have to prove that
$$s \,.\, 8b + (b - 2)^2 = \{b\,(2n - 1) + 2\}^2,$$
i.e. $$8bs = 4b^2n^2 - 4\,(b - 2)\, nb,$$
or $$2s = bn^2 - (b - 2)\, n$$
$$= n\,\{2 + (n - 1)\, b\}.$$
The proof being cumbrous, I shall add the generalised algebraic equivalent in a column parallel to the text.]

Let AB, CD, EF be the terms in A.P. after 1.	$1 + b,\ 1 + 2b,\ 1 + 3b, \ldots.$

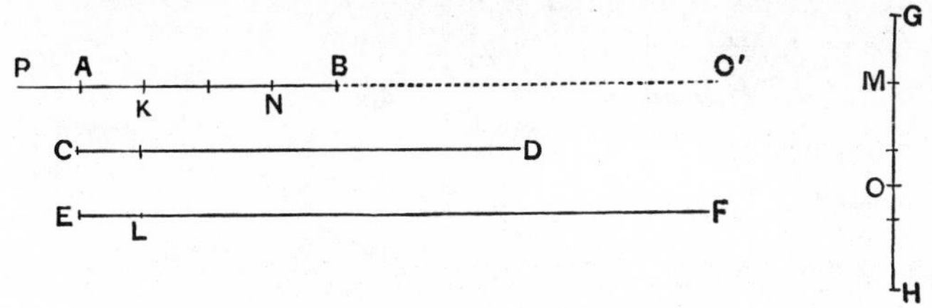

Let GH contain as many units as there are terms including 1.	n
Difference between EF and 1 = (diff. between AB and 1) × (GH − 1). [Prop. 2]	$l - 1 = (n - 1)\, b$

Put AK, EL, GM each equal to unity.

Therefore $LF = KB \, . \, MH$.

Make $KN = 2$, and we have to inquire whether

$$(\text{sum of terms}) \times 8KB + NB^2 = \{2 + KB(GH + HM)\}^2.$$

Call the expression on the left-hand side X.

Now sum of terms

$$= \tfrac{1}{2}(FE + EL) \, . \, GH \qquad \text{[Prop. 3]}$$
$$= \tfrac{1}{2}(LF + 2EL) \, . \, GH$$
$$= \tfrac{1}{2}(KB \, . \, MH \, . \, GH + 2GH),$$

since $LF = KB \, . \, MH$ [above].

$$s = \tfrac{1}{2}(l + 1)\, n$$
$$= \tfrac{1}{2}(l - 1 + 2)\, n$$
$$= \tfrac{1}{2}\{(n - 1)\, bn + 2n\}$$

Bisecting MH at O, we have

$$(\text{sum of terms}) = KB \, . \, GH \, . \, HO + GH.$$

We have therefore to inquire whether

$$(KB \, . \, GH \, . \, HO + GH) \, . \, 8KB + NB^2$$

is a square.

$$X = bn \, . \, \frac{n-1}{2} \, . \, 8b + 8bn + (b-2)^2$$

Now

$$KB \, . \, GH \, . \, HO \, . \, 8KB$$
$$= 8GH \, . \, HO \, . \, KB^2$$
$$= 4GH \, . \, HM \, . \, KB^2.$$

Is then

$$4GH \, . \, HM \, . \, KB^2 + 8KB \, . \, GH + NB^2$$

a square?

$$= 4n(n-1)\, b^2 + 8bn + (b-2)^2$$

Now

$$8GH \, . \, KB$$
$$= 4GM \, . \, KB + 4(GH + HM)\, KB.$$

Also $4GM \, . \, KB = 2NK \, . \, KB$;

and, adding NB^2, the right-hand side becomes $KB^2 + KN^2$. [Eucl. II. 7]

Is then

$$4GH \, . \, HM \, . \, KB^2 + 4(GH + HM)\, KB + KB^2 + KN^2$$

a square?

$$= 4n(n-1)\, b^2 + 4\{n + (n-1)\}\, b + b^2 + 2^2$$

Again,

$$KB^2 + 4GH \, . \, HM \, . \, KB^2$$
$$= GM^2 \, . \, KB^2 + 4GH \, . \, HM \, . \, KB^2$$
$$= (GH + HM)^2 \, . \, KB^2. \qquad \text{[Eucl. II. 8]}$$

Is then

$$(GH + HM)^2 \, . \, KB^2 + 4(GH + HM)\, KB + KN^2$$

a square?

$$= (n + n - 1)^2\, b^2 + 4\{n + (n-1)\}\, b + 2^2$$

Make the number NO' equal to

$$(GH + HM) \, . \, KB;$$

thus $(GH+HM)^2 . KB^2 = NO'^2$, as will be proved later[1].

Also $4NO' = 2 . NO' . NK$, since $NK = 2$.

Is then $NO'^2 + NK^2 + 2NO' . NK$ a square?

Yes; it is the square on KO'.

And

$$O'K - 2 = NO' = KB(GH + HM),$$

while $GH + HM + 1 =$ (twice number of terms).

Thus the proposition is proved.

Therefore

$$X = \{(n + n - 1) b + 2\}^2$$
$$= \{(2n - 1) b + 2\}^2.$$

"The above being premised, I say that,

[5] If there be as many terms as we please in A.P. beginning from 1, the sum of the terms is polygonal; for it has as many angles as the common difference increased by 2 contains units, and its side is the number of the terms set out including 1."

The numbers being as set out in the figure of Prop. 4, we have, by that proposition,

$$(\text{sum of terms}) . 8KB + NB^2 = KO'^2.$$

Taking another unit AP, we have $KP = 2$, while $KN = 2$; therefore PB, BK, BN are in A.P., so that

$$8PB . BK + NB^2 = (PB + 2KB)^2; \quad \text{[Prop. 1]}$$

and $PB + 2KB - 2 = PB + 2KB - PK = 3KB$,

while $3 + 1 = 2 . 2$, or 3 is one less than the double of 2.

Now, since the sum of the terms of the progression

[1] *Deferred lemma.*

To prove that $(GH+HM)^2 . KB^2$
$= \{(GH+HM) . KB\}^2$.

Let $\alpha = GH + HM$,
$\beta = KB$,
$\gamma = (GH + HM) . KB$.

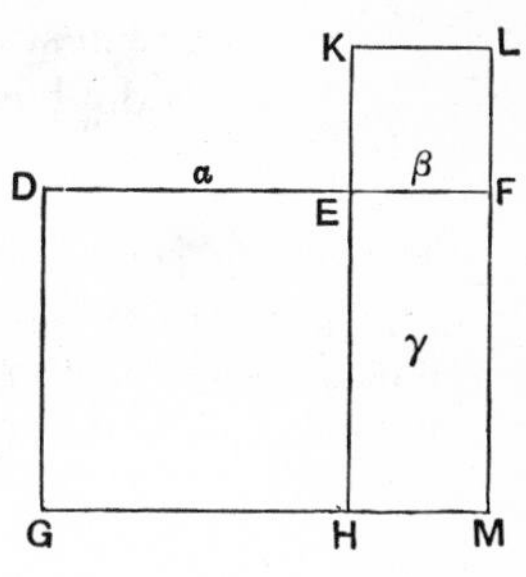

Place DE (equal to α) and EF (equal to β) in a straight line.

Describe squares DH, EL on DE, EF and complete the figure.

Then $DE : EF = DH : HF$,
and $HE : EK = HF : EL$.

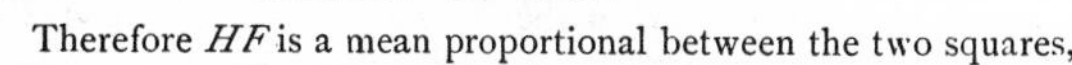

Therefore HF is a mean proportional between the two squares,

that is $DH . FK = HF^2$,

or $\alpha^2 . \beta^2 = (\alpha\beta)^2$.

including unity satisfies the same formula[1] [literally "does the same problem"] as PB does,

while PB is *any* number and is also always a polygonal, the first after unity (for AP is a unit and AB is the term next after it), and has 2 for its side,

it follows that the sum of all the terms of the progression is a polygonal with the same number of angles as PB, the number of its angles being the same as the number of units in the number which is greater by 2, or PK, than the common difference KB, and that its side is GH which is equal to the number of terms including 1.

And thus is demonstrated what is stated by Hypsicles in his definition, namely, that,

"If there are as many numbers as we please beginning from 1 and increasing by the same common difference, then, when the common difference is 1, the sum of all the terms is a triangular number; when 2, a square; when 3, a pentagonal number [and so on]. And the number of the angles is called after the number exceeding the common difference by 2, and the side after the number of terms including 1."

[In other words, if there be an arithmetical progression

$$1,\ 1+b,\ 1+2b, \ldots\ 1+(n-1)b,$$

the sum of the n terms, or $\frac{1}{2}n\{2+(n-1)b\}$, is the nth polygonal number which has $(b+2)$ angles.]

Hence, since we have triangles when the common difference is 1, the sides of the triangles will be the greatest term in each case, and the product of the greatest term and the greatest term increased by 1 is double the triangle.

[1] Nesselmann (pp. 475–6), exhibits this result thus.

Take the A.P. $\quad 1,\ 1+b,\ 1+2b, \ldots\ 1+(n-1)b.$

If s is the sum, $\quad 8sb+(b-2)^2=\{b(2n-1)+2\}^2.$

If now we take the three terms $b-2$, b, $b+2$, also in A.P.,

$$8b(b+2)+(b-2)^2=\{(b+2)+2b\}^2$$
$$=(3b+2)^2.$$

Now $b+2$ is the sum of the first two terms of the first series, and corresponds therefore to s when $n=2$; and $3=2.2-1$, so that 3 corresponds to $2n-1$.

Hence s and $b+2$ are subject to the same law; and therefore, as $b+2$ is a polygonal number with $b+2$ angles, s is also a polygonal number (the nth) with $b+2$ angles.

And, since PB is a polygonal with as many angles as there are units in it,

and $8PB.(PB-2)+(PB-4)^2=$ a square (from above, BK being equal to $PB-2$, and NB to $PB-4$),

the definition of polygonal numbers will be as follows:

Every polygonal multiplied by 8 times (number of angles -2) + square of (number of angles -4) = a square[1].

The Hypsiclean definition and the new one being thus simultaneously proved, it remains to show how, when the side is given, the prescribed polygonal is found.

For, having given the side GH and the number of angles, we know KB.

Therefore $(GH+HM)\,KB$, which is equal to NO', is also given; therefore $KO'(=NO'+NK$ or $NO'+2)$ is given.

Therefore KO'^2 is given;

and, subtracting from it the given square on NB, we obtain the remaining term which is equal to the required polygonal multiplied by $8KB$. Thus the required polygonal can be found.

Similarly, given the polygonal number, we can find its side GH. Q. E. D.

Rules for practical use.

(1) *To find the number from the side.*

Take the side, double it, subtract 1, and multiply the remainder by (number of angles -2). Add 2 to the product; and from the square of the sum subtract the square of (number of angles -4). Dividing the remainder by 8 times (number of angles -2), we have the required number.

[1] Hultsch points out (art. Diophantos in Pauly-Wissowa's *Real-Encyclopädie der classischen Altertumswissenschaften*) that this formula

$$8P(a-2)+(a-4)^2=\text{a square}$$

shows that Diophantus intended it to be applied not only to cases where a is greater than 4 but also where $a=4$ or less. For 36, as Diophantus must have known, besides being the second 36-gon, is also a triangle, a square, and a 13-gon, inasmuch as

$$8.36(3-2)+(3-4)^2=289=17^2,$$
$$8.36(4-2)+(4-4)^2=576=24^2,$$
$$8.36(13-2)+(13-4)^2=3249=57^2.$$

And indeed it is evident from Def. 9 of the *Arithmetica* that $(3-4)^2=1$, while it is equally obvious that $(4-4)^2=0$.

[If P be the nth a-gonal number,

$$P.8(a-2)+(a-4)^2=\{2+(2n-1)(a-2)\}^2,$$

or

$$P=\frac{\{2+(2n-1)(a-2)\}^2-(a-4)^2}{8(a-2)}.]$$

(2) *To find the side from the number.*

Multiply the number by 8 times (number of angles − 2); add to the product the square of (number of angles − 4). We thus get a square. Subtract 2 from the side of this square and divide the remainder by (number of angles − 2). Add 1 to the quotient, and half the result gives the side required[1].

$$\left[n=\frac{1}{2}\left(\frac{\sqrt{\{P.8(a-2)+(a-4)^2\}}-2}{a-2}+1\right).\right]$$

Given a number, to find in how many ways it can be polygonal.

Let AB be the given number, BC the number of angles, and in BC take $CD=2$, $CE=4$.

[*Algebraical equivalent.*]
Number $AB=P$.
Number of angles $BC=a$.

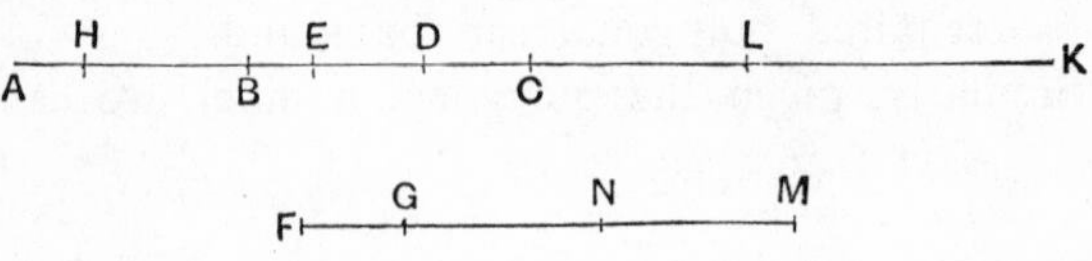

Since the polygonal AB has BC angles,

(1) $8AB.BD+BE^2=$ a square $=FG^2$, say.

Cut off AH equal to 1;

therefore $8AB.BD$

$$=4AH.BD+4(AB+BH)BD.$$

Make DK equal to $4(AB+BH)$, and for $4AH.BD$ put $2BD.DE$.

$$8P(a-2)+(a-4)^2$$
$$=\{2+(2n-1)(a-2)\}^2$$
$$=X^2, \text{ say.}$$

But $8P(a-2)$

$$=4(a-2)+4(2P-1)(a-2)$$
$$=2(a-2).2+4(2P-1)(a-2).$$
$$DK=4(2P-1)$$

[1] Fermat has the following note. "A very beautiful and wonderful proposition which I have discovered shall be set down here without proof. *If, in the series of natural numbers beginning with* 1, *any number n be multiplied into the next following*, $n+1$, *the product is twice the nth triangular number; if n be multiplied into the* $(n+1)$*th triangular number, the product is three times the nth tetrahedral number; if n be multiplied into the* $(n+1)$*th tetrahedral number, the product is four times the nth triangulo-triangular number* [*figured number of* 4*th order*]; *and so on, ad infinitum.* I do not think there can be, in the theory of numbers, any theorem more beautiful or more general. The margin is too small, and I am not at liberty, to give the proof." (Cf. Letter to Roberval of 4 November 1636, *Oeuvres de Fermat*, II. pp. 84, 85.) For a proof, see Wertheim's Diophantus, pp. 318–20.

Therefore

(2) $FG^2 = KD.DB + 2BD.DE + BE^2$,

$$X^2 = 4(2P-1)(a-2) + 2(a-2).2 + (a-4)^2$$

(3) $\quad = KD.DB + BD^2 + DE^2$, [Eucl. II. 7]

$$= 4(2P-1)(a-2) + (a-2)^2 + 2^2$$

(4) $\quad = KB.BD + DE^2$. [Eucl. II. 1]

$$= \{4(2P-1) + a - 2\}(a-2) + 2^2$$

But, since $DK = 4(AB + BH)$,

$$DK > 4AH > 4,$$

and $\quad DC =$ half 4 or 2;

therefore $\quad CK > CD$.

Therefore, if DK be bisected at L, L falls between C and K.

$$DL = 2(2P-1)$$

$$[BL = 2(2P-1) + a - 2]$$

And, since DK is bisected at L,

$$KB.BD + LD^2 = LB^2,$$

whence $KB.BD = LB^2 - LD^2$.

Therefore, by (4) above,

(5) $FG^2 = BL^2 - LD^2 + DE^2$,

or $\quad FG^2 + DL^2 = BL^2 + DE^2$,

$$X^2 = \{2(2P-1) + a - 2\}^2 - \{2(2P-1)\}^2 + 2^2$$

(6) or $LD^2 - DE^2 = LB^2 - FG^2$.

$$\{2(2P-1)\}^2 - 2^2 = \{2(2P-1) + a - 2\}^2 - X^2$$

Again, since $ED = DC$, and DC is produced to L,

$$EL.LC + CD^2 = DL^2;$$

therefore $EL.LC = DL^2 - DC^2$

$$= DL^2 - DE^2$$

(7) $\quad = LB^2 - FG^2$.

$$[EL = 2(2P-1) + 2, \quad CL = 2(2P-1) - 2]$$

$$\{2(2P-1)+2\}\{2(2P-1)-2\} = \{2(2P-1) + a - 2\}^2 - X^2$$

Put $FM = BL$ (for $BL > FG$, since $FG^2 + DL^2 = BL^2 + ED^2$, while $DL^2 > ED^2$).

$$FM = 2(2P-1) + a - 2$$

Therefore $FM^2 - FG^2 = EL.LC$.

Now, DK being bisected at L and being equal to $4(AB + BH)$,

$$DL = 2(AB + BH).$$

And $\quad DC = 2AH$.

Therefore $CL = 4BH$,

or $\quad BH = \frac{1}{4}CL$.

$$CL = 4(P-1)$$

But $\quad AH(=1) = \frac{1}{4}EC$;

therefore $\quad AB = \frac{1}{4}EL$,

while $\quad BH = \frac{1}{4}CL$.

$$EL = 4P$$

Therefore $AB.BH = \frac{1}{16}EL.LC$,

or $\quad EL.LC = 16AB.BH$.

(8) Therefore $16AB . BH = MF^2 - FG^2$	$16P(P-1)$ $= \{2(2P-1)+a-2\}^2 - X^2$
(9) $= GM^2 + 2FG . GM.$	$= \{2(2P-1)+a-2-X\}^2$ $+2X\{2(2P-1)+a-2-X\}$
Therefore GM is even.	$[=\{2(2P-2)-2(n-1)(a-2)\}^2$
Let GM be bisected at N	$+2\{2+(2n-1)(a-2)\}$
....	$\times\{2(2P-2)-2(n-1)(a-2)\}]$

[Here the fragment ends, and the question of course arises whether Diophantus ever actually solved the problem of finding in how many different ways a given number can be a polygonal. Tannery went so far as to call the whole of the fragment, from and including the enunciation of the problem, the "vain attempt of a commentator" to solve it[1]. Wertheim[2] has however shown grounds for thinking that Diophantus did solve the problem and that the fragment is a genuine part of his argument leading to that result. The equation

$$8P(a-2)+(a-4)^2 = \{2+(2n-1)(a-2)\}^2$$

easily reduces (by algebra) to

$$8P(a-2) = 4n(a-2)\{2+(n-1)(a-2)\},$$

or

$$2P = n\{2+(n-1)(a-2)\}.$$

Wertheim has shown how this result can be obtained by a continuation of the work, from the point where the fragment leaves off, in the same geometrical form which is used up to that point[3], and how, when the

[1] Dioph. I. pp. 476–7, notes.

[2] *Zeitschrift für Math. u. Physik*, hist. litt. Abtheilung, 1897, pp. 121–6.

[3] The only thing, so far as I can see, tending to raise doubt as to the correctness of this restoration is the fact that, supposing it to be required to prove geometrically, from the geometrical equivalent of

$$8P(a-2)+(a-4)^2 = \{2+(2n-1)(a-2)\}^2,$$

that

$$2P = n\{2+(n-1)(a-2)\},$$

it can be done much more easily than it is in Diophantus' proposition as extended by Wertheim.

For let $FG = 2+(2n-1)(a-2)$. Cut off FR equal to 2, and produce RF to S so that $RS = a-2$.

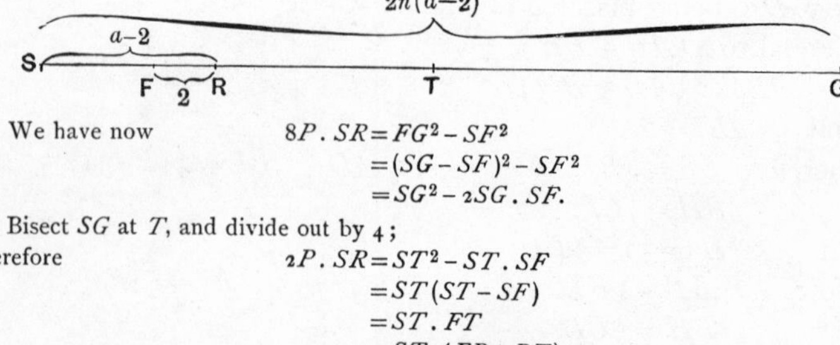

We have now $8P . SR = FG^2 - SF^2$
$= (SG - SF)^2 - SF^2$
$= SG^2 - 2SG . SF.$

Bisect SG at T, and divide out by 4;

therefore $2P . SR = ST^2 - ST . SF$
$= ST(ST - SF)$
$= ST . FT$
$= ST . (FR + RT).$

Now $ST = n . SR$, and $FR = 2$, while $RT = (n-1) . SR = (n-1)(a-2)$.

It follows that $2P = n\{2+(n-1)(a-2)\}.$

formula is thus obtained, it can be used for the purpose of finding the number of ways in which P can be a polygonal number. The portion of the geometrical argument which has to be supplied is, it is true, somewhat long, and its length and difficulty may, as Wertheim suggests, account for the copyist having failed, as it were, to see his way through it and having stopped through discouragement when he had lost his bearings.

I shall now reproduce Wertheim's suggested restoration of the rest of the problem. The figure requires some extension, and I accordingly give a new one after Wertheim.

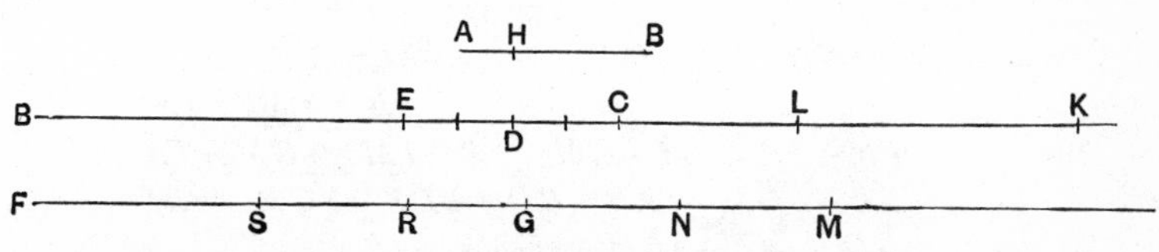

The last step in the above fragment is	
(9) $2FG \cdot GM + GM^2 = 16AB \cdot BH.$	$2\{2+(2n-1)(a-2)\}\{2(2P-2)-2(n-1)(a-2)\} + \{2(2P-2)-2(n-1)(a-2)\}^2 = 16P(P-1)$
Bisect GM in N, so that $GN = NM.$	$GN = NM = 2(P-1)-(n-1)(a-2)$
Therefore, if we divide by 4, (10) $FG \cdot GN + GN^2 = 4AB \cdot BH,$	$\{2+(2n-1)(a-2)\}\{2(P-1)-(n-1)(a-2)\} + \{2(P-1)-(n-1)(a-2)\}^2 = 4P(P-1)$
or (11) $FN \cdot NG = 4AB \cdot BH.$	$\{2P+n(a-2)\}\{2(P-1)-(n-1)(a-2)\} = 4P(P-1)$
Put now $FR = 2AB$, and $RS = GN$, so that $GS = RN$, and we have $FS = FR - RS = 2AB - RS,$	$FS = 2P - \{2(P-1)-(n-1)(a-2)\} = 2+(n-1)(a-2)$
$FN = FR + RN = 2AB + RN,$	$FN = 2P + n(a-2)$, from above
$GN = RS = 2AB - FS.$	$GN = 2(P-1)-(n-1)(a-2)$
Substituting in (11), we have	$RN = FN - 2AB = n(a-2)$
(12) $(2AB + RN)(2AB - FS) = 4AB \cdot BH,$	$\{2P+n(a-2)\}\{2(P-1)-(n-1)(a-2)\} = 4P(P-1)$

or (13) $4AB^2 - 2AB(FS - RN)$ $- RN.FS = 4AB^2 - 4AB.AH.$	$4P^2$ $-2P\{(n-1)(a-2)+2-n(a-2)\}$ $-n(a-2)\{(n-1)(a-2)+2\}$ $=4P^2-4P$
Therefore (14) $2AB(FS - RN) + RN.FS$ $= 4AB.AH,$	$2P\{2-(a-2)\}$ $+n(a-2)\{(n-1)(a-2)+2\}$ $=4P$
or (15) $2AB(2AH + RN - FS) = RN.FS.$	$2P(a-2)$ $= n(a-2)\{(n-1)(a-2)+2\}$

Now $RN = FN - FR = FM - NM - FR = FM - \frac{1}{2}GM - FR$

$= BL - \frac{1}{2}GM - 2AB = BD + \frac{1}{2}DK - \frac{1}{2}GM - 2AB$

$= BD + 2AB + 2BH - \frac{1}{2}GM - 2AB$

$= BD + 2BH - \frac{1}{2}GM,$

and $FS = FR - RS$

$= 2AB - \frac{1}{2}GM.$

Therefore $RN - FS = BD + 2BH - 2AB$

$= BD - 2AH,$

and $RN - FS + 2AH = BD.$

Again, we have

$RN = BD + 2BH - \frac{1}{2}GM = BD + 2BH - \frac{1}{2}BL + \frac{1}{2}FG$

$= BD + 2BH - \frac{1}{2}BD - \frac{1}{2}DL + \frac{1}{2}FG$

$= \frac{1}{2}BD + 2BH - \frac{1}{2}DL + \frac{1}{2}FG$

$= \frac{1}{2}BD + 2BH - (AB + BH) + \frac{1}{2}FG$

$= \frac{1}{2}BD + BH - AB + \frac{1}{2}FG$

$= \frac{1}{2}BD - AH + \frac{1}{2}FG$

$= \frac{1}{2}(BD + FG - 2AH).$

But, from the rule just preceding this proposition,

$FG = BD(2n-1) + 2;$

therefore $BD + FG = 2n.BD + 2,$

or $BD + FG - 2AH = 2n.BD;$

therefore $RN = n.BD.$

Accordingly the equation (15) above becomes

(16) $2AB.BD = n.BD.FS,$ or (17) $2AB = n.FS.$	$2P(a-2)$ $= n(a-2)\{(n-1)(a-2)+2\}$ $2P = n\{(n-1)(a-2)+2\}$

Thus the double of any polygonal number must be divisible by its side, and the quotient is the number arrived at by adding 2 to the product of (side − 1) and (number of angles − 2).

For a triangular number the quotient is $n+1$, and is therefore greater than the side; and, as the quotient increases by $n-1$ for every increase of 1 in the number of angles (a), it is always greater than the side.

We can therefore use the above formula (17) to find the number of ways in which a given number P can be a polygonal number. Separate $2P$ into two factors in all possible ways, excluding $1 . 2P$. Take the smaller factor as the side (n). Then take the other factor, subtract 2 from it, and divide the remainder by $(n-1)$. If $(n-1)$ divides it without a remainder, the particular factors taken answer the purpose, and the quotient increased by 2 gives the number of angles (a). If the second factor diminished by 2 is not divisible by $(n-1)$ without a remainder, the particular division into factors is useless for the purpose. The number of ways in which P can be a polygonal is the number of pairs of factors which answer the purpose. There is always one pair of factors which will serve, namely 2 and P itself.

The process of finding pairs of factors is shortened by the following considerations.

$$2P = n\{(n-1)(a-2)+2\};$$

therefore

$$2P/n = 4 + an - a - 2n,$$

and

$$a = 2 + \frac{2(P-n)}{n(n-1)};$$

therefore not only $2P/n$ but also $\frac{2(P-n)}{n(n-1)}$ must be a whole number and, as a is not less than 3,

$$\frac{2(P-n)}{n(n-1)} > \text{or} = 1,$$

and consequently

$$n < \text{or} = \frac{-1+\sqrt{(1+8P)}}{2}.$$

Thus in choosing values for the factor n we need not go beyond that shown in the right-hand expression.

Example 1. In what ways is 325 a polygonal number?

Here $-1+\sqrt{(1+8P)} = -1+\sqrt{(2601)} = 50$. Therefore n cannot be greater than 25. Now $2 . 325 = 2 . 5 . 5 . 13$, and the only possible values for n are therefore 2, 5, 10, 13, 25. The corresponding values for a are shown in the following table.

n	2	5	10	13	25
a	325	34	9	6	3

Example 2. $P = 120$.

n	2	3	4	5	6	8	10	12	15
a	120	41	—	—	—	6	—	—	3

CONSPECTUS OF THE ARITHMETICA

Equations of the first degree with one unknown.

I. 7. $x - a = m(x - b)$.

I. 8. $x + a = m(x + b)$.

I. 9. $a - x = m(b - x)$.

I. 10. $x + b = m(a - x)$.

I. 11. $x + b = m(x - a)$.

I. 39. $\left.\begin{array}{l}(a + x)b + (b + x)a = 2(a + b)x, \\ \text{or } (a + b)x + (b + x)a = 2(a + x)b, \\ \text{or } (a + b)x + (a + x)b = 2(b + x)a,\end{array}\right\} \quad (a > b)$.

Determinate systems of equations of the first degree.

I. 1. $x + y = a,\ x - y = b$.

I. 2. $x + y = a,\ x = my$.

I. 4. $x - y = a,\ x = my$.

I. 3. $x + y = a,\ x = my + b$.

I. 5. $x + y = a,\ \frac{1}{m}x + \frac{1}{n}y = b$.

I. 6. $x + y = a,\ \frac{1}{m}x - \frac{1}{n}y = b$.

I. 12. $x_1 + x_2 = y_1 + y_2 = a,\ x_1 = my_2,\ y_1 = nx_2, \quad (x_1 > x_2,\ y_1 > y_2)$.

I. 13. $\left.\begin{array}{l}x_1 + x_2 = y_1 + y_2 = z_1 + z_2 = a \\ x_1 = my_2,\ y_1 = nz_2,\ z_1 = px_2\end{array}\right\} \quad (x_1 > x_2,\ y_1 > y_2,\ z_1 > z_2)$.

I. 15. $x + a = m(y - a),\ y + b = n(x - b)$.

I. 16. $y + z = a,\ z + x = b,\ x + y = c$.

I. 17. $y + z + w = a,\ z + w + x = b,\ w + x + y = c,\ x + y + z = d$.

I. 18. $y + z - x = a,\ z + x - y = b,\ x + y - z = c$.

I. 19. $y + z + w - x = a,\ z + w + x - y = b,\ w + x + y - z = c,$
$x + y + z - w = d$.

I. 20. $x + y + z = a,\ x + y = mz,\ y + z = nx$.

I. 21. $x = y + \frac{1}{m}z,\ y = z + \frac{1}{n}x,\ z = a + \frac{1}{p}y, \quad (x > y > z)$.

II. 18*. $$\left.\begin{array}{l} x - \left(\frac{1}{m}x + a\right) + \left(\frac{1}{p}z + c\right) = y - \left(\frac{1}{n}y + b\right) + \left(\frac{1}{m}x + a\right) \\ \qquad = z - \left(\frac{1}{p}z + c\right) + \left(\frac{1}{n}y + b\right), \\ x + y + z = a. \end{array}\right\}$$

Determinate systems of equations reducible to the first degree

I. 26. $ax = \alpha^2,\ bx = \alpha$.

I. 29. $x + y = a,\ x^2 - y^2 = b$.

* Probably spurious.

I. 31. $x=my,\ x^2+y^2=n(x+y)$.
I. 32. $x=my,\ x^2+y^2=n(x-y)$.
I. 33. $x=my,\ x^2-y^2=n(x+y)$.
I. 34. $x=my,\ x^2-y^2=n(x-y)$.
I. 34. Cor. 1. $x=my,\ xy=n(x+y)$.
Cor. 2. $x=my,\ xy=n(x-y)$.

I. 35. $x=my,\ y^2=nx$.
I. 36. $x=my,\ y^2=ny$.
I. 37. $x=my,\ y^2=n(x+y)$.
I. 38. $x=my,\ y^2=n(x-y)$.
I. 38. Cor. $x=my,\ x^2=ny$.
" $x=my,\ x^2=nx$.
" $x=my,\ x^2=n(x+y)$.
" $x=my,\ x^2=n(x-y)$.
II. 6*. $x-y=a,\ x^2-y^2=x-y+b$.
IV. 36. $yz=m(y+z),\ zx=n(z+x),\ xy=p(x+y)$.

Determinate systems reducible to equations of second degree.

I. 27. $x+y=a,\ xy=b$.
I. 3 . $x-y=a,\ xy=b$.
I. 28. $x+y=a,\ x^2+y^2=b$.
IV. 1. $x^3+y^3=a,\ x+y=b$.
IV. 2. $x^3-y^3=a,\ x-y=b$.
IV. 15. $(y+z)x=a,\ (z+x)y=b,\ (x+y)z=c$.
IV. 34. $yz+(y+z)=a^2-1,\ zx+(z+x)=b^2-1,\ xy+(x+y)=c^2-1$.
IV. 35. $yz-(y+z)=a^2-1,\ zx-(z+x)=b^2-1,\ xy-(x+y)=c^2-1$.
IV. 37. $yz=m(x+y+z),\ zx=n(x+y+z),\ xy=p(x+y+z)$.
Lemma to V. 8. $yz=a^2,\ zx=b^2,\ xy=c^2$.

Systems of equations apparently indeterminate but really reduced, by arbitrary assumptions, to determinate equations of the first degree.

I. 14. $xy=m(x+y)$ [value of y arbitrarily assumed].
II. 3*. $xy=m(x+y)$ and $xy=m(x-y)$
II. 1*. (cf. I. 31.) $x^2+y^2=m(x+y)$
II. 2*. (cf. I. 34.) $x^2-y^2=m(x-y)$ [x assumed $=2y$].
II. 4*. (cf. I. 32.) $x^2+y^2=m(x-y)$
II. 5*. (cf. I. 33.) $x^2-y^2=m(x+y)$
II. 7*. $x^2-y^2=m(x-y)+a$ [Diophantus assumes $x-y=2$].

I. 22. $x-\frac{1}{m}x+\frac{1}{p}z=y-\frac{1}{n}y+\frac{1}{m}x=z-\frac{1}{p}z+\frac{1}{n}y$ [value of y assumed].

I. 23. $x-\frac{1}{m}x+\frac{1}{q}w=y-\frac{1}{n}y+\frac{1}{m}x$
$=z-\frac{1}{p}z+\frac{1}{n}y=w-\frac{1}{q}w+\frac{1}{p}z$ [value of y assumed].

* Probably spurious.

I. 24. $x + \frac{1}{m}(y+z) = y + \frac{1}{n}(z+x) = z + \frac{1}{p}(x+y)$

[value of $y + z$ assumed].

I. 25. $x + \frac{1}{m}(y+z+w) = y + \frac{1}{n}(z+w+x)$

$$= z + \frac{1}{p}(w+x+y) = w + \frac{1}{q}(x+y+z)$$

[value of $y + z + w$ assumed].

II. 17*. (cf. I. 22.) $x - \left(\frac{1}{m}x + a\right) + \left(\frac{1}{p}z + c\right)$

$$= y - \left(\frac{1}{n}y + b\right) + \left(\frac{1}{m}x + a\right) = z - \left(\frac{1}{p}z + c\right) + \left(\frac{1}{n}y + b\right)$$

[ratio of x to y assumed].

IV. 33. $x + \frac{1}{z}y = m\left(y - \frac{1}{z}y\right),\ y + \frac{1}{z}x = n\left(x - \frac{1}{z}x\right)$

[Diophantus assumes $\frac{1}{z}y = 1$].

Indeterminate equations of the first degree.

Lemma to IV. 34. $xy + (x+y) = a$
" " IV. 35. $xy - (x+y) = a$
" " IV. 36. $xy = m(x+y)$

[Solutions ἐν ἀορίστῳ. y practically found in terms of x.]

Indeterminate analysis of the second degree.

II. 8. $x^2 + y^2 = a^2$.
II. 9. $x^2 + y^2 = a^2 + b^2$.
II. 10. $x^2 - y^2 = a$.
II. 11. $x + a = u^2,\ x + b = v^2$.
II. 12. $a - x = u^2,\ b - x = v^2$.
II. 13. $x - a = u^2,\ x - b = v^2$.
II. 14 = III. 21. $x + y = a,\ x + z^2 = u^2,\ y + z^2 = v^2$.
II. 15 = III. 20. $x + y = a,\ z^2 - x = u^2,\ z^2 - y = v^2$.
II. 16. $x = my,\ a^2 + x = u^2,\ a^2 + y = v^2$.
II. 19. $x^2 - y^2 = m(y^2 - z^2)$.
II. 20. $x^2 + y = u^2,\ y^2 + x = v^2$.
II. 21. $x^2 - y = u^2,\ y^2 - x = v^2$.
II. 22. $x^2 + (x+y) = u^2,\ y^2 + (x+y) = v^2$.
II. 23. $x^2 - (x+y) = u^2,\ y^2 - (x+y) = v^2$.
II. 24. $(x+y)^2 + x = u^2,\ (x+y)^2 + y = v^2$.
II. 25. $(x+y)^2 - x = u^2,\ (x+y)^2 - y = v^2$.
II. 26. $xy + x = u^2,\ xy + y = v^2,\ u + v = a$.
II. 27. $xy - x = u^2,\ xy - y = v^2,\ u + v = a$.
II. 28. $x^2y^2 + x^2 = u^2,\ x^2y^2 + y^2 = v^2$.
II. 29. $x^2y^2 - x^2 = u^2,\ x^2y^2 - y^2 = v^2$.
II. 30. $xy + (x+y) = u^2,\ xy - (x+y) = v^2$.

* Probably spurious.

II. 31. $xy+(x+y)=u^2,\ xy-(x+y)=v^2,\ x+y=w^2.$

II. 32. $y^2+z=u^2,\ z^2+x=v^2,\ x^2+y=w^2.$

II. 33. $y^2-z=u^2,\ z^2-x=v^2,\ x^2-y=w^2.$

II. 34. $x^2+(x+y+z)=u^2,\ y^2+(x+y+z)=v^2,\ z^2+(x+y+z)=w^2.$

II. 35. $x^2-(x+y+z)=u^2,\ y^2-(x+y+z)=v^2,\ z^2-(x+y+z)=w^2.$

III. 1*. $(x+y+z)-x^2=u^2,\ (x+y+z)-y^2=v^2,\ (x+y+z)-z^2=w^2.$

III. 2*. $(x+y+z)^2+x=u^2,\ (x+y+z)^2+y=v^2,\ (x+y+z)^2+z=w^2.$

III. 3*. $(x+y+z)^2-x=u^2,\ (x+y+z)^2-y=v^2,\ (x+y+z)^2-z=w^2.$

III. 4*. $x-(x+y+z)^2=u^2,\ y-(x+y+z)^2=v^2,\ z-(x+y+z)^2=w^2.$

III. 5. $x+y+z=t^2,\ y+z-x=u^2,\ z+x-y=v^2,\ x+y-z=w^2.$

III. 6. $x+y+z=t^2,\ y+z=u^2,\ z+x=v^2,\ x+y=w^2.$

III. 7. $x-y=y-z,\ y+z=u^2,\ z+x=v^2,\ x+y=w^2.$

III. 8. $x+y+z+a=t^2,\ y+z+a=u^2,\ z+x+a=v^2,\ x+y+a=w^2.$

III. 9. $x+y+z-a=t^2,\ y+z-a=u^2,\ z+x-a=v^2,\ x+y-a=w^2.$

III. 10. $yz+a=u^2,\ zx+a=v^2,\ xy+a=w^2.$

III. 11. $yz-a=u^2,\ zx-a=v^2,\ xy-a=w^2.$

III. 12. $yz+x=u^2,\ zx+y=v^2,\ xy+z=w^2.$

III. 13. $yz-x=u^2,\ zx-y=v^2,\ xy-z=w^2.$

III. 14. $yz+x^2=u^2,\ zx+y^2=v^2,\ xy+z^2=w^2.$

III. 15. $yz+(y+z)=u^2,\ zx+(z+x)=v^2,\ xy+(x+y)=w^2.$

III. 16. $yz-(y+z)=u^2,\ zx-(z+x)=v^2,\ xy-(x+y)=w^2.$

III. 17. $xy+(x+y)=u^2,\ xy+x=v^2,\ xy+y=w^2.$

III. 18. $xy-(x+y)=u^2,\ xy-x=v^2,\ xy-y=w^2.$

III. 19. $(x_1+x_2+x_3+x_4)^2\pm x_1=\begin{Bmatrix}t^2\\ t'^2\end{Bmatrix},$

$(x_1+x_2+x_3+x_4)^2\pm x_2=\begin{Bmatrix}u^2\\ u'^2\end{Bmatrix},$

$(x_1+x_2+x_3+x_4)^2\pm x_3=\begin{Bmatrix}v^2\\ v'^2\end{Bmatrix},$

$(x_1+x_2+x_3+x_4)^2\pm x_4=\begin{Bmatrix}w^2\\ w'^2\end{Bmatrix}.$

IV. 4. $x^2+y=u^2,\ x+y=u.$

IV. 5. $x^2+y=u,\ x+y=u^2.$

IV. 13. $x+1=t^2,\ y+1=u^2,\ x+y+1=v^2,\ x-y+1=w^2.$

IV. 14. $x^2+y^2+z^2=(x^2-y^2)+(y^2-z^2)+(x^2-z^2)\quad (x>y>z).$

IV. 16. $x+y+z=t^2,\ x^2+y=u^2,\ y^2+z=v^2,\ z^2+x=w^2.$

IV. 17. $x+y+z=t^2,\ x^2-y=u^2,\ y^2-z=v^2,\ z^2-x=w^2.$

IV. 19. $yz+1=u^2,\ zx+1=v^2,\ xy+1=w^2.$

IV. 20. $x_2x_3+1=r^2,\ x_3x_1+1=s^2,\ x_1x_2+1=t^2,$

$x_1x_4+1=u^2,\ x_2x_4+1=v^2,\ x_3x_4+1=w^2.$

IV. 21. $xz=y^2,\ x-y=u^2,\ x-z=v^2,\ y-z=w^2\quad (x>y>z).$

IV. 22. $xyz+x=u^2,\ xyz+y=v^2,\ xyz+z=w^2.$

IV. 23. $xyz-x=u^2,\ xyz-y=v^2,\ xyz-z=w^2.$

* Probably spurious.

IV. 29. $x^2+y^2+z^2+w^2+x+y+z+w=a$.
IV. 30. $x^2+y^2+z^2+w^2-(x+y+z+w)=a$.
IV. 31. $x+y=1,\ (x+a)(y+b)=u^2$.
IV. 32. $x+y+z=a,\ xy+z=u^2,\ xy-z=v^2$.
IV. 39. $x-y=m(y-z),\ y+z=u^2,\ z+x=v^2,\ x+y=w^2$.
IV. 40. $x^2-y^2=m(y-z),\ y+z=u^2,\ z+x=v^2,\ x+y=w^2$.
V. 1. $xz=y^2,\ x-a=u^2,\ y-a=v^2,\ z-a=w^2$.
V. 2. $xz=y^2,\ x+a=u^2,\ y+a=v^2,\ z+a=w^2$.
V. 3. $x+a=r^2,\ y+a=s^2,\ z+a=t^2$,
$yz+a=u^2,\ zx+a=v^2,\ xy+a=w^2$.
V. 4. $x-a=r^2,\ y-a=s^2,\ z-a=t^2$.
$yz-a=u^2,\ zx-a=v^2,\ xy-a=w^2$.
V. 5. $y^2z^2+x^2=r^2,\ z^2x^2+y^2=s^2,\ x^2y^2+z^2=t^2$,
$y^2z^2+y^2+z^2=u^2,\ z^2x^2+z^2+x^2=v^2,\ x^2y^2+x^2+y^2=w^2$.
V. 6. $x-2=r^2,\ y-2=s^2,\ z-2=t^2$,
$yz-y-z=u^2,\ zx-z-x=v^2,\ xy-x-y=w^2$,
$yz-x=u'^2,\ zx-y=v'^2,\ xy-z=w'^2$.

Lemma 1 to V. 7. $xy+x^2+y^2=u^2$.

V. 7. $x^2\pm(x+y+z)=\begin{Bmatrix}u^2\\u'^2\end{Bmatrix},\ y^2\pm(x+y+z)=\begin{Bmatrix}v^2\\v'^2\end{Bmatrix}$,
$z^2\pm(x+y+z)=\begin{Bmatrix}w^2\\w'^2\end{Bmatrix}$.

V. 8. $yz\pm(x+y+z)=\begin{Bmatrix}u^2\\u'^2\end{Bmatrix},\ zx\pm(x+y+z)=\begin{Bmatrix}v^2\\v'^2\end{Bmatrix}$,
$xy\pm(x+y+z)=\begin{Bmatrix}w^2\\w'^2\end{Bmatrix}$.

V. 9. (cf. II. 11.) $x+y=1,\ x+a=u^2,\ y+a=v^2$.
V. 11. $x+y+z=1,\ x+a=u^2,\ y+a=v^2,\ z+a=w^2$.
V. 10. $x+y=1,\ x+a=u^2,\ y+b=v^2$.
V. 12. $x+y+z=1,\ x+a=u^2,\ y+b=v^2,\ z+c=w^2$.
V. 13. $x+y+z=a,\ y+z=u^2,\ z+x=v^2,\ x+y=w^2$.
V. 14. $x+y+z+w=a$,
$x+y+z=s^2,\ y+z+w=t^2,\ z+w+x=u^2,\ w+x+y=v^2$.
V. 21. $x^2y^2z^2+x^2=u^2,\ x^2y^2z^2+y^2=v^2,\ x^2y^2z^2+z^2=w^2$.
V. 22. $x^2y^2z^2-x^2=u^2,\ x^2y^2z^2-y^2=v^2,\ x^2y^2z^2-z^2=w^2$.
V. 23. $x^2-x^2y^2z^2=u^2,\ y^2-x^2y^2z^2=v^2,\ z^2-x^2y^2z^2=w^2$.
V. 24. $y^2z^2+1=u^2,\ z^2x^2+1=v^2,\ x^2y^2+1=w^2$.
V. 25. $y^2z^2-1=u^2,\ z^2x^2-1=v^2,\ x^2y^2-1=w^2$.
V. 26. $1-y^2z^2=u^2,\ 1-z^2x^2=v^2,\ 1-x^2y^2=w^2$.
V. 27. $y^2+z^2+a=u^2,\ z^2+x^2+a=v^2,\ x^2+y^2+a=w^2$.
V. 28. $y^2+z^2-a=u^2,\ z^2+x^2-a=v^2,\ x^2+y^2-a=w^2$.
V. 30. $mx+ny=u^2,\ u^2+a=(x+y)^2$.

Lemma 2 to VI. 12. $ax^2+b=u^2$ (where $a+b=c^2$).
Lemma to VI. 15. $ax^2-b=u^2$ (where $ad^2-b=c^2$ is known).

[III. 15]. $xy + x + y = u^2,\ x + 1 = \frac{v^2}{w^2}(y + 1).$

[III. 16]. $xy - (x + y) = u^2,\ x - 1 = \frac{v^2}{w^2}(y - 1).$

[IV. 32]. $x + 1 = \frac{u^2}{v^2}(x - 1).$

[V. 21]. $x^2 + 1 = u^2,\ y^2 + 1 = v^2,\ z^2 + 1 = w^2.$

Indeterminate analysis of the third degree.

IV. 3. $x^2y = u,\ xy = u^3.$

IV. 6. $x^3 + y^2 = u^3,\ z^2 + y^2 = v^2.$

IV. 7. $x^3 + y^2 = u^2,\ z^2 + y^2 = v^3.$

IV. 8. $x + y^3 = u^3,\ x + y = u$

IV. 9. $x + y^3 = u,\ x + y = u^3$

IV. 10. $x^3 + y^3 = x + y$

IV. 11. $x^3 - y^3 = x - y$ } the same problem

IV. 12. $x^3 + y = y^3 + x$ }

(IV. 8–12:) Really reducible to second degree.

IV. 18. $x^3 + y = u^3,\ y^2 + x = v^2.$

IV. 24. $x + y = a,\ xy = u^3 - u.$

IV. 25. $x + y + z = a,\ xyz = \{(x-y) + (x-z) + (y-z)\}^3 \quad (x > y > z).$

IV. 26. $xy + x = u^3,\ xy + y = v^3.$

IV. 27. $xy - x = u^3,\ xy - y = v^3.$

IV. 28. $xy + (x + y) = u^3,\ xy - (x + y) = v^3.$

[IV. 28]. $\{\frac{1}{4}(x^3 - y^3)\}^2 - \frac{1}{2}(x^3 + y^3) = u^2.$

IV. 38. $(x + y + z)\,x = \frac{1}{2}u\,(u + 1),\ (x + y + z)\,y = v^2,\ (x + y + z)\,z = w^3.$

V. 15. $(x + y + z)^3 + x = u^3,\ (x + y + z)^3 + y = v^3,\ (x + y + z)^3 + z = w^3.$

V. 16. $(x + y + z)^3 - x = u^3,\ (x + y + z)^3 - y = v^3,\ (x + y + z)^3 - z = w^3.$

V. 17. $x - (x + y + z)^3 = u^3,\ y - (x + y + z)^3 = v^3,\ z - (x + y + z)^3 = w^3.$

V. 18. $x + y + z = t^2,\ (x + y + z)^3 + x = u^2,\ (x + y + z)^3 + y = v^2,\ (x + y + z)^3 + z = w^2.$

V. 19. $x + y + z = t^2,\ (x + y + z)^3 - x = u^2,\ (x + y + z)^3 - y = v^2,\ (x + y + z)^3 - z = w^2.$

V. 19 *a*. $x + y + z = t^2,\ x - (x + y + z)^3 = u^2,\ y - (x + y + z)^3 = v^2,\ z - (x + y + z)^3 = w^2.$

V. 19 *b*. $x + y + z = a,\ (x + y + z)^3 + x = u^2,\ (x + y + z)^3 + y = v^2,\ (x + y + z)^3 + z = w^2.$

V. 19 *c*. $x + y + z = a,\ (x + y + z)^3 - x = u^2,\ (x + y + z)^3 - y = v^2,\ (x + y + z)^3 - z = w^2.$

V. 20. $x + y + z = \frac{1}{m},\ x - (x + y + z)^3 = u^2,\ y - (x + y + z)^3 = v^2,\ z - (x + y + z)^3 = w^2.$

[IV. 8]. $x - y = 1,\ x^3 - y^3 = u^2.$

[IV. 9, 10]. $x^3 + y^3 = \frac{u^2}{v^2}(x + y).$

[IV. 11]. $x^3 - y^3 = \frac{u^2}{v^2}(x - y).$

[V. 15]. $x^3+y^3+z^3-3=u^2$.

[V. 16]. $3-(x^3+y^3+z^3)=u^2$.

[V. 17]. $x^3+y^3+z^3+3=u^2$.

Indeterminate analysis of the fourth degree.

V. 29. $x^4+y^4+z^4=u^2$.

[V. 18]. $x^2+y^2+z^2-3=u^4$.

Problems of constructing right-angled triangles with sides in rational numbers and satisfying various other conditions.

[N.B. I shall use x, y for the perpendicular sides and z for the hypotenuse in all cases, so that the condition $x^2+y^2=z^2$ must be understood to apply in every case in addition to the other conditions specified.]

Lemma to V. 7. $xy=x_1y_1=x_2y_2$.

{VI. 1. $z-x=u^3$, $z-y=v^3$.
VI. 2. $z+x=u^3$, $z+y=v^3$.

{VI. 3. $\frac{1}{2}xy+a=u^2$.
VI. 4. $\frac{1}{2}xy-a=u^2$.
VI. 5. $a-\frac{1}{2}xy=u^2$.

{VI. 6. $\frac{1}{2}xy+x=a$.
VI. 7. $\frac{1}{2}xy-x=a$.

{VI. 8. $\frac{1}{2}xy+(x+y)=a$.
VI. 9. $\frac{1}{2}xy-(x+y)=a$.

{VI. 10. $\frac{1}{2}xy+(x+z)=a$.
VI. 11. $\frac{1}{2}xy-(x+z)=a$.

Lemma 1 to VI. 12. $x=u^2$, $x-y=v^2$, $\frac{1}{2}xy+y=w^2$.

{VI. 12. $\frac{1}{2}xy+x=u^2$, $\frac{1}{2}xy+y=v^2$.
VI. 13. $\frac{1}{2}xy-x=u^2$, $\frac{1}{2}xy-y=v^2$.

{VI. 14. $\frac{1}{2}xy-z=u^2$, $\frac{1}{2}xy-x=v^2$.
VI. 15. $\frac{1}{2}xy+z=u^2$, $\frac{1}{2}xy+x=v^2$.

VI. 16. $\xi+\eta=x$, $\xi/\eta=y/z$.

{VI. 17. $\frac{1}{2}xy+z=u^2$, $x+y+z=v^3$.
VI. 18. $\frac{1}{2}xy+z=u^3$, $x+y+z=v^2$.

{VI. 19. $\frac{1}{2}xy+x=u^2$, $x+y+z=v^3$.
VI. 20. $\frac{1}{2}xy+x=u^3$, $x+y+z=v^2$.

{VI. 21. $x+y+z=u^2$, $\frac{1}{2}xy+(x+y+z)=v^3$.
VI. 22. $x+y+z=u^3$, $\frac{1}{2}xy+(x+y+z)=v^2$.

VI. 23. $z^2=u^2+u$, $z^2/x=v^3+v$.

VI. 24. $z=u^3+u$, $x=v^3-v$, $y=w^3$.

[VI. 6, 7]. $(\frac{1}{2}x)^2+\frac{1}{2}mxy=u^2$.

[VI. 8, 9]. $\{\frac{1}{2}(x+y)\}^2+\frac{1}{2}mxy=u^2$.

[VI. 10, 11]. $\{\frac{1}{2}(z+x)\}^2+\frac{1}{2}mxy=u^2$.

[VI. 12]. $y+(x-y)\cdot\frac{1}{2}xy=u^2$, $x=v^2$ $(x>y)$.

[VI. 14, 15]. $u^2zx-\frac{1}{2}xy\cdot x(z-x)=v^2$ $(u^2 < \text{or} > \frac{1}{2}xy)$.

SUPPLEMENT

ADDITIONAL NOTES, THEOREMS AND PROBLEMS BY FERMAT, TO WHICH ARE ADDED SOME SOLUTIONS BY EULER

I HAVE generally referred to the notes of Fermat, and allied propositions of his, on the particular problems of Diophantus which were the occasion of such notes, illustrations or extensions; but there are some cases where the notes would have been of disproportionate length to give in the places where they occur. Again, some further explanations and additional theorems and problems given by Fermat are not in the notes to Diophantus but elsewhere, namely in his correspondence or in the *Doctrinae Analyticae Inventum Novum* of Jacques de Billy "based on various letters sent to him from time to time by Pierre de Fermat" and originally included at the beginning of the 2nd (1670) edition of Bachet's Diophantus (the *Inventum Novum* is also published, in a free French translation by Tannery, in *Oeuvres de Fermat*, Vol. III. pp. 323–398). Some of these theorems and problems are not so closely connected with particular problems in Diophantus as to suggest that they should be given as notes in one place rather than another. In these circumstances it seemed best to collect the additional matter at the end of the book by way of Supplement.

In the chapter on the Porisms and other assumptions in Diophantus (pp. 106–110 above) I quoted some famous propositions of Fermat on the subject of numbers which are the sums of two, three or four square numbers respectively. The first section of this Supplement shall be devoted to completing, so far as possible, the story of Fermat's connexion with these theorems.

SECTION I.

ON NUMBERS SEPARABLE INTO INTEGRAL SQUARES.

As already noted, Fermat enunciated, on Diophantus IV. 29, a very general theorem of which one part states that *Every number is either a square or the sum of two, three or four squares.* We shall return to this later, and shall begin with the case of numbers which are the sum of two squares.

1. *On numbers which are the sum of two squares.*

I may repeat the beginning of the note on III. 19 already quoted (p. 106).

"A prime number of the form $4n+1$ is the hypotenuse of a right-angled triangle in one way only, its square is so in two ways, its cube in three, its biquadrate in four ways, and so on *ad infinitum*.

"The same prime number $4n+1$ and its square are the sum of two squares in one way only, its cube and its biquadrate in two ways, its fifth and sixth powers in three ways, and so on *ad infinitum*.

"If a prime number which is the sum of two squares be multiplied into another prime number which is also the sum of two squares, the product will be the sum of two squares in two ways; if the first prime be multiplied into the square of the second prime, the product will be the sum of two squares in three ways; if the first prime be multiplied into the cube of the second, the product will be the sum of two squares in four ways, and so on *ad infinitum*."

Before proceeding further with this remarkable note, it is natural to ask how Fermat could possibly have proved the general proposition that (α) *Every prime number of the form* $4n+1$ *is the sum of two square numbers*, which was actually proved by Euler[1]. Fortunately we have in this case a clear statement by Fermat himself of the line which his argument took. In his "Relation des nouvelles découvertes en la science des nombres" sent by Fermat to Carcavi and shortly after (14 August, 1659) communicated by the latter to Huygens, Fermat begins by a reference to his method of proof by *indefinite diminution* (*descente infinie* or *indéfinie*) and proceeds[2] thus: "I was a long time before I was able to apply my method to *affirmative* questions because the way and manner of getting at them is much more difficult than that which I employ with *negative* theorems. So much so that, when I had to prove that *every prime number of the form* $4n+1$ *is made up of two squares*, I found myself in a pretty fix. But at last a certain reflection many times repeated gave me the necessary light, and affirmative questions yielded to my method, with the aid of some new principles by which sheer necessity compelled me to supplement it. This development of my argument in the case of these affirmative questions takes the following line: if a prime number of the form $4n+1$ selected at random is not made up of two squares, there will exist another prime number of the same sort but less than the given number, and again a third still smaller and so on, descending *ad infinitum*, until you arrive at the number 5 which is the smallest of all numbers of

[1] *Novi Commentarii Academiae Petropolitanae* 1752 and 1753, Vol. IV. (1758), pp. 3–40, 1754 and 1755, Vol. V. (1760), pp. 3–58 = *Commentationes arithmeticae collectae*, 1849, I. pp. 155–173 and pp. 210–233.

[2] *Oeuvres de Fermat*, II. p. 432.

the kind in question and which the argument would require *not* to be made up of two squares, although, in fact, it is so made up. From which we are obliged to infer, by *reductio ad absurdum*, that all numbers of the kind in question are in consequence made up of two squares."

The rest of the note to Diophantus III. 19 is as follows.

"From this consideration it is easy to deduce a solution of the problem

"*To find in how many ways a given number can be the hypotenuse of a right-angled triangle.*

"Take all the primes of the form $4n+1$, *e.g.* 5, 13, 17, which measure the given number.

"If *powers* of these primes measure the given number, set out the *exponents* of the powers; *e.g.* let the given number be measured by the cube of 5, the square of 13, and by 17 itself but no other power of 17; and set out the exponents in order, as 3, 2, 1.

"Take now the product of the first of these and twice the second, and add to the product the sum of the first and second: this gives 17. Multiply this by twice the third exponent and add to the product the sum of 17 and the third exponent: this gives 52, which is *the number of the different right-angled triangles which have the given number for hypotenuse.* [If a, b, c be the exponents, the number of the triangles is $4abc+2(bc+ca+ab)+a+b+c$.] We proceed similarly whatever the number of divisors and exponents.

"Other prime factors which are not of the form $4n+1$, and their powers, do not increase or diminish the number of the right-angled triangles which have the given hypotenuse.

"PROBLEM I. *To find a number which is a hypotenuse in any assigned number of ways.*

"Let the given number of times be 7. We double 7: this gives 14. Add 1, which makes 15. Then seek all the prime numbers which measure it, *i.e.* 3 and 5. Next subtract 1 from each and bisect the remainders. This gives 1 and 2. [In explanation of the process it is only necessary to observe that, for example, $2\{4abc+2(bc+ca+ab)+a+b+c\}+1$ is equal to $(2a+1)(2b+1)(2c+1)$, and so on.] Now choose as many prime numbers of the form $4n+1$ as there are numbers in the result just arrived at, *i.e.* in this case two. Give to these primes the exponents 1, 2 respectively and multiply the results, *i.e.* take one of the primes and multiply it into the square of the other.

"It is clear from this that it is easy to find the *smallest* number which is the hypotenuse of a right-angled triangle in a given number of ways."

[Fermat illustrates the above further in a letter of 25 December 1640 to Mersenne[1].

To find a number which is the hypotenuse of 367 different right-angled triangles and no more.

[1] *Oeuvres de Fermat*, II. pp. 214 sq.

Double the number and add 1; this gives 735. Take all the divisors which are prime numbers: these are 3, 5, 7, 7. Subtract 1 from each and then divide by 2; this gives 1, 2, 3, 3. We have then to take four prime numbers of the form $4n+1$ and give them 1, 2, 3, 3 respectively as exponents. The product of these powers is the number required.

To find the least such number, we must take the four *least* primes of the form $4n+1$, *i.e.* 5, 13, 17, 29, and we must give the smallest of them, in order, the largest exponent; *i.e.* we must take 5^3, 13^3, 17^2 and 29 in this case, and the product of these four numbers is the least number which is the hypotenuse of 367 right-angled triangles and no more.

If the double of the given number + 1 is a prime number, then there is only one possible divisor. Suppose the given number is 20; the double of it *plus* 1 is 41. Subtracting unity and bisecting, we have 20, so that the number to be taken is some prime number of the form $4n+1$ to the power of 20.]

"PROBLEM 2. *To find a number which shall be the sum of two squares in any assigned number of ways.*

"Let the given number be 10. Its double is 20, which, when separated into its prime factors, is 2.2.5. Subtract 1 from each, leaving 1, 1, 4. Take three different prime numbers of the form $4n+1$, say 5, 13, 17, and multiply the biquadrate of one (the exponent being 4) by the product of the other two. The result is the required number.

"By means of this it is easy to find the smallest number which is the sum of two squares in a given number of ways.

"In order to solve the converse problem,

"*To find in how many ways a given number is the sum of two squares*,

"let the given number be 325. The prime factors of the form $4n+1$ contained in this number are 5, 13, the latter being so contained once only, the former to the second power. Set out the exponents 2, 1. Multiply them and add to the product the sum of the two: this gives 5. Add 1, making 6, and take the half of this, namely 3. This is the number of ways in which 325 is the sum of two squares.

"If there were three exponents, as 2, 2, 1, we should proceed thus. Take the product of the first two and add it to their sum: this gives 8. Multiply 8 into the third and add the product to the sum of 8 and the third: this gives 17. Add 1, making 18, and take half of this or 9. This is the number of ways in which the number taken in this second case is the sum of two squares. [If a, b, c be the three exponents, the number of ways is $\frac{1}{2}\{abc+(bc+ca+ab)+(a+b+c)+1\}$ provided that the number represented by this expression is an integer.]

"If the last number which has to be bisected should be odd, we must subtract 1 and take half the remainder.

"But suppose we are next given the following problem to solve:

"*To find a whole number which, when a given number is added to it, becomes a square, and which is the hypotenuse of any assigned number of right-angled triangles.*

"This is difficult. Suppose *e.g.* that a number has to be found which is a hypotenuse in two ways and which, when 2 is added to it, becomes a square.

"The required number will be 2023, and there are an infinite number of others with the same property, as 3362 etc."

2. *On numbers which cannot be the sum of two squares.*

In his note on Diophantus v. 9 Fermat took up a remark of Bachet's to the effect that he believes it to be impossible to divide 21 into two squares because "it is neither a square nor by its nature made up of two squares." Fermat's note was: "The number 21 cannot be divided into two squares (even) in fractions. That I can easily prove. And generally a number divisible by 3 which is not also divisible by 9 cannot be divided into two squares either integral or fractional."

He discusses the matter more generally in a letter of August 1640 to Roberval[1].

"I have made a discovery à propos of the 12th [9th] proposition of the fifth Book of Diophantus (that on which I have supplied what Bachet confesses that he did not know and at the same time restored the corrupted text, a story too long to develop here). I need only enunciate to you my theorem, while reminding you that I proved some time ago that

"*A number of the form $4n-1$ is neither a square nor the sum of two squares, either in integers or fractions.*"

[This proposition was sent by Mersenne to Descartes, on 22 March 1638, as having been proved by Fermat.]

"For the time I rested there, although there are many numbers of the form $4n+1$ which are not squares or the sums of squares either, *e.g.* 21, 33, 77, etc., a fact which made Bachet say on the proposed division of 21 into two squares 'It is, I believe, impossible since 21 is neither a square nor by its nature made up of two squares,' where the word *reor* (I think) clearly shows that he was not aware of the proof of the impossibility. This I have at last discovered and comprehended in the following general proposition.

"*If a given number is divided by the greatest square which measures it, and the quotient is measured by a prime number of the form $4n-1$, the given number is neither a square nor the sum of two squares either integral or fractional.*

[1] *Oeuvres de Fermat*, II. pp. 203–4.

"EXAMPLE. Let the given number be 84. The greatest square which measures it is 4, and the quotient is 21 which is measured by 3 or by 7, both 3 and 7 being of the form $4n-1$. I say that 84 is neither a square nor the sum of two squares either integral or fractional.

"Let the given number be 77. The greatest square which measures it is 1, and the quotient is 77 which is here the same as the given number and is measured by 11 or by 7, each of these numbers being of the form $4n-1$. I say that 77 is neither a square nor the sum of two squares, either in integers or fractions.

"I confess to you frankly that I have found nothing in the theory of numbers which has pleased me so much as the proof of this proposition, and I shall be glad if you will try to discover it, if only for the purpose of showing me whether I think more of my discovery than it deserves.

"Following on this I have proved the following proposition, which is of assistance in the finding of prime numbers.

"*If a number is the sum of two squares prime to one another, I say that it cannot be divided by any prime number of the form* $4n-1$.

"For example, add 1, if you will, to an even square, say the square 10 000 000 000, making 10 000 000 001. I say that 10 000 000 001 cannot be divided by any prime number of the form $4n-1$, and accordingly, when you would try whether it is a prime number, you need not divide by 3, 7, 11 etc."

(The theorem that *Numbers which are the sum of two squares prime to one another have no divisors except such as are likewise the sum of two squares* was proved by Euler[1].)

3. *Numbers* (1) *which are always,* (2) *which can never be, the sum of three squares.*

(1) *The number which is double of any prime number of the form* $8n-1$ *is the sum of three squares* (Letter to Kenelm Digby of June 1658)[2].

E.g. the numbers 7, 23, 31, 47 etc. are primes of the form $8n-1$; the doubles are 14, 46, 62, 94 etc.; and the latter numbers are the sums of three squares.

Fermat adds "I assert that this proposition is true, though I do so in the manner of Conon, an Archimedes not having yet arisen to assert it or prove it."

Lagrange[3] remarks that he has not yet been able to prove the proposition completely. The form $8n-1$ reduces to one or other of the three

[1] *Novi Commentarii Acad. Petropol.* 1752 and 1753, Vol. IV. (1758), pp. 3–40= *Commentationes arithmeticae*, I. pp. 155–173.

[2] *Oeuvres de Fermat*, II. pp. 402 sqq.

[3] "Recherches d'Arithmétique" in Berlin *Mémoires* 1773 and 1775=*Oeuvres de Lagrange*, III. p. 795.

forms $24n-1$, $24n+7$, $24n+15$, of which the first two only are primes. Lagrange had previously proved that every prime number of the form $24n+7$ is of the form x^2+6y^2. The double of this is $2x^2+12y^2$, and

$$2x^2+12y^2=(x+2y)^2+(x-2y)^2+(2y)^2,$$

that is, $2x^2+12y^2$ is the sum of three squares.

The theorem was thus proved for prime numbers of the form $8n-1$, wherever n is not a multiple of 3, but not for prime numbers of the form $24n-1$.

Legendre[1], however, has the theorem that *Every number which is the double of an odd number is the sum of three squares.*

(2) *No number of the form* $24n+7$ *or* $4^m(24n+7)$ *can be the sum of three squares.*

This theorem is substantially stated in Fermat's note on Dioph. v. 11. We may, as a matter of fact, substitute for the forms which he gives the forms $8n+7$ and $4^m(8n+7)$ respectively.

Legendre[2] proved that numbers of the form $8n+7$ are the *only* odd numbers which are not the sum of three squares.

4. *Every number is either a square or the sum of two, three or four squares.*

This theorem is also mentioned in the "Relation des nouvelles découvertes en la science des nombres" already quoted, as a case to which Fermat ultimately found himself able to apply the method of proof by *descente.* He says[3] that there are some other problems which require new principles in order to enable the method of *descente* to be applied, and the discovery of such new principles is sometimes so difficult that they cannot be arrived at except after very great trouble.

"Such is the following question which Bachet on Diophantus admits that he could never prove, and as to which Descartes in one of his letters makes the same statement, going so far as to admit that he regards it as so difficult that he does not see any means of solving it.

"*Every number is a square or the sum of two, three or four squares.*

"I have at last brought this under my method, and I prove that, if a given number were not of this nature, there would exist a number smaller than it which would not be so either, and again a third number smaller than the second, etc. *ad infinitum*; whence we infer that all numbers are of the nature indicated."

In another place (letter to Pascal of 25 September, 1654)[4], after quoting the more general proposition, including the above, that every number is

[1] Legendre, *Zahlentheorie*, tr. Maser, I. p. 387.

[2] *Ibid.* p. 386.

[3] *Oeuvres de Fermat*, II. p. 433.

[4] *Ibid.* p. 313.

made up (1) of one, two, or three triangles, (2) of one, two, three or four squares, (3) of one, two, three, four or five pentagons, and so on *ad infinitum*, Fermat adds that "to arrive at this it is necessary—

(1) To prove that *every prime number of the form* $4n+1$ *is the sum of two squares, e.g.* 5, 13, 17, 29, 37, *etc.*;

(2) Given a prime number of the form $4n+1$, as 53, to *find*, by a general rule, the two squares of which it is the sum.

(3) *Every prime number of the form* $3n+1$ *is of the form* x^2+3y^2, *e.g.* 7, 13, 19, 31, 37, *etc.*

(4) *Every prime number of the form* $8n+1$ *or* $8n+3$ *is of the form* x^2+2y^2, *e.g.* 11, 17, 19, 41, 43, *etc.*

(5) *There is no rational right-angled triangle in whole numbers the area of which is a square.*

"This will lead to the discovery of many propositions which Bachet admits to have been unknown to him and which are wanting in Diophantus.

"I am persuaded that, when you have become acquainted with my method of proof in this kind of proposition, you will think it beautiful, and it will enable you to make many new discoveries, for it is necessary, as you know, that *multi pertranseant ut augeatur scientia* [Bacon]."

Propositions (3) and (4) will be mentioned again, and a full account will be given in Section III. of this Supplement of Fermat's method, or methods, of proving (5).

The main theorem now in question that every integral number is the sum of four or fewer squares was attacked by Euler in the paper[1] (1754–1755) in which he finally proved the proposition (1) above about primes of the form $4n+1$; but, though he obtained important results, he did not then succeed in completing the proof. Lagrange followed up Euler's results and finally established the proposition in 1770[2]. Euler returned to the subject in 1772; he found Lagrange's proof long and difficult, and set himself to simplify it[3].

(The rest of the more general theorem of Fermat quoted above, the portion of it, that is, which relates to numbers as the sum of n or fewer *n-gonal numbers*, was proved by Cauchy[4].)

[1] *Novi Commentarii Acad. Petropol.* for 1754–5, Vol. V. (1760), pp. 3–58 = *Commentationes arithmeticae collectae*, 1849, I. pp. 210–233.

[2] *Nouveaux Mémoires de l'Acad. Roy. des Sciences de Berlin*, année 1770, Berlin 1772, pp. 123–133 = *Oeuvres de Lagrange*, III. pp. 187–201: cf. Wertheim's account in his Diophantus, pp. 324–330.

[3] "Novae demonstrationes circa resolutionem numerorum in quadrata," *Acta Erudit. Lips.* 1773, p. 193; *Acta Petrop.* I. II. 1775, p. 48; *Comment. arithm.* I. pp. 538–548.

[4] Cauchy, "Démonstration du théorème général de Fermat sur les nombres polygones," *Oeuvres*, IIe Série, Vol. VI. pp. 320–353. See also Legendre, *Zahlentheorie*, tr. Maser, II. pp. 332–343.

Under this heading may be added the further proposition that

"*Any number whatever of the form* $8n - 1$ *can only be represented as the sum of four squares, not only in integers* (as others may have seen) *but in fractions also*, as I promise that I will prove[1]."

5. *On numbers of the forms* $x^2 + 2y^2$, $x^2 + 3y^2$, $x^2 + 5y^2$ *respectively.*

(1) *Every prime number of the form* $8n + 1$ *or* $8n + 3$ *is of the form* $x^2 + 2y^2$.

This is one of the theorems enunciated in the letter of 25 Sept., 1654, to Pascal[2] and also in the letter of June, 1658, to Kenelm Digby[3].

[In a paper of 1754 Euler says that he does not yet see his way to prove either part of the theorem[4]. In 1759 he says[5] he can prove the truth of the theorem for a prime number of the form $8n + 1$, but not for a prime of the form $8n + 3$. Later, however, he proved it for prime numbers of both forms[6]. Lagrange[7] also proved it for primes of the form $8n + 3$.]

(2) *Every prime number of the form* $3n + 1$ *is of the form* $x^2 + 3y^2$.

The theorem is stated in the same two letters to Pascal and Digby respectively.

Lagrange naturally quotes it as "All prime numbers of the form $6n + 1$ are of the form $x^2 + 3y^2$," for of course $3n + 1$ is not a prime number unless n is even.

The proposition was proved by Euler[8]. Lagrange proved[9] (*a*) that all prime numbers of the form $12n - 5$ are of the form $x^2 + 3y^2$, (*b*) that all prime numbers of the form $12n - 1$ are of the form $3x^2 - y^2$, and (*c*) that all prime numbers of the form $12n + 1$ are of *both* the forms $x^2 + 3y^2$ and $x^2 - 3y^2$.

(3) *No number of the form* $3n - 1$ *can be of the form* $x^2 + 3y^2$.

In the "Relation des nouvelles découvertes en la science des nombres[10]" Fermat says that this was one of the negative propositions which he proved by his method of *descente*.

[1] Letter to Mersenne of Sept. or Oct. 1636, *Oeuvres de Fermat*, II. p. 66.

[2] *Oeuvres de Fermat*, II. p. 313.

[3] *Ibid.* II. p. 403.

[4] "Specimen de usu observationum in mathesi pura (De numeris formae $2aa + bb$)" in *Novi Commentarii Acad. Petrop.* 1756–7, Vol. VI. (1761), pp. 185–230 = *Comment. arithm.* I. pp. 174–192.

[5] *Novi Commentarii Acad. Petrop.* 1760–1, Vol. VIII. (1763), pp. 126–8 = *Comment. arithm.* I. p. 296.

[6] *Commentationes arithmeticae*, II. p. 607.

[7] "Recherches d'Arithmétique" in *Oeuvres de Lagrange*, III. pp. 776, 784.

[8] "Supplementum quorundam theorematum arithmeticorum, quae in nonnullis demonstrationibus supponuntur (De numeris formae $aa + 3bb$)" in *Novi Comment. Acad. Petrop.* 1760–1, Vol. VIII. (1763), pp. 105–128 = *Comment. arithm.* I. pp. 287–296.

[9] *Op. cit.*, *Oeuvres de Lagrange*, III. pp. 784, 791.

[10] *Oeuvres de Fermat*, II. p. 431.

(4) *If two prime numbers ending in either 3 or 7 which are also of the form $4n+3$ are multiplied together, the product is of the form x^2+5y^2.*

This theorem also is enunciated in the letter of June, 1658, to Kenelm Digby. Fermat instances 3, 7, 23, 43, 47, 67 etc. as numbers of the kind indicated. Take, he says, two of these, *e.g.* 7 and 23. The product 161 will be the sum of a square and 5 times another square, namely $81+5.16$.

He admits, however, that he has not yet proved the theorem generally: "I assert that this theorem is true generally, and I am only waiting for a proof of it. Moreover the square of each of the said numbers is the sum of a square and 5 times another square: this, too, I should like to see proved."

Lagrange proved this theorem also[1]. He observes that the numbers described are either of the form $20n+3$ or of the form $20n+7$, and he proves that all prime numbers of these forms are necessarily of the form $2x^2 \pm 2xy+3y^2$. He has then only to prove that the product of two numbers of the latter form is of the form x^2+5y^2.

This is easy, for

$$(2x^2+2xy+3y^2)(2x'^2+2x'y'+3y'^2)=(2xx'+xy'+yx'+3yy')^2+5(xy'-yx')^2.$$

6. *Numbers of the forms x^2-2y^2 and $2x^2-y^2$.*

Fermat's way of expressing the fact that a number is of one of these forms is to say that it is the sum of, or the difference between, the two smaller sides, *i.e.* the perpendicular sides, of a right-angled triangle. Like Diophantus, he "forms" a rational right-angled triangle from two numbers x, y, taking as the three sides the numbers x^2+y^2, x^2-y^2, $2xy$ respectively. The sum therefore of the perpendicular sides is $x^2+2xy-y^2$ or $(x+y)^2-2y^2$, and their difference is either $x^2-2xy-y^2$ or $2xy-(x^2-y^2)$, that is, either $(x-y)^2-2y^2$ or $2y^2-(x-y)^2$.

The main theorem on the subject of numbers of these forms is, as a matter of fact, contained, not in a letter of Fermat's, but in two letters of Frénicle to Fermat dated 2nd August and 6th Sept., 1641, respectively[2]. It is, however, clear (cf. the letter in which Fermat had on 15th June, 1641, propounded to Frénicle a problem on such numbers) that the theorem was at any rate common property between the two.

Frénicle's two statements of the theorem are as follows:

"Every prime number of the form $8n \pm 1$ is the sum of the two smaller sides of a (right-angled) triangle, and every number which is the sum of the two smaller sides of a (right-angled) triangle with sides prime to one another is of the form $8n \pm 1$."

"Every prime number of the form $8n \pm 1$, or which is the product of such prime numbers exclusively, is the difference between the two smaller sides of an infinite number of primitive right-angled triangles."

[1] *Op. cit.*, *Oeuvres de Lagrange*, II. pp. 784, 788–9.

[2] *Oeuvres de Fermat*, II. pp. 231, 235.

Lagrange[1] quotes the theorem in the form

All prime numbers of the form $8n \pm 1$ *are of the form* $y^2 - 2t^2$.

Lagrange himself proves[2] that all prime numbers of the form $8n - 1$ are of *both* the forms $x^2 - 2y^2$ and $2x^2 - y^2$, and observes[3] that this theorem is more general than that of Fermat so far as prime numbers of the form $8n - 1$ are concerned. This, however, seems scarcely correct if the further explanations given by Frénicle are taken into account. For Frénicle shows clearly, in the second of the two letters referred to[4], that he was fully alive to the fact that numbers which are of the form $x^2 - 2y^2$ are also of the form $2x^2 - y^2$; and indeed it is obvious that he was aware that

$$x^2 - 2y^2 = 2(x+y)^2 - (x+2y)^2.$$

Lagrange proved in addition[5] that

Every prime number of the form $8n + 1$ *is at the same time of the three forms* $x^2 + 2y^2$, $x^2 - 2y^2$, $2x^2 - y^2$.

This is, I think, really included in Frénicle's statements when combined with Fermat's theorem (1) above to the effect that every prime number of the form $8n + 1$ is of the form $x^2 + 2y^2$.

The problem propounded by Fermat to Frénicle in connexion with the numbers now under consideration was:—

Given a number, to find in how many ways it can be the sum of the two smaller sides of a right-angled triangle.

Frénicle replied that this involved also the problem of finding a number which will be the sum of the two smaller sides of a right-angled triangle in an assigned number of ways and no more, and tried, but unsuccessfully[6], to bring these problems under a rule corresponding to that by which Fermat found the number of ways in which a prime number of the form $4n + 1$ can be the hypotenuse of a right-angled triangle (see p. 269 above), but with a prime number of the form $8n \pm 1$ substituted for the prime number of the form $4n + 1$. I cannot find that Fermat ever communicated his own solution, at all events in the correspondence which we possess.

SECTION II.

EQUATION $x^2 - Ay^2 = 1$.

History of the equation up to Fermat's time.

Fermat was not the first to propound, or even to discover a general method of solving, the problem of finding any number of integral values of x, y satisfying the above equation, wherein A is any integral number not a square. But Fermat rediscovered the problem and was perhaps the first

[1] *Op. cit., Oeuvres de Lagrange*, III. p. 775. [2] *Ibid.* p. 784. [3] *Ibid.* p. 788.

[4] *Oeuvres de Fermat*, II. pp. 235–240.

[5] *Op. cit., Oeuvres de Lagrange*, III. p. 790.

[6] See *Oeuvres de Fermat*, II. pp. 231, 238 sqq.

to assert that the general solution is always possible whatever be the (non-square) value of A. The equation has a history of over 2000 years, and that history, even in outline, requires, as it has now obtained, a book to itself[1]. This note will therefore be confined, practically, to recalling, in the briefest possible way, the recorded stages anterior to Fermat, and then to setting out somewhat fully the passages in Fermat's writings which throw the most light on his connexion with the subject.

The Pythagoreans.

We have seen (p. 117 above) that the Pythagoreans had already discovered a general solution of a particular equation of this type, namely

$$2x^2 - y^2 = \pm 1,$$

by which all the successive values of x, y satisfying the equation were ascertained. If $x = p$, $y = q$ satisfies the equation $2x^2 - y^2 = \pm 1$, they proved that the equation $2x^2 - y^2 = \mp 1$ is satisfied by

$$p_1 = p + q, \quad q_1 = 2p + q,$$

the equation $2x^2 - y^2 = \pm 1$ again by

$$p_2 = p_1 + q_1, \quad q_2 = 2p_1 + q_1,$$

and so on. As $p = 1$, $q = 1$ satisfies $2x^2 - y^2 = +1$, we have all the successive solutions of $2x^2 - y^2 = \pm 1$ by forming (p_1, q_1), (p_2, q_2) etc. in accordance with the law.

Archimedes.

The solution of the above equation by the Pythagoreans was evidently used in order to obtain successive approximations to $\sqrt{2}$.

Consequently, when we find Archimedes giving, without explanation, the fractions $\frac{265}{153}$ and $\frac{1351}{780}$ as being approximately equal to $\sqrt{3}$, the hypothesis of Zeuthen and Tannery that he arrived at these approximations by obtaining successive solutions of equations of a similar form, but with 3 substituted for 2, is one of the most natural that have been suggested[2]. The equations are in this case

$$x^2 - 3y^2 = 1,$$
$$x^2 - 3y^2 = -2.$$

Tannery shows how the law for forming successive solutions of such simple cases as these can easily be found when we have found by trial (which is not difficult) the three simplest solutions. If we take the more general equation

$$x^2 - ay^2 = r,$$

[1] H. Konen, *Geschichte der Gleichung* $t^2 - Du^2 = 1$, Leipzig (S. Hirzel), 1901.

[2] Zeuthen, "Nogle hypotheser om Arkhimedes kvadratrodsberegning," *Tidsskrift for Mathematik*, VI. Raekke, 3. Aargang, pp. 150 sqq.; P. Tannery, "Sur la mesure du cercle d'Archimède" in *Mémoires de la soc. des sciences phys. et nat. de Bordeaux*, IIe Sér. IV., 1882, p. 303; see Günther, "Die quadratischen Irrationalitäten der Alten und deren Entwickelungsmethoden" in *Abhandlungen zur Gesch. der Mathematik*, Heft IV. 1882, pp. 87–91; Konen, *op. cit.* p. 15.

of which $x = p, y = q$ is a known solution, and put

$$p_1 = \alpha p + \beta q, \quad q_1 = \gamma p + \delta q,$$

it is sufficient to know the three simplest solutions in order to find $\alpha, \beta, \gamma, \delta$; for, substituting the values of (p, q), (p_1, q_1) and (p_2, q_2) where (p_2, q_2) are formed from (p_1, q_1) by the same law as (p_1, q_1) are formed from (p, q), we have four simultaneous equations in four unknown quantities. Taking the particular equation

$$x^2 - 3y^2 = 1,$$

we easily find the first three solutions, namely $(p = 1, q = 0)$, $(p_1 = 2, q_1 = 1)$ and $(p_2 = 7, q_2 = 4)$, whence

$$2 = \alpha, \qquad 1 = \gamma,$$
$$7 = 2\alpha + \beta, \quad 4 = 2\gamma + \delta,$$

and $\alpha = 2$, $\beta = 3$, $\gamma = 1$, $\delta = 2$, so that

$$p_1 = 2p + 3q, \quad q_1 = p + 2q.$$

But there is evidence that Archimedes dealt with much more difficult equations of the type, for (as stated above, p. 123) the Cattle-Problem attributed to him requires us to solve in positive integers the equation

$$x^2 - 4729494y^2 = 1.$$

There is this difference between this equation and the simpler ones above that, while the first solutions of the latter can be found by trial, the simplest solution of this equation cannot, so that some general method, *e.g.* that of continued fractions, is necessary to find even the least solution in integers. Whether Archimedes was actually able to solve this particular equation is a question on which there is difference of opinion; Tannery thought it not impossible, but, as the smallest values of x, y satisfying the equation have 46 and 41 digits respectively, we may, with Günther, feel doubt on the subject[1]. There is, however, nothing impossible in the supposition that Archimedes was in possession of a general method of solving such equations where the numbers involved were not too great for manipulation in the Greek numeral notation.

Diophantus.

Tannery[2] was of opinion that Diophantus dealt with the equation

$$x^2 - Ay^2 = 1$$

somewhere in the lost Books of the *Arithmetica*. Diophantus does indeed say (Lemma to VI. 15) that, if a, b are any numbers and $ax^2 - b$ is a square when x is given a certain value p, then other values of x greater than p can also be found which have the same property; and Tannery points out that

[1] Günther, *op. cit.*, pp. 92–93 note. Cf. Konen, *op. cit.*, p. 14.

[2] Tannery, "L'Arithmétique des Grecs dans Pappus" in *Mémoires de la soc. des sciences phys. et nat. de Bordeaux*, IIe Sér. III., 1880, pp. 370 sq.

we can, by making suppositions of the same kind as Diophantus makes, deduce a more general solution of the equation

$$x^2 - Ay^2 = 1$$

when one solution (p, q) is known.

Put

$$p_1 = mx - p, \quad q_1 = x + q,$$

and suppose

$$p_1^2 - Aq_1^2 = m^2x^2 - 2mpx + p^2 - Ax^2 - 2Aqx - Aq^2 = 1;$$

therefore (since $p^2 - Aq^2 = 1$)

$$x = 2\frac{mp + Aq}{m^2 - A},$$

and, by substitution in the expressions for p_1, q_1, we have

$$p_1 = \frac{(m^2 + A)p + 2Amq}{m^2 - A}, \quad q_1 = \frac{2mp + (m^2 + A)q}{m^2 - A},$$

and in fact $p_1^2 - Aq_1^2 = 1$.

If an integral solution is wanted, one way of obtaining it is to substitute u/v for m where $u^2 - Av^2 = 1$, *i.e.* where u, v is another solution of the original equation, and we then have

$$p_1 = (u^2 + Av^2)p + 2Auvq, \quad q_1 = 2puv + (u^2 + Av^2)q.$$

But this is all that we can get out of Diophantus as we have him, and it will be observed that here too we must have ascertained two solutions of the one equation, or one solution of it and a solution of an auxiliary equation, before we can apply the method[1].

[1] It may be observed that, in the particular case of the equation $x^2 - 3y^2 = 1$, the assumption of u, v satisfying the equation will not enable us to obtain from the formula

$$p_1 = (u^2 + Av^2)p + 2Auvq, \quad q_1 = 2puv + (u^2 + Av^2)q$$

above given the simpler formula otherwise obtained by Tannery (p. 279 above), namely

$$p_1 = 2p + 3q, \quad q_1 = p + 2q;$$

for, if (p_1, q_1) is to be a different solution from (p, q), we cannot make $u = 1$, $v = 0$, but must take $u = 2$, $v = 1$, whence, putting $A = 3$, we obtain

$$p_1 = 7p + 12, \quad q_1 = 4p + 7q,$$

which is the same as p_2, q_2, the next solution to $p_1 = 2p + 3q$, $q_1 = p + 2q$.

In order to get the latter we have to take u, v satisfying, not $x^2 - 3y^2 = 1$, but

$$x^2 - 3y^2 = -2.$$

The values $u = 1$, $v = 1$ satisfy $x^2 - 3y^2 = -2$, and

$$p_1 = \frac{(u^2 + 3v^2)p + 6uvq}{u^2 - 3v^2} = \frac{4p + 6q}{-2} = -(2p + 3q),$$

$$q_1 = \frac{2uvp + (u^2 + 3v^2)q}{u^2 - 3v^2} = \frac{2p + 4q}{-2} = -(p + 2q);$$

and of course $p_1 = +(2p + 3q)$, $q_1 = +(p + 2q)$ can be taken, since they equally satisfy

$$p_1^2 - 3q_1^2 = 1.$$

The Indian Solution.

If the Greeks did not accomplish the general solution of our equation, it is all the more extraordinary that we should have such a general solution in practical use among the Indians as early as the time of Brahmagupta (born 598 A.D.) under the name of the "cyclic method." Whether this method was evolved by the Indians themselves, or was due to Greek influence and inspiration, is disputed. Hankel held the former view[1]; Tannery held the latter and showed how, from the Greek manner of deducing from one approximation to a surd a nearer approximation, it is possible, by simple steps, to pass to the Indian method[2]. The question presumably cannot be finally decided unless by the discovery of fresh documents; but, so far as the other cases of solution of indeterminate equations by the Indians help to suggest a presumption on the subject, they are, I think, rather in favour of the hypothesis of ultimate Greek origin. Thus the solution of the equation $ax - by = c$ given by Āryabhata (born 476 A.D.) as well as by Brahmagupta and Bhāskara, though it anticipated Bachet's solution which is really equivalent to our method of solution by continued fractions, is an easy development from Euclid's method of finding the greatest common measure or proving by that process that two numbers have no common factor (Eucl. VII. 1, 2, X. 2, 3)[3], and it would be strange if the Greeks had not taken this step. The Indian solution of the equation $xy = ax + by + c$, by the geometrical form in which it was clothed, suggests Greek origin[4].

The "cyclic method" of solving the equation

$$x^2 - Ay^2 = 1$$

is found in Brahmagupta and Bhāskara[5] (born 1114 A.D.) and is well described by Hankel, Cantor and Konen[6].

The method is given in the form of dogmatic rules, without any proof of the assumptions made, but is equivalent to a preliminary lemma followed by the solution proper.

[1] Hankel, *Zur Geschichte der Math. im Alterthum und Mittelalter*, pp. 203–4.

[2] Tannery, "Sur la mesure du cercle d'Archimède" in *Mém. de la soc. des sciences phys. et nat. de Bordeaux*, 2e Sér. IV., 1882, p. 325; cf. Konen, pp. 27–28; Zeuthen, "L'Oeuvre de Paul Tannery comme historien des mathématiques" in *Bibliotheca Mathematica*, VI3, 1905–6, pp. 271–273.

[3] G. R. Kaye, "Notes on Indian mathematics, No. 2, Āryabhata" in *Journal of the Asiatic Society of Bengal*, Vol. IV. No. 3, 1908, pp. 135–138.

[4] Cf. the description of the solution in Hankel, p. 199; Cantor, *Gesch. d. Math.* I3, p. 631.

[5] The mathematical chapters in the works of these writers containing the solution in question are contained in H. T. Colebrooke's *Algebra with arithmetic and mensuration from the Sanskrit of Brahmegupta and Bhaskara*, London, 1817.

[6] Hankel, pp. 200–203; Cantor, I3, pp. 632–633; Konen, *op. cit.*, pp. 19–26.

Lemma.

If $x=p,\ y=q$ be a solution of the equation

$$Ay^2+s=x^2,$$

and $x=p',\ y=q'$ a solution of the equation

$$Ay^2+s'=x^2,$$

then, say the Indians, $x=pp'\pm Aqq',\ y=pq'\pm p'q$ is a solution of the equation

$$Ay^2+ss'=x^2.$$

In other words, if

$$\left.\begin{aligned}Aq^2+s&=p^2\\ Aq'^2+s'&=p'^2\end{aligned}\right\},$$

then $$A(pq'\pm p'q)^2+ss'=(pp'\pm Aqq')^2.$$

This is easily verified[1].

In particular, taking $s=s'$, we find, from any solution $x=p,\ y=q$ of the equation

$$Ay^2+s=x^2,$$

a solution $x=p^2+Aq^2,\ y=2pq$ of the equation

$$Ay^2+s^2=x^2.$$

Again, particular use of the lemma can be made when $s=\pm 1$ or $s=\pm 2$.

(*a*) If $s=+1$, and $x=p,\ y=q$ is a solution of

$$Ay^2+1=x^2,$$

then $x=p^2+Aq^2,\ y=2pq$ is another solution of the same equation.

If $s=-1$, and $x=p,\ y=q$ is a solution of

$$Ay^2-1=x^2,$$

then $x=p^2+Aq^2,\ y=2pq$ is a solution of

$$Ay^2+1=x^2.$$

(*b*) If $s=\pm 2$, and $x=p,\ y=q$ is a solution of

$$Ay^2\pm 2=x^2,$$

then $x=p^2+Aq^2,\ y=2pq$ is a solution of

$$Ay^2+4=x^2.$$

In this case, since $2pq$ is even, the whole result when the values of x, y are substituted must be divisible by 4, and we have $x=\frac{1}{2}(p^2+Aq^2)$, $y=pq$ as a solution of the equation

$$Ay^2+1=x^2.$$

[1] For, since $s=p^2-Aq^2,\ s'=p'^2-Aq'^2$,

$$\begin{aligned}ss'&=(p^2-Aq^2)(p'^2-Aq'^2)\\&=(pp')^2+(Aqq')^2-A(pq')^2-A(p'q)^2\\&=\{(pp')^2\pm 2App'qq'+(Aqq')^2\}-A\{(pq')^2\pm 2pp'qq'+(p'q)^2\}\\&=(pp'\pm Aqq')^2-A(pq'\pm p'q)^2.\end{aligned}$$

Solution proper of the equation $x^2 - Ay^2 = 1$.

We take two numbers prime to one another, p, q, and a third number s with no square factor, such that

$$Aq^2 + s = p^2,$$

the numbers being also chosen (in order to abbreviate the solution) such that s is as small as possible, though this is not absolutely necessary. (This is a purely empirical matter; we have only to take a rough approximation to $\sqrt{A}$ in the form of a fraction p/q.)

[It follows that s, q can have no common factor; for, if δ were a common factor of s, q, it would also be a factor of p^2, and p^2, q^2 would have a common factor. But p, q are prime to one another.]

Now find a number r such that

$$q_1 \equiv \pm\frac{p + qr}{s} \text{ is a whole number.}$$

[This would be done by the Indian method called *cuṭṭaca* ("pulveriser"), corresponding to our method by continued fractions.]

Of the possible values of r a value is taken which will make $r^2 - A$ as small as possible.

Now, say the Indians, we shall have:

$$s_1 = \pm\frac{r^2 - A}{s} \text{ is an integral number,}$$

and
$$Aq_1^2 + s_1 = \left(\frac{pq_1 - 1}{q}\right)^2 = p_1^2.$$

(Again the proofs are not given; they are however supplied by Hankel[1].)

[1] Since $q_1 = \frac{p+qr}{s}$ is an integral number, all the letters in $q_1 s = p + qr$ represent integers.

Further, $$s = p^2 - Aq^2;$$
therefore, eliminating s, we have
$$q_1(p^2 - Aq^2) = p + qr,$$
or
$$p(pq_1 - 1) = q(r + Aqq_1).$$

Since p, q have no common factor, q must divide $pq_1 - 1$; that is,

$$\frac{pq_1 - 1}{q} = \text{an integer.}$$

We have next to prove that $s_1 = (r^2 - A)/s$ is an integer.

Now $$r^2 - A = \frac{(q_1 s - p)^2 - Aq^2}{q^2} = \frac{q_1^2 s^2 - 2pq_1 s + s}{q^2}, \text{ since } s = p^2 - Aq^2;$$

therefore $$\frac{s(q_1^2 s - 2pq_1 + 1)}{q^2} \text{ is an integer,}$$

and, since s, q have no common factor, it follows that

$$\frac{q_1^2 s - 2pq_1 + 1}{q^2} = \frac{r^2 - A}{s} \text{ is an integer.}$$

Also $$s_1 = \frac{r^2 - A}{s} = \frac{q_1^2 s - 2pq_1 + 1}{q^2} = \frac{q_1^2(p^2 - Aq^2) - 2pq_1 + 1}{q^2} = \left(\frac{pq_1 - 1}{q}\right)^2 - Aq_1^2.$$

We have therefore satisfied a new equation of the same form as that originally taken[1].

We proceed in this way, obtaining fresh results of this kind, until we arrive at one in which $s = \pm 1$ or ± 2 or ± 4, when, by means of the lemma, we obtain a solution of

$$Ay^2 + 1 = x^2.$$

Example. To solve the equation $67y^2 + 1 = x^2$.

Since 8^2 is the nearest square to 67, we take as our first auxiliary equation $67 . 1^2 - 3 = 8^2$, so that $p = 8$, $q = 1$, $s = -3$.

Thus $q_1 = -\dfrac{8+r}{3}$. We put $r = 7$, which makes q_1 an integer and at the same time makes $s_1 = -\dfrac{7^2 - 67}{3} = 6$ as small as possible.

Thus
$$q_1 = -5,\ p_1 = (pq_1 - 1)/q = -41,$$
and we have satisfied the new equation

$$67 . 5^2 + 6 = 41^2.$$

Next we take $q_2 = \dfrac{41 + 5r_2}{6}$, and we put $r_2 = 5$, giving $q_2 = 11$; thus $s_2 = \dfrac{r_2^2 - 67}{6} = -7$, and $p_2 = (p_1 q_2 - 1)/q_1 = 90$, and

$$67 . (11)^2 - 7 = 90^2.$$

Next $q_3 = -\dfrac{90 + 11r_3}{7}$, and we put $r_3 = 9$, giving $q_3 = -27$; therefore

$$s_3 = \frac{r_3^2 - 67}{-7} = -2,\quad p_3 = \frac{-90 . 27 - 1}{11} = -221, \text{ and}$$

$$67 . (27)^2 - 2 = (221)^2.$$

As we have now brought our s down to 2, we can use the lemma, and

$$67\,(2 . 27 . 221)^2 + 4 = (221^2 + 67 . 27^2)^2,$$

or,
$$67\,(11934)^2 + 4 = (97684)^2;$$

therefore, dividing by 4, we have

$$67\,(5967)^2 + 1 = (48842)^2.$$

Of this Indian method Hankel says, "It is above all praise; it is certainly the finest thing which was achieved in the theory of numbers

[1] Hankel conjectures that the Indian method may have been evolved somewhat in this way.

If $Aq^2 + s = p^2$ is given, and if we put $Aq'^2 + s' = p'^2$, then

$$A\,(pq' - p'q)^2 + ss' = (pp' - Aqq')^2.$$

Now suppose p', q' to be determined as whole numbers from the equation $pq' - p'q = 1$, and let the resulting integral value of $pp' - Aqq'$ be r.

Then $A + ss' = r^2$, and accordingly $r^2 - A$ must be divisible by s, or $s' = (A - r^2)/s$ is a whole number.

Eliminating p' from the two equations in p', q', we obtain

$$q' = (p + qr)/(p^2 - Aq^2) = (p + qr)/s,$$

and, as stated in the rule, r has therefore to be so chosen that $(p + qr)/s$ is an integer.

before Lagrange"; and, although this may seem an exaggeration when we think of the extraordinary achievements of a Fermat, it is true that the Indian method is, remarkably enough, the same as that which was rediscovered and expounded by Lagrange in his memoir of 1768[1]. Nothing is wanting to the cyclic method except the proof that it will in every case lead to the desired result whenever A is a number which is not a square; and it was this proof which Lagrange first supplied.

Fermat.

As we have already said, Fermat rediscovered our problem and was the first to assert that the equation

$$x^2 - Ay^2 = 1,$$

where A is any integer not a square, always has an unlimited number of solutions in integers.

His statement was made in a letter to Frénicle of February, 1657[2]. Fermat asks Frénicle for *a general rule for finding, when any number not a square is given, squares which, when they are respectively multiplied by the given number and unity is added to the product, give squares.* If, says Fermat, Frénicle cannot give a general rule, will he give the smallest value of y which will satisfy the equations $61y^2 + 1 = x^2$ and $109y^2 + 1 = x^2$?[3]

At the same time Fermat issued a challenge to the same effect to mathematicians in general, prefacing it by some remarks which are worth quoting in full[4].

"There is hardly any one who propounds purely arithmetical questions, hardly any one who understands them. Is this due to the fact that up to now arithmetic has been treated geometrically rather than arithmetically? This has indeed generally been the case both in ancient and modern works; even Diophantus is an instance. For, although he has freed himself from geometry a little more than others have in that he confines his analysis to the consideration of rational numbers, yet even there geometry is not entirely absent, as is sufficiently proved by the *Zetetica* of Vieta, where the method of Diophantus is extended to continuous magnitude and therefore to geometry.

"Now arithmetic has, so to speak, a special domain of its own, the theory of integral numbers. This was only lightly touched upon by Euclid in his *Elements*, and was not sufficiently studied by those who followed him (unless, perchance, it is contained in those Books of Diophantus of

[1] "Sur la solution des problèmes indéterminés du second degré" in *Mémoires de l'Acad. Royale des Sciences et Belles-Lettres de Berlin*, t. XXIII. 1769 (= *Oeuvres de Lagrange*, II. pp. 377 sqq.). The comparison between Lagrange's procedure and the Indian is given by Konen, pp. 75–77.

[2] *Oeuvres de Fermat*, II. pp. 333–4.

[3] Fermat evidently chose these cases for their difficulty; the smallest values satisfying the first equation are $y = 226153980$, $x = 1766319049$, and the smallest values satisfying the second are $y = 15140424455100$, $x = 158070671986249$.

[4] *Oeuvres de Fermat*, II. pp. 334–5.

which the ravages of time have robbed us); arithmeticians have therefore now to develop it or restore it.

"To arithmeticians therefore, by way of lighting up the road to be followed, I propose the following theorem to be proved or problem to be solved. If they succeed in discovering the proof or solution, they will admit that questions of this kind are not inferior to the more celebrated questions in geometry in respect of beauty, difficulty or method of proof.

"*Given any number whatever which is not a square, there are also given an infinite number of squares such that, if the square is multiplied into the given number and unity is added to the product, the result is a square.*

"Example. Let 3, which is not a square, be the given number; when it is multiplied into the square 1, and 1 is added to the product, the result is 4, being a square.

"The same 3 multiplied by the square 16 gives a product which, if increased by 1, becomes 49, a square.

"And an infinite number of squares besides 1 and 16 can be found which have the same property.

"But I ask for a general rule of solution when any number not a square is given.

"*E.g.* let it be required to find a square such that, if the product of the square and the number 149, or 109, or 433 etc. be increased by 1, the result is a square."

The challenge was taken up in England by William, Viscount Brouncker, first President of the Royal Society, and Wallis[1]. At first, owing apparently to some misunderstanding, they thought that only rational, and not necessarily integral, solutions were wanted, and found of course no difficulty in solving this easy problem. Fermat was, naturally, not satisfied with this solution, and Brouncker, attacking the problem again, finally succeeded in solving it. The method is set out in letters of Wallis[2] of 17th December, 1657, and 30th January, 1658, and in Chapter XCVIII. of Wallis' *Algebra*; Euler also explains it fully in his *Algebra*[3], wrongly attributing it to Pell[4].

[1] An excellent summary of the whole story is given in Wertheim's paper "Pierre Fermat's Streit mit John Wallis" in *Abhandlungen zur Gesch. der Math.* IX. Heft (Cantor-Festschrift), 1899, pp. 557–576. See also Konen, pp. 29–43.

[2] *Oeuvres de Fermat*, III. pp. 457–480, 490–503. Wallis gives the solution of each of the three difficult cases last mentioned.

[3] Euler, *Algebra*, Part II. chap. VII.

[4] This was the origin of the erroneous description of our equation as the "Pellian" equation. Hankel (p. 203) supposed that the equation was so called because the solution was reproduced by Pell in an English translation (1668) by Thomas Brancker of Rahn's *Algebra*; but this is a misapprehension, as the so-called "Pellian" equation is not so much as mentioned in Pell's additions (Wertheim in *Bibliotheca Mathematica*, III_3, 1902, pp. 124–6; Konen, pp. 33–4 note). The attribution of the solution to Pell was a pure mistake of Euler's, probably due to a cursory reading by him of the second volume of Wallis' *Opera* where the solution of the equation $ax^2+1=y^2$ is given as well as information as to Pell's work in indeterminate analysis. But Pell is not mentioned in connexion with the equation at all (Eneström in *Bibliotheca Mathematica*, III_3, 1902, p. 206).

Fermat appears to have been satisfied with the actual *solution*[1], but later he points out that, although Frénicle and Wallis had given many particular solutions, they had not supplied a general *proof*[2] (*i.e.* presumably that the solution is always possible and that the method will always lead to the solution sought for). He says, "I prove it by the method of *descente* applied in a quite special manner....The general demonstration will be found by means of the *descente* duly and appropriately applied."

Further on, Fermat says he has discovered "general rules for solving the simple and double equations of Diophantus."

"Suppose, for example, that we have to make

$$2x^2 + 7967 \text{ equal to a square.}$$

"*I have a general rule for solving this equation, if it is possible, or discovering its impossibility, and similarly in all cases and for all values of the coefficient of* x^2 *and of the absolute term.*

"Suppose we have to solve the double-equation

$$\left.\begin{aligned} 2x + 3 &= \text{square} \\ 2x + 5 &= \text{square} \end{aligned}\right\}.$$

"Bachet boasts, in his commentary on Diophantus[3], of having discovered a rule for solving in two particular cases; I make it general for all kinds of cases and can determine, by rule, whether it is possible or not[4]."

Thus Fermat asserts that he can solve, when it is possible to solve it, and can determine, by a general method, whether it is possible or impossible to solve, for any particular values of the constants, the more general equation

$$x^2 - Ay^2 = B.$$

This more general equation was of course solved by Lagrange. How Fermat solved it we do not know. It is true that he has sometimes been

[1] Letter of June, 1658, to Kenelm Digby, *Oeuvres de Fermat*, II. p. 402.

[2] "Relation des nouvelles découvertes en la science des nombres," *Oeuvres*, II. p. 433.

[3] See on Diophantus IV. 39, and above, pp. 80–82.

[4] With this should be compared Fermat's note on Dioph. IV. 39, where he says, similarly:

"Suppose, if you will, that the double-equation to be solved is

$$\left.\begin{aligned} 2x + 5 &= \text{square} \\ 6x + 3 &= \text{square} \end{aligned}\right\}.$$

"The first square must be made equal to 16 and the second to 36; and others will be found *ad infinitum* satisfying the question. Nor is it difficult to propound a general rule for the solution of this kind of question."

No doubt the double-equation in this case, as in the others referred to in the "Relation," would be transformed into the single equation

$$t^2 - Au^2 = B$$

by eliminating x. I think this shows how Fermat was led to investigate our equation: a question which seems to have puzzled Konen (p. 29), in view of the fact that the actual equation is not mentioned in the notes to Diophantus. The comparison of the two places seems to make the matter clear. For example, the two equations mentioned above in this note lead to the equation $t^2 - 3u^2 = -12$, and the solution $t = 6$, $u = 4$ is easily obtained.

credited with the very same solution of the equation $x^2 - Ay^2 = 1$ as that given by Brouncker and Wallis; but this idea seems to be based on a misapprehension of a sentence in Ozanam's *Algebra* (1702). Ozanam gives the Brouncker-Wallis solution as "une règle générale pour résoudre cette question, qui est de M. de Fermat"; and possibly the ambiguity of the reference of "qui" may have misled Lagrange and others into supposing that the "règle" was due to Fermat.

For the history of the equation after Fermat's time I must refer to other works and particularly that of Konen[1]. Euler, Lagrange, Gauss, Jacobi, Dirichlet, Kronecker are the great names associated with it. I will only add a few particulars with regard to Euler[2] as coming nearest to Fermat.

In a letter to Goldbach[3] of 10th August, 1730, Euler mentions that he requires the solution of the equation $x^2 - Ay^2 = 1$ in order to make $ax^2 + bx + c$ a complete square. He goes on to observe that the problem of solving $x^2 - Ay^2 = 1$ in integers was discussed between Wallis and Fermat and that the solution (which he already attributes to Pell) was set out in Wallis' *Opera*. There is an indication in this very passage that Euler had then only read the Brouncker-Wallis correspondence cursorily, for he speaks of the equation $109y^2 + 1 = x^2$ as being the most difficult case solved by them, whereas the most difficult examples actually solved were $433y^2 + 1 = x^2$ and $313y^2 + 1 = x^2$.

A paper of a year or two later[4] contained the proof that the evolution of successive solutions of $ax^2 + bx + c = y^2$ when one is known requires that one solution of $a\xi^2 + 1 = \eta^2$ must also be known. Similarly, in his *Algebra*[5], he shows that the solution of the latter equation is necessary for finding all the possible solutions of the equation $ax^2 + b = y^2$, the importance of which remark is emphasised by Lagrange[6].

In the paper quoted in the last paragraph Euler finds any number of successive solutions of $ax^2 + bx + c = y^2$, and the law for forming them, when we are given one value n of x which will make $ax^2 + bx + c$ a complete square and one value p of ξ which will make $a\xi^2 + 1$ a complete square, or, in other words, when $an^2 + bn + c = m^2$ and $ap^2 + 1 = q^2$. He then takes the particular case $ax^2 + bx + d^2 = y^2$ where (since $x = 0$, $y = d$ satisfies the equation) we can substitute 0 for n and d for m in the expressions representing the successive solutions of $ax^2 + bx + c = y^2$. Then again, putting $b = 0$ and $d = 1$, he is in a position to write down any

[1] Konen, *op. cit.*; cf. Cantor's *Geschichte der Mathematik*, IV. Abschnitt XX., as regards Euler and Lagrange.

[2] Cf. Konen, *op. cit.* pp. 47–58.

[3] *Correspondance mathématique et physique de quelques célèbres géomètres du* XVIII*ième siècle*, publiée par P. H. Fuss, Pétersbourg, 1843, I. p. 37.

[4] "De solutione problematum Diophanteorum per numeros integros" in *Commentarii Acad. Petropol.* 1732–3, VI. (1738), pp. 175 sqq. = *Commentationes arithm.* I. pp. 4–10.

[5] *Algebra*, Part II. ch. VI.

[6] Additions to Euler's *Algebra*, ch. VIII.

number of successive solutions of $a\xi^2 + 1 = \eta^2$ when one solution $\xi = p$, $\eta = q$ is known. The successive values of ξ are

$$0,\ p,\ 2pq,\ 4pq^2 - p, \ldots$$

and the corresponding values of η are

$$1,\ q,\ 2q^2 - 1,\ 4q^3 - 3q, \ldots$$

the law of formation being in each case that, if A, B be consecutive values in either series, the next following is $2qB - A$.

The question then arises how to find the first values p, q which will satisfy the equation. Euler first points out that, when a has one of many particular forms, values of p, q can at once be written down which satisfy the equation. The following are such cases with the obvious values of p and q.

$$a = e^2 - 1; \qquad p = 1,\ q = e,$$

$$a = e^2 + 1; \qquad p = 2e,\ q = 2e^2 + 1,$$

$$a = \alpha^2 e^{2b} \pm 2\alpha e^{b-1}; \ p = e, \quad q = \alpha e^{b+1} \pm 1$$

(where α may even be fractional provided αe^{b-1} is an integer),

$$a = (\alpha e^b + \beta e^\mu)^2 + 2\alpha e^{b-1} + 2\beta e^{\mu-1}; \ p = e, \quad q = \alpha e^{b+1} + \beta e^{\mu+1} + 1,$$

$$a = \tfrac{1}{4}\alpha^2 k^2 e^{2b} \pm \alpha e^{b-1}; \qquad p = ke,\ q = \tfrac{1}{2}\alpha k^2 e^{b+1} \pm 1.$$

But, if a cannot be put into such forms as the above, then the method explained by Wallis must be used. Euler illustrates by finding the least values p, q which will satisfy the equation $31\xi^2 + 1 = \eta^2$, and then adds a table of the least solutions of the equation $a\xi^2 + 1 = \eta^2$ for all values of a (which are not squares) from 2 to 68.

The important remark follows (§ 18) that the above procedure at once gives a very easy way of finding closer and closer approximations to the value of any surd $\sqrt{a}$. For, since $ap^2 + 1 = q^2$, we have $\sqrt{a} = \sqrt{(q^2 - 1)}/p$, and, if q (and therefore p also) is large, q/p is a close approximation to $\sqrt{a}$; the error is not greater than $1/(2p^2\sqrt{a})$. Euler illustrates by taking $\sqrt{6}$. The first solution of $6\xi^2 + 1 = \eta^2$ (after $\xi = 0$, $\eta = 1$) is $p = 2$, $q = 5$. Taking then the series of values above given for $a\xi^2 + 1 = \eta^2$, namely

$$\xi = 0,\ p,\ 2pq,\quad 4pq^2 - p, \ldots A,\ B,\ 2qB - A,$$

$$\eta = 1,\ q,\ 2q^2 - 1,\ 4q^3 - 3q, \ldots E,\ F,\ 2qF - E,$$

and substituting $p = 2$, $q = 5$, the successive corresponding values P, Q of ξ, η respectively become

$$P = 0,\ 2,\ 20,\ 198,\ 1960,\ 19402,\ 192060,\ 1901198, \ldots$$

$$Q = 1,\ 5,\ 49,\ 485,\ 4801,\ 47525,\ 470449,\ 4656965, \ldots$$

and the successive values Q/P are closer and closer approximations to $\sqrt{6}$. It will be observed that the method of obtaining successive approximations to $\sqrt{a}$ from successive solutions of $a\xi^2 + 1 = \eta^2$ is the same as that which, according to the hypothesis of Zeuthen and Tannery, Archimedes used in order to find his approximations to $\sqrt{3}$.

The converse process of finding successive solutions of $a\xi^2 + 1 = \eta^2$ by developing $\sqrt{a}$ as a continued fraction did not apparently occur to Euler till later. In two letters[1] to Goldbach of 4th Sept. 1753 and 23rd Sept. 1755 he speaks of a "certain" method and of improvements which he had made in the "Pellian" method but gives no details. His next paper on the same subject[2] returns to the problem of finding all the solutions of $ax^2 + bx + c = y^2$ or $ax^2 + b = y^2$ when one is known, and in the course of his discussion of the latter he arrives at "the following remarkable theorem which contains within it the foundation of higher solutions.

"If $x = a,\ y = b$ satisfies $\alpha x^2 + p = y^2$,

and $x = c,\ y = d$ satisfies $\alpha x^2 + q = y^2$,

then $x = bc \pm ad,\ y = bd \pm \alpha ac$ satisfies $\alpha x^2 + pq = y^2$."

That is to say, Euler rediscovers and recognises the importance of the lemma to the Indian solution, as Lagrange did later.

More important is the paper of about three years later[3] in which Euler obtained the solution of the equation $x^2 - Ay^2 = 1$ by the process of converting $\sqrt{A}$ into a continued fraction, this course being the reverse of that which was, according to the hypothesis of Tannery and Zeuthen, followed by Archimedes, and to the feasibility of which Euler had called attention in 1732–3. He begins by stating, without proof, that, if $q^2 = lp^2 + 1$, then q/p is an approximation to $\sqrt{l}$, and q/p is "such a fraction as expresses the value of $\sqrt{l}$ so nearly or exceeds it so little that a closer approximation cannot be made except by bringing in greater numbers." Next he develops certain particular surds, namely $\sqrt{(13)}$, $\sqrt{(61)}$ and $\sqrt{(67)}$, after which he states the process generally thus. If $\sqrt{z}$ be the given surd and v the root of the greatest integral square which is less than z, the process will give

$$\sqrt{z} = v + \cfrac{1}{a + \cfrac{1}{b + \cfrac{1}{c + \cfrac{1}{d + \text{etc.}}}}}$$

the successive quotients a, b, c, d, being found by means of the process shown in the following table:

[1] *Correspondance etc.*, ed. Fuss, pp. 614 sq., 629 sq.

[2] "De resolutione formularum quadraticarum indeterminatarum per numeros integros" in *Novi Commentarii Acad. Petropol.* 1762–3, IX. (1764), pp. 3 sqq. = *Commentat. arithm.* I. pp. 297–315.

[3] "De usu novi algorithmi in problemate Pelliano solvendo" in *Novi Commentarii Acad. Petropol.* 1765, XI. (1767), pp. 28–66 = *Commentat. arithm.* I. pp. 316–336. The paper seems to have been read as early as 15 Oct. 1759.

	Take	and	It follows that
I.	$A=v$	$\alpha=z-A^2=z-v^2$	$a\leqq\frac{v+A}{\alpha}$
II.	$B=\alpha a-A$	$\beta=\frac{z-B^2}{\alpha}=1+a(A-B)$	$b\leqq\frac{v+B}{\beta}$
III.	$C=\beta b-B$	$\gamma=\frac{z-C^2}{\beta}=\alpha+b(B-C)$	$c\leqq\frac{v+C}{\gamma}$
IV.	$D=\gamma c-C$	$\delta=\frac{z-D^2}{\gamma}=\beta+c(C-D)$	$d\leqq\frac{v+D}{\delta}$
V.	$E=\delta d-D$	$\epsilon=\frac{z-E^2}{\delta}=\gamma+d(D-E)$	$e\leqq\frac{v+E}{\epsilon}$

etc. etc.

(This is of course exactly the process given in text-books of Algebra, *e.g.* Todhunter's.)

Euler now remarks as follows.

1. The numbers $A, B, C, D\ldots$ cannot exceed v; the first, A, is equal to v; since $a\leqq(v+A)/\alpha$, $\alpha a-A=B\leqq v$, and so on.

2. Unless where one of the numbers $\alpha, \beta, \gamma, \delta\ldots$ is equal to unity, none of the corresponding quotients $a, b, c, d\ldots$ can exceed v.

3. When we arrive at a quotient equal to $2v$, the next quotients will be $a, b, c, d\ldots$ in the same order.

4. Similar periods occur with the letters $\alpha, \beta, \gamma, \delta\ldots$ and the term of this series corresponding to a quotient $2v$ is always 1.

The successive convergents to the continued fraction are then investigated and it is shown that, for successive convergents q/p beginning with $v/1$,

$$q^2-zp^2=-\alpha,\ +\beta,\ -\gamma,\ +\delta,\ -\epsilon \text{ etc. in order.}$$

It follows that the problem is solved whenever one of the terms with a positive sign, β, δ, ζ etc., becomes 1.

Since unity for one of the terms $\alpha, \beta, \gamma, \delta$ corresponds to the quotient $2v$, and each fresh period begins with $2v$, the first period will produce a convergent q/p such that $q^2-zp^2=\pm 1$; and the negative sign will apply if the number of quotients constituting the period is odd, while the positive sign will apply if the number of quotients is even. In the latter case we have a solution of our equation at once; if, however, $q^2-zp^2=-1$, we must go on to the end of the second period in order to get an even number of quotients and so satisfy the equation $q^2-zp^2=+1$. Or, says Euler, instead of going on and completing the second period, we can satisfy the latter equation more easily thus.

Suppose $q^2-zp^2=-1$, and assume

$$p'=2pq,\quad q'=2q^2+1.$$

Then
$$\begin{aligned} q'^2-zp'^2&=4q^4+4q^2+1-4zp^2q^2\\ &=1+4q^2(q^2-zp^2+1)\\ &=1.\end{aligned}$$

[This last derivation of a solution of $y^2 - zx^2 = 1$ from a known solution of $y^2 - zx^2 = -1$ is of course the same as the Indian method of doing the same thing, for they assumed $p' = 2pq$, $q' = q^2 + zp^2$, and $q^2 + zp^2 = q^2 + (q^2 + 1)$.]

We thus see that in Euler's method there is everything necessary to the complete solution of our equation except the proof that it must always lead to the desired result. Unless it is proved that the quotient $2v$ will actually occur in the development of the continued fraction in every case, we cannot be sure that the equation has any solution except $x = 0$, $y = 1$.

I cannot, I think, do better than conclude by a quotation from H. J. S. Smith[1], the first part of which is well known[2]. "Euler observed that [if $T^2 - DU^2 = 1$] T/U is itself necessarily a convergent to the value of $\sqrt{D}$, so that to obtain the numbers T and U it suffices to develop $\sqrt{D}$ as a continued fraction. It is singular, however, that it never seems to have occurred to him that, to complete the theory of the problem, it was necessary to demonstrate that the equation is always resoluble and that all its solutions are given by the development of $\sqrt{D}$. His memoir contains all the elements necessary to the demonstration, but here, as in some other instances, Euler is satisfied with an induction which does not amount to a rigorous proof. The first admissible proof of the resolubility of the equation was given by Lagrange in the *Mélanges de la Société de Turin*, Vol. IV. p. 41[3]. He there shows that in the development of $\sqrt{D}$ we shall obtain an infinite number of solutions of some equation of the form $T^2 - DU^2 = A$ and that, by multiplying together a sufficient number of these equations, we can deduce solutions of the equation $T^2 - DU^2 = 1$. But the simpler demonstration of its solubility which is now to be found in most books on algebra, and which depends on the completion of the theory (left unfinished by Euler) of the development of a quadratic surd as a continued fraction, was first given by Lagrange in the *Hist. de l'Académie de Berlin* for 1767 and 1768, Vol. XXIII. p. 272, and Vol. XXIV. p. 236[4], and, in a simpler form, in the Additions to Euler's *Algebra*[5], Art. 37."

[1] "Report on the Theory of Numbers, Part III.," *British Association Reports for* 1861, London, 1862, p. 315 = *Collected Works*, Vol. I., Oxford, 1894, p. 192.

[2] It is given in Cantor, *Gesch. d. Math.* IV. 1908, p. 159, and referred to by Konen, *op. cit.* p. 51.

[3] "Solution d'un problème d'Arithmétique," finished at Berlin on 20th Sept. 1768 and published in *Miscellanea Taurinensia*, IV. 1766–1769 = *Oeuvres de Lagrange*, I. pp. 671–731.

[4] The references are: "Sur la solution des problèmes indéterminés du second degré," read 24th Nov. 1768 and published in the *Mémoires de l'Académie Royale des Sciences et Belles-lettres de Berlin*, Vol. XXIII., 1769, pp. 165–310 = *Oeuvres de Lagrange*, II. pp. 377–535; "Nouvelle méthode pour résoudre les problèmes indéterminés en nombres entiers," read 21st June, 1770, and published in *Mémoires de l'Académie Royale des Sciences et Belles-lettres de Berlin*, Vol. XXIV., 1770, pp. 181–256 = *Oeuvres de Lagrange*, II. pp. 655–726.

[5] The Additions of Lagrange were first printed as an appendix to *Élémens d'Algèbre par M. L. Euler traduits de l'allemand*, Vol. II., Lyons, 1774; second edition, Paris, 1798; they were thence incorporated in *Oeuvres de Lagrange*, VII. pp. 158 sqq.

SECTION III.

THEOREMS AND PROBLEMS ON RATIONAL RIGHT-ANGLED TRIANGLES.

1. On No. 20 of the problems about right-angled triangles added by Bachet to Book VI. ("To find a right-angled triangle such that its area is equal to a given number") Fermat has a note which shall be quoted in full, not only for the sake of the famous theorem enunciated in it, but because, exceptionally, it indicates the lines on which his proof of the theorem proceeded.

"**The area of a right-angled triangle the sides of which are rational numbers cannot be a square number.**

"This proposition, which is my own discovery, I have at length succeeded in proving, though not without much labour and hard thinking. I give the proof here, as this method will enable extraordinary developments to be made in the theory of numbers.

"If the area of a right-angled triangle were a square, *there would exist two biquadrates the difference of which would be a square number.* Consequently *there would exist two square numbers the sum and difference of which would both be squares.* Therefore we should have a square number which would be equal to the sum of a square and the double of another square, while the squares of which this sum is made up would themselves [*i.e.* taken once each] have a square number for their sum. But if a square is made up of a square and the double of another square, its side, as I can very easily prove, is also similarly made up of a square and the double of another square. From this we conclude that the said side is the sum of the sides about the right angle in a right-angled triangle, and that the simple square contained in the sum is the base and the double of the other square the perpendicular.

"This right-angled triangle will thus be formed from two squares, the sum and the difference of which will be squares. But both these squares can be shown to be smaller than the squares originally assumed to be such that both their sum and their difference are squares. Thus, if there exist two squares such that their sum and difference are both squares, there will also exist two other integer squares which have the same property but have a smaller sum. By the same reasoning we find a sum still smaller than that last found, and we can go on *ad infinitum* finding integer square numbers smaller and smaller which have the same property. This is, however, impossible because there cannot be an infinite series of numbers smaller than any given integer we please.—The margin is too small to enable me to give the proof completely and with all detail.

"By means of these considerations I have also discovered and proved that *no triangular number except* 1 *can be a biquadrate.*"

As Wertheim says, it may have been by following out the indications thus given by Fermat that Euler succeeded in proving the propositions that $x^4 - y^4$ and $x^4 + y^4$ cannot be squares, as well as a number of other theorems connected therewith (*Commentationes arithmeticae collectae*, I. pp. 24 sqq.; *Algebra*, Part II. Chapter XIII.).

Zeuthen[1] suggests a method of filling out Fermat's argument, thus.

The sides of a rational right-angled triangle can be expressed as

$$x^2 + y^2,\ x^2 - y^2,\ 2xy.$$

As a common factor in the sides would appear as a square in the number representing the area, we can neglect such a factor, and assume that $x^2 - y^2$ and therefore also $x + y$ and $x - y$ are odd numbers and that x, y are prime to one another, so that x, y, $x + y$, $x - y$ are all prime to one another.

We have now to test the assumption that the area of the triangle

$$xy(x - y)(x + y)$$

is a square. If so, the separate factors must be squares, or

$$x = u^2,\ y = v^2,$$

$$u^2 + v^2 = p^2,\ u^2 - v^2 = q^2.$$

("*There would exist two biquadrates the difference of which* $[u^4 - v^4]$ *would be a square, and consequently there would exist two squares the sum and difference of which* $[u^2 + v^2,\ u^2 - v^2]$ *would both be squares*," Fermat.)

From the last two equations we obtain

$$2v^2 = p^2 - q^2 = (p - q)(p + q).$$

("*We should have a square number which would be equal to the sum of a square and the double of another square* $[p^2 = 2v^2 + q^2]$," Fermat.)

Now $p + q$ and $p - q$ are both even numbers because, on the above assumptions, p^2 and q^2 are both odd; but they cannot have any other common factor except 2, since u^2 and v^2 are prime to one another. It follows therefore from the last equation that

$$p + q = \begin{cases} 2m^2 \\ n^2 \end{cases},\quad p - q = \begin{cases} n^2 \\ 2m^2 \end{cases},$$

where n is an even number.

We obtain, therefore,

$$u^2 = \frac{p^2 + q^2}{2} = (m^2)^2 + \left(\frac{n^2}{2}\right)^2.$$

The whole numbers m^2 and $\frac{n^2}{2}$ are therefore sides of a new right-angled triangle with the square area $\frac{m^2 n^2}{4}$.

[1] Zeuthen, *Geschichte der Mathematik im* XVI. *und* XVII. *Jahrhundert*, 1903, p. 163.

("If a square is made up of a square and the double of another square [$p^2 = 2v^2 + q^2$], its side is, as I can very easily prove, also made up of a square and the double of another square $\left[p = m^2 + 2\left(\frac{n}{2}\right)^2\right]$. From this we conclude that the said side is the sum of the sides about the right angle in a right-angled triangle, the square [m^2] being the base and the double of the other square $\left[2\left(\frac{n}{2}\right)^2\right]$ the perpendicular," Fermat.)

That the sides of the new triangle are less than those of the original triangle is clear from the fact that the square on its hypotenuse u^2 or x is a factor of one of the perpendicular sides of the original triangle[1].

As now an infinite series of diminishing positive whole numbers is impossible, the original assumption from which we started is also impossible.

It will be observed, as Zeuthen says, that the proof includes also the proof of the fact that $u^4 - v^4$ cannot be a square and therefore cannot be a fourth power, from which it follows that the equation $u^4 = v^4 + w^4$ cannot be solved in whole numbers, and consequently cannot be solved in rational numbers either.

The history of this theorem would not be complete without an account of a "proof originating with Fermat" which Wertheim has reproduced[2]. In the small paper of Fermat's entitled "Relation des nouvelles découvertes en la science des nombres[3]" containing a statement of his method of "diminution without limit" (*descente infinie* or *indéfinie*) and of a number of theorems which he proved by means of it, there is a remark that he had sent to Carcavi and Frénicle some proofs based on this method. And, sure enough, Frénicle gives a proof by this method of the theorem now in question in his "Traité des triangles rectangles en nombres[4]." Wertheim accordingly concludes that we have here a proof of Fermat's. A short explanation is necessary before we come to Frénicle's proof.

We obtain a right-angled triangle z, x, y in rational numbers ($z^2 = x^2 + y^2$) if, a, b being any integers and $a > b$, we put

$$z = a^2 + b^2, \quad x = a^2 - b^2, \quad y = 2ab.$$

If a is prime to b and one of these numbers is even, the other odd, then it is easily shown that the greatest common measure of x, y, z is 1.

In the right-angled triangle $a^2 - b^2$ and $2ab$ are the perpendicular sides,

[1] Zeuthen's inference at this point diverges slightly in form from what we actually find in Fermat's own statement of his argument. Fermat does not actually say that the new right-angled triangle is a triangle in smaller numbers than the original triangle and with the same assumed property, but that its formation gives us two new square numbers the sum and difference of which are squares, and which are smaller than the two squares originally assumed to have this property.

[2] *Zeitschrift für Math. u. Physik*, hist. litt. Abtheilung XLIV. 1899, pp. 4–6.

[3] *Oeuvres de Fermat*, Vol. II. pp. 431–6.

[4] *Mémoires de l'Académie Royale des Sciences*, V., Paris, 1729, pp. 83–166.

and $(a^2 - b^2)ab$ is the area. a, b are called the *generating* numbers (the numbers from which the triangle is formed) and if a is prime to b, and one of them is odd and the other even, so that x, y, z have no common factor except 1, the triangle is called a *primitive* triangle.

If $(a^2-b^2)ab$ is the area of a *primitive* right-angled triangle—and it is enough to prove the proposition for such—each of the three numbers a^2-b^2, a, b is prime to the other two. If, then, the product is a square number, each of the three factors must be square, and in that case a^2-b^2 will be the difference between two fourth powers. The theorems

(1) *the area of a right-angled triangle in rational numbers cannot be a square number*, and

(2) *the difference of two fourth powers cannot be a square*,

accordingly state essentially the same fact.

The proof which Frénicle gives of the first of these propositions depends on the following Lemmas.

Lemma I. *If the odd perpendicular of a primitive right-angled triangle is a square number, there exists a second primitive right-angled triangle with smaller sides which has for its odd perpendicular the root of the said square number.*

If $a^2-b^2=c^2$, it follows that $a^2=b^2+c^2$, so that a, b, c are the sides of a right-angled triangle. The odd perpendicular of this second triangle is c, for by hypothesis c^2 is odd; consequently the even perpendicular is b, while a is the hypotenuse. The triangle is "primitive" because a common divisor of any two of the three numbers a, b, c would divide the third, while by hypothesis a, b have no common factor except 1. Next, the second triangle has smaller sides than the first, since $c<c^2$, $a<a^2+b^2$, $b<2ab$.

By this lemma we can from the triangle 9, 40, 41 derive the triangle 3, 4, 5, and from the triangle 225, 25312, 25313 the triangle 15, 112, 113.

Lemma II. *If in a primitive right-angled triangle the hypotenuse as well as the even perpendicular were square, there would exist a second primitive right-angled triangle with smaller sides which would have for hypotenuse the root of the hypotenuse of the first, for odd perpendicular a square number, and for even perpendicular the double of a square number.*

Let the sides of the first triangle be a^2+b^2, a^2-b^2, $2ab$. If $2ab$ were a square, ab would be double of a square; therefore, since a, b are prime to one another, one of these two numbers, namely the odd one, would be a square, and the other, the even one, would be double of a square. Let a be the odd one of the two, b the even. If now the hypotenuse a^2+b^2 were a square number c^2, we should have a second right-angled triangle a, b, c which would necessarily be primitive and in which the sides would be smaller than those of the first triangle; for $c<c^2$, $b<2ab$ and $a<a^2-b^2$ since $a+b>a$, $a-b \geqq 1$.

By means of the above two lemmas combined we can now prove that *the area of a primitive right-angled triangle cannot be a square number.*

Let the sides of the triangle be a^2+b^2, a^2-b^2, $2ab$. If now the area were square, the product of the perpendicular sides would be double of a square. But the perpendicular sides are prime to one another. Therefore the odd perpendicular a^2-b^2 would be a square, and the even perpendicular $2ab$ the double of a square. But, if a^2-b^2 were equal to c^2, we could (by the first Lemma) find a second primitive triangle with smaller sides in which the odd perpendicular would be c, the even perpendicular b, and the hypotenuse a. Again, since $2ab$ would be double of a square, ab would be a square, and, since a is prime to b, both a and b would be squares. The second triangle would accordingly have a square number both for its hypotenuse (a) and for its even perpendicular (b). That is, the second primitive triangle would satisfy the conditions of the second Lemma, and we could accordingly derive from the second primitive triangle a third primitive triangle with still smaller sides which would, *exactly like the first triangle*, have a square number for its odd perpendicular, and for its even perpendicular the double of a square number.

From this third triangle we could obtain a fourth, and by means of the fourth we could obtain a fifth with the same property as the first, and so we should have an unending series of primitive right-angled triangles, each successive triangle having smaller sides than the one before, and all being such that the odd perpendicular would be a square number, the even perpendicular the double of a square number, and consequently the area a square number. This, however, is impossible since there cannot be an unending series of integral numbers less than any given integral number.

Frénicle proves, by similar considerations, that *neither can the area of a right-angled triangle in rational numbers be the double of a square number.*

In enunciating Fermat's problems on right-angled triangles I shall in future for brevity and uniformity use ξ, η, ζ to denote the three sides, while ζ will always represent the hypotenuse and ξ, η the two perpendicular sides.

2. *To find a right-angled triangle* (ζ, ξ, η) *such that*

$$\left.\begin{array}{c}\zeta=u^2\\ \xi+\eta=v^2\end{array}\right\}.$$

[Since $\zeta^2=\xi^2+\eta^2$, this problem is equivalent to that of finding x, y such that

$$\left.\begin{array}{c}x+y=v^2\\ x^2+y^2=w^4\end{array}\right\},$$

which is Question 17 in Chapter XIV. of Euler's *Algebra*, Part II.]

First method.

Form a right-angled triangle from the numbers $x+1$, x; the sides will then be

$$\zeta=2x^2+2x+1,\quad \xi=2x+1,\quad \eta=2x^2+2x.$$

We have then the double-equation

$$\left.\begin{aligned} 2x^2 + 2x + 1 &= u^2 \\ 2x^2 + 4x + 1 &= v^2 \end{aligned}\right\}.$$

The ordinary method of Diophantus gives the solution $x = -\frac{12}{7}$; the triangle will therefore be formed from $-\frac{5}{7}$ and $-\frac{12}{7}$ or, if we take the numerators only, -5 and -12, and the triangle is $(169, -119, 120)$ which is equally the result of forming a triangle from $+5$ and $+12$.

But, as one of the perpendiculars is negative, we must find another value of x which will make all three sides positive.

We accordingly form a triangle from $x + 5$ and 12, instead of from 5 and 12, and repeat the operation. This gives for the sides

$$\zeta = x^2 + 10x + 169, \quad \xi = x^2 + 10x - 119, \quad \eta = 24x + 120,$$

and we have to solve the double-equation

$$\begin{aligned} x^2 + 10x + 169 &= u^2, \\ x^2 + 34x + 1 &= v^2. \end{aligned}$$

Making the absolute term the same in each, we have to solve

$$\begin{aligned} x^2 + 10x + 169 &= u^2, \\ 169x^2 + 5746x + 169 &= v'^2. \end{aligned}$$

The difference is $168x^2 + 5736x$, which we may separate into the factors $14x$, $12x + \frac{2868}{7}$ (the sum of the terms in x being $26x$ or $2 \cdot 13x$).

Equating the square of half the sum of these factors to the larger expression, or the square of half their difference to the smaller, we find in the usual way

$$x = \frac{2048075}{20566}.$$

The triangle is therefore formed from $\frac{2150905}{20566}$, 12, or from 2150905, 246792, and the triangle itself is

$$4687298610289, \quad 4565486027761, \quad 1061652293520,$$

the hypotenuse and the sum of the other two sides being severally squares.

Second method.

This is the same as the first method up to the forming of the triangle from $x + 5$ and 12 and the arrival at the double-equation

$$\begin{aligned} x^2 + 10x + 169 &= u^2, \\ x^2 + 34x + 1 &= v^2. \end{aligned}$$

Multiply the two expressions together, and we must have

$$\begin{aligned} x^4 + 44x^3 + 510x^2 + 5756x + 169 &= \text{a square} \\ &= \left(13 + \tfrac{2878}{13}x - x^2\right)^2, \text{ say;} \end{aligned}$$

this gives, as a matter of fact, the same value of x, namely

$$x = \frac{2048075}{20566},$$

and the triangle is the same as before[1].

In his note on Diophantus VI. 22 Fermat says that he confidently asserts that the above right-angled triangle is the smallest right-angled triangle in rational numbers which satisfies the conditions.

[The truth of this latter assertion was proved by Lagrange[2]. Lagrange observes that, since $\xi+\eta=y^2$, $\xi^2+\eta^2=x^4$, say, we have, if we put z for $\xi-\eta$,

$$z^2+y^4=2x^4,$$

or

$$2x^4-y^4=z^2,$$

and, if x, y is any solution of the latter equation,

$$\xi=\tfrac{1}{2}(y^2+z), \quad \eta=\tfrac{1}{2}(y^2-z).$$

[1] For comparison we may give Euler's solution (*Algebra*, Part II., Art. 240; *Commentationes arithmeticae*, II. p. 398).

We have to solve the equations

$$\left.\begin{array}{r} x+y=u^2 \\ x^2+y^2=v^4 \end{array}\right\}.$$

First make x^2+y^2 a square by putting $x=a^2-b^2$, $y=2ab$, so that

$$x^2+y^2=(a^2+b^2)^2.$$

To make the last expression a fourth power put $a=p^2-q^2$, $b=2pq$, so that

$$a^2+b^2=(p^2+q^2)^2,$$

and accordingly

$$x^2+y^2=(p^2+q^2)^4.$$

We have now only to make $x+y$ a square.

Now $\quad x=a^2-b^2=p^4-6p^2q^2+q^4, \quad y=2ab=4p^3q-4pq^3;$

therefore $\quad p^4+4p^3q-6p^2q^2-4pq^3+q^4=$ a square.

In solving this we have to note that p, q should be positive, p must be $>q$ (for otherwise y would be negative), and $a>b$ in order that x may be positive.

Put

$$p^4+4p^3q-6p^2q^2-4pq^3+q^4=(p^2-2pq+q^2)^2,$$

and we obtain

$$4p^3q-6p^2q^2=-4p^3q+6p^2q^2, \text{ whence } p/q=\frac{3}{2}.$$

But, if we put $p=3$, $q=2$, we find $x=-119$, a negative value.

To find fresh values, we can substitute for p the expression $\frac{3}{2}q+r$ and solve for the ratio q/r; then, by taking for q the numerator and for r the denominator of the fraction so found, we find a value for p and thence for x, y. This is Euler's method in the *Algebra*. But we avoid the necessity for clearing of fractions if (as in the *Comment. arithm.*) we leave 2 as the value of q and substitute $3+v$ for 3 as the value of p.

We then have

$$\begin{aligned} p^4 &= 81+108v+54v^2+12v^3+v^4, \\ +4p^3q &= 216+216v+72v^2+8v^3, \\ -6p^2q^2 &= -216-144v-24v^2, \\ -4pq^3 &= -96-32v, \\ +q^4 &= 16, \end{aligned}$$

whence $\quad x+y=1+148v+102v^2+20v^3+v^4=$ a square $=(1+74v-v^2)^2$, say;

and we obtain

$$1343=42v, \text{ or } v=\frac{1343}{42}, \text{ and } p=3+v=\frac{1469}{42}, \text{ while } q=2.$$

Taking integral values, we put $p=1469$, $q=84$.

Therefore $\quad a=1385\cdot 1553=2150905, \quad b=168\cdot 1469=246792,$

and $\quad x=4565486027761, \quad y=1061652293520,$

which is the same as Fermat's solution.

[2] *N. Mémoires de l'Acad. Royale des Sciences et Belles-lettres de Berlin*, année 1777, Berlin, 1779 = *Oeuvres de Lagrange*, IV. pp. 377–398.

He sets himself therefore to find a general solution of the equation $2x^4 - y^4 = z^2$ and effects it by a method which is a variation of Fermat's *descente*, one of the most fruitful methods, as Lagrange observes, in the whole theory of numbers. The modified method consists of two parts, (1) a proof that, assuming that there exist integral values of x, y greater than 1 which satisfy the condition $2x^4 - y^4 = z^2$, there are still smaller integral values which will also satisfy it, (2) the discovery of a general method of deducing the latter from the former. This being done, and it being known that $x = 1$, $y = 1$ are the minimum values, the successive higher values are found by reversing the process. Lagrange found that the four lowest values for x, y give the following pairs of values for ξ, η, namely

$$\begin{aligned}
&(1)\quad \xi = 1, &&\eta = 0,\\
&(2)\quad \xi = 120, &&\eta = -119,\\
&(3)\quad \xi = 2276953, &&\eta = -473304,\\
&(4)\quad \xi = 1061652293520, &&\eta = 4565486027761,
\end{aligned}$$

so that the last pair (4) are in truth, as Fermat asserts, the smallest possible values in positive integers.]

3. *To find a right-angled triangle ζ, ξ, η such that*

$$\left.\begin{aligned} \zeta &= u^2 \\ \xi - \eta &= v^2 \end{aligned}\right\}.$$

[This is of course equivalent to solving

$$\left.\begin{aligned} x - y &= t^2 \\ x^2 + y^2 &= w^4 \end{aligned}\right\}.]$$

Form a triangle from the numbers $x + 1$, 1; the sides will then be

$$\zeta = x^2 + 2x + 2,\quad \xi = x^2 + 2x,\quad \eta = 2x + 2.$$

We have then to solve the double-equation

$$\left.\begin{aligned} x^2 + 2x + 2 &= u^2 \\ x^2 - 2 &= v^2 \end{aligned}\right\}.$$

Solved in the ordinary way, this gives $x = -\frac{17}{12}$; consequently the triangle is formed from $-\frac{5}{12}$, 1, or from -5, 12.

We could proceed, as in the last problem, to deduce a new value for x, but we observe that the triangle formed from 5, 12, *i.e.* the triangle 169, 119, 120, satisfies the conditions.

4. *To find a right-angled triangle ζ, ξ, η such that*

$$\left.\begin{aligned} \zeta &= u^2 \\ \xi + m\eta &= v^2 \end{aligned}\right\},$$

where m is any number.

Fermat takes the case where $m = 2$.

Form a triangle from x, 1; the sides are then $\zeta = x^2 + 1$, $\xi = x^2 - 1$, $\eta = 2x$.

Therefore

$$\left.\begin{matrix} x^2+1 \\ x^2+4x-1 \end{matrix}\right\} \text{ must both be squares.}$$

The difference $= 2-4x$, and by the usual method we find $x=\frac{5}{12}$.

But $\xi = x^2-1$ is negative unless $x>1$. We therefore begin afresh and form a triangle from $x+5$, 12.

The sides of this triangle are

$$x^2+10x+169,\quad x^2+10x-119,\quad 24x+120.$$

We have therefore to solve the double-equation

$$\left.\begin{aligned} x^2+10x+169&=u^2 \\ x^2+58x+121&=v^2 \end{aligned}\right\}.$$

Fermat multiplies the two expressions together and puts

$$x^4+68x^3+870x^2+11012x+20449 = \text{a square}$$
$$= \left(143+\tfrac{5506}{143}x-\tfrac{6262703}{2924207}x^2\right)^2, \text{ say;}$$

therefore $$x=\frac{96051795411}{14790092510},$$

and the triangle is formed from 103447257961, 17749110120.

The double-equation could also have been solved by the usual Diophantine method, as in the next problem to be given.

5. *To find a right-angled triangle* ζ, ξ, η *such that*

$$\left.\begin{aligned} \zeta&=u^2 \\ \xi-m\eta&=v^2 \end{aligned}\right\},$$

where m *is any number.*

Suppose that $m=2$.

Form a triangle from $x+1$, 1, so that the sides are

$$\zeta=x^2+2x+2,\quad \xi=x^2+2x,\quad \eta=2x+2.$$

Therefore we have to solve

$$\left.\begin{aligned} x^2+2x+2&=u^2 \\ x^2-2x-4&=v^2 \end{aligned}\right\}.$$

Solving in the usual manner, we obtain $x=-\frac{17}{12}$, so that the triangle is formed from $-\frac{5}{12}$, 1, or from -5, 12, and is therefore $(169, 119, -120)$.

We have to replace the value of x by a value which will avoid the negative sign. Form a triangle, then, from $x-5$, 12.

The sides are $x^2-10x+169$, $x^2-10x-119$, $24x-120$.

The double-equation now becomes

$$\left.\begin{aligned} x^2-10x+169&=u^2 \\ x^2-58x+121&=v^2 \end{aligned}\right\}.$$

Multiply the second equation by $\frac{169}{121}$, and we have to solve

$$\left.\begin{aligned} x^2-10x+169&=u^2 \\ \tfrac{169}{121}x^2-\tfrac{9802}{121}x+169&=v'^2 \end{aligned}\right\}.$$

The difference $= \frac{48}{121}x^2 - \frac{8592}{121}x = \frac{2}{11}x\left(\frac{24}{11}x - \frac{4296}{11}\right)$.

Equating the square of half the difference of the factors to the smaller expression (or the square of half the sum to the larger), we have

$$x = \frac{4593455}{46046},$$

and the required triangle is formed from 4363225, 552552, the sides being

$$19343046113329, \quad 18732418687921, \quad 4821817400400.$$

Or again in this case we can multiply the expressions $x^2 - 10x + 169$ and $x^2 - 58x + 121$ and put their product

$$x^4 - 68x^3 + 870x^2 - 11012x + 20449 = \text{a square}$$
$$= \left(143 - \frac{5506}{143}x + x^2\right)^2, \text{ say,}$$

and the result will be the same as before,

$$x = \frac{4593455}{46046}.$$

6. *To find a right-angled triangle ζ, ξ, η such that*

$$\left.\begin{aligned} \xi &= u^2 \\ \xi + m\eta &= v^2 \end{aligned}\right\},$$

where m is any given number.

Let $m = 3$. Form a triangle from $x + 1$, 1; its sides will be

$$\zeta = x^2 + 2x + 2, \quad \xi = x^2 + 2x, \quad \eta = 2x + 2.$$

We have therefore to solve the double-equation

$$\left.\begin{aligned} x^2 + 2x &= u^2 \\ x^2 + 8x + 6 &= v^9 \end{aligned}\right\}.$$

Solving this in the ordinary manner, we shall find $x = \frac{1}{12}$.

Hence the triangle is formed from $\frac{13}{12}$, 1, or (in whole numbers) from 13, 12; the sides are therefore 313, 25, 312.

Fermat also finds the solution by multiplying the two expressions and making the product a square;

$$x^4 + 10x^3 + 22x^2 + 12x = \text{a square}$$
$$= \left(x^2 + 5x - \tfrac{3}{2}\right)^2, \text{ say.}$$

This gives the same value of x as before, $x = \frac{1}{12}$; and the triangle is 313, 25, 312.

7. *To find a right-angled triangle ζ, ξ, η such that*

$$\left.\begin{aligned} \xi &= u^2 \\ \xi - m\eta &= v^2 \end{aligned}\right\},$$

where m is a given number.

Fermat takes the case $m = 3$.

Remembering that in the corresponding problem with a *plus* sign we found the triangle 313, 25, 312 which is formed from 13, 12, we form the triangle in this case from $x - 13$, 12; its sides are

$$\zeta = x^2 - 26x + 313, \quad \xi = x^2 - 26x + 25, \quad \eta = 24x - 312.$$

We have then

$$\left.\begin{aligned} x^2 - 26x + 25 &= u^2 \\ x^2 - 98x + 961 &= v^2 \end{aligned}\right\}.$$

Multiplying the first expression by $\frac{961}{25}$, we have to solve the double-equation

$$\left.\begin{aligned} \tfrac{961}{25}x^2 - \tfrac{24986}{25}x + 961 &= u'^2 \\ x^2 - 98x + 961 &= v^2 \end{aligned}\right\}.$$

The difference $= \frac{936}{25}x^2 - \frac{22536}{25}x = \frac{26}{5}x\left(\frac{36}{5}x - \frac{11268}{65}\right)$.

Proceeding as usual, we find $x = \frac{27681731}{318370}$; the triangle is formed from $x - 13$, 12, or (in whole numbers) from 23542921, 3820440, and the sides are

$$568864891005841, \quad 539673367418641, \quad 179888634210480.$$

The same result is obtained by multiplying the expressions $x^2 - 26x + 25$ and $x^2 - 98x + 961$ and making the product a square; we put

$$\begin{aligned} x^4 - 124x^3 + 3534x^2 - 27436x + 24025 &= \text{a square} \\ &= \left(x^2 - \tfrac{13718}{155}x + 155\right)^2, \end{aligned}$$

and the result is $x = \frac{27681731}{318370}$, as before.

8. *To find a right-angled triangle ζ, ξ, η such that*

$$\left.\begin{aligned} \xi &= u^2 \\ \zeta + m\eta &= v^2 \end{aligned}\right\},$$

where m is any given number.

Suppose $m = 2$. Form a triangle from $x + 1$, 1; the sides are

$$\zeta = x^2 + 2x + 2, \quad \xi = x^2 + 2x, \quad \eta = 2x + 2.$$

We have then to solve the double-equation

$$\left.\begin{aligned} x^2 + 2x &= u^2 \\ x^2 + 6x + 6 &= v^2 \end{aligned}\right\}.$$

The usual method gives $x = \frac{1}{4}$, and the triangle is formed from $\frac{5}{4}$, 1, or (in whole numbers) from 5, 4, being the triangle (41, 9, 40).

Since $\zeta + \eta = x^2 + 4x + 4 =$ a square, we have actually solved the problem of *finding a right-angled triangle ζ, ξ, η such that*

$$\left.\begin{aligned} \xi &= u^2 \\ \zeta + \eta &= v^2 \\ \zeta + 2\eta &= w^2 \end{aligned}\right\}.$$

9. *To find a right-angled triangle ζ, ξ, η such that*

$$\left.\begin{aligned} \xi &= u^2 \\ \zeta - m\eta &= v^2 \end{aligned}\right\},$$

where m is a given number.

Suppose $m = 2$.

Since the corresponding problem with a *plus* sign just preceding has the solution (41, 9, 40) formed from the numbers 5, 4, we form a triangle in this case from $x - 5$, 4; the sides are

$$\zeta = x^2 - 10x + 41, \quad \xi = x^2 - 10x + 9, \quad \eta = 8x - 40.$$

We have then to solve the double-equation

$$\left.\begin{aligned} x^2 - 10x + \quad 9 &= u^2 \\ x^2 - 26x + 121 &= v^2 \end{aligned}\right\}.$$

De Billy (or Fermat) observes that this double-equation "seems to admit of solution in several ways, but it will be found that it is hardly possible to find a practical solution except by the new method" (expounded earlier in the *Inventum Novum*) of making the *absolute* terms equal (instead of using the equal terms in x^2, which method gives, in fact, the value $x = 0$). That is to say, we make the absolute terms in the two expressions equal by multiplying the first by $\frac{121}{9}$, and the double-equation becomes

$$\left.\begin{aligned} \tfrac{121}{9}x^2 - \tfrac{1210}{9}x + 121 &= u'^2 \\ x^2 - 26x + 121 &= v^2 \end{aligned}\right\}.$$

The difference $= \frac{112}{9}x^2 - \frac{976}{9}x = \frac{8}{3}x\left(\frac{14}{3}x - \frac{122}{3}\right)$.

Equating the square of half the difference of the factors to v^2, or the square of half their sum to u'^2, we find $x = \frac{658}{33}$.

Therefore the triangle is formed from $\frac{493}{33}$, 4 or (in whole numbers) from 493, 132, and the sides are 260473, 225625, 130152.

Since $\zeta - \eta = x^2 - 18x + 81 =$ a square, the above actually amounts to the solution of the problem of *finding a right-angled triangle* ζ, ξ, η *such that the three conditions*

$$\left.\begin{aligned} \xi &= u^2 \\ \zeta - \eta &= v^2 \\ \zeta - 2\eta &= w^2 \end{aligned}\right\}$$

are simultaneously satisfied.

De Billy (or Fermat) observes however that, while the above *one* solution satisfies the conditions of both problems, it is not so with all solutions of the problem involving the two conditions only; but only *primitive* triangles satisfying the conditions of that problem satisfy the additional condition. Thus the triangle (624, 576, 240) is such that one of the perpendicular sides is a square and the difference between the hypotenuse and twice the other perpendicular is also a square, but the hypotenuse *minus* the latter perpendicular is not a square.

10. *To find a right-angled triangle* ζ, ξ, η *such that*

$$\left.\begin{aligned} \eta &= t^2 \\ \xi + \eta &= u^2 \\ \xi - \xi\eta &= v^2 \\ \eta - \xi\eta &= w^2 \end{aligned}\right\}.$$

Assume x, $1 - x$ for the sides ξ, η about the right angle respectively.

This supposition satisfies the second condition.

Again, since $\xi\eta = x - x^2$, the third and fourth conditions are satisfied, for $v^2 = x^2$, $w^2 = 1 - 2x + x^2$.

It remains to satisfy the conditions

$$\left.\begin{array}{r}\eta = 1 - x = t^2 \\ \text{and} \quad \zeta^2 = \xi^2 + \eta^2 = 1 - 2x + 2x^2 = \text{a square}\end{array}\right\}.$$

The difference $= 2x^2 - x = \frac{1}{2}x(4x - 2)$, and we find, in the usual way, $x = \frac{40}{49}$.

The triangle is $(\frac{41}{49}, \frac{40}{49}, \frac{9}{49})$.

11. *To find a right-angled triangle ζ, ξ, η such that*

$$\left.\begin{array}{r}\xi = a \text{ cube} \\ \xi - \frac{1}{2}\xi\eta = a \text{ square}\end{array}\right\}.$$

Fermat assumes $\xi = 1$, $\eta = x$, so that the first condition is satisfied, 1 being a cube.

We must now have

$$\left.\begin{array}{r}1 - \frac{1}{2}x = u^2 \\ \text{and also} \quad \zeta^2 = \xi^2 + \eta^2 = 1 + x^2 = v^2\end{array}\right\}.$$

The difference $= x^2 + \frac{1}{2}x = \frac{1}{4}x(4x + 2)$, and we find $x = -\frac{272}{225}$.

In order to derive a positive value for x we substitute $y - \frac{272}{225}$ for x in the equations, which gives

$$\frac{361}{225} - \frac{1}{2}y = u^2,$$

$$y^2 - \frac{544}{225}x + \frac{124609}{50625} = v^2.$$

Make the absolute term in the first equation equal to that in the latter by multiplying by $\dfrac{124609}{361 \cdot 225}$, and we have to solve

$$\left.\begin{array}{r}\frac{124609}{50625} - \frac{124609}{162450}y = u'^2 \\ y^2 - \frac{544}{225}y + \frac{124609}{50625} = v^2\end{array}\right\}.$$

The difference $= y^2 - \frac{268159}{162450}y = y\left(y - \frac{268159}{162450}\right)$.

We find accordingly

$$y = \frac{187917462543}{80970928200}$$

and

$$x = y - \frac{272}{225} = \frac{90032607119}{80970928200}.$$

The triangle is then

$$\frac{121087412881}{80970928200}, \ 1, \ \frac{90032607119}{80970928200}.$$

12. *To find a right-angled triangle ζ, ξ, η such that*

$$\zeta + \tfrac{1}{2}\xi\eta = u^2.$$

Form a triangle from the numbers $x + 1$, x; the sides are

$$\zeta = 2x^2 + 2x + 1, \quad \xi = 2x + 1, \quad \eta = 2x^2 + 2x.$$

Thus $\zeta + \frac{1}{2}\xi\eta = 2x^3 + 5x^2 + 3x + 1$ must be a square.

Suppose $\qquad 2x^3 + 5x^2 + 3x + 1 = (\frac{3}{2}x + 1)^2,$

and we have $\qquad x = -\frac{11}{8}.$

Now substitute $y - \frac{11}{8}$ for x in the expression to be made a square, and we have

$$2y^3 - \frac{13}{4}y^2 + \frac{19}{32}y + \frac{289}{256} = \text{a square}$$
$$= (\tfrac{19}{68}y + \tfrac{17}{16})^2, \text{ say,}$$

whence $y = \frac{15389}{9248}$, and $x = \frac{15389}{9248} - \frac{11}{8} = \frac{2673}{9248}$.

The triangle is accordingly found.

13. *To find a right-angled triangle* ζ, ξ, η *such that*

$$\xi + \tfrac{1}{2}\xi\eta = u^2.$$

Form a triangle as before from $x + 1$, x, and in this case we shall have

$$2x^3 + 3x^2 + 3x + 1 = \text{a square}$$
$$= (\tfrac{3}{2}x + 1)^2, \text{ say,}$$

whence $x = -\frac{3}{8}$.

Substitute $y - \frac{3}{8}$ for x in the expression to be made a square; thus

$$2y^3 + \tfrac{3}{4}y^2 + \tfrac{51}{32}y + \tfrac{49}{256} = \text{a square}$$
$$= (\tfrac{51}{28}y + \tfrac{7}{16})^2, \text{ say,}$$

whence $y = \frac{2013}{1568}$, and $x = \frac{2013}{1568} - \frac{3}{8} = \frac{1425}{1568}$,

the triangle being therefore

$$\frac{5494337}{1229312}, \quad \frac{3463712}{1229312}, \quad \frac{4265025}{1229312}.$$

14. *To find a right-angled triangle* ζ, ξ, η *such that*

$$(\xi + \eta)^2 - \tfrac{1}{2}\xi\eta = u^2.$$

Let $\xi = x$, $\eta = 1$; then $\zeta^2 = x^2 + 1 = \text{a square}$

Also, by the condition of the problem, $x^2 + \frac{3}{2}x + 1 = \text{a square}$.

The usual method of solution gives $x = -\frac{55}{48}$.

Substitute therefore $y - \frac{55}{48}$ for x in the two expressions, and we have the double-equation

$$y^2 - \tfrac{19}{24}y + \tfrac{1369}{2304} = v^2,$$
$$y^2 - \tfrac{55}{24}y + \tfrac{5329}{2304} = w^2.$$

Or, if we make the absolute term in the first expression the same as in the second by multiplying by $\frac{5329}{1369}$,

$$\left.\begin{aligned} \tfrac{5329}{1369}y^2 - \tfrac{101251}{32856}y + \tfrac{5329}{2304} &= v'^2 \\ y^2 - \tfrac{55}{24}y + \tfrac{5329}{2304} &= w^2 \end{aligned}\right\}.$$

The difference $= \frac{3960}{1369}y^2 - \frac{2163}{2738}y = \frac{36}{37}y(\frac{110}{37}y - \frac{2163}{2664})$,

and we find $y = \frac{94105}{64824}$, so that $x = y - \frac{55}{48} = \frac{39655}{129648}$.

Therefore the two perpendicular sides of the triangle, in whole numbers, are 39655, 129648, and the hypotenuse is 135577.

15. *To find a right-angled triangle ζ, ξ, η such that*

$$(\xi+\eta)^2+\tfrac{1}{2}\xi\eta = a \text{ square}.$$

This problem is mentioned in Fermat's letters to St Martin of 31st May and to Mersenne of 1st September 1643[1]. The result only is given (in the letter to Mersenne), and not the solution; but it can easily be worked out on the lines of the solution of the preceding problem.

Let $\xi=x$, $\eta=1$; we must therefore have

$$\left.\begin{array}{l} x^2+1 \\ x^2+\frac{5}{2}x+1 \end{array}\right\} \text{both squares.}$$

Solving in the usual way by splitting the difference $\frac{5}{2}x$ into the factors $\frac{5}{4}\cdot 2x$ we find $x=-\frac{39}{80}$.

Substitute $y-\frac{39}{80}$ for x in the two expressions, and we have to solve

$$y^2-\tfrac{39}{40}y+(\tfrac{89}{80})^2=u^2,$$
$$y^2+\tfrac{61}{40}y+(\tfrac{11}{80})^2=v^2.$$

Multiply the last by $(\frac{89}{11})^2$ so as to make the absolute terms the same; and we have to solve

$$y^2-\tfrac{39}{40}y+(\tfrac{89}{80})^2=u^2,$$
$$(\tfrac{89}{11})^2y^2+(\tfrac{89}{11})^2\cdot\tfrac{61}{40}y+(\tfrac{89}{80})^2=v'^2.$$

The difference $=\{(\frac{89}{11})^2-1\}y^2+\frac{24395}{242}y$

$=\frac{100}{11}y\left(\frac{78}{11}y+\frac{4879}{440}\right)$.

We therefore put $(y-\frac{4879}{880})^2=y^2-\frac{39}{40}y+(\frac{89}{80})^2$,

whence $y\left(\frac{4879}{440}-\frac{39}{40}\right)=(\frac{4879}{880})^2-(\frac{89}{80})^2$,

and $y=\frac{114231}{39160}$, so that $x=y-\frac{39}{80}=\frac{190281}{78320}$.

The required triangle is therefore $(\frac{205769}{78320}, \frac{190281}{78320}, 1)$ or, in whole numbers, (205769, 190281, 78320).

16. *To find a right-angled triangle ζ, ξ, η such that*

$$\zeta^2+m\cdot\tfrac{1}{2}\xi\eta = a \text{ square}.$$

Fermat takes the case where $m=2$.

Form a triangle from the numbers x, 1; the sides are then

$$\zeta=x^2+1,\quad \xi=x^2-1,\quad \eta=2x.$$

Thus we must have $(x^2+1)^2+2x(x^2-1)$ a square, that is,

$$x^4+2x^3+2x^2-2x+1 = \text{a square}$$
$$=(x^2+x+\tfrac{1}{2})^2,\text{ say,}$$

whence $x=\frac{1}{4}$.

[1] *Oeuvres de Fermat*, II. pp. 260, 263.

But this value makes $x^2 - 1$ negative; so we must seek another by putting $y + \frac{1}{4}$ for x in the expression to be made a square.

We have $y^4 + 3y^3 + \frac{31}{8}y^2 - \frac{9}{16}y + \frac{169}{256} =$ a square

$$= (\tfrac{13}{16} - \tfrac{9}{26}y + \tfrac{5077}{2197}y^2)^2, \text{ say.}$$

This gives $y = \frac{462553}{436440}$, and $x = y + \frac{1}{4} = \frac{571663}{436440}$.

Therefore the triangle is generated (in whole numbers) from 571663 and 436440.

De Billy adds that there is one case in which the problem is impossible. Tannery observes in a note that this remark seems to refer to the case in which $m = 8$.

17. *To find a right-angled triangle* ζ, ξ, η *such that*

$$\xi^2 - \tfrac{1}{2}\xi\eta = a \text{ square.}$$

Form a triangle from $x - 1$, 4; the sides will then be

$$\zeta = x^2 - 2x + 17, \quad \xi = x^2 - 2x - 15, \quad \eta = 8x - 8.$$

Thus $(x^2 - 2x - 15)^2 - (4x - 4)(x^2 - 2x - 15)$ must be a square, that is,

$$x^4 - 8x^3 - 14x^2 + 112x + 165 = \text{a square}$$

$$= (x^2 - 4x - 15)^2, \text{ say.}$$

This gives $x = -\frac{15}{2}$, and accordingly, to find another value, we substitute $y - \frac{15}{2}$ for x in the expression to be made a square.

We must therefore have

$$y^4 - 38y^3 + \tfrac{1007}{2}y^2 - \tfrac{5431}{2}y + \tfrac{81225}{16} = \text{a square}$$

$$= (y^2 - 19y - \tfrac{285}{4})^2, \text{ say.}$$

This gives $y = \frac{5423}{285}$, and $x = y - \frac{15}{2} = \frac{6571}{570}$.

The triangle is therefore formed from $\frac{6001}{570}$, 4, or (in whole numbers) from 6001, 2280.

The sides are therefore 41210401, 30813601, 27364560.

18. *To find a right-angled triangle* ζ, ξ, η *such that* (*if* $\xi > \eta$)

$$(\xi - \eta)^2 - 2\eta^2 = a \text{ square.}$$

This problem is enunciated in Fermat's note on VI. 22. He merely adds that the triangle (1525, 1517, 156) formed from 39, 2 satisfies the conditions, but does not give the solution.

The solution is however easy to obtain by his usual method, thus.

Form a triangle from x, 1, so that

$$\zeta = x^2 + 1, \quad \xi = x^2 - 1, \quad \eta = 2x.$$

Then $$(\xi - \eta)^2 - 2\eta^2 = (x^2 - 2x - 1)^2 - 8x^2$$

$$= x^4 - 4x^3 - 6x^2 + 4x + 1.$$

This has to be a square; let it be equal to $(x^2-2x-5)^2$, say; this gives

$$4x+1=20x+25,$$

or

$$x=-\tfrac{3}{2}.$$

The triangle formed from $-\frac{3}{2}$, 1, or from -3, 2, will have one side negative. To avoid this, we proceed as usual to form a triangle from $y-3$, 2.

Thus $\quad \zeta=y^2-6x+13, \quad \xi=y^2-6y+5, \quad \eta=4y-12,$

and

$$(\xi-\eta)^2-2\eta^2=(y^2-10y+17)^2-2(4y-12)^2$$
$$=y^4-20y^3+102y^2-148y+1.$$

In order that this may be a square, suppose it equal to $(y^2-10y-1)^2$ or $y^4-20y^3+98y^2+20y+1$.

It follows that $\quad 102y^2-148y=98y^2+20y,$

and $y=42$.

The triangle required is formed from $y-3$, 2, that is, from 39, 2, and is accordingly 1525, 1517, 156.

Fermat does not tell us in the note on VI. 22 what use he made of this problem, but the omission is made good in a letter to Carcavi[1], where he says that it was propounded to him by Frénicle (who admitted frankly that he had not been able to solve it), and that it served to solve another problem which had occupied Frénicle. The latter problem is the following.

19. *To find a right-angled triangle* ζ, ξ, η *such that*

$$\left.\begin{matrix}\zeta\\ \zeta-\eta\\ \xi-\eta\end{matrix}\right\}\text{ are all squares.}$$

Fermat does not actually give the solution, but presumably it was somewhat as follows.

Form a triangle from two numbers x, y; the sides are then

$$\zeta=x^2+y^2, \quad \xi=x^2-y^2, \quad \eta=2xy.$$

Now $\zeta-\eta=x^2+y^2-2xy$ and is *ipso facto* a square.

The other conditions give

$$x^2+y^2=\text{a square},$$

and

$$x^2-y^2-2xy=(x-y)^2-2y^2=\text{a square}.$$

These conditions are satisfied by the two perpendicular sides of the triangle of the last problem, that is, by $x=1517$, $y=156$.

[1] *Oeuvres de Fermat*, II. p. 265.

The triangle required is therefore formed from 1517, 156 and is

$$(2325625, 2276953, 473304).$$

The present seems to be the appropriate place for a problem contained in a letter from Fermat to Frénicle the date of which was probably 15 June 1641[1].

20. *To find all the right-angled triangles in integral numbers such that the perpendicular sides differ by* 1.

If a right-angled triangle is formed from x, y, the difference between the two perpendiculars is either x^2-y^2-2xy or $2xy-(x^2-y^2)$, that is to say, either $(x-y)^2-2y^2$ or $2y^2-(x-y)^2$. As this difference is to be 1, we have to find all the integral solutions of the equation

$$2y^2-(x-y)^2=\pm 1.$$

Those who are familiar with the history of Greek mathematics will here recognise an old friend. The equation is in fact the indeterminate equation

$$2\xi^2-\eta^2=\pm 1,$$

which the Pythagoreans had already solved by evolving the series of "side-" and "diagonal-" numbers described by Theon of Smyrna, the property of which they proved by means of the geometrical theorems of Eucl. II. 9, 10.

If x, y are two numbers such that

$$2x^2-y^2=+1,$$

then the numbers $x+y$, $2x+y$ will satisfy the equation

$$2\xi^2-\eta^2=-1;$$

fresh numbers formed from $x+y$, $2x+y$ by the same law will satisfy the equation

$$2\xi^2-\eta^2=+1,$$

and so on.

Take now the equation

$$2y^2-(x-y)^2=\pm 1,$$

where x, y are two numbers from which a right-angled triangle has been formed. We can deduce a right-angled triangle formed from x', y' where

$$2y'^2-(x'-y')^2=\mp 1;$$

for by the above law of formation we have only to take

$$y'=y+(x-y)=x,$$

$$x'-y'=2y+(x-y)=x+y,$$

whence also $x'=2x+y$.

[1] *Oeuvres de Fermat*, II. pp. 221 sqq.

Fermat gave two rules for the formation of this second triangle. The first rule is in the letter above quoted.

First Rule. If h, p, b be any right-angled triangle satisfying the condition (h being the hypotenuse, $p > b$ and $p - b = 1$), then, if a triangle be taken in which

$$\text{the least side} = 2h + p + 2b,$$

$$\text{the middle side} = 2h + p + 2b + 1,$$

$$\text{the greatest side} = 3h + 2(p + b),$$

this triangle also will be a right-angled triangle satisfying the condition.

To verify this from the above considerations we have to consider two cases, according as $2xy$ is greater or less than $x^2 - y^2$.

Take the case in which $2xy > x^2 - y^2$; then

$$2y^2 - (x - y)^2 = +1,$$

and accordingly

$$2y'^2 - (x' - y')^2 = -1,$$

or

$$x'^2 - y'^2 > 2x'y'.$$

The least side, therefore, of the second triangle

$$2x'y' = 2x(2x + y) = 2(x^2 + y^2) + (2xy) + 2(x^2 - y^2);$$

the middle side

$$x'^2 - y'^2 = 2x'y' + 1;$$

and the hypotenuse

$$x'^2 + y'^2 = (2x + y)^2 + x^2 = 3(x^2 + y^2) + 2(x^2 - y^2 + 2xy).$$

The expressions on the right hand are those given by Fermat's rule.

Second Rule.

This rule is given in a letter of 31 May 1643 probably addressed to St Martin[1].

Fermat says: Given any triangle having the desired property, then, to find another such triangle from it, "subtract from double the sum of all three sides each of the perpendiculars separately [this gives two of the sides of the new triangle], and add to the same sum the greatest side [this gives the third side]."

That is to say, the sides of the new triangle are respectively

$$2(2x^2 + 2xy) - (x^2 - y^2),$$

$$2(2x^2 + 2xy) - 2xy,$$

$$2(2x^2 + 2xy) + (x^2 + y^2).$$

[1] *Oeuvres de Fermat*, II. p. 259.

In fact the three expressions reduce as follows:

$$2(2x^2+2xy)-(x^2-y^2)=3x^2+4xy+y^2=(2x+y)^2-x^2,$$
$$2(2x^2+2xy)-2xy=2x(2x+y),$$
$$2(2x^2+2xy)+x^2+y^2=(2x+y)^2+x^2;$$

and the result agrees with the formation of the triangle from x', y' above.

From the triangle (3, 4, 5) we get (20, 21, 29); from the latter the triangle (119, 120, 169), and so on. The sixth such triangle is (23660, 23661, 33461).

21. *To find all the rational right-angled triangles in whole numbers which are such that the two perpendiculars differ by any given number.*

To his explanation of the First Rule above, applicable to the case where the given number is 1, Fermat adds in his curt way: "same method for finding a triangle such that the difference of the two smaller sides is *a given number*. I omit the rules, and the limitations, for finding all the possible triangles of the kind required, for the rule is easy, when the principles are once admitted."

He adds, however, to his Second Rule[1] its application to the case where the given number is 7.

There are, he says, two fundamental triangles with the desired property, namely 5, 12, 13 and 8, 15, 17. [In the case of the former $2xy > x^2-y^2$, and in the case of the second $x^2-y^2 > 2xy$.]

From the first triangle (5, 12, 13) we deduce, by the Rule, a triangle with the sides $2.30-12$, $2.30-5$, $2.30+13$ or (48, 55, 73); from the second a triangle with the sides $2.40-15$, $2.40-8$, $2.40+17$, or (65, 72, 97).

And so on, *ad infinitum*.

Next to the explanation of the first of the above Rules Fermat mentions, in the same letter, the problem

22. *To find right-angled triangles in integral numbers ζ, ξ, η $(\xi > \eta)$ such that*

$$\left.\begin{matrix}\zeta-\eta\\ \xi-\eta\end{matrix}\right\}\text{ are both squares.}$$

He observes that alternate triangles of the series in which the two smaller sides differ by 1 satisfy the conditions, those namely in which the smallest side η is $2xy$ and not x^2-y^2; for x^2+y^2-2xy is a square, and $\xi-\eta$, being equal to 1, is also a square.

[1] *Oeuvres de Fermat*, II. p. 259.

Thus, while 3, 4, 5 does not satisfy the conditions, (20, 21, 29) does, and, while the next (119, 120, 169) does not satisfy the conditions, the triangle after that, namely (696, 697, 985), does.

Frénicle naturally objected, in his reply, that the triangles should not be limited to those in which the smaller square representing the difference between the perpendicular sides is 1, and proposed the problem in the form

To find all the triangles (ζ, ξ, η) *such that*

$$\left.\begin{matrix}\zeta-\eta\\ \xi-\eta\end{matrix}\right\}\text{ are both squares,}$$

and one square does not measure the other.

Fermat seems to have, in the first instance, formed the triangle from two numbers x, y where

$$x = r^2 + 1, \quad y = 2r - 2,$$

and then to have given the more general rule of forming a triangle from

$$x = r^2 + s^2, \quad y = 2(r - s)s,$$

where r, s are prime to one another (Letter from Frénicle of 6 Sept. 1641)[1].

It appears from a letter of Fermat's to Mersenne of 27th January 1643[2] that St Martin propounded to Fermat the problem, apparently suggested by Frénicle[3],

Given a number, to find how many times it is the difference between the [perpendicular?] sides of a triangle which has a square number for the difference between its least side and each of the two others respectively.

The number given was 1803601800, and Fermat replies that there are 243 triangles, and no more, which satisfy the conditions. He adds "The universal method, which I will communicate to him if he asks for it, is beautiful and noteworthy, although I doubt not that Frénicle has already given him everything on the subject of these questions."

23. *To find two triangles,* ζ, ξ, η *and* ζ', ξ', η' $(\xi > \eta, \xi' > \eta')$ *such that*

$$\left.\begin{matrix}\zeta-\xi=\xi'-\eta'\\ \xi-\eta=\zeta'-\xi'\end{matrix}\right\}.$$

Suppose the two triangles formed from (x, y) and (x', y') respectively, the sides being

$$\zeta = x^2 + y^2, \quad \xi = 2xy, \quad \eta = x^2 - y^2.$$
$$\zeta' = x'^2 + y'^2, \quad \xi' = 2x'y', \quad \eta' = x'^2 - y'^2.$$

[1] *Oeuvres de Fermat*, II. p. 233.

[2] *Ibid.*, p. 250.

[3] *Ibid.*, p. 247.

Then we must have

$$\left.\begin{aligned}(x-y)^2 &= 2y'^2-(x'-y')^2\\ 2y^2-(x-y)^2 &= (x'-y')^2\end{aligned}\right\},$$

and

which equations show that $y=y'$, and that

$$(x-y)^2,\quad y^2,\quad (x'-y)^2$$

are three squares in arithmetical progression.

Suppose that these squares are 1, 25, 49 respectively; thus $y=5$; $x-y=1$, so that $x=1+5$; $x'-y=7$, so that $x'=5+7$.

Fermat accordingly gives the rule: Find three squares in arithmetical progression; then form the first triangle from (1) the sum of the sides of the first and second squares and (2) the side of the second, and the second triangle from (1) the sum of the sides of the second and third squares and (2) the side of the second[1].

In the particular case, the triangles are formed from (6, 5) and from (12, 5) respectively; the triangles are therefore (61, 60, 11) and (169, 120, 119) respectively.

For solving the problem of *finding three square numbers in arithmetical progression* Fermat seems first to have given a rule which was not general, and then in a later document to have formed the sides of the three squares as follows:

$$r^2-2s^2,\quad r^2+2rs+2s^2,\quad r^2+4rs+2s^2.$$

Frénicle formed them thus[2]:

$$p^2-2pq-q^2,\quad p^2+q^2,\quad p^2+2pq-q^2,$$

the latter form agreeing with Fermat's if $p=r+s$, and $q=s$.

Frénicle expresses his formula neatly by saying that we take for the side of the middle square the hypotenuse of any primitive triangle formed from p, q, i.e. p^2+q^2, for the side of the smallest square the difference between the perpendicular sides of the same triangle, i.e. p^2-q^2-2pq, and for the side of the largest square the sum of the perpendicular sides of the same triangle.

Suppose the primitive triangle is (28, 45, 53) formed from (7, 2). Then the sides of the three squares in arithmetical progression are 17, 53 and 73, the squares themselves being 289, 2809, 5329. The triangles derived from these squares and having the above property are formed from (70, 53) and from (126, 53) respectively, and are therefore (7709, 7420, 2091) and (18685, 13356, 13067).

[1] *Oeuvres de Fermat*, II. p. 225.

[2] *Ibid.*, II. pp. 234–5.

24. *To find two right-angled triangles* (ζ, ξ, η) *and* (ζ', ξ', η') *such that*

$$\left.\begin{aligned} \xi' - \eta' &= \xi - \eta \\ \xi' &= \zeta \end{aligned}\right\}.$$

Form the triangle ζ, ξ, η from the numbers x, 1; then

$$\zeta = x^2 + 1, \quad \xi = x^2 - 1, \quad \eta = 2x.$$

Thus $\xi' = x^2 + 1$; and, since $\xi' - \eta' = \xi - \eta = x^2 - 2x - 1$, it follows that $\eta' = 2x + 2$.

It remains to secure that $\xi'^2 + \eta'^2 = (x^2 + 1)^2 + (2x + 2)^2$ shall be a square, that is,

$$x^4 + 6x^2 + 8x + 5 = \text{a square}$$
$$= (x^2 + 3)^2, \text{ say};$$

therefore $x = \frac{1}{2}$.

Hence the triangle ζ, ξ, η is formed from $\frac{1}{2}$, 1 or from 1, 2; but this solution will not do, as it gives a negative value for ξ. Accordingly we must find a fresh value for x, which we obtain by forming the triangle from $x + 1$, 2.

The sides are then

$$\zeta = x^2 + 2x + 5, \quad \xi = x^2 + 2x - 3, \quad \eta = 4x + 4;$$

thus $$\xi' = x^2 + 2x + 5, \quad \eta' = \xi' - (x^2 - 2x - 7) = 4x + 12.$$

Therefore $(x^2 + 2x + 5)^2 + (4x + 12)^2$ must be a square, or

$$x^4 + 4x^3 + 30x^2 + 116x + 169 = \text{a square}$$
$$= (13 + \tfrac{58}{13}x - x^2)^2, \text{ say},$$

from which we obtain $x = -\frac{1525}{546}$, and the triangle is formed from $-\frac{979}{546}$, 2, or (in whole numbers) from -979, 1092.

"We can use these numbers as if both were real and form the triangle from 1092, 979. We thus obtain the two triangles

2150905, 2138136, 234023,

2165017, 2150905, 246792,

which satisfy the conditions of the question."

25. *To find two right-angled triangles* (ζ, ξ, η) *and* (ζ', ξ', η') *such that*

$$\left.\begin{aligned} \xi' + \eta' &= \xi + \eta \\ \xi' &= \zeta \end{aligned}\right\}. \qquad (\xi' > \eta')$$

Form the triangle ζ, ξ, η from the numbers $x + 1$, 1; then

$$\zeta = x^2 + 2x + 2, \quad \xi = x^2 + 2x, \quad \eta = 2x + 2.$$

Thus $\xi' = x^2 + 2x + 2$, and $\eta' = \xi + \eta - \xi' = 2x$.

We must now have $\xi'^2+\eta'^2=(x^2+2x+2)^2+(2x)^2$ a square; that is,

$$x^4+4x^3+12x^2+8x+4=\text{a square}$$
$$=(x^2+2x+4)^2, \text{ say};$$

whence $x=-\frac{3}{2}$.

Accordingly we substitute $y-\frac{3}{2}$ for x, and we must have

$$y^4-2y^3+\tfrac{15}{2}y^2-\tfrac{29}{2}y+\tfrac{169}{16}=\text{a square}$$
$$=(\tfrac{13}{4}-\tfrac{29}{13}y+y^2)^2, \text{ say}.$$

This gives $y=\frac{21}{13}$, and $x=\frac{21}{13}-\frac{3}{2}=\frac{3}{26}$.

The triangle ζ, ξ, η is therefore formed from $\frac{29}{26}$, 1, or from 29, 26, and is therefore 1517, 165, 1508; the triangle ζ', ξ', η' is 1525, 1517, 156.

Or again we may proceed thus from the point where we found $x=-\frac{3}{2}$. The triangle ζ, ξ, η may be formed from $-\frac{1}{2}$, 1 or from -1, 2.

We therefore form a triangle from $x-1$, 2 and start afresh.

The sides are

$$\zeta=x^2-2x+5,\quad \xi=x^2-2x-3,\quad \eta=4x-4.$$

Thus $\xi'=x^2-2x+5$, and $\eta'=\xi+\eta-\xi'=4x-12$.

Hence $(x^2-2x+5)^2+(4x-12)^2$ must be a square; that is,

$$x^4-4x^3+30x^2-116x+169=\text{a square}$$
$$=(13-\tfrac{58}{13}x+x^2)^2, \text{ say}.$$

This gives $x=\frac{42}{13}$, and the triangle ζ, ξ, η is therefore formed from $\frac{29}{13}$, 2, or from 29, 26, as before.

The remaining problems on rational right-angled triangles in the *Inventum Novum* are cases given in Part II. of that collection to illustrate the method of the Triple-Equation due to Fermat and explained by him on Diophantus VI. 22 as well as, at greater length, in the *Inventum Novum*. An account of the method will be found in a later section of this Supplement; but the problems applying the method to right-angled triangles will be enunciated here.

26. *To find a right-angled triangle ζ, ξ, η such that*

$$\left.\begin{aligned}\zeta(\xi+\eta)&=t^2\\ \zeta^2+2\zeta&=u^2\\ \zeta^2+\xi&=v^2\\ \zeta^2+\eta&=w^2\end{aligned}\right\}.$$

By Problem 2 above find a right-angled triangle h, p, b (h being the hypotenuse) in which h, $p+b$ are both squares; the first condition is thus satisfied.

To find ζ, ξ, η, put $\zeta = hx, \xi = px, \eta = bx$.

The three remaining conditions thus give a "triple-equation" in x. [The numbers would of course be enormous.]

27. *To find a right-angled triangle ζ, ξ, η such that*

$$\left.\begin{array}{r}(\xi+\eta+\zeta)^2+\xi=u^2\\(\xi+\eta+\zeta)^2+\eta=v^2\\(\xi+\eta+\zeta)^2+m\zeta=w^2\end{array}\right\},$$

where m is any given number.

Fermat supposes $m = 2$.

Assume for the required triangle $(3x, 4x, 5x)$; we have then the triple-equation

$$\left.\begin{array}{r}144x^2+3x=u^2\\144x^2+4x=v^2\\144x^2+10x=w^2\end{array}\right\},$$

the solution of which gives $x = \frac{169}{38016}$, and the triangle is

$$\frac{507}{38016},\quad \frac{676}{38016},\quad \frac{845}{38016}.$$

28. *To find a right-angled triangle ζ, ξ, η such that*

$$\left.\begin{array}{r}\zeta(\xi-\eta)=t^2\\(\xi+\eta+\zeta)^2+\xi=u^2\\(\xi+\eta+\zeta)^2+\eta=v^2\\(\xi+\eta+\zeta)^2+m\zeta=w^2\end{array}\right\}.$$

Suppose $m = 2$.

Find a triangle (Problem 3 above) in which $\zeta, \xi-\eta$ are both squares, say the triangle (119, 120, 169). Put $119x, 120x, 169x$ for the sides of the required triangle, and we have the "triple-equation"

$$\left.\begin{array}{r}166464x^2+119x=u^2\\166464x^2+120x=v^2\\166464x^2+338x=w^2\end{array}\right\}.$$

29. *To find a right-angled triangle ζ, ξ, η such that*

$$\left.\begin{array}{r}\xi^2-\frac{1}{2}\xi\eta=t^2 \;*\\(\xi+\eta+\zeta)^2+\xi=u^2\\(\xi+\eta+\zeta)^2+\eta=v^2\\(\xi+\eta+\zeta)^2+m\zeta=w^2\end{array}\right\},$$

where m is any given number.

* The enunciation has $\xi(\xi-\frac{1}{2}\xi\eta)$ instead of $\xi^2-\frac{1}{2}\xi\eta$; but $\xi(\xi-\frac{1}{2}\xi\eta)$ is inconsistent with the solution given, and I have therefore altered it so as to correspond to the solution.

Take a right-angled triangle in which 1, p are the sides about the right angle and are such that $1-\frac{1}{2}p$ is a square (Problem 11 above).

Let q be the hypotenuse of the triangle so taken, so that $q=\sqrt{(p^2+1)}$, and take as the sides of the required triangle x, px, qx; we thus have the triple-equation

$$\left.\begin{aligned}(1+p+q)^2x^2+x&=u^2\\(1+p+q)^2x^2+px&=v^2\\(1+p+q)^2x^2+mqx&=w^2\end{aligned}\right\}.$$

30. *To find a right-angled triangle* ζ, ξ, η *such that*

$$\left.\begin{aligned}\xi(\xi+\eta)&=t^2\\(\xi+\eta+\zeta)^2+\xi&=u^2\\(\xi+\eta+\zeta)^2+\eta&=v^2\\(\xi+\eta+\zeta)^2+\zeta&=w^2\end{aligned}\right\}.$$

First find a triangle in which one of the perpendiculars is a square, and the sum of the perpendiculars is also a square, say 40, 9, 41.

Take $40x$, $9x$, $41x$ as the sides of the required triangle; and we therefore have the triple-equation

$$\left.\begin{aligned}8100x^2+40x&=u^2\\8100x^2+9x&=v^2\\8100x^2+41x&=w^2\end{aligned}\right\}.$$

SECTION IV.

OTHER PROBLEMS BY FERMAT.

31. *To find two numbers* ξ, η *such that*

$$\left.\begin{array}{ll}(1) & \xi-(\xi^2-\eta^2)\\(2) & \eta-(\xi^2-\eta^2)\\(3),(4) & \xi\pm\eta-(\xi^2-\eta^2)\end{array}\right\}\text{ are all squares.}$$

Let $\xi+\eta=1-2x$, $\xi-\eta=2x$, so that $\xi=\frac{1}{2}$, $\eta=\frac{1}{2}-2x$, and

$$\xi^2-\eta^2=2x-4x^2.$$

Thus (3), (4) are both satisfied.

The other conditions (1) and (2) give

$$\left.\begin{aligned}4x^2-2x+\tfrac{1}{2}&=u^2\\4x^2-4x+\tfrac{1}{2}&=v^2\end{aligned}\right\}.$$

The difference $=2x=4x\cdot\frac{1}{2}$; and, putting $(2x+\frac{1}{4})^2=4x^2-2x+\frac{1}{2}$, we find $x=\frac{7}{48}$.

The required numbers are therefore $\frac{1}{2}$, $\frac{5}{24}$.

Another pair of numbers satisfying the conditions will be obtained by substituting $y+\frac{7}{48}$ for x in the expressions to be made squares, and so on.

32. *To find two numbers* ξ, η *such that*

$$\left.\begin{array}{l}\xi+\eta\pm(\xi-\eta)\\ \xi+\eta\pm(\xi^2-\eta^2)\end{array}\right\}\ \textit{are all squares.}$$

Let the numbers be $\frac{1}{2}+x$, $\frac{1}{2}-x$; therefore $\xi-\eta$, as well as $\xi^2-\eta^2$, is equal to $2x$. The sum $\xi+\eta=1$.

Therefore $1\pm 2x$ must be a square, or we have the double-equation

$$\left.\begin{array}{l}1+2x=u^2\\ 1-2x=v^2\end{array}\right\}.$$

Replace x by $\frac{1}{2}y^2+y$ so as to make $1+2x$ a square; therefore

$$\begin{aligned}1-2y-y^2 &= \text{a square}\\ &= (1-3y)^2, \text{ say,}\end{aligned}$$

whence $y=\frac{2}{5}$, and $x=\frac{1}{2}y^2+y=\frac{12}{25}$.

The required numbers are therefore $\frac{49}{50}$, $\frac{1}{50}$.

33. *To find two numbers* ξ, η *such that*

$$(\xi+\eta)(\xi^2+\eta^2)=\textit{a cube.}$$

Assume $\xi=x$, $\eta=2-x$; therefore

$$\begin{aligned}(\xi+\eta)(\xi^2+\eta^2)=2(2x^2-4x+4) &= \text{a cube}\\ &= (2-\tfrac{2}{3}x)^3, \text{ say.}\end{aligned}$$

This gives $x=-\frac{9}{2}$; and to get a "real" value of x we must substitute $y-\frac{9}{2}$ for x in the expression to be made a cube.

Thus

$$\begin{aligned}4y^2-44y+125 &= \text{a cube}\\ &= (5-\tfrac{44}{75}y)^3, \text{ say}\\ &= 125-44y+\tfrac{1936}{375}y^2-\tfrac{85184}{421875}y^3,\end{aligned}$$

and $y=\frac{122625}{21296}$, so that $x=y-\frac{9}{2}=\frac{26793}{21296}$.

The required numbers are therefore $\frac{26793}{21296}$, $\frac{15799}{21296}$.

COR. We observe:

(1) that the numerators 26793, 15799 satisfy the conditions;

(2) that we have in fact solved the problem *To divide 2 into two parts such that twice the sum of their squares is a cube*;

(3) that we can solve in the same manner the problem *To find two numbers such that any multiple of the sum of their squares is a cube.* Thus suppose that the multiple is 5; we then assume x and $5-x$ for the numbers and proceed as above;

(4) that we can also deduce the solution of the following "very fine problem":

To find two numbers such that their difference is equal to the difference of their biquadrates or fourth powers.

In other words, we can solve the indeterminate equation

$$\xi - \eta = \xi^4 - \eta^4.$$

For we have only to take the two numbers found above, namely 26793 and 15799, and divide by (as a common denominator) the root of the cube formed by multiplying their sum by the sum of their squares.

This common denominator is 34540, and the two required numbers are $\frac{26793}{34540}$, $\frac{15799}{34540}$.

This latter problem is alluded to in Fermat's note to Diophantus IV. 11 in these terms: "But whether it is possible *to find two biquadrates the difference between which is equal to the difference between their sides* is a question to be investigated by trying the device furnished by our method, which will doubtless succeed. For let two biquadrates be sought such that the difference of their sides is 1, while the difference between the biquadrates themselves is a cube. The sides will, in the first instance, be $-\frac{9}{22}$ and $\frac{13}{22}$. But, as one is negative, let the operation be repeated, in accordance with my method, and let the first side be $x - \frac{9}{22}$; the second side will be $x + \frac{13}{22}$, and the new operation will give real numbers satisfying the condition of the problem[1]."

34. *To find two numbers* ξ, η *such that*

$$\xi^4 + 3\eta^4 = \textit{a square}.$$

Fermat (or De Billy) observes that it must be required that the first biquadrate (ξ^4) shall not be unity, for in that case the problem would be too easy, since $1 + 3 \cdot 1 = 4$ and $1 + 3 \cdot 16 = 49$.

Assume $\xi = x$, $\eta = x - 1$; therefore

$$4x^4 - 12x^3 + 18x^2 - 12x + 3 = \text{a square}$$
$$= (2x^2 - 3x + \tfrac{9}{4})^2, \text{ say}.$$

This gives $x = \frac{11}{8}$, $x - 1 = \frac{3}{8}$; and a solution in whole numbers is $\xi = 11$, $\eta = 3$. In fact $11^4 + 3 \cdot 3^4 = 14641 + 243 = 14884$ or 122^2.

We can also take any equimultiples of (11, 3), as (22, 6) and (33, 9); and the latter pairs of numbers severally satisfy the condition of the problem.

[1] It gives in fact $\frac{26793}{10994}$, $\frac{15799}{10994}$ as a solution of the subsidiary problem, and from this we can obtain the same solution of the main problem as that given above

$$\left(\frac{26793}{34540}, \frac{15799}{34540}\right).$$

SECTION V.

FERMAT'S TRIPLE-EQUATIONS.

Fermat's own description of his method of "triple-equations," which is contained in his note on VI. 22, is as follows:

"Where double-equations do not suffice, we must have recourse to *triple-equations*, which are my discovery and lead to the solution of a multitude of elegant problems.

If, for example, the three expressions

$$x+4, \quad 2x+4, \quad 5x+4$$

have to be made squares, we have a triple-equation the solution of which can be effected by means of a double-equation. If for x we substitute a number which when increased by 4 gives a square, *e.g.* y^2+4y [Fermat says x^2+4x], the expressions to be made squares become

$$y^2+4y+4, \quad 2y^2+8y+4, \quad 5y^2+20y+4.$$

The first is already a square; we have therefore only to make

$$\left.\begin{array}{l} 2y^2+\ \ 8y+4 \\ 5y^2+20y+4 \end{array}\right\}$$

severally squares.

That is to say, the problem is reduced to a double-equation.

This double-equation gives, it is true, only one solution; but from this solution we can deduce another, from the second a third, and so on. In fact, when we have obtained one value for y [say $y=a$], we substitute for y in the equations the binomial expression consisting of y *plus* the value found [*i.e.* $y+a$]. In this way we can find any number of successive solutions each derived from the preceding one."

The subject is developed in the *Doctrinae Analyticae Inventum Novum* of De Billy already mentioned so often.

It will be observed that the absolute term in all the three expressions to be made squares is a square. It need not be the *same* square in the original expressions; if the absolute terms are different squares, the three expressions can, so far as necessary, be multiplied by squares which will make the absolute terms the same, when the method will apply.

We may put the solution generally thus. Suppose that

$$\left.\begin{array}{l} ax+p^2 \\ bx+q^2 \\ cx+r^2 \end{array}\right\}$$

have to be made squares (a, b, c or some of them may be negative as well as positive).

Put $$ax=y^2+2py,$$

which makes the first expression a square (or of course we could put $ax=a^2y^2+2apy$).

Substitute $(y^2+2py)/a$ for x in the second and third expressions.

Therefore
$$\left.\begin{array}{l}\dfrac{b}{a}(y^2+2py)+q^2\\[2ex] \dfrac{c}{a}(y^2+2py)+r^2\end{array}\right\}$$

must both be squares; or, if we multiply the first expression by r^2 and the second by q^2 (so as to make the absolute terms the same), we have to solve the double-equation

$$\frac{b}{a}r^2(y^2+2py)+q^2r^2=u^2,$$

$$\frac{c}{a}q^2(y^2+2py)+q^2r^2=v^2.$$

The difference $=\dfrac{br^2-cq^2}{a}\cdot y^2+2p\cdot\dfrac{br^2-cq^2}{a}\cdot y.$

This has to be separated into two factors of the form λy, $\mu y+\nu$, where ν must be equal to $2qr$ (in order that, when $\frac{1}{2}\{(\lambda+\mu)y+\nu\}$ is squared and equated to the first, or when $\frac{1}{4}\{(\lambda-\mu)y-\nu\}^2$ is equated to the second, of the two expressions, the absolute terms q^2r^2 may cancel each other).

A different separation into factors is possible if b/a and c/a are both squares; but otherwise, as Fermat says, the method gives only one solution in the first instance; the above difference must necessarily be split into the factors

$$\frac{p(br^2-cq^2)}{aqr}y \text{ and } \frac{qr}{p}y+2qr.$$

Half the sum of these factors

$$=\tfrac{1}{2}y\left\{\frac{p(br^2-cq^2)}{aqr}+\frac{qr}{p}\right\}+qr$$

$$=\tfrac{1}{2}y\left(\frac{aq^2r^2+br^2p^2-cp^2q^2}{apqr}\right)+qr.$$

Squaring this and equating it to $\dfrac{br^2}{a}(y^2+2py)+q^2r^2$, we have

$$\left\{\tfrac{1}{2}y\left(\frac{aq^2r^2+br^2p^2-cp^2q^2}{apqr}\right)+qr\right\}^2=\frac{br^2}{a}y^2+\frac{2pbr^2}{a}y+q^2r^2;$$

therefore

$$y^2\left\{\frac{1}{4a^2p^2q^2r^2}(aq^2r^2+br^2p^2-cp^2q^2)^2-\frac{br^2}{a}\right\}$$
$$=y\left\{\frac{2pbr^2}{a}-\frac{aq^2r^2+br^2p^2-cp^2q^2}{ap}\right\},$$

or
$$\frac{y^2}{4a^2p^2q^2r^2}\{(aq^2r^2+br^2p^2-cp^2q^2)^2-4abp^2q^2r^4\}$$
$$=\frac{y}{ap}(br^2p^2+cp^2q^2-aq^2r^2)$$

that is,

$$y(a^2q^4r^4 + b^2r^4p^4 + c^2p^4q^4 - 2bcp^4q^2r^2 - 2cap^2q^4r^2 - 2abp^2q^2r^4)$$
$$= 4apq^2r^2(br^2p^2 + cp^2q^2 - aq^2r^2),$$

or $$y = \frac{4apq^2r^2(br^2p^2 + cp^2q^2 - aq^2r^2)}{a^2q^4r^4 + b^2r^4p^4 + c^2p^4q^4 - 2bcp^4q^2r^2 - 2cap^2q^4r^2 - 2abp^2q^2r^4},$$

whence $x\left(=\frac{y^2 + 2py}{a}\right)$ is found.

Exx. from the *Inventum Novum.*

(1) $$\left.\begin{matrix} 2x+4 \\ 3x+4 \\ 6x+4 \end{matrix}\right\} \text{ to be made squares.}$$

Here $a = 2$, $b = 6$, $c = 3$, $p = q = r = 2$; therefore

$$y = \frac{4 \cdot 2 \cdot 32(6 \cdot 16 + 3 \cdot 16 - 2 \cdot 16)}{16^2(4 + 36 + 9 - 2 \cdot 6 \cdot 3 - 2 \cdot 3 \cdot 2 - 2 \cdot 2 \cdot 6)}$$
$$= -\frac{16 \cdot 7}{23},$$

and $$x = \frac{1}{2}(y^2 + 4y) = \frac{1}{2}\left\{\frac{112^2}{23^2} - \frac{4 \cdot 112}{23}\right\} = \frac{56}{23^2}(112 - 4 \cdot 23) = \frac{1120}{529}.$$

(2) $$\left.\begin{matrix} x+1 \\ 3x+4 \\ 2x+9 \end{matrix}\right\} \text{ to be made squares.}$$

Here $a = 1$, $b = 3$, $c = 2$, $p = 1$, $q = 2$, $r = 3$; therefore

$$y = \frac{4 \cdot 36(3 \cdot 9 + 2 \cdot 4 - 36)}{36^2 + 9 \cdot 81 + 4 \cdot 16 - 12 \cdot 36 - 16 \cdot 36 - 6 \cdot 36 \cdot 9}$$
$$= \frac{-4 \cdot 36}{-36 \cdot 46 + 9 \cdot 81 + 4 \cdot 16} = \frac{144}{863},$$

and $x = y^2 + 2y = \left(\frac{144}{863}\right)^2 + 2\left(\frac{144}{863}\right) = \frac{269280}{744769}$.

The disadvantage of the method is that it leads so soon to such very large numbers.

Other examples from the *Inventum Novum* are the following, which, like those above given, can be readily solved *ab initio* without using the above general formula.

(3) To solve $$\left.\begin{matrix} 1 + x = u^2 \\ 1 + 2x = v^2 \\ 1 + 5x = w^2 \end{matrix}\right\}.$$

Put $x = y^2 + 2y$, and substituting in the second and third expressions we have only to solve the double-equation

$$\left.\begin{matrix} 2y^2 + 4y + 1 = v^2 \\ 5y^2 + 10y + 1 = w^2 \end{matrix}\right\}.$$

The difference $= 3(y^2 + 2y) = 3y(y+2)$.

Equate the square of half the difference of the factors to the smaller expression; thus

$$(y-1)^2 = 2y^2 + 4y + 1,$$

whence $y = -6$, and $x = y^2 + 2y = 24$.

(4) Equations
$$\left.\begin{aligned} x+9&=u^2\\ 3x+9&=v^2\\ 5x+9&=w^2\end{aligned}\right\}.$$

In this case we put $x = y^2 + 6y$, and we have to solve

$$\left.\begin{aligned} 3(y^2+6y)+9&=v^2\\ 5(y^2+6y)+9&=w^2\end{aligned}\right\}.$$

The difference $= 2(y^2 + 6y) = 2y(y+6)$; we then have

$$(\tfrac{1}{2}y-3)^2 = 3y^2 + 18y + 9,$$

and $y = -\frac{84}{11}$, so that $x = y^2 + 6y = \frac{1512}{121}$.

(5) Equations
$$\left.\begin{aligned} 1+\ x&=u^2\\ 1-2x&=v^2\\ 1+5x&=w^2\end{aligned}\right\}.$$

If we assume $x = y^2 + 2y$, we find $y = \frac{2}{11}$ and $x = \frac{48}{121}$.

There are two other problems of the same sort which are curiously enunciated.

(6) "To find three cubes such that, if we add their sum to numbers proportional to the cubes respectively, we may have three squares."

What Fermat really does is to take three cubes (a^3, b^3, c^3) such that their sum is a square (this is necessary in order to make the term independent of x in each of the three expressions a square) and then to assume a^3x, b^3x, c^3x for the numbers proportional to the cubes. He takes as the cubes 1, 8, 27, the sum of which is 36. Thus we have the triple-equation

$$\left.\begin{aligned} 36+\ \ x&=u^2\\ 36+\ 8x&=v^2\\ 36+27x&=w^2\end{aligned}\right\}.$$

We put $x = y^2 + 12y$ in order to make the first expression a square. Then, solving the double-equation

$$\left.\begin{aligned} 36+\ 8(y^2+12y)&=v^2\\ 36+27(y^2+12y)&=w^2\end{aligned}\right\},$$

we obtain $y = \frac{204}{73}$ and $x = y^2 + 12y = \frac{220320}{5329}$.

(7) "To find three different square numbers such that, if we add to them respectively three numbers in harmonic progression, the three resulting numbers will be squares."

Fermat first assumes three square numbers 1, 4, 16 and then takes $2x$, $3x$, $6x$ as the required numbers in harmonic progression. (He observes that, of the three numbers in harmonic progression, the greatest must be greater than the sum of the other two.) We thus have the triple-equation

$$\left.\begin{aligned} 1 + 2x &= u^2 \\ 4 + 3x &= v^2 \\ 16 + 6x &= w^2 \end{aligned}\right\},$$

or, if we make the absolute terms the same square,

$$\left.\begin{aligned} 16 + 32x &= u'^2 \\ 16 + 12x &= v'^2 \\ 16 + 6x &= w^2 \end{aligned}\right\}.$$

Making the last expression a square by putting $\frac{1}{6}y^2 + \frac{4}{3}y$ for x, we solve as usual and obtain $y = -\frac{912}{23}$ and $x = \frac{1}{6}(y^2 + 8y) = \frac{110656}{529}$.

Fermat observes that triple-equations of the form

$$\left.\begin{aligned} x^2 + x &= u^2 \\ x^2 + 2x &= v^2 \\ x^2 + 5x &= w^2 \end{aligned}\right\},$$

that is to say, of the form

$$\left.\begin{aligned} p^2x^2 + ax &= u^2 \\ q^2x^2 + bx &= v^2 \\ r^2x^2 + cx &= w^2 \end{aligned}\right\},$$

can be similarly solved, because they can be reduced to the above linear form by putting $x = 1/y$ and multiplying up by y^2.

Examples.

(1) To solve the triple-equation

$$\left.\begin{aligned} 4x^2 + 2x &= u^2 \\ 4x^2 + 6x &= v^2 \\ 4x^2 + 9x &= w^2 \end{aligned}\right\}.$$

If $x = 1/y$, this is equivalent to

$$\left.\begin{aligned} 2y + 4 &= u'^2 \\ 6y + 4 &= v'^2 \\ 9y + 4 &= w'^2 \end{aligned}\right\}.$$

Putting $y = \frac{1}{2}z^2 + 2z$ and solving as usual, we find

$$z = -\tfrac{208}{47},\ y = \tfrac{1}{2}z^2 + 2z = \tfrac{2080}{2209},\ \text{and } x = \tfrac{2209}{2080}.$$

(2) Equations

$$\left.\begin{aligned} x^2 + x &= u^2 \\ 4x^2 + 3x &= v^2 \\ 9x^2 + 2x &= w^2 \end{aligned}\right\}.$$

This is equivalent to

$$\left.\begin{aligned} y + 1 &= u'^2 \\ 3y + 4 &= v'^2 \\ 2y + 9 &= w'^2 \end{aligned}\right\}.$$

We put $y = z^2 + 2z$ and, solving the double-equation

$$\left.\begin{aligned} 27(z^2 + 2z) + 36 &= \alpha^2 \\ 8(z^2 + 2z) + 36 &= \beta^2 \end{aligned}\right\},$$

we find $z = \frac{144}{863}$, $y = \frac{269280}{744769}$, so that $x = \frac{744769}{269280}$.

(3) "To find three square numbers such that, if we add their sum to each of their roots respectively, we obtain a square."

Choose, says Fermat, three squares such that their sum is a square and such that the root of the greatest is greater than the sum of the roots of the other two (the reason for this last condition will shortly appear); *e.g.* let the squares be 4, 36, 81, the sum of which is 121.

Let $4x^2$, $36x^2$, $81x^2$ be the three square numbers required; therefore

$$\left.\begin{array}{l} 121x^2 + 2x = u^2 \\ 121x^2 + 6x = v^2 \\ 121x^2 + 9x = w^2 \end{array}\right\}.$$

The solution, arrived at as above, is $x = \frac{2209}{62920}$.

Fermat actually used his triple-equations for the purpose, mainly, of extending problems in Diophantus where three numbers are found satisfying certain conditions so as to find *four* numbers satisfying like conditions. The cases which occur are in his notes to the problems III. 15, IV. 19, 20, V. 3, 27, 28; they are referred to in my notes on those problems.

De Billy observes (what he says Fermat admitted he had not noticed) that the method fails when, the absolute terms being the *same* square, the coefficient of x in one of the linear expressions to be made squares is equal to the sum of the coefficients of x in the other two. Thus suppose that

$$1 + 2x, \quad 1 + 3x, \quad 1 + 5x$$

have to be made squares. To make the first expression a square put $x = 2y^2 + 2y$. The other expressions then become

$$1 + 6y + 6y^2, \quad 1 + 10y + 10y^2.$$

The difference is $4y^2 + 4y = 2y(2y + 2)$, and the usual method gives

$$(2y + 1)^2 = 10y^2 + 10y + 1,$$

or

$$6y^2 + 6y = 0,$$

so that $y = -1$, and consequently $x = 2y^2 + 2y = 0$.

It does not however follow, says De Billy, that a set of expressions so related cannot be made squares by one value of x. Thus $1 + 5x$, $1 + 16x$ and $1 + 21x$ are all squares if $x = 3$, the squares being 16, 49, 64. He adds (§ 11) that "we must observe with Fermat" that the triple-equation

$$\left.\begin{array}{l} 1 + x = u^2 \\ 1 + 2x = v^2 \\ 1 + 3x = w^2 \end{array}\right\}$$

not only cannot be solved by the above method, but cannot be solved at all, because "*there cannot be four squares in arithmetical progression*," which however would be the case if the above equations had a solution and we took 1 for the first of the four squares.

The subject of triple-equations has been taken up afresh in a recent paper by P. v. Schaewen[1]. The following are the main points made.

(1) The equations
$$\left.\begin{aligned} ax + p^2 &= u^2 \\ bx + q^2 &= v^2 \\ cx + r^2 &= w^2 \end{aligned}\right\}$$
can be reduced to the form
$$\left.\begin{aligned} 1 + a'x' &= u'^2 \\ 1 + b'x' &= v'^2 \\ 1 + c'x' &= w'^2 \end{aligned}\right\}$$
by substituting mx' for x, where m is the least common multiple of p^2, q^2, r^2.

(2) The method of Fermat has the disadvantage that, with one operation, it only gives one value for x and not by any means always the smallest solution. From this point of view there is a better method, namely that of finding the *general* solution of the first two equations, substituting the general value of x so found in the third equation and solving the resulting equation in a new unknown. Consider the equations
$$\left.\begin{aligned} 1 + ax &= u^2 \\ 1 + bx &= v^2 \\ 1 + cx &= w^2 \end{aligned}\right\}.$$

Suppose $1 + ax = p^2$, some square. Therefore
$$1 + bx = 1 + \frac{b}{a}(p^2 - 1),$$
and, multiplying by a^2, we have to make
$$abp^2 + a^2 - ab \text{ a square.}$$

This is a square if $p = 1$; and we therefore substitute $q + 1$ for p. Thus
$$\begin{aligned} abq^2 + 2abq + a^2 &= \text{a square} \\ &= \left(\frac{m}{n}q + a\right)^2, \text{ say.} \end{aligned}$$

Therefore
$$\left(ab - \frac{m^2}{n^2}\right) q = 2\left(\frac{m}{n}a - ab\right),$$
and
$$q = \frac{2an(m - nb)}{abn^2 - m^2},$$
whence
$$p = q + 1 = \frac{2amn - abn^2 - m^2}{abn^2 - m^2},$$
and
$$\begin{aligned} x = \frac{p^2 - 1}{a} &= \frac{1}{a}\left\{\frac{(2amn - abn^2 - m^2)^2 - (abn^2 - m^2)^2}{(abn^2 - m^2)^2}\right\} \\ &= \frac{-4mn\{m^2 - (a+b)mn + abn^2\}}{(abn^2 - m^2)^2}. \end{aligned}$$

Substituting this value of x in the expression $1 + cx$, we have a biquadratic expression in $\frac{m}{n}$ which has to be made a square, namely
$$m^4 - 4cm^3n + \{4(a+b)c - 2ab\} m^2n^2 - 4abcmn^3 + a^2b^2n^4.$$

[1] *Bibliotheca Mathematica*, IX$_3$, 1909, pp. 289–300.

Example. Find x such that

$$1 - x, \ 1 + 4x, \ 1 + 7x \text{ are all squares.}$$

First find the general value of x which will make the first two expressions squares; this is

$$x = \frac{-4mn(m^2 - 3mn - 4n^2)}{(m^2 + 4n^2)^2},$$

or, if we substitute k for $2n/m$,

$$x = \frac{k(2k^2 + 3k - 2)}{(k^2 + 1)^2}.$$

We have now to make $1 + 7x$ a square; that is,

$$k^4 + 14k^3 + 23k^2 - 14k + 1 = \text{a square.}$$

The first solution of this is $k = \pm 1$, and by means of these values we get the further values $k = \frac{2}{5}$ and $k = \frac{14}{15}$ (cf. Euler's solution of the problem of making $x^2 + 1$ and $x + 1$ simultaneously squares quoted in my note on pp. 84, 85). The corresponding values of x are respectively

$$\frac{3}{4}, \ -\frac{120}{29^2} \text{ and } \frac{120120}{421^2}.$$

Fermat's method gives, as the next solution after $\frac{3}{4}$, the value

$$x = \frac{51294243}{16989923524}.$$

(3) v. Schaewen observes that the problem of finding x such that three different expressions of the form $mx + n$ are all squares can always be solved provided that we know *one* solution; in this case the absolute terms need not be squares. I doubt however if he is right in supposing that the possibility of solution in this case was not known to Fermat or De Billy. I think it probable that Fermat at least was aware of the fact; for this case of the triple-equation is precisely parallel to that of the double-equation

$$\left. \begin{array}{l} 2x + 5 = u^2 \\ 6x + 3 = w^2 \end{array} \right\},$$

given as a possible case by Fermat in his note on Bachet's conditions for the possibility of solving double-equations (cf. note on p. 287 above). Fermat says that the square to which $2x + 5$ should be made equal is 16 and that to which $6x + 3$ should be made equal is 36 (corresponding to $x = 5\frac{1}{2}$), adding that an infinite number of other solutions can be found.

(4) Lastly, v. Schaewen investigates the conditions under which the equations

$$1 + ax = u^2, \ 1 + bx = v^2, \ 1 + (a + b)x = w^2,$$

which cannot be solved by Fermat's method, are nevertheless capable of solution, and shows how to solve them when they *have* a solution other than $x = 0$.

SECTION VI.

SOME SOLUTIONS BY EULER.

PROBLEM I. *To solve generally the indeterminate equation*[1]

$$x^3 + y^3 + z^3 = v^3.$$

Vieta solved this equation on the assumption that two of the four numbers are taken as known.

[I noted on p. 102 Euler's remark that, if $3^3 + 4^3$ is turned into the difference between two cubes by the direct use of Vieta's second formula, the formula gives $3^3 + 4^3 = (\frac{472}{37})^3 - (\frac{465}{37})^3$ but not $3^3 + 4^3 = 6^3 - 5^3$. I ought however to have observed[2] that the latter can be obtained from Vieta's *first* formula if we multiply throughout by $a^3 + b^3$. The formula then becomes

$$a^3(a^3 + b^3)^3 = b^3(a^3 + b^3)^3 + a^3(a^3 - 2b^3)^3 + b^3(2a^3 - b^3)^3.$$

Putting $a=2$, $b=1$, we have $18^3=9^3+12^3+15^3$, which gives (after division by 3^3) $6^3 = 3^3 + 4^3 + 5^3$. The next solution, obtained by putting $a = 3$, $b=1$, is $84^3 = 28^3 + 53^3 + 75^3$; if $a = 3$, $b = 2$, we have $105^3 = 33^3 + 70^3 + 92^3$; and so on. Similarly Vieta's second formula gives

$$a^3(a^3 + 2b^3)^3 = a^3(a^3 - b^3)^3 + b^3(a^3 - b^3)^3 + b^3(2a^3 + b^3)^3,$$

and we obtain other integral solutions; thus

if $a = 2$, $b = 1$, we have $20^3 = 7^3 + 14^3 + 17^3$,

if $a = 3$, $b = 1$, we have $87^3 = 26^3 + 55^3 + 78^3$;

and so on.]

(1) A more general solution can be obtained by treating only one of the three numbers x, y, z as known.

To solve $$a^3 + x^3 + y^3 = v^3,$$

put $$x = pu + r,\ y = qu - r;$$

therefore

$$a^3 + 3r^2(p+q)u + 3r(p^2 - q^2)u^2 + (p^3 + q^3)u^3 = v^3$$
$$= \left\{a + \frac{r^2}{a^2}(p+q)u\right\}^3, \text{ say};$$

and we obtain, after dividing out by $(p+q)u^2$,

$$3r(p-q) + (p^2 - pq + q^2)u = \frac{3r^4}{a^3}(p+q) + \frac{r^6}{a^6}(p+q)^2 u,$$

[1] *N. Comment. Acad. Petrop.* 1756–57, Vol. VI. (1761), pp. 155 sqq. = *Comment. arithm.* I. pp. 193–206. Cf. pp. 101–2 above.

[2] See Nesselmann's "Anmerkungen zu Diophant" in the *Zeitschrift für Math. u. Physik*, XXXVII. (1892), Hist. litt. Abt. p. 123.

or
$$u = \frac{3a^3r^4(p+q) - 3a^6r(p-q)}{a^6(p^2-pq+q^2) - r^6(p+q)^2},$$

$$x = pu + r = \frac{3a^3pr^4(p+q) - a^6r(2p^2-2pq-q^2) - r^7(p+q)^2}{a^6(p^2-pq+q^2) - r^6(p+q)^2},$$

$$y = qu - r = \frac{3a^3qr^4(p+q) - a^6r(p^2+2pq-2q^2) + r^7(p+q)^2}{a^6(p^2-pq+q^2) - r^6(p+q)^2},$$

$$v = a + \frac{r^2}{a^2}(p+q)u = \frac{a^7(p^2-pq+q^2) - 3a^4r^3(p^2-q^2) + 2ar^6(p+q)^2}{a^6(p^2-pq+q^2) - r^6(p+q)^2},$$

where a, r and the ratio $p : q$ may be given any values we please.

(2) A more general solution still is obtained if we regard none of the first three cubes as known.

Suppose that, in the equation

$$x^3 + y^3 + z^3 = v^3,$$

$$x = mt + pu, \; y = nt + qu, \; z = -nt + ru.$$

Therefore

$$x^3 + y^3 + z^3 = m^3t^3 + \left.\begin{matrix} 3m^2p \\ +3n^2q \\ +3n^2r \end{matrix}\right\} t^2u + \left.\begin{matrix} 3mp^2 \\ +3nq^2 \\ -3nr^2 \end{matrix}\right\} tu^2 + \left.\begin{matrix} p^3 \\ +q^3 \\ +r^3 \end{matrix}\right\} u^3.$$

Put now
$$v = mt + \frac{m^2p + n^2(q+r)}{m^2}u,$$

and we have, after division by u^2,

$$3t\{mp^2 + n(q^2 - r^2)\} + u(p^3 + q^3 + r^3) = \frac{3t}{m^3}\{m^2p + n^2(q+r)\}^2 + \frac{u}{m^6}\{m^2p + n^2(q+r)\}^3,$$

whence, neglecting a common factor which may be chosen arbitrarily, we have

$$t = m^6(p^3 + q^3 + r^3) - \{m^2p + n^2(q+r)\}^3,$$
$$u = 3m^3\{m^2p + n^2(q+r)\}^2 - 3m^6\{mp^2 + n(q^2 - r^2)\},$$

or, if we divide by the factor $q + r$,

$$t = m^6(q^2 - qr + r^2) - 3m^4n^2p^2 - 3m^2n^4p(q+r) - n^6(q+r)^2,$$
$$u = -3m^6n(q-r) + 6m^5n^2p + 3m^3n^4(q+r),$$

so that x, y, z and v can be written down.

The solution is, however, still not general.

(3) **General solution.**

To find generally all the sets of three cubes the sum of which is a cube.

Suppose $A^3 + B^3 + C^3 = D^3$, or $A^3 + B^3 = D^3 - C^3$,

and assume $A = p + q$, $B = p - q$, $C = r - s$, $D = r + s$.

Then $A^3 + B^3 = 2p^3 + 6pq^2$, $D^3 - C^3 = 2s^3 + 6r^2s$,

so that
$$p(p^2 + 3q^2) = s(s^2 + 3r^2).$$

This equation cannot subsist unless p^2+3q^2, s^2+3r^2 have a common divisor. Now it is known that numbers of this form have no divisors except such as are of the same form.

To find them, we introduce six new letters to take the place of p, q, r, s, thus: let

$$p = ax+3by,\quad s = 3cy-dx,$$
$$q = bx-ay,\quad r = dy+cx,$$

whence $\quad p^2+3q^2 = (a^2+3b^2)(x^2+3y^2),\ s^2+3r^2 = (d^2+3c^2)(x^2+3y^2),$
and our equation, divided by x^2+3y^2, becomes

$$(ax+3by)(a^2+3b^2) = (3cy-dx)(d^2+3c^2);$$

so that
$$\frac{x}{y} = \frac{-3b(a^2+3b^2)+3c(d^2+3c^2)}{a(a^2+3b^2)+d(d^2+3c^2)},$$

and we may put
$$x = -3nb(a^2+3b^2)+3nc(d^2+3c^2),$$
$$y = na(a^2+3b^2)+nd(d^2+3c^2).$$

Hence the values of p, q, r, s are found to be

$$p = 3n(ac+bd)(d^2+3c^2),$$
$$q = n(3bc-ad)(d^2+3c^2)-n(a^2+3b^2)^2,$$
$$r = n(d^2+3c^2)^2-n(3bc-ad)(a^2+3b^2),$$
$$s = 3n(ac+bd)(a^2+3b^2),$$

and
$$A = n(3ac+3bc-ad+3bd)(d^2+3c^2)-n(a^2+3b^2)^2,$$
$$B = n(3ac-3bc+ad+3bd)(d^2+3c^2)+n(a^2+3b^2)^2,$$
$$C = n(d^2+3c^2)^2-n(3ac+3bc-ad+3bd)(a^2+3b^2),$$
$$D = n(d^2+3c^2)^2+n(3ac-3bc+ad+3bd)(a^2+3b^2).$$

These values satisfy the equation

$$A^3+B^3+C^3 = D^3,$$

and, since no restriction has been introduced, the solution is capable of giving all the sets of three cubes which have a cube for their sum.

More special forms for A, B, C, D can of course be obtained by putting zero for one of the letters a, b, c, d, and still more special forms by combining with the assumption $a=0$ or $b=0$ the assumption $d=\pm c$, or combining with the assumption $c=0$ or $d=0$ the assumption $b=\pm a$.

Two cases are worth noting.

First, suppose $b=0$, $d=c$, and we have

$$A = 8nac^3-na^4,\ B = 16nac^3+na^4,\ C = 16nc^4-2na^3c,\ D = 16nc^4+4na^3c.$$

If further we write $2a$ for a and $n/16$ for n, we have

$$A = na(c^3-a^3),\ B = na(2c^3+a^3),\ C = nc(c^3-a^3),\ D = nc(c^3+2a^3),$$

which is equivalent to Vieta's solution of his second problem.

Secondly, suppose $d=0$, $b=a$, and we have

$$A = 18nac^3-16na^4,\ B = 16na^4,\ C = 9nc^4-24na^3c,\ D = 9nc^4,$$

or, if we write $\frac{1}{2}a$ for a,

$$A = 9nac^3-na^4,\ B = na^4,\ C = 9nc^4-3na^3c,\ D = 9nc^4,$$

which, if $n = a = c = 1$, gives the simplest solution of all

$$A = 8, \ B = 1, \ C = 6, \ D = 9, \text{ and } 1^3 + 6^3 + 8^3 = 9^3.$$

In proceeding to other solutions we have to remember that, while A, B, C, D must be integral, they should all be prime to one another; for those solutions in which A, B, C, D have a common factor are not new solutions in addition to that from which the common factor is eliminated.

Thus, while giving any values, positive or negative, to the numbers a, b, c, d in the formulae

$$x = 3nc\,(d^2 + 3c^2) - 3nb\,(a^2 + 3b^2),$$
$$y = nd\,(d^2 + 3c^2) + na\,(a^2 + 3b^2),$$

we have to choose for n such a fraction as will make x, y prime to one another. We then form

$$p = ax + 3by, \ q = bx - ay, \ r = dy + cx, \ s = 3cy - dx;$$

and, after again eliminating any common factor, we put

$$A = p + q, \ B = p - q, \ C = r - s, \ D = r + s,$$

and we shall have $$A^3 + B^3 + C^3 = D^3.$$

(The cases in which one of the three cubes A^3, B^3, C^3 is negative will give the solutions of the equation $x^3 + y^3 = z^3 + v^3$.)

While any values of a, b, c, d may be taken, it is necessary, if we want a solution in which A, B, C, D will be *small* numbers, to choose a, b, c, d so that $a^2 + 3b^2$, $d^2 + 3c^2$ may have a common factor. Euler accordingly sets out a table of all numbers of the form $m^2 + 3n^2$ less than 1000 (giving m values from 1 to 31 and n values from 1 to 18), and then chooses out cases in which $a^2 + 3b^2$, $d^2 + 3c^2$ have a tolerably large common factor.

Now, assuming that
$$a^2 + 3b^2 = mk,$$
$$d^2 + 3c^2 = nk,$$

we have (supposing further that $ac + bd = f$, $3bc - ad = g$)

$$A = n\,(3f + g) - m^2k,$$
$$B = n\,(3f - g) + m^2k,$$
$$C = n^2k - m\,(3f + g),$$
$$D = n^2k + m\,(3f - g).$$

In these formulae f, g may be either positive or negative, the signs of a, b, c, d being ambiguous; and we may put

$$\text{either } \left.\begin{array}{l} f = \pm\,(ac + bd) \\ g = \pm\,(3bc - ad) \end{array}\right\} \text{ or } \left.\begin{array}{l} f = \pm\,(ac - bd) \\ g = \pm\,(3bc + ad) \end{array}\right\}.$$

But, if f changes sign while g remains unaltered, we get numbers of the same form, only in different order; therefore we may confine ourselves to the positive sign in f.

Example 1. Let

$$a^2+3b^2=19, \text{ so that } a=4,\ b=1,$$

$$d^2+3c^2=76, \text{ so that } \left.\begin{array}{l}d=1\\c=5\end{array}\right\} \text{ or } \left.\begin{array}{l}d=7\\c=3\end{array}\right\} \text{ or } \left.\begin{array}{l}d=8\\c=2\end{array}\right\}.$$

Then $m=1$, $n=4$, $k=19$.

The following values for f, g result, viz.

I. $f=21$,	II. $f=19$,	III. $f=19$,
$g=\pm 11$,	$g=\pm 19$,	$g=\pm 19$,
IV. $f=5$,	V. $f=16$,	VI. $f=0$,
$g=\pm 37$,	$g=\pm 26$,	$g=\pm 38$,

while, since $m=1$, $n=4$, $k=19$,

$$A=12f+4g-19,$$
$$B=12f-4g+19,$$
$$C=304-3f-g,$$
$$D=304+3f-g.$$

The values (VI) $f=0$, $g=\pm 38$ are excluded because, if $f=0$, $A=-B$ and $C=D$.

The values (I) give

	that is,		
$A=233\pm 44$,	$A=277$	$A=189$ or	$A=3$
$B=271\mp 44$	$B=227$	$B=315$	$B=5$
$C=241\mp 11$	$C=230$	$C=252$	$C=4$
$D=367\mp 11$	$D=356$	$D=378$	$D=6$

The values (II) and (III) give, after division by 19,

	that is,		
$A=11\pm 4$,	$A=15$ or	$A=5$	$A=7$
$B=13\mp 4$	$B=9$	$B=3$	$B=17$
$C=13\mp 1$	$C=12$	$C=4$	$C=14$
$D=19\mp 1$	$D=18$	$D=6$	$D=20$

The values (IV) give

	that is,		
$A=41\pm 148$,	$A=189$ or	$A=63$	$A=-107$
$B=79\mp 148$	$B=-69$	$B=-23$	$B=227$
$C=289\mp 37$	$C=252$	$C=84$	$C=326$
$D=319\mp 37$	$D=282$	$D=94$	$D=356$

Lastly, the values (V) give

	that is,		
$A=173\pm 104$,	$A=277$	$A=69$ or	$A=23$
$B=211\mp 104$	$B=107$	$B=315$	$B=105$
$C=256\mp 26$	$C=230$	$C=282$	$C=94$
$D=352\mp 26$	$D=326$	$D=378$	$D=126$

Thus from the one assumption for a^2+3b^2, d^2+3c^2 we have the following solutions:

$227^3+230^3+277^3=356^3$	$107^3+356^3=227^3+326^3$
$107^3+230^3+277^3=326^3$	$23^3+94^3=63^3+84^3$
$23^3+94^3+105^3=126^3$	
$7^3+14^3+17^3=20^3$	
$3^3+4^3+5^3=6^3$	

Example 2. Assuming

$$a^2+3b^2=28, \text{ so that } \left.\begin{matrix}a=1\\b=3\end{matrix}\right\} \text{ or } \left.\begin{matrix}a=4\\b=2\end{matrix}\right\} \text{ or } \left.\begin{matrix}a=5\\b=1\end{matrix}\right\},$$

$$d^2+3c^2=84, \text{ so that } \left.\begin{matrix}d=3\\c=5\end{matrix}\right\} \text{ or } \left.\begin{matrix}d=6\\c=4\end{matrix}\right\} \text{ or } \left.\begin{matrix}d=9\\c=1\end{matrix}\right\},$$

we have $k=28$, $m=1$, $n=3$, and the following solutions will be obtained:

$1^3+6^3+8^3=9^3$	$1^3+12^3=9^3+10^3$
$34^3+39^3+65^3=72^3$	$10^3+27^3=19^3+24^3$
$20^3+54^3+79^3=87^3$	$17^3+39^3=26^3+36^3$
$3^3+4^3+5^3=6^3$	
$38^3+48^3+79^3=87^3$	

PROBLEM 2. *To find three numbers x, y, z such that*

$$x+y,\ x+z,\ y+z,$$

$$x-y,\ x-z,\ y-z,$$

are all squares.

First solution[1].

Assume that $x-y=p^2$, $x-z=q^2$, $y-z=r^2$;

therefore $y=x-p^2$, $z=x-q^2$, and $q^2=p^2+r^2$.

The first three formulae now become

$$x+y=2x-p^2,\ x+z=2x-q^2,\ y+z=2x-p^2-q^2.$$

Suppose that $2x-p^2-q^2=t^2$, so that $2x=t^2+p^2+q^2$; therefore we have to make t^2+q^2 and t^2+p^2 squares, while in addition $q^2=p^2+r^2$.

Let $q=a^2+b^2$, $p=a^2-b^2$, $r=2ab$;

then $t^2+(a^2+b^2)^2=t^2+a^4+b^4+2a^2b^2$

and $t^2+(a^2-b^2)^2=t^2+a^4+b^4-2a^2b^2$

must be made squares.

Comparing now $t^2+a^4+b^4$ with c^2+d^2 and $2a^2b^2$ with $2cd$, let us suppose $cd=a^2b^2=f^2g^2h^2k^2$, $c=f^2g^2$, $d=h^2k^2$, $a^2=f^2h^2$, $b^2=g^2k^2$ (or $a=fh$, $b=gk$); then the assumption $t^2+a^4+b^4=c^2+d^2$ will assume the form

$$t^2+f^4h^4+g^4k^4=f^4g^4+h^4k^4,$$

or $$t^2=f^4g^4-f^4h^4+h^4k^4-g^4k^4=(f^4-k^4)(g^4-h^4).$$

[1] *Algebra*, Part II. Art. 235.

Hence the problem is reduced to finding the differences of two pairs of fourth powers, namely $f^4 - k^4$ and $g^4 - h^4$, the product of which is a square.

For this purpose Euler sets out a table of values of $m^4 - n^4$ corresponding to different values of m, n, with a view of selecting pairs of values of $m^4 - n^4$ the products of which are squares.

m^2	n^2	$m^2 - n^2$	$m^2 + n^2$	$m^4 - n^4$
4	1	3	5	3 · 5
9	1	8	10	16 . 5
9	4	5	13	5 · 13
16	1	15	17	3 · 5 · 17
16	9	7	25	25 · 7
25	1	24	26	16 . 3 · 13
25	9	16	34	16 . 2 . 17
49	1	48	50	25 · 16 . 2 . 3
49	16	33	65	3 · 5 · 11 . 13
64	1	63	65	9 · 5 · 7 · 13
81	49	32	130	64 . 5 · 13
121	4	117	125	25 · 9 · 5 · 13
121	9	112	130	16 . 2 . 5 · 7 · 13
121	49	72	170	144 · 5 · 17
144	25	119	169	169 . 7 · 17
169	1	168	170	16 . 3 · 5 · 7 · 17
169	81	88	250	25 · 16 . 5 · 11
225	64	161	289	289 . 7 · 23

One solution is obtained from $f^2 = 9$, $k^2 = 4$, $g^2 = 81$, $h^2 = 49$, whence

$$t^2 = (f^4 - k^4)(g^4 - h^4) = 5 \cdot 13 \cdot 64 \cdot 5 \cdot 13 = (520)^2 = 270400.$$

Therefore

$$a = fh = 21,\ b = gk = 18,\ p = a^2 - b^2 = 117,\ q = a^2 + b^2 = 765,\ r = 2ab = 756;$$

therefore

$$\left.\begin{aligned} 2x = t^2 + p^2 + q^2 = 869314, \text{ or } x &= 434657 \\ y = x - p^2 &= 420968 \\ z = x - q^2 &= -150568 \end{aligned}\right\}.$$

The last number z may be taken positively; the difference then becomes the sum and the sum becomes the difference; therefore

$$\begin{aligned} x &= 434657, & x + y &= 855625 = (925)^2, & x - y &= 13689 = (117)^2, \\ y &= 420968, & x + z &= 585225 = (765)^2, & x - z &= 284089 = (533)^2, \\ z &= 150568, & y + z &= 571536 = (756)^2, & y - z &= 270400 = (520)^2. \end{aligned}$$

We might also have taken $f^2 = 9$, $k^2 = 4$, $g^2 = 121$, $h^2 = 4$, which would equally have given a solution.

Second solution[1].

This later solution (1780) of Euler's is worth giving on account of the variety of the artifices used.

We can make $x+y$ and $x-y$ squares by putting $x=p^2+q^2$, $y=2pq$. Similarly $x+z$, $x-z$ will be squares if $x=r^2+s^2$, $z=2rs$.

Therefore four conditions will be satisfied if only $p^2+q^2=r^2+s^2$.

Now [cf. Diophantus III. 19 and pp. 105–6 above] if we put

$$x=(a^2+b^2)(c^2+d^2),$$

x can be made the sum of two squares in two ways; in fact

$$p=ac+bd, \quad r=ad+bc,$$
$$q=ad-bc, \quad s=ac-bd,$$

and

$$y=2pq=2(a^2cd+abd^2-abc^2-b^2cd), \quad z=2rs=2(a^2cd+abc^2-abd^2-b^2cd),$$

so that $$y+z=4cd(a^2-b^2), \quad y-z=4ab(d^2-c^2).$$

These latter expressions have to be made squares.

First make their product y^2-z^2 a square; this means that

$$ab(a^2-b^2)\,.\,cd(d^2-c^2) \text{ must be made a square.}$$

To effect this, let us assume that $cd(d^2-c^2)=n^2ab(a^2-b^2)$; we may further, since the question depends on the relations between the pairs of letters a, b and c, d, suppose that $d=a$.

We have then $$c(a^2-c^2)=n^2b(a^2-b^2),$$

whence $a^2=\dfrac{n^2b^3-c^3}{n^2b-c}$, which fraction has accordingly to be made a square.

Suppose that $a=b-c$, so that $\dfrac{n^2b^3-c^3}{n^2b-c}=b^2-2bc+c^2$, and we have

$$0=-(2n^2+1)b^2c+(n^2+2)bc^2;$$

therefore $$\frac{b}{c}=\frac{n^2+2}{2n^2+1}.$$

Put $b=n^2+2$ and $c=2n^2+1$; therefore $a=1-n^2=d$.

As we have now made the product of the expressions $ab(d^2-c^2)$ and $cd(a^2-b^2)$ a square, it only remains to make either of them singly a square, say $ab(d^2-c^2)$.

But $$ab(d^2-c^2)=ab(d-c)(d+c)=3n^2(n^2-1)(n^2+2)^2.$$

We have therefore only to make $3(n^2-1)$ a square, which is easy, since n^2-1 has factors; for we have only to put

$$3(n^2-1)=\frac{f^2}{g^2}(n+1)^2,$$

which gives $$3(n-1)=\frac{f^2}{g^2}(n+1), \text{ or } n=\frac{f^2+3g^2}{3g^2-f^2}.$$

[1] *Mémoires de l'Académie Impériale des Sciences de St Pétersbourg*, 1813–14, VI. (1818), pp. 54 sqq. = *Commentationes arithmeticae*, II. pp. 392–5.

[Euler had previously tried the supposition $a=b+c$, which would require $3(n^2+1)$ to be made a square, which is impossible.]

All the conditions are now satisfied, and we have to find a, b, c, d etc. in terms of f, g:

$$a=d=1-n^2=-\frac{12f^2g^2}{(3g^2-f^2)^2},\quad b=n^2+2=\frac{3f^4-6f^2g^2+27g^4}{(3g^2-f^2)^2},$$

$$c=2n^2+1=\frac{3f^4+6f^2g^2+27g^4}{(3g^2-f^2)^2}.$$

As the whole solution depends on the ratios of a, b, c, d, we can multiply throughout by the common denominator, divide by 3, and put

$$a=d=-4f^2g^2,\quad b=f^4-2f^2g^2+9g^4,\quad c=f^4+2f^2g^2+9g^4,$$

whence
$$p=-8f^2g^2(f^4+9g^4),\quad r=f^8+30f^4g^4+81g^8,$$
$$q=-f^8+2f^4g^4-81g^8,\quad s=-16f^4g^4.$$

[Euler took a to be n^2-1 instead of $1-n^2$ and consequently obtained positive signs for the values of p and s; he also has $q=-(f^4-9g^4)^2$, which appears to be a slip.]

Assuming therefore any values for f, g in the first instance, we first find values for a, b, c, d, then values for p, q, r, s, and lastly values for x, y, z. It is to be observed that it is a matter of indifference whether we get negative values or not; for positive values can be substituted without danger.

Euler gives four examples.

If $f=1$, $g=1$, we find that x, y have equal values; this solution therefore does not serve our purpose.

The same is the case if $f=3$, $g=1$.

Suppose then that $f=2$, $g=1$; therefore $a=d=-16$, $b=17$, $c=33$; and (taking positive signs) we have

$$p=800,\quad q=305,\quad r=817,\quad s=256,$$

and
$$x=733025,\quad y=488000,\quad z=418304,$$

$$x+y=1105^2,\quad x-y=495^2,$$

$$x+z=1073^2,\quad x-z=561^2,$$

$$y+z=952^2,\quad y-z=264^2.$$

If $f=1$, $g=2$, we have $a=d=16$, $b=137$, $c=153$, and

$$p=4640,\quad q=20705,\quad r=21217,\quad s=256,$$

leading to large numbers for x, y, z.

Euler adds that, if x, y, z satisfy the conditions of the problem, another solution is furnished by X, Y, Z where

$$X=\tfrac{1}{2}(y^2+z^2-x^2),\quad Y=\tfrac{1}{2}(z^2+x^2-y^2),\quad Z=\tfrac{1}{2}(x^2+y^2-z^2).$$

PROBLEM 3. *To find three squares such that the difference of any pair is a square, or to find x, y, z such that*

$$x^2-y^2,\ x^2-z^2,\ y^2-z^2 \text{ are all squares.}$$

Any solution of the preceding problem will satisfy this, but the numbers would be large and we can get smaller solutions[1].

Dividing by z^2, we have to find three squares, $\frac{x^2}{z^2}$, $\frac{y^2}{z^2}$ and 1, such that

$$\left(\frac{x^2}{z^2}-\frac{y^2}{z^2}\right),\ \left(\frac{x^2}{z^2}-1\right),\ \left(\frac{y^2}{z^2}-1\right)$$

are all squares.

The last two conditions are satisfied if we put

$$\frac{x}{z}=\frac{p^2+1}{p^2-1} \text{ and } \frac{y}{z}=\frac{q^2+1}{q^2-1};$$

and we have only to make $\frac{x^2}{z^2}-\frac{y^2}{z^2}=\frac{(p^2+1)^2}{(p^2-1)^2}-\frac{(q^2+1)^2}{(q^2-1)^2}$ a square.

Now

$$\frac{(p^2+1)^2}{(p^2-1)^2}-\frac{(q^2+1)^2}{(q^2-1)^2}=\left(\frac{p^2+1}{p^2-1}+\frac{q^2+1}{q^2-1}\right)\left(\frac{p^2+1}{p^2-1}-\frac{q^2+1}{q^2-1}\right)$$

$$=\frac{4(p^2q^2-1)(q^2-p^2)}{(p^2-1)^2(q^2-1)^2}.$$

Therefore $(p^2q^2-1)(q^2-p^2)$ or $(p^2q^2-1)\left(\frac{q^2}{p^2}-1\right)$ has to be made a square.

(1) The latter expression is a square if

$$pq=\frac{f^2+g^2}{2fg},\ \frac{q}{p}=\frac{h^2+k^2}{2hk}.$$

And $pq\cdot\frac{q}{p}=q^2$, a square; therefore

$$\frac{f^2+g^2}{2fg}\cdot\frac{h^2+k^2}{2hk} \text{ or } fg(f^2+g^2)\cdot hk(h^2+k^2) \text{ must be a square.}$$

If $f=a+b$, $g=a-b$, $h=c+d$, $k=c-d$, the expression becomes $4(a^4-b^4)(c^4-d^4)$, which must be a square.

From the Table to the last problem we may take the values

$$a^2=9,\ b^2=4,\ c^2=81,\ d^2=49,$$

which make the expression a square.

Then $f=5$, $g=1$, $h=16$, $k=2$, $pq=\frac{13}{5}$, $q/p=\frac{260}{64}=\frac{65}{16}$, so that $q^2=\frac{169}{16}$, $q=\frac{13}{4}$, and therefore $p=\frac{4}{5}$.

Therefore $\frac{x}{z}=\frac{p^2+1}{p^2-1}=-\frac{41}{9}$, $\frac{y}{z}=\frac{q^2+1}{q^2-1}=\frac{185}{153}$ is the solution.

[1] *Algebra*, Part II., Arts. 236, 237.

To obtain whole numbers, we put $z=153$ and then $x=-697$ and $y=185$.

Thus
$$\left.\begin{aligned} x^2 &= 485809 \\ y^2 &= 34225 \\ z^2 &= 23409 \end{aligned}\right\} \text{ and } \begin{aligned} x^2-y^2 &= 451584=(672)^2, \\ y^2-z^2 &= 10816=(104)^2, \\ x^2-z^2 &= 462400=(680)^2. \end{aligned}$$

(2) Without using the Table, we may make $(p^2q^2-1)\left(\frac{q^2}{p^2}-1\right)$ a square in another way.

Put $q/p=m$ or $q=mp$, and $(m^2p^4-1)(m^2-1)$ has to be made a square.

This is a square when $p=1$; substitute therefore $1+s$ for p and we have

$$(m^2-1)(m^2-1+4m^2s+6m^2s^2+4m^2s^3+m^2s^4).$$

Dividing out by $(m^2-1)^2$ and, for brevity, putting a for $m^2/(m^2-1)$, we have

$$1+4as+6as^2+4as^3+as^4,$$

which has to be made a square.

Equating this to $(1+fs+gs^2)^2$, let us determine f, g so that the first three terms disappear;

therefore $$2f=4a, \text{ or } f=2a,$$

and $$6a=2g+f^2 \text{ or } g=\tfrac{1}{2}(6a-f^2)=3a-2a^2.$$

Lastly, the equation gives $4a+as=2fg+g^2s$, so that

$$s=\frac{4a-2fg}{g^2-a}=\frac{4a-12a^2+8a^3}{4a^4-12a^3+9a^2-a}=\frac{4-12a+8a^2}{4a^3-12a^2+9a-1}=\frac{4(2a-1)}{4a^2-8a+1}.$$

Now m in the expression for a may have any value.

Ex. 1. Let $m=2$, so that $a=\frac{4}{3}$;

therefore $$s=4\cdot\frac{5\cdot 3}{-23}=-\frac{60}{23},\quad p=-\frac{37}{23},\quad q=-\frac{74}{23};$$

whence $$\frac{x}{z}=\frac{949}{420},\quad \frac{y}{z}=\frac{6005}{4947}.$$

Ex. 2. Let $m=\frac{3}{2}$, so that $a=\frac{9}{5}$;

therefore $$s=4\cdot\frac{13\cdot 5}{-11}=-\frac{260}{11},\quad p=-\frac{249}{11},\quad q=-\frac{747}{22},$$

whence x/z, y/z are determined.

Euler considers also the particular case in which $a=m^2/(m^2-1)$ is a square, b^2 say.

The expression $1+4b^2s+6b^2s^2+4b^2s^3+b^2s^4$ is then equated to

$$(1+2b^2s+bs^2)^2,$$

and we obtain $$s=\frac{1-2b-2b^2}{2b} \text{ and } p=\frac{1-2b^2}{2b}.$$

Ex. a is a square if $m=\frac{5}{3}$, and in that case $b=\frac{5}{4}$. Therefore $p=-\frac{17}{20}$ $q=mp=-\frac{17}{12}$, and accordingly

$$\frac{x}{z}=\frac{689}{111}, \frac{y}{z}=\frac{433}{145}.$$

Problem 4. *To find three square numbers such that the sum of each pair is also a square, i.e. to find numbers x, y, z such that*

$$x^2+y^2,\ x^2+z^2,\ y^2+z^2$$

are all squares[1].

Dividing by z^2, we have to make

$$\frac{x^2}{z^2}+\frac{y^2}{z^2},\ \frac{x^2}{z^2}+1,\ \frac{y^2}{z^2}+1$$

all squares.

The second and third are made squares by putting

$$\frac{x}{z}=\frac{p^2-1}{2p} \text{ and } \frac{y}{z}=\frac{q^2-1}{2q};$$

and it only remains to make

$$\frac{(p^2-1)^2}{4p^2}+\frac{(q^2-1)^2}{4q^2}, \text{ or } q^2(p^2-1)^2+p^2(q^2-1)^2, \text{ a square.}$$

This can hardly be solved generally, and accordingly we resort to particular artifices.

1. Let us make the expression divisible by $(p+1)^2$, which is easily done by supposing $p+1=q-1$, or $q=p+2$, so that $q+1$ becomes $p+3$.

Thus $(p+2)^2(p-1)^2+p^2(p+3)^2$, or $2p^4+8p^3+6p^2-4p+4$, must be a square.

Suppose $$2p^4+8p^3+6p^2-4p+4=(gp^2+fp+2)^2,$$

and let us choose f, g such that the terms in p, p^2 vanish; therefore $f=-1$, and $4g+1=6$, or $g=\frac{5}{4}$.

We now have
$$\begin{aligned}2p+8&=g^2p+2fg\\&=\tfrac{25}{16}p-\tfrac{5}{2},\end{aligned}$$

so that $p=-24$, and $q=-22$, whence

$$\frac{x}{z}=\frac{p^2-1}{2p}=-\frac{575}{48}, \frac{y}{z}=\frac{q^2-1}{2q}=-\frac{483}{44}.$$

Making $z=16.3.11$, the least common multiple of 48 and 44, we have the solution

$$x=11.23.25=6325,\ y=12.21.23=5796,\ z=3.11.16=528,$$

and
$$\begin{aligned}x^2+y^2&=23^2(275^2+252^2)=23^2.373^2,\\x^2+z^2&=11^2(575^2+48^2)=11^2.577^2,\\y^2+z^2&=12^2(483^2+44^2)=12^2.485^2.\end{aligned}$$

[1] *Algebra*, Part II., Art. 238.

2, 3. Euler obtains fresh solutions by assuming, first, that

$$q-1=2(p+1),$$

and, secondly, that
$$q-1=\tfrac{4}{3}(p-1).$$

4. Lastly, he makes our expression divisible by both $(p+1)^2$ and $(p-1)^2$ at the same time.

For this purpose he takes

$$q=\frac{pt+1}{p+t},$$

whence
$$q+1=\frac{(p+1)(t+1)}{p+t}, \text{ and } q-1=\frac{(p-1)(t-1)}{p+t}.$$

Substituting in the formula $q^2(p^2-1)^2+p^2(q^2-1)^2$ the value of q in terms of p, t and then dividing by $(p^2-1)^2$, we have the expression

$$\frac{(pt+1)^2}{(p+t)^2}+\frac{p^2(t^2-1)^2}{(p+t)^4},$$

and we have to make $(pt+1)^2(p+t)^2+p^2(t^2-1)^2$ a square,

or
$$t^2p^4+2t(t^2+1)p^3+\{2t^2+(t^2+1)^2+(t^2-1)^2\}p^2+2t(t^2+1)p+t^2$$

must be a square.

We now equate this to $\{tp^2+(t^2+1)p-t\}^2$,

whence we have

$$\{2t^2+(t^2+1)^2+(t^2-1)^2\}p+2t(t^2+1)=\{(t^2+1)^2-2t^2\}p-2t(t^2+1),$$

which gives
$$\{4t^2+(t^2-1)^2\}p+4t(t^2+1)=0,$$

and
$$p=-\frac{4t}{t^2+1};$$

therefore
$$pt+1=\frac{-3t^2+1}{t^2+1}, \quad p+t=\frac{t^3-3t}{t^2+1},$$

and
$$q=\frac{-3t^2+1}{t^3-3t},$$

where t can be chosen arbitrarily.

Ex. Let $t=2$; then $p=-\frac{8}{5}$, $q=-\frac{11}{2}$, and

$$\frac{x}{z}=\frac{p^2-1}{2p}=-\frac{39}{80}, \quad \frac{y}{z}=\frac{q^2-1}{2q}=-\frac{117}{44}.$$

Putting $z=4\cdot4\cdot5\cdot11$, the least common multiple of 80 and 44, we have

$$x=-3\cdot11\cdot13 = -429,$$
$$y=-4\cdot5\cdot9\cdot13=-2340,$$
$$z=4\cdot4\cdot5\cdot11=880,$$

and $$x^2+y^2=3^2 \cdot 13^2(121+3600)=3^2 \cdot 13^2 \cdot 61^2,$$
$$x^2+z^2=11^2(1521+6400) \quad =11^2 \cdot 89^2,$$
$$y^2+z^2=20^2(13689+1936) \quad =20^2 \cdot 125^2.$$

PROBLEM 5. (Extension of Dioph. IV. 20 to *five* numbers.)

To find five numbers such that the product of every pair increased by unity becomes a square[1].

Euler had already shown (see pp. 181, 182 above) that, if $mn+1=l^2$, then the following *four* numbers which we will call a, b, c, d have the property, viz.

$$a=m, \quad b=n, \quad c=m+n+2l, \quad d=4l(l+m)(l+n).$$

If now z is the fifth required number, the four expressions

$$1+az, \quad 1+bz, \quad 1+cz, \quad 1+dz$$

must all be squares.

If, says Euler, we had to satisfy these conditions singly, the difficulties would be insuperable. But here too it happens, as in the former case, that, if we make the product of the four expressions a square, the expressions are all severally squares.

Let the product be $\quad 1+pz+qz^2+rz^3+sz^4,$

where accordingly

$$p=a+b+c+d, \quad q=ab+ac+ad+bc+bd+cd,$$
$$r=abc+abd+acd+bcd, \quad s=abcd.$$

Suppose now that

$$1+pz+qz^2+rz^3+sz^4=\{1+\tfrac{1}{2}pz+(\tfrac{1}{2}q-\tfrac{1}{8}p^2)z^2\}^2;$$

therefore, since the absolute term and the terms in z, z^2 vanish, we have

$$r+sz=p(\tfrac{1}{2}q-\tfrac{1}{8}p^2)+(\tfrac{1}{2}q-\tfrac{1}{8}p^2)^2 z,$$

whence $$z=\frac{r-p(\frac{1}{2}q-\frac{1}{8}p^2)}{(\frac{1}{2}q-\frac{1}{8}p^2)^2-s}.$$

Now it will be found (see the proof lower down) that

$$\tfrac{1}{2}q-\tfrac{1}{8}p^2=-\tfrac{1}{2}(s+1);$$

the denominator of the fraction will therefore be $\frac{1}{4}(s-1)^2$; that is, the said denominator fortunately turns out to be a square; if it were not so, the single expressions $1+az$, $1+bz$, $1+cz$, $1+dz$ could not have been made squares.

As it is however, substituting for $\frac{1}{2}q-\frac{1}{8}p^2$ its value in the numerator and denominator of the fraction for z, we have

$$z=\frac{4r+2p(s+1)}{(s-1)^2},$$

[1] *Commentationes arithmeticae*, II. pp. 50–52.

and all the conditions will be fulfilled, that is, all the expressions

$$ab+1,\quad ac+1,\quad ad+1,\quad bc+1,\quad bd+1,$$
$$cd+1,\quad az+1,\quad bz+1,\quad cz+1,\quad dz+1$$

will be squares.

Lemma. To prove the fact (assumed above) that

$$\tfrac{1}{2}q-\tfrac{1}{8}p^2=-\tfrac{1}{2}(s+1).$$

For brevity, put $m+n+l=f$, $l(l+m)(l+n)=k$, so that $k=fl^2+lmn$; and, since $a=m$, $b=n$, $c=f+l$, $d=4k$, we have $a+b+c=2f$, and therefore

$$p=2f+4k.$$

Again, since $$q=(a+b+c)d+(a+b)c+ab,$$
$$q=8fk+(m+n)^2+2l(m+n)+mn;$$

and, since $mn+1=l^2$, the latter expression becomes

$$q=8fk+f^2-1.$$

Moreover, $$s=abcd=4mnk(f+l);$$

therefore $$1+q+s=8fk+f^2+4mnk(f+l),$$

and we have to see whether the right-hand expression is equal to $\tfrac{1}{4}p^2$.

Now $$\tfrac{1}{4}p^2=f^2+4fk+4k^2.$$

Assume then, as a hypothesis, that

$$8fk+f^2+4mnk(f+l)=f^2+4fk+4k^2,$$

i.e. $$4fk+4mnk(f+l)=4k^2,$$

or, if we divide throughout by $4k$,

$$f+mn(f+l)=k=fl^2+lmn, \text{ from above};$$

that is, $$f+fmn=fl^2,$$

which is of course true, since $mn+1=l^2$.

Consequently it is proved that

$$1+q+s=\tfrac{1}{4}p^2, \text{ or } (\tfrac{1}{2}q-\tfrac{1}{8}p^2)=-\tfrac{1}{2}(s+1)$$

Ex. 1. Assume $m=1$, $n=3$, so that $l=2$; therefore

$$a=1,\quad b=3,\quad c=8,\quad d=120,$$

whence $$p=132,\quad q=1475,\quad r=4224,\quad s=2880,$$

and we deduce that

$$z=\frac{4\cdot 4224+264\cdot 2881}{2879^2}=\frac{777480}{8288641}.$$

The conditions are satisfied, for

$$ab+1=2^2,\qquad ac+1=3^2,\qquad ad+1=11^2,$$
$$bc+1=5^2,\qquad bd+1=19^2,\qquad cd+1=31^2,$$
$$az+1=(\tfrac{3011}{2879})^2,\qquad bz+1=(\tfrac{3259}{2879})^2,\qquad cz+1=(\tfrac{3809}{2879})^2,$$
$$dz+1=(\tfrac{10079}{2879})^2.$$

Ex. 2. To get smaller numbers (since we must put up with fractions) let us put $m=\frac{1}{2}$, $n=\frac{5}{2}$, so that $l=\frac{3}{2}$; therefore

$$a=\tfrac{1}{2},\quad b=\tfrac{5}{2},\quad c=6,\quad d=48,$$

whence $$p=57,\quad q=451\tfrac{1}{4},\quad r=931\tfrac{1}{2},\quad s=360,$$

and $$z=\frac{4\cdot 931\frac{1}{2}+114\cdot 361}{359^2}=\frac{44880}{128881}.$$

Problem 6. Euler has a general solution of the problem of Dioph. III. 15, viz.

To find three numbers x, y, z such that

$$xy+x+y,\quad xz+x+z,\quad yz+y+z$$

are all squares[1].

(1) Put $x+1=A$, $y+1=B$, $z+1=C$, so that $AB-1$, $AC-1$ and $BC-1$ have to be made squares.

Let $$AB=p^2+1,\quad AC=q^2+1,\quad BC=r^2+1;$$

therefore $$ABC=\sqrt{\{(p^2+1)(q^2+1)(r^2+1)\}}.$$

To make this expression rational, let us regard p, q as given and put $(p^2+1)(q^2+1)=m^2+n^2$, so that $m=pq\pm 1$, $n=p\mp q$; therefore

$$ABC=\sqrt{\{(m^2+n^2)(r^2+1)\}}=\sqrt{\{(mr+n)^2+(nr-m)^2\}}.$$

Put the latter root equal to $mr+n+t(nr-m)$; therefore

$$nr-m=2mrt+2nt+nrt^2-mt^2,$$

and $$r=\frac{m(t^2-1)-2nt}{n(t^2-1)+2mt}.$$

Therefore $$r^2+1=\frac{(m^2+n^2)(t^2+1)^2}{\{n(t^2-1)+2mt\}^2},\ \text{and}\ ABC=\frac{(m^2+n^2)(t^2+1)}{n(t^2-1)+2mt};$$

thus, since $BC=r^2+1$, we have

$$A=\frac{n(t^2-1)+2mt}{t^2+1},$$

and, since $m^2+n^2=(p^2+1)(q^2+1)$,

$$B=\frac{(p^2+1)(t^2+1)}{n(t^2-1)+2mt},$$

$$C=\frac{(q^2+1)(t^2+1)}{n(t^2-1)+2mt},$$

where $m=pq\pm 1$, $n=p\mp q$.

This solution is very general, inasmuch as we may choose p, q as we please, thus equating $AB-1$, $AC-1$ to any given squares; and, as t can be chosen arbitrarily, we have an infinite number of square values for $BC-1$.

(2) Euler adds two methods of obtaining solutions in integers, the second of which is interesting.

1 "Considerationes circa analysin Diophanteam," *Commentationes arithmeticae*, II. p. 577.

Take two fractions $\frac{a}{b}$ and $\frac{c}{d}$ so related that $ad-bc=\pm 1$; and form a third fraction $\frac{c\pm a}{d\pm b}$, which is similarly related to either of the former fractions.

Then the following three numbers will satisfy the conditions:

$$A=a^2+b^2,\quad B=c^2+d^2,\quad C=(c\pm a)^2+(d\pm b)^2.$$

For, since $ad-bc=\pm 1$,

$$AB=(ac+bd)^2+1,$$
$$AC=(ac\pm a^2+bd\pm b^2)^2+1,$$
$$BC=(c^2\pm ac+d^2\pm bd)^2+1.$$

(Cf. Dioph. III. 19.)

Simple solutions are seen thus:

$\frac{a}{b}$	$\frac{c}{d}$	$\frac{a+c}{b+d}$	A	B	C
$\frac{0}{1}$	$\frac{1}{f}$	$\frac{1}{f+1}$	1	f^2+1	f^2+2f+2
$\frac{1}{1}$	$\frac{f-1}{f}$	$\frac{f}{f+1}$	2	$2f^2-2f+1$	$2f^2+2f+1$
$\frac{1}{2}$	$\frac{f}{2f-1}$	$\frac{f+1}{2f+1}$	5	$5f^2-4f+1$	$5f^2+6f+2$

and so on.

(3) If two of the numbers A, B are given such that $AB-1=p^2$, we can find an infinite number of values for a third, C, which with A, B will satisfy the conditions.

For, since $AC-1$ and $BC-1$ have to be squares, take their product $ABC^2-(A+B)C+1$ and equate it to $(mC+1)^2$; we have then

$$C=\frac{A+B+2m}{AB-m^2},\ \text{whence}\ AC-1=\frac{(A+m)^2}{AB-m^2}\ \text{and}\ BC-1=\frac{(B+m)^2}{AB-m^2}.$$

Therefore we have only to make $AB-m^2$ a square; that is,

$$p^2+1-m^2=\text{a square}=n^2\ \text{say, so that}\ m^2+n^2=p^2+1.$$

Take now two fractions a and α such that $a^2+\alpha^2=1$, and let $m=ap+\alpha$, $n=\alpha p-a$; then

$$C=\frac{A+B\pm 2(ap+\alpha)}{(\alpha p-a)^2},$$

where a, α are determined by giving any values whatever to f, g in the expressions

$$a=\frac{f^2-g^2}{f^2+g^2},\quad \alpha=\frac{2fg}{f^2+g^2}.$$

Problem 7. *To find four numbers such that the product of any pair plus the sum of that pair gives a square; or, in other words, to find four numbers A, B, C, D such that the product of any pair diminished by* 1 *is a square, that is, such that*

$$AB-1, \quad AC-1, \quad AD-1, \quad BC-1, \quad BD-1, \quad CD-1$$

are all squares[1]. (Cf. Diophantus IV. 20.)

Let us regard two of the numbers A, B as given, being such that $AB-1=p^2$, or $AB=p^2+1$.

Let a, α be such fractions that $a^2+\alpha^2=1$, and put

$$C=\frac{A+B+2(ap+\alpha)}{(\alpha p-a)^2}.$$

Similarly let $b^2+\beta^2=1$, and put for the fourth number

$$D=\frac{A+B+2(bp+\beta)}{(\beta p-b)^2}.$$

Thus five conditions are satisfied, namely, that

$$AB-1, \quad AC-1, \quad BC-1, \quad AD-1, \quad BD-1 \text{ are all squares.}$$

The sixth condition, that $CD-1$ shall be a square, gives

$$(A+B)^2+2(A+B)\{(a+b)p+\alpha+\beta\}+4(ap+\alpha)(bp+\beta)$$
$$-(\alpha p-a)^2(\beta p-b)^2=\text{a square},$$

where AB has at the same time to be equal to p^2+1.

Regarding a, α, b, β and p as given, we have

$$A+B=A+\frac{p^2+1}{A}=\frac{A^2+p^2+1}{A},$$

and the expression to be made a square becomes the following expression in powers of A,

$$A^4+2A^3(a+b)p+2A^2(p^2+1) \qquad +2A(p^2+1)(a+b)p+(p^2+1)^2$$
$$+2A^3(\alpha+\beta) \quad +4A^2(ap+\alpha)(bp+\beta) \quad +2A(p^2+1)(\alpha+\beta)$$
$$-\quad A^2(\alpha p-a)^2(\beta p-b)^2$$

Equate this to the square of

$$A^2+A(a+b)p-(p^2+1)$$
$$+A(\alpha+\beta),$$

and we have

$$A^2\{(a+b)^2p^2+2(a+b)(\alpha+\beta)p+(\alpha+\beta)^2-4(p^2+1)$$
$$-4(ap+\alpha)(bp+\beta)+(\alpha p-a)^2(\beta p-b)^2\}$$
$$=4A(p^2+1)\{(a+b)p+\alpha+\beta\},$$

whence A is found.

Euler goes on to some particular cases, of which the following may be given.

[1] *Commentationes arithmeticae*, II. pp. 579–582.

Suppose $b=-a$ and $\beta=-\alpha$; we then have

$$C=\frac{A+B+2(ap+\alpha)}{(\alpha p-a)^2},\quad D=\frac{A+B-2(ap+\alpha)}{(\alpha p-a)^2},$$

and the expression above in A which had to be made a square becomes

$$\begin{aligned}&A^4+2A^2(p^2+1)+(p^2+1)^2\\&-4A^2(ap+\alpha)^2\\&-\;A^2(\alpha p-a)^4.\end{aligned}$$

This can be put in the form

$$\{A^2-(p^2+1)\}^2+A^2(\alpha p-a)^2\{4-(\alpha p-a)^2\},$$

by virtue of the relation $a^2+\alpha^2=1$.

Our expression is clearly a square if $4-(\alpha p-a)^2=0$, or $\alpha p-a=2$, that is, $p=(2+a)/\alpha$, and

$$ap+\alpha=\frac{(2+a)a}{\alpha}+\alpha=\frac{2a+1}{\alpha},$$

and in that case

$$B=\frac{p^2+1}{A},\quad C=\frac{A+B+2(2a+1)/\alpha}{4}=\frac{\alpha(A+B)+4a+2}{4\alpha},$$

$$D=\frac{\alpha(A+B)-4a-2}{4\alpha},$$

where A can be chosen quite arbitrarily.

Putting $a=(f^2-g^2)/(f^2+g^2)$, $\alpha=2fg/(f^2+g^2)$, we obtain the following as a solution, where m, n can be any integers whatever.

$$A=\frac{m(f^2+g^2)}{2nfg},\qquad B=\frac{n(9f^2+g^2)}{2mfg},$$

$$C=\frac{(m+3n)^2f^2+(m-n)^2g^2}{8mnfg},\quad D=\frac{(m-3n)^2f^2+(m+n)^2g^2}{8mnfg}.$$

Ex. Suppose $f=1$, $g=2$, $m=5$, $n=6$;

therefore $A=\frac{25}{24}$, $B=\frac{39}{10}$, $C=\frac{533}{480}$, $D=\frac{653}{480}$,

and $AB-1=(\frac{7}{4})^2$, $AC-1=(\frac{19}{48})^2$, $AD-1=(\frac{31}{48})^2$,

$BC-1=(\frac{73}{40})^2$, $BD-1=(\frac{83}{40})^2$, $CD-1=(\frac{343}{480})^2$.

PROBLEM 8. *To find four numbers such that the product of any pair added to a given number n gives a square*[1].

(1) A particular solution is found in this way. Let A, B, C, D be the required numbers, and, since $AB+n$ has to be a square, put

$$A=na^2-b^2,\quad B=nc^2-d^2,$$

so that $AB=(nac-bd)^2-n(ad-bc)^2$. [Cf. the Indian formula above, p. 282.]

[1] *Commentationes arithmeticae*, II. pp. 582–3.

The condition that $AB+n$ is a square is therefore fulfilled, provided that $ad-bc=\pm 1$; therefore we have to take fractions $\frac{a}{b}, \frac{c}{d}$ such that $ad-bc=\pm 1$; and, when this is done, the fractions $\frac{a+c}{b+d}$ and $\frac{a-c}{b-d}$ will have the same property in relation to either of the former fractions.

We accordingly put

$$A=na^2-b^2, \qquad B=nc^2-d^2,$$
$$C=n(a+c)^2-(b+d)^2, \quad D=n(a-c)^2-(b-d)^2.$$

Thus five conditions are satisfied, and it only remains to make $CD+n$ a square; that is,

$$\left.\begin{array}{l} n^2(a^2-c^2)^2-2n(ab-cd)^2+(b^2-d^2)^2 \\ \qquad -2n(ad-bc)^2 \\ \qquad +n \end{array}\right\} = \text{a square.}$$

or, since $(ad-bc)^2=1$,

$$n^2(a^2-c^2)^2-n\{2(ab-cd)^2+1\}+(b^2-d^2)^2 = \text{a square.}$$

(2) We obtain a general solution by the same method as that applied above (p. 345) in the problem of making $AB-1$, $BC-1$, etc. squares.

Put $AB=p^2-n$; then, to make $AC+n$, $BC+n$ both squares, take the product of these expressions and equate it to $(n+Cx)^2$; therefore

$$n^2+n(A+B)C+ABC^2=n^2+2nCx+C^2x^2,$$

whence $$C=\frac{n(A+B-2x)}{x^2-AB}, \text{ and } AC+n=\frac{n(A-x)^2}{x^2-AB},$$

so that $(x^2-AB)/n$ must be a square.

Let then $x^2-AB=x^2-p^2+n=ny^2$, or $x^2-ny^2=p^2-n$.

Similarly let us put $v^2-nz^2=p^2-n$, so as to get

$$C=\frac{A+B-2x}{y^2}, \quad D=\frac{A+B-2v}{z^2};$$

and it remains to make $CD+n$ a square,

that is, $$(A+B)^2-2(x+v)(A+B)+ny^2z^2+4xv$$
must be a square.

But, since $B=\frac{p^2-n}{A}$ and $A+B=\frac{A^2+p^2-n}{A}$, the expression becomes (after multiplication by A^2)

$$\begin{array}{l} A^4-2A^3(x+v)+2A^2(p^2-n)-2A(p^2-n)(x+v)+(p^2-n)^2 \\ \qquad +nA^2y^2z^2 \\ \qquad +4A^2xv, \end{array}$$

which must be a square $=\{A^2-A(x+v)-(p^2-n)\}^2$ say; therefore

$$A^2\{(x+v)^2-4(p^2-n)-ny^2z^2-4xv\}+4A(x+v)(p^2-n)=0,$$

so that

$$A=\frac{4(x+v)(p^2-n)}{ny^2z^2+4(p^2-n)-(x+v)^2+4xv}=\frac{4(x+v)(p^2-n)}{n(y^2-1)(z^2-1)+2xv+2p^2-3n},$$

or

$$A=\frac{4(x+v)(p^2-n)}{ny^2z^2-2n(y^2+z^2)+(v+x)^2}.$$

(3) A particular solution is obtained by assuming that $v=-x$, so that $z=y$, and

$$C=\frac{A+B-2x}{y^2},\quad D=\frac{A+B+2x}{y^2},$$

while $AB=p^2-n=x^2-ny^2$.

For then we have to make

$$A^4+A^2\{2(p^2-n)+ny^4-4x^2\}+(p^2-n)^2 \text{ a square};$$

that is, $$(A^2-p^2+n)^2+nA^2y^2(y^2-4)=\text{a square}.$$

This is satisfied if we put $y=2$, so that $p^2=x^2-3n$.

Suppose $p=x-t$, and we have

$$x=\frac{t^2+3n}{2t} \text{ and } p=\frac{3n-t^2}{2t}, \text{ or } p=\frac{3nu^2-t^2}{2tu} \text{ and } x=\frac{3nu^2+t^2}{2tu},$$

and hence $$AB=\frac{(nu^2-t^2)(9nu^2-t^2)}{4t^2u^2}.$$

We may therefore put

$$A=\frac{f(nu^2-t^2)}{2gtu},\qquad B=\frac{g(9nu^2-t^2)}{2ftu},$$

$$C=\frac{n(f-3g)^2u^2-(f+g)^2t^2}{8fgtu},\quad D=\frac{n(f+3g)^2u^2-(f-g)^2t^2}{8fgtu}.$$

It will be seen that in this solution $C+D=\frac{1}{2}(A+B)$.

PROBLEM 9. *To find four numbers such that the product of any pair added to the sum of all gives a square*[1].

First find four numbers A, B, C, D such that the product of any pair increased by a number n gives a square (Problem 8).

Take as the numbers sought mA, mB, mC, mD, and, since $m^2(AB+n)$ is a square or m^2AB+m^2n is a square, we have only to make m^2n equal to the sum of the four numbers or $m(A+B+C+D)$, whence

$$m=\frac{A+B+C+D}{n}.$$

[1] *Commentationes arithmeticae*, II. pp. 583–5.

But, since in the other problem $C+D=\frac{1}{2}(A+B)$, this gives

$$m=\frac{3(A+B)}{2n}=\frac{3n(f^2+9g^2)u^2-3(f^2+g^2)t^2}{4nfgtu},$$

where n as well as f, g, t and u can be chosen as we please.

Since n may be chosen arbitrarily, take $p^2=x^2-3n$, as in the last problem, so that $n=\frac{1}{3}(x^2-p^2)$, and $AB=p^2-n=\frac{1}{3}(4p^2-x^2)$.

Accordingly we may put

$$A=\frac{f(2p+x)}{3g}, \quad B=\frac{g(2p-x)}{f};$$

therefore $$A+B=\frac{2(f^2+3g^2)p+(f^2-3g^2)x}{3fg},$$

and hence $$C=\frac{2(f^2+3g^2)p+(f^2-6fg-3g^2)x}{12fg},$$

$$D=\frac{2(f^2+3g^2)p+(f^2+6fg-3g^2)x}{12fg},$$

and $$A+B+C+D=\frac{2(f^2+3g^2)p+(f^2-3g^2)x}{2fg};$$

therefore $$m=(A+B+C+D)/n=\frac{6(f^2+3g^2)p+3(f^2-3g^2)x}{2fg(x^2-p^2)}.$$

Now two of the numbers, A, B, can be chosen arbitrarily, and

$$2p+x=\frac{3Ag}{f}, \quad 2p-x=\frac{Bf}{g};$$

therefore $$p=\frac{3Ag^2+Bf^2}{4fg} \text{ and } x=\frac{3Ag^2-Bf^2}{2fg},$$

so that $$n=\frac{1}{3}(x^2-p^2)=\frac{(9Ag^2-Bf^2)(Ag^2-Bf^2)}{16f^2g^2},$$

and $$C=\frac{A+B}{4}-\frac{3Ag^2-Bf^2}{4fg}, \quad D=\frac{A+B}{4}+\frac{3Ag^2-Bf^2}{4fg},$$

while $$m=\frac{3(A+B)}{2n}.$$

If, in order to get rid of fractions, we put $A=4afg$, $B=4bfg$, we have

$$C=(a+b)fg-3ag^2+bf^2, \quad D=(a+b)fg+3ag^2-bf^2,$$

$$n=(9ag^2-bf^2)(ag^2-bf^2), \quad m=\frac{6(a+b)fg}{(9ag^2-bf^2)(ag^2-bf^2)}.$$

Ex. Let $f=2$, $g=1$; therefore

$$A=8a, \quad B=8b, \quad C=6b-a, \quad D=5a-2b,$$

$$m=\frac{12(a+b)}{(9a-4b)(a-4b)}=\frac{12(a+b)}{(4b-9a)(4b-a)}.$$

The following are simple cases:

(1) $a = 5$, $b = 1$, whence $A = 40$, $B = 8$, $C = 1$, $D = 23$, $m = \frac{72}{41}$.

(2) $a = 11$, $b = 2$, whence $A = 88$, $B = 16$, $C = 1$, $D = 51$, $m = \frac{4}{7}$.

If $f = 5$, $g = 1$, we can obtain integral solutions, thus.

$$A = 20a, \quad B = 20b, \quad C = 30b + 2a, \quad D = 8a - 20b,$$

$$m = \frac{30(a+b)}{(25b - 9a)(25b - a)}.$$

Assuming then $a = 19$, $b = 7$, we have

$$A = 380, \quad B = 140, \quad C = 248, \quad D = 12, \quad m = \frac{5}{4},$$

so that the required numbers are

$$475, \quad 175, \quad 310, \quad 15,$$

the sum of which is 975.

We can also solve the corresponding problem:

9 A. *To find four numbers such that the product of any pair minus the sum of all gives a square.*

For we have only to give m a negative value.

PROBLEM 10. *To find three numbers x, y, z such that*

$$\left.\begin{array}{l} x+y+z \\ yz+zx+xy \\ xyz \end{array}\right\} \text{ are all squares}^1.$$

(This may be expressed as the problem of finding p, q, r such that the equation $\xi^3 - p\xi^2 + q\xi - r = 0$ has all its roots rational while p, q, r are all squares.)

Take nx, ny, nz for the numbers required, so that

$$\left.\begin{array}{l} n(x+y+z) \\ n^2(xy+xz+yz) \\ n^3xyz \end{array}\right\} \text{ must all be squares.}$$

If the first and third conditions are satisfied, we must have, by multiplication,

$$xyz(x+y+z) = \text{a square}.$$

Put therefore $$xyz(x+y+z) = v^2(x+y+z)^2,$$

whence $$xyz = v^2(x+y+z), \text{ and } z = \frac{v^2(x+y)}{xy - v^2}.$$

Since $xyz = \dfrac{v^2xy(x+y)}{xy - v^2}$, we must have, in order that $nxyz$ may be a square,

$$n = m^2xy(x+y)(xy - v^2).$$

[1] *Novi Commentarii Acad. Petropol.* 1760–61, Vol. VIII. (1763), p. 64 sqq. = *Commentationes arithmeticae*, I. pp. 239–244.

If the values of z, n thus found be taken, the first and third conditions are satisfied, and the three numbers will be

$$nx = m^2x^2y(x+y)(xy-v^2),$$
$$ny = m^2xy^2(x+y)(xy-v^2),$$
$$nz = m^2v^2xy(x+y)^2.$$

The second condition requires that

$$xy + z(x+y) = xy + \frac{v^2(x+y)^2}{xy-v^2} = \text{a square.}$$

Suppose for this purpose that $xy - v^2 = u^2$ (this introduces a restriction because there are doubtless plenty of solutions where $xy - v^2$ is not a square); therefore

$$y = \frac{v^2+u^2}{x}, \quad z = \frac{v^2(x+y)}{u^2},$$

and $xy = v^2 + u^2$, $x + y = \dfrac{x^2+v^2+u^2}{x}$, so that we must make

$$v^2 + u^2 + \frac{v^2(x^2+v^2+u^2)^2}{u^2x^2} \text{ a square.}$$

Put $x = tv$, so that $y = \dfrac{v^2+u^2}{tv}$, and

$$v^2 + u^2 + \frac{\{v^2(t^2+1)+u^2\}^2}{t^2u^2} = \text{a square,}$$

or $$t^2u^2v^2 + t^2u^4 + v^4(t^2+1)^2 + 2u^2v^2(t^2+1) + u^4 = \text{a square,}$$

i.e. $$v^4(t^2+1)^2 + u^2v^2(3t^2+2) + u^4(t^2+1) = \text{a square}$$
$$= \{v^2(t^2+1) + su^2\}^2, \text{ say.}$$

Therefore $$v^2(3t^2+2) + u^2(t^2+1) = 2sv^2(t^2+1) + s^2u^2,$$

and $$\frac{v^2}{u^2} = \frac{t^2+1-s^2}{2s(t^2+1)-3t^2-2} = \text{a square.}$$

Further, let $s = t - r$, and we shall have

$$\frac{v^2}{u^2} = \frac{2rt-r^2+1}{2t^3-(2r+3)t^2+2t-2(r+1)}.$$

Multiply the numerator and denominator by $2rt - r^2 + 1$, and we have

$$\frac{v^2}{u^2} = \frac{(2rt-r^2+1)^2}{4rt^4-2(3r^2+3r-1)t^3+(2r^3+3r^2+2r-3)t^2-2(3r-1)(r+1)t+2(r-1)(r+1)^2}.$$

The problem is accordingly reduced to making the denominator of this fraction a square. If we suppose this done, and Q to be the square root, while t and r are determined as the result of equating the denominator to Q^2, we shall have

$$\frac{v}{u} = \frac{2rt-r^2+1}{Q}, \text{ and } x = tv, \; y = \frac{v^2+u^2}{tv},$$

whence we can derive the numbers required.

Now the denominator to be made a square is easily made such if the coefficient of t^4, or the absolute term, is a square; and the absolute term is a square if $2(r-1)$ is a square.

Case I. Suppose $r=1$; the coefficient of t^4 is then a square and the absolute term vanishes.

We have $\quad 4t^4-10t^3+4t^2-8t=Q^2$, while $v/u=2t/Q$.

Suppose $Q=2t^2-\frac{5}{2}t$, and we have

$$4t^2-8t=\tfrac{25}{4}t^2,\quad\text{and } t=-\tfrac{32}{9},\quad \frac{v}{u}=\frac{4}{4t-5}=\frac{-36}{173};$$

we therefore put $v=-36$, $u=173$, $t=-\frac{32}{9}$, and $x=tv=128$; further

$$y=\frac{v^2+u^2}{tv}=\frac{31225}{128}=\frac{25\,.\,1249}{128},$$

$$x+y=\tfrac{47609}{128},\quad z=\frac{36^2\,.\,47609}{173^2\,.\,128};$$

and, since $xy-v^2=u^2$, the required numbers will be

$$nx=\frac{128^2\,.\,25\,.\,1249\,.\,47609\,.\,173^2}{128\,.\,128}m^2,$$

$$ny=\frac{128\,.\,25^2\,.\,1249^2\,.\,47609\,.\,173^2}{128^2\,.\,128}m^2,$$

$$nz=\frac{36^2\,.\,128\,.\,25\,.\,1249\,.\,47609^2}{128\,.\,128^2}m^2.$$

In order to get rid of fractions, put $m=\frac{128}{5}$, and we have

$$nx=128^2\,.\,173^2\,.\,1249\,.\,47609=490356736\,.\,59463641,$$
$$ny=5^2\,.\,173^2\,.\,1249^2\,.\,47609\quad=934533025\,.\,59463641,$$
$$nz=36^2\,.\,1249\,.\,47609^2\qquad=61701264\,.\,59463641.$$

The product of the three numbers is obviously a square; their sum is found to be $25\,.\,59463641^2$; and the sum of the products of pairs

$$=173^2\,.\,59463641^2\,.\,18248924559376$$
$$=(173\,.\,59463641\,.\,4271876)^2.$$

Case II. Put $r=\frac{3}{2}$; then $\dfrac{v}{u}=\dfrac{12t-5}{4Q}$, and

$$6t^4-\tfrac{41}{2}t^3+\tfrac{27}{2}t^2-\tfrac{35}{2}t+\tfrac{25}{4}=Q^2$$
$$=(\tfrac{5}{2}-\tfrac{7}{2}t+\tfrac{1}{4}t^2)^2,\text{ say,}$$

whence $\quad 6t^4-\frac{41}{2}t^3=\frac{1}{16}t^4-\frac{7}{4}t^3$, and $t=\frac{60}{19}$.

Accordingly $Q=\frac{4375}{722}$, $\dfrac{v}{u}=\frac{19}{14}$, and we put $v=19$, $u=14$.

Therefore $\quad x=tv=60,\quad y=\dfrac{v^2+u^2}{tv}=\frac{557}{60},\quad x+y=\frac{4157}{60},$

and the required numbers are

$$\left.\begin{aligned} nx &= \frac{60^2 \cdot 557 \cdot 4157 \cdot 196}{60 \cdot 60} m^2 = 14^2 \cdot 60^2 \cdot 557 \cdot 4157 \\ ny &= \frac{60 \cdot 557^2 \cdot 4157 \cdot 196}{60 \cdot 60 \cdot 60} m^2 = 14^2 \cdot 557^2 \cdot 4157 \\ nz &= \frac{361 \cdot 60 \cdot 557 \cdot 4157^2}{60 \cdot 60 \cdot 60} m^2 = 19^2 \cdot 557 \cdot 4157^2 \end{aligned}\right\} \text{if } m = 60.$$

That is,

$$\begin{aligned} nx &= 705600 \cdot 2315449 = 1633780814400, \\ ny &= 109172 \cdot 2315449 = 252782198228, \\ nz &= 1500677 \cdot 2315449 = 3474741058973. \end{aligned}$$

The product of the three numbers is clearly a square; their sum will be found to be 2315449^2; and the sum of the products of pairs

$$\begin{aligned} &= 14^2 \cdot 2315449^2 \cdot 6631333489 \\ &= (14 \cdot 2315449 \cdot 81433)^2. \end{aligned}$$

These numbers are much smaller than those first obtained.

If fractional numbers are admitted, we may divide those found in the last solution by 2315449^2, and the solution will be

$$\frac{705600}{2315449}, \quad \frac{196}{4157}, \quad \frac{361}{557}.$$

PROBLEM 11. *To find four numbers x, y, z, u such that*

$$\left.\begin{aligned} &x + y + z + u \\ &xy + yz + \ldots \\ &xyz + yzu + zux + uxy \\ &xyzu \end{aligned}\right\} \textit{are all squares}^{1}.$$

A general solution being apparently impossible, some particular assumption simplifying the problem had to be made. Euler therefore assumed as the four numbers

$$Mab, \quad Mbc, \quad Mcd, \quad Mda,$$

which assumption, although five letters are used, involves the restriction that the product of the first and third numbers is equal to the product of the second and fourth.

We must therefore have

$$\left.\begin{aligned} &M(ab + bc + cd + da) \\ &M^2(ab^2c + bc^2d + cd^2a + da^2b + 2abcd) \\ &M^3(ab^2c^2d + abc^2d^2 + a^2bcd^2 + a^2b^2cd) \\ &M^4a^2b^2c^2d^2 \end{aligned}\right\} \text{all squares.}$$

[1] *Novi Commentarii Acad. Petrop.*, 1772, XVII. (1773), pp. 24 sqq. = *Commentationes arithmeticae*, I. pp. 450–5.

The above assumption therefore has the advantage of making the product of the four numbers automatically a square and also of making the third formula take the form

$$M^3abcd\,(ab+bc+cd+da).$$

Since the first formula $M(ab+bc+cd+da)$ must be a square, it follows that $abcd$ must be made a square.

In order to make the first and third formulae squares, take

$$M=ab+bc+cd+da,$$

or, if the latter expression has a square factor, say f^2, put

$$M=(ab+bc+cd+da)/f^2.$$

We now have only two conditions remaining to be satisfied, namely

$$abcd=\text{a square} \quad\ldots\ldots\ldots\ldots\ldots\ldots\ldots\ldots(1),$$

$$ab^2c+bc^2d+cd^2a+da^2b+2abcd=\text{a square} \quad\ldots\ldots\ldots\ldots(2).$$

The expression in (2) reduces to

$$(a^2+c^2)\,bd+ac\,(b^2+d^2)+2abcd,$$

or $$bd\,(a^2+c^2)+(b+d)^2\,ac=\text{a square}.$$

We have therefore only to find numbers a, b, c, d satisfying these two conditions. It is further to be noted that a, c are connected by a relation similar to that between b, d, and the whole question depends on the ratios $a:c$ and $b:d$. We may therefore assume a, c prime to one another and likewise b, d prime to one another, for, if either pair had a common divisor, it could be omitted and the relation would still be satisfied.

Consider now the second condition as being the more difficult. Although two ratios $a:c$, $b:d$ are involved, neither can be arbitrarily assumed. For suppose *e.g.* that $b:d=2:1$; then $2a^2+2c^2+9ac$ would have to be made a square; this however is seen to be impossible, for, if we put $a=p+q$, $c=p-q$, we obtain the expression $13p^2-5q^2$, which cannot be made a square. The same impossibility results if we put $b:d=3:1$. Therefore the ratios $a:c$ and $b:d$ can only be certain particular ratios.

Obviously the first class of ratios adapted for our purpose are *square* ratios. Assume then that $b:d=p^2:q^2$, and put

$$p^2q^2\,(a^2+c^2)+ac\,(p^2+q^2)^2=\left(pqa+\frac{m}{n}\,c\right)^2,\ \text{say};$$

therefore $$n^2\,(p^2+q^2)^2\,a+n^2p^2q^2c=2mnpqa+m^2c,$$

so that $$\frac{a}{c}=\frac{m^2-n^2p^2q^2}{n^2\,(p^2+q^2)^2-2mnpq},$$

or, if $m=\pm kpq$,

$$\frac{b}{d}=\frac{p^2}{q^2},\quad \frac{a}{c}=\frac{(k^2-n^2)\,p^2q^2}{n^2\,(p^2+q^2)^2\pm 2knp^2q^2}. \qquad (k>n)$$

Now, if values could be found for k, n, p, q such as would make ac or

$$n(k^2-n^2)\{n(p^2+q^2)^2 \pm 2kp^2q^2\} \text{ a square,}$$

we should have a solution of the problem, since, bd being already a square, $abcd$ would then be a square. Euler however abandons the investigation of this general problem as too troublesome and as certain, in any case, to lead to very large numbers; and, instead, he proceeds to seek solutions by trial of particular assumptions.

Particular values of a/c in terms of p, q are the following, which are obtained by putting $k=2$, $n=1$; $k=3$, $n=1$; etc.

$$\text{I.}\quad \frac{a}{c}=\frac{3p^2q^2}{(p^2+q^2)^2 \pm 4p^2q^2}, \qquad \text{II.}\quad \frac{a}{c}=\frac{8p^2q^2}{(p^2+q^2)^2 \pm 6p^2q^2},$$

$$\text{III.}\quad \frac{a}{c}=\frac{5p^2q^2}{4(p^2+q^2)^2 \pm 12p^2q^2}, \qquad \text{IV.}\quad \frac{a}{c}=\frac{15p^2q^2}{(p^2+q^2)^2 \pm 8p^2q^2},$$

$$\text{V.}\quad \frac{a}{c}=\frac{7p^2q^2}{9(p^2+q^2)^2 \pm 24p^2q^2}, \qquad \text{VI.}\quad \frac{a}{c}=\frac{24p^2q^2}{(p^2+q^2)^2 \pm 10p^2q^2},$$

$$\text{VII.}\quad \frac{a}{c}=\frac{21p^2q^2}{4(p^2+q^2)^2 \pm 20p^2q^2}, \qquad \text{VIII.}\quad \frac{a}{c}=\frac{16p^2q^2}{9(p^2+q^2)^2 \pm 30p^2q^2},$$

$$\text{IX.}\quad \frac{a}{c}=\frac{9p^2q^2}{16(p^2+q^2)^2 \pm 40p^2q^2}, \qquad \text{etc.}$$

Taking now the simplest values of $b/d=p^2/q^2$, let us write down the simplest corresponding values for a/c:

$$\text{if } \frac{b}{d}=\tfrac{1}{1},\quad \frac{a}{c} \text{ becomes } \tfrac{3}{8},\ -\tfrac{4}{1},\ \tfrac{4}{5},\ \tfrac{5}{28},\ -\tfrac{15}{4},\ \tfrac{7}{12},\ \tfrac{7}{60},\ \tfrac{8}{33};$$

$$\text{if } \frac{b}{d}=\tfrac{4}{1},\quad \frac{a}{c} \text{ becomes } \tfrac{4}{3},\ \tfrac{12}{41},\ \tfrac{32}{1},\ \tfrac{32}{49},\ \tfrac{5}{13},\ \tfrac{5}{37},\ -\tfrac{60}{7},\ \tfrac{20}{19};$$

$$\text{if } \frac{b}{d}=\tfrac{9}{1},\quad \frac{a}{c} \text{ becomes } \tfrac{27}{64},\ \tfrac{27}{136},\ \tfrac{36}{23},\ \tfrac{36}{77},\ \tfrac{45}{292},\ \tfrac{108}{5};$$

$$\text{if } \frac{b}{d}=\tfrac{9}{4},\quad \frac{a}{c} \text{ becomes } \tfrac{108}{25},\ \tfrac{45}{61},\ \tfrac{28}{73},\ \tfrac{64}{49},\ \tfrac{64}{289}.$$

The last assumption gives, "praeter exspectationem," two cases in which a/c becomes a square; and these give two solutions of our problem.

1. Putting $a=64$, $b=9$, $c=49$, $d=4$, we have

$$M=ab+bc+cd+da=576+441+196+256$$
$$=1469,$$

and the four numbers are

$$1469 \cdot 196,\quad 1469 \cdot 256,\quad 1469 \cdot 441,\quad 1469 \cdot 576.$$

2. Putting $a=64$, $b=9$, $c=289$, $d=4$, we obtain

$$M=576+2601+1156+256=4589,$$

and the four numbers are

$$4589 \cdot 256,\quad 4589 \cdot 576,\quad 4589 \cdot 1156,\quad 4589 \cdot 2601.$$

Again, the form of the expressions $abcd$, $bd(a^2+c^2)+ac(b+d)^2$ to be made squares shows that any values for a/c obtained by the above process may be taken as values for b/d. Also a and c may be interchanged. Euler accordingly sets down as values of b/d to be tried the following:

$$\frac{4}{3},\ \frac{5}{4},\ \frac{8}{3},\ \frac{12}{7},\ \frac{13}{5},\ \frac{20}{19},\ \frac{28}{5},\ \frac{32}{1},\ \frac{33}{8}\ \text{etc.}$$

He obtains no solution from the assumption $b/d=\frac{4}{3}$, but he is more successful with the assumption $b/d=\frac{5}{4}$.

Putting $b/d=\frac{5}{4}$, we have to make

$$20(a^2+c^2)+81ac=\text{a square.}$$

This is satisfied by $a/c=1$; let therefore $a/c=1+x$, and we have to make $20\{(1+x)^2+1\}+81(1+x)$ a square; that is,

$$121+121x+20x^2=\text{a square}=(11+xy)^2,\ \text{say;}$$

therefore $x=\dfrac{121-22y}{y^2-20}$, and $\dfrac{a}{c}=\dfrac{y^2-22y+101}{y^2-20}=\dfrac{m^2\pm 22mn+101n^2}{m^2-20n^2}$,

and, by putting $m=5$, $n=1$ we obtain $a/c=\frac{16}{5}$.

This solution serves our purpose, since it makes $abcd$ a square.

Putting $a=16$, $b=5$, $c=5$, $d=4$, we have

$$M=\frac{80+25+20+64}{f^2}=\frac{189}{f^2},$$

and, if $f=3$, $M=21$; the four numbers are therefore

$$21\cdot 20,\quad 21\cdot 25,\quad 21\cdot 64,\quad 21\cdot 80.$$

This is a solution in much smaller numbers; and

the sum of the numbers $=9\cdot 21^2$,

the sum of products of pairs $=110^2\cdot 21^2$,

the sum of products of sets of three $=120^2\cdot 21^4$,

and the product of all four $=1600^2\cdot 21^4$.

When one solution is known, others can be found. Take, for example, the last solution in which, for $b/d=\frac{5}{4}$, we found that

$$\frac{a}{c}=\frac{y^2-22y+101}{y^2-20}.$$

In order that $abcd$ may be a square, we must have

$$5(y^2-20)(y^2-22y+101)=\text{a square.}$$

This is satisfied by $y=5$. Substitute $z+5$ for y, and we have

$$5(z^2+10z+5)(z^2-12z+16)=\text{a square,}$$

or

$$400+500z-495z^2-10z^3+5z^4=\text{a square.}$$

Equate this expression to $(20+\frac{25}{2}z-\frac{521}{32}z^2)^2$, and we have

$$\left(\frac{521^2}{32^2}-5\right)z=\frac{25\cdot 521}{32}-10,$$

whence $$z=\frac{32\cdot 12705}{266321}=\frac{32\cdot 1155}{24211}=\frac{32\cdot 105}{2201}=\frac{3360}{2201};$$

therefore $y=z+5=\frac{14365}{2201}$; and the resulting values of a, c are large numbers which Euler does not trouble to develop. As a matter of fact,

$$\frac{a}{c}=\frac{55696}{109465205}=\frac{4\cdot 118^2}{5\cdot 4679^2}.$$

It follows that

$$\begin{aligned} f^2M &= 5\cdot 55696+5\cdot 109465205+4\cdot 109465205+4\cdot 55696\\ &= 278480+547326025+437860820+222784\\ &= 985688109; \end{aligned}$$

and, putting $f=9$, we have

$$M=12168989.$$

The four numbers are therefore

$12168989\cdot 278480$, $12168989\cdot 547326025$, $12168989\cdot 437860820$, $12168989\cdot 222784$.

PROBLEM 12. *To find three numbers x, y, z such that the expressions*

$$x^2+y^2+z^2,\quad x^2y^2+x^2z^2+y^2z^2$$

are both squares[1].

In order to satisfy the first condition, we have only to put

$$x=p^2+q^2-r^2,\quad y=2pr,\quad z=2qr,$$

for then $$x^2+y^2+z^2=(p^2+q^2+r^2)^2=P^2,\text{ say.}$$

The second condition requires that

$$x^2y^2+x^2z^2+y^2z^2=Q^2;$$

therefore, since $y^2+z^2=4r^2(p^2+q^2)$,

$$Q^2=4r^2(p^2+q^2)(p^2+q^2-r^2)^2+16p^2q^2r^4,$$

or $$Q^2/4r^2=(p^2+q^2)(p^2+q^2-r^2)^2+4p^2q^2r^2.$$

In order to get rid of the sixth power of p and so make p^4 the highest power of p, suppose that $r=p-nq$ (which introduces no restriction); therefore

$$Q^2/4(p-nq)^2=(p^2+q^2)\{2npq+(1-n^2)q^2\}^2+4p^2q^2(p-nq)^2,$$

or $$Q^2/4q^2(p-nq)^2=(p^2+q^2)\{2np+(1-n^2)q\}^2+4p^2(p-nq)^2.$$

[1] *Acta Acad. Scient. Imp. Petropol.*, 1779, Vol. III. (1782), pp. 30 sqq. = *Commentationes arithmeticae*, II. pp. 457 sqq.

Let the latter expression be denoted by R^2, so that $Q = 2q(p - nq) R$; and

$$R^2 = 4(1 + n^2)p^4 - 4n(1 + n^2)p^3q + (1 + 6n^2 + n^4)p^2q^2 + 4n(1 - n^2)pq^3 + (1 - n^2)^2q^4.$$

This may be made a square in two ways, either (1) by taking advantage of the fact that the last term is a square, or (2) by making the first term, *i.e.* making $1 + n^2$, a square.

(1) Put $R^2 = \{(1 - n^2)q^2 + 2npq + \alpha p^2\}^2$, and make the term in q^2 disappear by choosing α so that $1 + 6n^2 + n^4 = 4n^2 + 2\alpha(1 - n^2)$, or $\alpha = \dfrac{1 + 2n^2 + n^4}{2(1 - n^2)}$; we then have

$$4p^4 - 4np^3q = \frac{(1 + n^2)^3}{4(1 - n^2)^2} p^4 + \frac{2n(1 + n^2)}{1 - n^2} p^3q,$$

whence $$(15 - 35n^2 + 13n^4 - n^6)p = 8n(1 - n^2)(3 - n^2)q;$$

this divides throughout by $3 - n^2$, and

$$\frac{p}{q} = \frac{8n(1 - n^2)}{5 - 10n^2 + n^4}.$$

Let $p = 8n(1 - n^2)$, $q = 5 - 10n^2 + n^4$; then $r = p - nq = n(3 + 2n^2 - n^4)$, while

$$R = (1 - n^2)q^2 + 2npq + \frac{(1 + n^2)^2}{2(1 - n^2)}p^2, \quad Q = 2q(p - nq)R;$$

and x, y, z can be expressed in terms of n.

Ex. 1. Suppose $n = 2$; then

$$p = -48, \quad q = -19, \quad r = -10, \quad R = 7035, \quad Q = 380 \cdot 7035;$$

$x = 2565$, $y = 960$, $z = 380$, or (dividing throughout by 5) $x = 513$, $y = 192$, $z = 76$ (in which case $Q = 106932$, $P = 553$).

Ex. 2. Suppose $n = 3$; then $p = -192$, $q = -4$, $r = -180$, or (dividing by -4)

$$p = 48, \quad q = 1, \quad r = 45, \quad R = 14120, \quad Q = 1270800;$$

$$x = 280, \quad y = 90 \cdot 48, \quad z = 90.$$

Dividing the values of x, y, z by 10, we have

$$x = 28, \quad y = 432, \quad z = 9, \quad \text{and} \quad Q = 12708, \quad P = 433.$$

(2) To make the first term in R^2 a square, suppose $1 + n^2 = m^2$, which is the case whenever $n = (a^2 - b^2)/2ab$.

We have then

$$R^2 = 4m^2p^4 - 4nm^2p^3q + (m^4 + 4n^2)p^2q^2 + 4n(1 - n^2)pq^3 + (1 - n^2)^2q^4.$$

Euler solves this in three ways.

First, he puts $R = 2mp^2 - nmpq + (1 - n^2)q^2$; and from this, by taking $a = 2$, $b = 1$, so that $n = \frac{3}{4}$, $m = \pm\frac{5}{4}$, he obtains the particular solution

$$x = -392, \quad y = 1386, \quad z = -1056,$$

or

$$x = 196, \quad y = 693, \quad z = 528.$$

Secondly, he puts $R = 2mp^2 + 2npq + (1 - n^2)q^2$, and deduces, by the same particular assumptions,

$$x = 936, \quad y = 74, \quad z = 3552,$$

or

$$x = 468, \quad y = 37, \quad z = 1776.$$

Thirdly, he supposes

$$R = 2mp^2 - mnpq + \frac{m^4 + 3n^2}{4m}q^2,$$

where however the last term should apparently be $\dfrac{m^2 + 4n^2}{4m}q^2$.

Euler's son, J. A Euler, gave, in a Supplement to his father's paper, another solution as follows.

We know that

$$(p^2 - 1)^2 + 4p^2 = (p^2 + 1)^2 \text{ and } (q^2 - 1)^2 + 4q^2 = (q^2 + 1)^2.$$

Multiply the first equation by $4q^2$ and the second by $(p^2 + 1)^2$; this gives

$$4q^2(p^2 - 1)^2 + 16p^2q^2 = 4q^2(p^2 + 1)^2$$
$$= (p^2 + 1)^2(q^2 + 1)^2 - (p^2 + 1)^2(q^2 - 1)^2,$$

or

$$(q^2 - 1)^2(p^2 + 1)^2 + 4q^2(p^2 - 1)^2 + 16p^2q^2 = (p^2 + 1)^2(q^2 + 1)^2.$$

Therefore the three numbers

$$(q^2 - 1)(p^2 + 1), \quad 2q(p^2 - 1), \quad 4pq$$

satisfy the first of the conditions.

The sum of the squares of the products of pairs of these numbers must now be a square; after dividing out by $4q^2$, this gives

$$(q^2 - 1)^2(p^4 - 1)^2 + 4p^2(q^2 - 1)^2(p^2 + 1)^2 + 16p^2q^2(p^2 - 1)^2 = \text{a square}.$$

But

$$(p^4 - 1)^2 + 4p^2(p^2 + 1)^2 = (p^2 + 1)^4;$$

therefore $(p^2 + 1)^4(q^2 - 1)^2 + 16p^2q^2(p^2 - 1)^2$ must be a square.

For brevity, let $A^2 = (p^2 + 1)^4$, $B^2 = 16p^2(p^2 - 1)^2$, and

$$A^2(q^2 - 1)^2 + B^2q^2, \text{ or } A^2q^4 + (B^2 - 2A^2)q^2 + A^2,$$

must be a square.

Put

$$A^2q^4 + (B^2 - 2A^2)q^2 + A^2 = (Aq^2 + v)^2,$$

whence

$$q^2 = \frac{A^2 - v^2}{2A^2 - B^2 + 2Av}.$$

Now both the numerator and denominator of this fraction are squares if $v^2 = A^2 - B^2$, for the numerator becomes B^2 and the denominator

$$2A^2 - B^2 + 2A\sqrt{(A^2 - B^2)},$$

which is the square of $A + \sqrt{(A^2 - B^2)}$.

But, putting for A, B their values in terms of p as above, we have

$$A^2 - B^2 = p^8 - 12p^6 + 38p^4 - 12p^2 + 1 = (p^4 - 6p^2 + 1)^2;$$

therefore

$$q = \frac{B}{A + \sqrt{(A^2 - B^2)}} = \frac{4p(p^2 - 1)}{(p^2 + 1)^2 + p^4 - 6p^2 + 1} = \frac{4p(p^2 - 1)}{2p^4 - 4p^2 + 2} = \frac{2p}{p^2 - 1}.$$

Thus $$q^2 - 1 = \frac{6p^2 - p^4 - 1}{(p^2 - 1)^2},$$

and the numbers required will be

$$\frac{(6p^2 - p^4 - 1)(p^2 + 1)}{(p^2 - 1)^2}, \quad 4p, \quad \frac{8p^2}{p^2 - 1},$$

or, if we multiply by $(p^2 - 1)^2$,

$$(6p^2 - p^4 - 1)(p^2 + 1), \quad 4p(p^2 - 1)^2, \quad 8p^2(p^2 - 1).$$

The sum of the squares of these numbers turns out to be $(p^2 + 1)^6$, which is not only a square but a sixth power, while the sum of the squares of the products of pairs is found to be

$$16p^2(p^2 - 1)^2(p^8 - 4p^6 + 22p^4 - 4p^2 + 1)^2,$$

or $$16p^2(p^2 - 1)^2\{(p^2 - 1)^4 + 16p^4\}^2.$$

Ex. Put $p = 2$, and we have

$$x = 5 \cdot 7 = 35, \quad y = 72, \quad z = 96, \quad x^2 + y^2 + z^2 = 125^2 = 5^6,$$
$$x^2y^2 + x^2z^2 + y^2z^2 = 16 \cdot 4 \cdot 9 \cdot 337^2 = 8088^2,$$

the solution being in smaller numbers than Euler's own.

PROBLEM 13. *To find*[1] *three positive integral numbers x, y, z such that*

$$\left.\begin{aligned} x + y + z &= u^2 \\ x^2 + y^2 + z^2 &= v^4 \end{aligned}\right\}.$$

To make $x^2 + y^2 + z^2$ a square, put $x = a^2 + b^2 - c^2$, $y = 2ac$, $z = 2bc$, and we have $x^2 + y^2 + z^2 = (a^2 + b^2 + c^2)^2$.

We have now to make $a^2 + b^2 + c^2$ a square, and we put similarly

$$a = p^2 + q^2 - r^2, \quad b = 2pr, \quad c = 2qr;$$

we have then $$x^2 + y^2 + z^2 = (p^2 + q^2 + r^2)^4.$$

Now let us express x, y, z in terms of p, q, r; this gives

$$x = p^4 + q^4 + r^4 + 2p^2q^2 + 2p^2r^2 - 6q^2r^2,$$
$$y = 4qr(p^2 + q^2 - r^2),$$
$$z = 8pqr^2;$$

[1] *Commentationes arithmeticae*, II. pp. 399–400.

therefore

$$x+y+z=p^4+q^4+r^4+2p^2q^2+2p^2r^2-6q^2r^2+4p^2qr+4q^3r-4qr^3+8pqr^2.$$

(1) Arrange this according to powers of p, and

$$x+y+z=p^4+2(q+r)^2p^2+8pqr^2+q^4+4q^3r-6q^2r^2-4qr^3+r^4.$$

In making this a square, we have to see that p, q, r are all positive, and also $p^2+q^2>r^2$. Also a^2+b^2 must be $>c^2$.

Equate the expression to $\{p^2+(q+r)^2\}^2$, and we have

$$8pqr^2+q^4+4q^3r-6q^2r^2-4qr^3+r^4=(q+r)^4,$$

whence $$8pqr^2=12q^2r^2+8qr^3, \text{ or } p=\tfrac{3}{2}q+r.$$

Therefore $$a=\tfrac{13}{4}q^2+3qr, \quad b=3qr+2r^2, \quad c=2qr,$$

where both the letters q, r may be given any positive values.

Ex. 1. Suppose $q=2$, $r=1$; therefore

$$p=4, \quad a=19, \quad b=8, \quad c=4;$$

accordingly the numbers are

$$x=409, \quad y=152, \quad z=64,$$

and $$x+y+z=625=25^2, \quad x^2+y^2+z^2=194481=441^2=21^4.$$

Ex. 2. Let $q=2$, $r=2$; therefore

$$p=5, \quad a=25, \quad b=20, \quad c=8,$$

and $$x=961, \quad y=400, \quad z=320;$$

therefore $$x+y+z=1681=41^2, \quad x^2+y^2+z^2=1185921=33^4.$$

(2) Arrange the expression for $x+y+z$ according to powers of q; this gives

$$x+y+z=q^4+4q^3r+2q^2(p^2-3r^2)+4qr(p^2+2pr-r^2)+(p^2+r^2)^2.$$

In order that the terms in q^4 and q^3 and the absolute term may vanish, equate the expression to

$$\{q^2+2qr-(p^2+r^2)\}^2,$$

whence we obtain $$q=\frac{2pr(p+r)}{2r^2-p^2}.$$

Ex. Suppose $p=1$, $r=1$; therefore

$$q=4, \quad a=16, \quad b=2, \quad c=8,$$

or (if we divide by 2) $$a=8, \quad b=1, \quad c=4;$$

therefore $$x=49, \quad y=64, \quad z=8;$$

and $$x+y+z=11^2, \quad x^2+y^2+z^2=6561=81^2=9^4.$$

These numbers are no doubt the smallest which satisfy the conditions.

The case of three numbers is thus easier than that of two (see p. 299, note). Euler solves the same problem for four and five numbers, and shows how the method may be extended to six numbers, and so on indefinitely.

PROBLEM 14. *To find three numbers x, y, z, positive and prime to one another, such that both $x+y+z$ and $x^2+y^2+z^2$ are fourth powers*[1].

As in the above problem, put

$$x = a^2 + b^2 - c^2, \quad y = 2ac, \quad z = 2bc,$$

and further
$$a = p^2 + q^2 - r^2, \quad b = 2pr, \quad c = 2qr,$$

and make the expression in p, q, r for $x+y+z$ a square by equating it to $\{p^2+(q+r)^2\}^2$ as before. This gives $p = \frac{3}{2}q + r$; but we have now, in addition, to make $p^2+(q+r)^2$ a square.

Put
$$p^2 + (q+r)^2 = \left\{p + \frac{f(q+r)}{g}\right\}^2;$$

therefore
$$g^2(q+r) = 2fgp + f^2(q+r).$$

Substitute $\frac{3}{2}q + r$ for p, and this becomes

$$(f^2-g^2)(q+r) + fg(3q+2r) = 0,$$

whence
$$\frac{q}{r} = \frac{f^2+2fg-g^2}{g^2-3fg-f^2}.$$

The problem may therefore be solved in this way.

Take
$$q = f^2+2fg-g^2 \text{ and } r = g^2-3fg-f^2,$$

so that $p = \frac{1}{2}(f^2-g^2)$, then find a, b, c, and then again x, y, z, in terms of f, g.

Ex. Let $f=1$, $g=3$; therefore

$$q=-2, \quad r=-1, \quad p=-4,$$

or
$$q=2, \quad r=1, \quad p=4.$$

Thus
$$a=19, \quad b=8, \quad c=4,$$

and
$$x=409, \quad y=152, \quad z=64;$$

so that
$$x+y+z=625=5^4, \quad x^2+y^2+z^2=194481=21^4.$$

To find limits for the values of f, g, change the signs of q, r, putting

$$q=g^2-2fg-f^2, \quad r=f^2+3fg-g^2, \quad p=\tfrac{1}{2}(g^2-f^2).$$

In order that q may be positive,

$$g/f > 1+\sqrt{2} > 2.414\ldots,$$

and, in order that r may be positive,

$$g/f < \tfrac{1}{2}(3+\sqrt{13}) < 3.302\ldots.$$

Suppose *e.g.* that $f=2$, $g=5$; then

$$q=1, \quad r=9, \quad p=\tfrac{21}{2},$$

or in integers
$$q=2, \quad r=18, \quad p=21;$$

hence
$$a=121, \quad b=756, \quad c=72,$$

$$x=580993, \quad y=17424, \quad z=108864,$$

$$x+y+z=707281=29^4, \quad x^2+y^2+z^2=349707832321=769^4.$$

[1] *Commentationes arithmeticae*, II. p. 402.

PROBLEM 15. (Problem in Fermat's note on VI. 13.)

To find a right-angled triangle (in rational numbers) such that either of the sides about the right angle less the area gives a square[1].

Let the perpendiculars be $\frac{2x}{z}$, $\frac{y}{z}$, so that the area is $\frac{xy}{z^2}$; and

$$\left.\begin{array}{ll} \frac{2x}{z}-\frac{xy}{z^2} & \text{or } 2xz-xy \\ \frac{y}{z}-\frac{xy}{z^2} & \text{or } yz-xy \\ \text{as well as } \frac{4x^2+y^2}{z^2} & \text{or } 4x^2+y^2 \end{array}\right\} \text{have to be made squares.}$$

Since the first two expressions are to be squares, their product must be so also; therefore

$$2xyz^2-2x^2yz-xy^2z+x^2y^2=\text{a square}$$
$$=\left(xy-\frac{p}{q}yz\right)^2, \text{ say,}$$

and, after dividing by yz, we have

$$2xz-2x^2-xy=-\frac{2p}{q}xy+\frac{p^2}{q^2}yz,$$

whence
$$z=\frac{2q^2x^2+q^2xy-2pqxy}{2q^2x-p^2y}.$$

Thus
$$2z-y=\frac{4q^2x^2-4pqxy+p^2y^2}{2q^2x-p^2y}=\frac{(2qx-py)^2}{2q^2x-p^2y},$$

$$z-x=\frac{p^2xy+q^2xy-2pqxy}{2q^2x-p^2y}=\frac{xy(p-q)^2}{2q^2x-p^2y};$$

and
$$2xz-xy=\frac{x(2qx-py)^2}{2q^2x-p^2y}=\frac{x^2(2qx-py)^2}{2q^2x^2-p^2xy},$$

$$yz-xy=\frac{xy^2(p-q)^2}{2q^2x-p^2y}=\frac{x^2y^2(p-q)^2}{2q^2x^2-p^2xy}.$$

Therefore the two expressions are squares if $2q^2x^2-p^2xy$ is a square.

Put
$$2q^2x^2-p^2xy=r^2x^2;$$

therefore
$$(2q^2-r^2)x=p^2y, \text{ or } x/y=p^2/(2q^2-r^2).$$

It is sufficient for our solution to know the ratio x/y, since a common denominator z has already been introduced.

Therefore we may put

$$x=p^2, \quad y=2q^2-r^2,$$

[1] *Novi Commentarii Acad. Petrop.*, 1749, Vol. II. (1751), pp. 49 sqq. = *Commentationes arithmeticae*, I. pp. 62–72.

whence $$z - x = \frac{p^2(2q^2 - r^2)(p-q)^2}{p^2 r^2},$$

and $$z = p^2 + \frac{(2q^2 - r^2)(p-q)^2}{r^2}.$$

It only remains to make $4x^2 + y^2$ a square; that is,

$$4p^4 + 4q^4 - 4q^2r^2 + r^4 \text{ must be a square.}$$

A general solution of this equation giving all possible values of p, q, r is impossible. We must therefore be satisfied with particular solutions.

Particular solutions (1) *and* (2).

Put $$4p^4 + 4q^4 - 4q^2r^2 + r^4 = (2p^2 \mp r^2)^2;$$

therefore $$4q^4 - 4q^2r^2 = \mp 4p^2r^2,$$

and $$p^2 = \mp \frac{q^2}{r^2}(q^2 - r^2),$$

that is, either

$$(1)\quad p = \frac{q}{r}\sqrt{(q^2 - r^2)},\quad \text{or}\quad (2)\quad p = \frac{q}{r}\sqrt{(r^2 - q^2)}.$$

(1) Now $p = \frac{q}{r}\sqrt{(q^2 - r^2)}$ is satisfied by $q = c^2 + d^2$, $r = 2cd$, whence

$$p = \frac{(c^2 + d^2)(c^2 - d^2)}{2cd},$$

or we may put

$$p = (c^2 + d^2)(c^2 - d^2),\quad q = 2cd(c^2 + d^2),\quad r = 4c^2d^2,$$

and we thus find values for

$$x = p^2,\quad y = 2q^2 - r^2,\quad \sqrt{(4x^2 + y^2)} = 2p^2 + r^2,\quad z = x + \frac{y(p-q)^2}{r^2}.$$

Ex. 1. Suppose $c = 2$, $d = 1$; then

$$p = 5 \cdot 3 = 15,\quad q = 4 \cdot 5 = 20,\quad r = 4 \cdot 4 = 16,$$

$$x = 225,\quad y = 544,\quad z = 225 + \frac{544 \cdot 25}{256} = \frac{25 \cdot 89}{8} = \frac{2225}{8},$$

$$\sqrt{(4x^2 + y^2)} = 2p^2 + r^2 = 706,$$

and the triangle is

$$\frac{2x}{z} = \frac{144}{89},\quad \frac{y}{z} = \frac{4352}{25 \cdot 89},\quad \frac{\sqrt{(4x^2 + y^2)}}{z} = \frac{5648}{25 \cdot 89}.$$

Ex. 2. If $c = 3$, $d = 1$, we get the triangle

$$\frac{2x}{z} = \frac{32 \cdot 9}{185},\quad \frac{y}{z} = \frac{81 \cdot 41}{25 \cdot 185},\quad \frac{\sqrt{(4x^2 + y^2)}}{z} = \frac{9 \cdot 881}{25 \cdot 185}.$$

And so on.

(2) In this case $p = \frac{q}{r}\sqrt{(r^2 - q^2)}$, and we have to put

$$r = c^2 + d^2, \quad q = 2cd, \quad \text{whence } p = \frac{2cd\,(c^2 - d^2)}{c^2 + d^2},$$

or

$$p = 2cd\,(c^2 - d^2), \quad q = 2cd\,(c^2 + d^2), \quad r = (c^2 + d^2)^2,$$

while

$$x = p^2, \quad y = 2q^2 - r^2, \quad \sqrt{(4x^2 + y^2)} = 2p^2 - r^2, \quad z = x + \frac{y\,(p - q)^2}{r^2}.$$

Here, since $2q^2$ must be $> r^2$,

$$8c^2d^2 > (c^2 + d^2)^2 \text{ and } 2cd\sqrt{2} > c^2 + d^2;$$

therefore $d^2 > (c - d\sqrt{2})^2$, and

$$\textit{either } d > c - d\sqrt{2}, \text{ so that } \frac{d}{c} > \frac{1}{1 + \sqrt{2}},$$

$$\textit{or} \quad d > d\sqrt{2} - c, \text{ so that } \frac{d}{c} < \frac{1}{\sqrt{2} - 1}.$$

If therefore $d = 1$, either $c < \sqrt{2} + 1$ or $c > \sqrt{2} - 1$. The second alternative is satisfied by $c > 1$.

Ex. Let $c = 2$, $d = 1$, and we have

$$p = 4 \cdot 3 = 12, \quad q = 4 \cdot 5 = 20, \quad r = 5 \cdot 5 = 25;$$

therefore

$$x = 144, \quad y = 175, \quad \sqrt{(4x^2 + y^2)} = 337, \quad z = 144 + \frac{175 \cdot 64}{625} = \frac{4048}{25}.$$

The triangle is therefore

$$\frac{2x}{z} = \frac{288 \cdot 25}{4048} = \frac{450}{253}; \quad \frac{y}{z} = \frac{25 \cdot 175}{4048} = \frac{4375}{4048}; \quad \frac{\sqrt{(4x^2 + y^2)}}{z} = \frac{25 \cdot 337}{4048} = \frac{8425}{4048}.$$

Particular solution (3).

Put $$4p^4 + 4q^4 - 4q^2r^2 + r^4 = (2p^2 \pm 2q^2)^2;$$

therefore $$r^4 - 4q^2r^2 = \pm 8p^2q^2, \text{ and } p^2 = \pm \frac{2r^2(r^2 - 4q^2)}{16q^2};$$

therefore $$\text{either } p = \frac{r}{4q}\sqrt{(2r^2 - 8q^2)}, \text{ or } p = \frac{r}{4q}\sqrt{(8q^2 - 2r^2)}.$$

The first value is however useless, since $2q^2 - r^2 > 0$, or $2q^2 > r^2$.

We have therefore $$p = \frac{r}{4q}\sqrt{(8q^2 - 2r^2)},$$

while

$$x = p^2, \quad y = 2q^2 - r^2, \quad \sqrt{(4x^2 + y^2)} = 2p^2 - 2q^2, \text{ and } z = x + \frac{y\,(p - q)^2}{r^2}.$$

Since $8q^2 - 2r^2$ must be a square, put

$$8q^2 - 2r^2 = \left\{\frac{c}{d}(2q + r)\right\}^2;$$

therefore $$4q - 2r = \frac{c^2}{d^2}(2q + r), \text{ or } 4d^2q - 2d^2r = 2c^2q + c^2r,$$

whence $$q = c^2 + 2d^2, \quad r = 4d^2 - 2c^2,$$

$$2q + r = 8d^2, \quad \sqrt{(8q^2 - 2r^2)} = 8cd, \text{ and therefore } p = \frac{4cd(2d^2 - c^2)}{2d^2 + c^2}.$$

Multiplying by $2d^2 + c^2$, we have in integers

$$p = 4cd(2d^2 - c^2), \quad q = (2d^2 + c^2)^2, \quad r = 2(2d^2 - c^2)(2d^2 + c^2),$$

while x, y, z have the values above stated.

Ex. 1. Put $c = 1$, $d = 1$; therefore

$$p = 4, \quad q = 9, \quad r = 6; \quad x = 16, \quad y = 126, \quad \sqrt{(4x^2 + y^2)} = 130,$$

and $$z = 16 + \frac{126 \cdot 25}{36} = \frac{207}{2}.$$

The triangle is therefore

$$\frac{2x}{z} = \frac{64}{207}, \quad \frac{y}{z} = \frac{252}{207}, \quad \frac{\sqrt{(4x^2 + y^2)}}{z} = \frac{260}{207}.$$

This is the triangle in the smallest numbers satisfying the conditions, as Euler proves later.

Ex. 2. Since $2q^2 > r^2$, it follows that $c/d > 2 - \sqrt{2}$; but it does not matter whether $2d^2 > c^2$ or not, since p, q, r may be negative as well as positive.

Put then $d = 2$, $c = 3$; therefore $2d^2 - c^2 = -1$, and $2d^2 + c^2 = 17$.

We then have $\quad p = -24, \quad q = 289, \quad r = -34;$

$$x = 576, \quad y = 2 \cdot 7 \cdot 41 \cdot 17^2, \quad \sqrt{(4x^2 + y^2)} = 2 \cdot 5 \cdot 53 \cdot 313, \quad z = \frac{28118255}{2}.$$

The triangle is therefore

$$\frac{2x}{z} = \frac{2304}{28118255}, \quad \frac{y}{z} = \frac{28 \cdot 41 \cdot 17^2}{28118255}, \quad \frac{\sqrt{(4x^2 + y^2)}}{z} = \frac{4 \cdot 5 \cdot 53 \cdot 313}{28118255}.$$

It is to be observed that in all the above examples it matters not whether c, d are negative; it will only result in the values of p or q or r becoming negative, but the values of x and y will not be thereby changed. Only z will vary, since z may be either

$$x + \frac{y(p - q)^2}{r^2} \text{ or } x + \frac{y(p + q)^2}{r^2}.$$

After remarking that the problem of making

$$4p^4 + 4q^4 - 4q^2r^2 + r^4 \text{ or } 4p^4 + (2q^2 - r^2)^2 \text{ a square}$$

may be solved generally by equating it to

$$\left(2q^2 - r^2 + \frac{2m}{n}p^2\right)^2,$$

Euler passes to his general solution.

General solution.

If $\frac{2x}{z}$, $\frac{y}{z}$ are the perpendicular sides of the triangle, let $x = ab$, $y = a^2 - b^2$; the triangle is then

$$\frac{2ab}{z}, \quad \frac{a^2-b^2}{z}, \quad \frac{a^2+b^2}{z};$$

and the area is

$$\frac{ab(a^2-b^2)}{z^2}.$$

Now we found above, at the beginning of the investigation, that

$$z = \frac{2q^2x^2 + q^2xy - 2pqxy}{2q^2x - p^2y} = x + \frac{xy(p-q)^2}{2q^2x - p^2y},$$

or, since q can be taken positively as well as negatively,

$$z = x + \frac{xy(p \pm q)^2}{2q^2x - p^2y},$$

where $x = ab$, $y = a^2 - b^2$.

And we took

$$2q^2x^2 - p^2xy = r^2x^2,$$

whence

$$z = x + \frac{y(p \pm q)^2}{r^2} = ab + \frac{(a^2-b^2)(p \pm q)^2}{r^2}.$$

We have therefore only to satisfy the equation

$$2q^2x^2 - p^2xy = r^2x^2,$$

or

$$xy = \frac{x^2}{p^2}(2q^2 - r^2);$$

and, since $xy = ab(a^2-b^2)$, *we have to find such numbers for* a, b *that* $ab(a^2-b^2)$ *may be of the form* $2f^2 - g^2$ *or* $(2f^2-g^2)h^2$.

Suppose now that such numbers a, b have been found that

$$ab(a^2-b^2) = (2f^2-g^2)h^2.$$

Then, since $x = ab$,

$$(2f^2-g^2)h^2 = \frac{a^2b^2}{p^2}(2q^2 - r^2),$$

and a natural inference is suggested, namely that

$$\frac{abq}{p} = fh, \quad \frac{abr}{p} = gh.$$

Let now $p = ab$, and accordingly

$$q = fh, \quad r = gh, \quad z = ab + \frac{(a^2-b^2)(ab \pm fh)^2}{g^2h^2};$$

the triangle is then

$$\frac{2ab}{z} = \frac{2abg^2h^2}{abg^2h^2 + (a^2-b^2)(ab \pm fh)^2},$$

$$\frac{a^2-b^2}{z} = \frac{(a^2-b^2)g^2h^2}{abg^2h^2 + (a^2-b^2)(ab \pm fh)^2},$$

$$\frac{a^2+b^2}{z} = \frac{(a^2+b^2)g^2h^2}{abg^2h^2 + (a^2-b^2)(ab \pm fh)^2}.$$

Also from any particular values of a, b any number of triangles can be derived satisfying the conditions.

For, if $p = ab$, and

$$ab(a^2 - b^2) = (2f^2 - g^2)h^2,$$

we have

$$(2f^2 - g^2)h^2 = 2q^2 - r^2,$$

or

$$2(f^2h^2 - q^2) = g^2h^2 - r^2.$$

Put $2(fh + q) = \frac{m}{n}(gh + r)$, and $fh - q = \frac{n}{m}(gh - r)$;

therefore

$$q = \frac{2mngh - (2n^2 + m^2)fh}{2n^2 - m^2},$$

$$r = \frac{(2n^2 + m^2)gh - 4mnfh}{2n^2 - m^2};$$

or, in integers,

$$p = (2n^2 - m^2)ab,$$
$$q = 2mngh - (2n^2 + m^2)fh,$$
$$r = (2n^2 + m^2)gh - 4mnfh,$$

while

$$z = \frac{abr^2 + (a^2 - b^2)(p \pm q)^2}{r^2}.$$

Thus the triangle $\left(\frac{2ab}{z}, \frac{a^2 - b^2}{z}, \frac{a^2 + b^2}{z}\right)$ is known.

Lastly, to find suitable values for a, b, Euler writes down all the numbers from 1 to 200 which are of the form $2t^2 - u^2$, including all the squares arising from the supposition that $u = t$, and all the doubles of squares corresponding to $u = 0$. Inspection shows that the table contains (within the limits) all the prime numbers of the form $8m \pm 1$, and no other primes, the doubles of the primes, the products of the primes into all squares and into one another, and the doubles of those products.

Now, since the product $a . b(a + b)(a - b)$ is to be of the form $2t^2 - u^2$, and the factors a, b, $a + b$, $a - b$ are either prime to one another or at the most have 2 as a common divisor, while 2 is itself contained in the form $2t^2 - u^2$, the several factors must all be of that form, in which case the product will be of that form.

We have therefore first to take some value of b in the table and then see whether there are in the table three other numbers $a - b$, a, $a + b$ differing by b. Euler gives a second table showing values of a corresponding to values 1, 7, 8, 9, 16, 17 etc. of b.

The values of a in the table corresponding to $b = 1$ are 8, 17, 63, 72, 127.

Ex. 1. Take $b = 1$, $a = 8$; therefore

$$ab = 8, \quad a^2 - b^2 = 63, \quad ab(a^2 - b^2) = 8 . 9 . 7 = 4 . 9 . 14,$$

and $4 . 9 . 14 = h^2(2f^2 - g^2)$, so that $h = 6$, $2f^2 - g^2 = 14$, and accordingly $f = 3$, $g = 2$.

We have therefore in this case

$$p = 8(2n^2 - m^2), \quad q = 24mn - 18(2n^2 + m^2), \quad r = 12(2n^2 + m^2) - 72mn;$$

or, dividing by 2,

$$p = 8n^2 - 4m^2, \quad q = 12mn - 18n^2 - 9m^2, \quad r = 12n^2 + 6m^2 - 36mn,$$

whence $p + q = 12mn - 10n^2 - 13m^2, \quad -p + q = 12mn - 26n^2 - 5m^2,$

while
$$z = 8 + \frac{63(p \pm q)^2}{r^2}.$$

Thus there are any number of values of z from which triangles may be obtained satisfying the conditions.

The simplest value is found by putting $m = 1$, $n = 0$, whence

$$r = 6, \quad p + q = -13, \quad p - q = 5,$$

and either
$$z = 8 + \tfrac{7}{4} \cdot 25 = \tfrac{207}{4},$$
or
$$z = 8 + \tfrac{7}{4} \cdot 169 = \tfrac{1215}{4}.$$

The first value gives the triangle in smallest numbers above found (p. 367),

$$\frac{2ab}{z} = \frac{64}{207}, \quad \frac{a^2 - b^2}{z} = \frac{252}{207}, \quad \frac{a^2 + b^2}{z} = \frac{260}{207}.$$

Substituting 1215 for 207, we have the sides of the triangle corresponding to the second value of z.

The particular triangles are also directly obtained from the values of a, b, f, g, h without bringing in m, n; for

$$z = ab + \frac{(a^2 - b^2)(ab \pm fh)^2}{g^2h^2},$$

that is,
$$z = 8 + \frac{63(8 \pm 18)^2}{12^2} = \frac{207}{4} \text{ or } \frac{1215}{4}.$$

Ex. 2. Take $b = 41$, $a = 112$; therefore

$$ab = 7 \cdot 16 \cdot 41, \quad a^2 - b^2 = 71 \cdot 9 \cdot 17,$$

and
$$ab(a^2 - b^2) = 16 \cdot 9 \cdot 7 \cdot 17 \cdot 41 \cdot 71 = (2f^2 - g^2)h^2,$$

whence $h = 12$, and $7 \cdot 17 \cdot 41 \cdot 71 = 2f^2 - g^2$.

The simplest solution is $f = 417$, $g = 37$.

Thus
$$z = ab + \frac{(a^2 - b^2)(ab \pm fh)^2}{g^2h^2}$$

is easily found, and consequently the triangle

$$\frac{2ab}{z}, \quad \frac{a^2 - b^2}{z}, \quad \frac{a^2 + b^2}{z}.$$

[Euler finds values for f, g by using the formulae

$$(2\alpha^2 - \beta^2)(2\gamma^2 - \delta^2) = (2\alpha\gamma \pm \beta\delta)^2 - 2(\beta\gamma \pm \alpha\delta)^2$$

and
$$x^2 - 2y^2 = 2(x \pm y)^2 - (x \pm 2y)^2.$$

He does not actually give the steps leading up to the particular solution $f=417$, $g=37$, but it can be obtained thus.

Since $7=2.2^2-1$ and $17=2.3^2-1$, we have

$$7.17=(2.2.3+1.1)^2-2(3.1+2.1)^2$$
$$=13^2-2.5^2=2(13-5)^2-(13-2.5)^2=2.8^2-3^2.$$

Again, since $41=2.5^2-3^2$ and $71=2.6^2-1^2$, it follows that

$$41.71=(2.5.6-3.1)^2-2(3.6-5.1)^2$$
$$=57^2-2.13^2=2(57-13)^2-(57-2.13)^2=2.44^2-31^2.$$

Therefore, by multiplication,

$$7.17.41.71=(2.8^2-3^2)(2.44^2-31^2)=(2.8.44+3.31)^2-2(8.31+3.44)^2$$
$$=797^2-2.380^2=2(797-380)^2-(797-2.380)^2=2.417^2-37^2.]$$

PROBLEMS 16. "De problematibus indeterminatis, quae videntur plus quam determinata[1]."

We have seen that by means of certain "Porisms" stated without proof Diophantus is able to obtain relations between three numbers x, y, z which have the effect that, when they are satisfied, a quite appreciable number of symmetrical expressions in x, y, z are automatically (as it were) made squares.

It is clear therefore, says Euler, that, if a general method of finding "porisms" of this kind can be discovered, the whole subject of Diophantine analysis will be appreciably advanced. Accordingly he proceeds to discuss such a method.

The method depends on a Lemma the truth of which is evident.

Lemma. *If values have been found for the letters z, y, x etc. which satisfy the equation $W=0$, where W is any function of those letters, and P, Q, R etc. are other functions of the letters such that $P\pm W$, $Q\pm W$, $R\pm W$ etc. are squares, then, if the values of z, y, x etc. are taken which satisfy $W=0$, the resulting values of P, Q, R etc. will also be made squares.*

Cor. P, Q, R etc. will similarly be made squares if $P+\alpha W$, $Q+\beta W$, $R+\gamma W$ etc. or, more generally, if

$$P+\alpha W+\zeta W^2, \quad Q+\beta W+\eta W^2, \quad R+\gamma W+\theta W^2 \text{ etc.}$$

are squares.

Conversely, If such values for z, y, x etc. have been assigned as will satisfy $W=0$, all formulae such as $P^2+\alpha W$, $Q^2+\beta W$, $R^2+\gamma W$ etc. will at the same time be made squares.

[1] *Novi Commentarii Acad. Petropol.*, 1756–57, VI. (1761), pp. 85 sqq. = *Commentationes arithmeticae*, I. pp. 245–259.

And, as the number of such formulae is subject to no limit, it is clear that an unlimited number of conditions can be prescribed which are all satisfied provided that the one condition $W = 0$ has been satisfied.

The same Lemma can be extended to the case of cubes or any higher powers; for, if $W = 0$ has been satisfied by certain values, all expressions of the form $P^3 + \alpha W$ will thereby be made cubes, all expressions of the form $P^4 + \alpha W$ will be made fourth powers, and so on.

While it is plain that, if values for z, y, x etc. are found which satisfy the condition $W = 0$, all the expressions $P^2 + \alpha W$, $Q^2 + \beta W$, $R^2 + \gamma W$ etc. will be made squares by the same values of x, y, z, the difficulty will be, when a number of expressions $P^2 + \alpha W$, $Q^2 + \beta W$ etc. are given which are capable of being made squares in this way, to identify and separate the expression W the equating of which to zero will make the rest of the several expressions automatically squares. It would indeed be easy so to hide away the composition of the expressions as to make this separation itself a most arduous problem. On the other hand it is easy and interesting to begin with $W = 0$, and then investigate the simpler formulae which can by this means be made squares. Before proceeding to the particular cases, Euler observes further that it is convenient to take for W an expression in which z, y, x etc. enter symmetrically and can be interchanged; for then, if P^2 is such a square that $P^2 + \alpha W$ is a square, and z, y, x etc. are interchanged so as to turn P^2 into Q^2, R^2 etc., $Q^2 + \alpha W$, $R^2 + \alpha W$ etc. will also be squares. Also, since solutions in rational numbers are required, z, y, x etc. should not enter in any higher power than the second into the expression W. Euler begins with expressions containing two unknowns z, y only.

Problem (1). *Given* $W = y + z - a = 0$, *to find the more simple formulae which by means of this equation can be made squares.*

When the equation $y + z - a = 0$ is satisfied, it is clear that the general formula $P^2 + M(-a + y + z)$ will become a square whatever quantities are put for P and M. Accordingly Euler, by giving P, M various values, obtains without difficulty 44 different expressions which become squares when $y + z - a = 0$.

He supposes $M = 2,\ -2,\ 2n,\ -y,\ -z-y,\ y+z+a,\ n(y+z+a)$, $(y+z+a)(y-z+a)(z-y+a)$, and 3 and $n^2 - 1$ times the last expression respectively, and with each of these assumptions he combines one or more forms for P. I need only quote a few expressions which are thus made squares, *e.g.*

$$\left.\begin{aligned}(y-1)^2 + 2(-a+y+z) &= y^2 + 2z + 1 - 2a\\ (z-1)^2 + 2(-a+y+z) &= z^2 + 2y + 1 - 2a\end{aligned}\right\},$$

$$\left.\begin{aligned}(y-z+1)^2-2(-a+y+z)&=(y-z)^2-4z+1+2a\\(z-y+1)^2-2(-a+y+z)&=(y-z)^2-4y+1+2a\end{aligned}\right\},$$

$$(y-n)^2+2n(-a+y+z)=y^2+2nz+n^2-2na,$$

$$(y-z-n)^2+2n(-a+y+z)=(y-z)^2+4nz+n^2-2na,$$

$$y^2-y(-a+y+z)=-yz+ay,$$

$$(y+z)^2-(y+z)(-a+y+z)=ay+az,$$

$$(y+z-a)^2-(y+z)(-a+y+z)=a^2-ay-az,$$

$$(yz-1)^2+(y+z+a)(-a+y+z)=y^2z^2+y^2+z^2+1-a^2,$$

$$(yz-n)^2+n(y+z+a)(-a+y+z)=y^2z^2+ny^2+nz^2+n^2-na^2,$$

$$(y^2+z^2+a^2)^2+(y+z+a)(y-z+a)(z-y+a)(-a+y+z)=4(y^2z^2+a^2y^2+a^2z^2),$$

and so on. Wherever a new expression can be got by interchanging z and y, this may be done.

Taking the more particular case of $W=y+z-1=0$, Euler obtains the following expressions which are thereby made squares,

$$y^2+4z,\quad y^2-y+z,\quad y+z,\quad y-yz,$$
$$z^2+4y,\quad z^2-z+y,\quad z-yz,$$
$$y^2z^2+y^2+z^2,\quad 2y^2+2z^2-1,$$

which indeed are easily seen to reduce to squares if we put $y+z=1$ or $y=1-z$.

The fact that $y^2z^2+y^2+z^2$ is a square if $y=1-z$ or, more generally, if $y=\pm1\pm z$, is included in the Porism in Dioph. v. 5. Similarly

$$y^2z^2+a^2y^2+a^2z^2$$

is made a square if we put $y=\pm a\pm z$.

The last expression but one in the first of the above lists, namely $y^2z^2+ny^2+nz^2+n^2-na^2$, becomes a square whatever value n has. If $a=1$, it becomes

$$y^2z^2+ny^2+nz^2+n^2-n$$

or

$$(y^2+n)(z^2+n)-n.$$

That this is a square when $z=y\pm1$ is part of Diophantus' assumption in v. 4 (see p. 104 above).

Euler's Problems (2) and (3) similarly show how to find a number of formulae which are all made squares by values of y, z satisfying the equations $W=yz-a(y+z)+b=0$ and $W=y^2+z^2-2nyz-a=0$.

He then passes to the cases where there are three unknowns.

Problem (4). *Given $W=x+y+z-a=0$, to find the more noteworthy formulae which can be made squares by satisfying this equation.*

In this case the general expression $r^2+M(x+y+z-a)$ becomes a square.

Put $M=2n$ and $P=$ one of the expressions $x-n, y-n, z-n$, or one of the expressions $y+z-n, z+x-n, x+y-n$.

These assumptions make the following expressions squares:

$z^2+2n(x+y)+n^2-2na$, and the two other similar expressions,

$(y+z)^2+2nx+n^2-2na$, " " "

If $M=2nyz$, $P=yz-ny-nz$, and so on,

$$y^2z^2+2nxyz+n^2y^2+n^2z^2+2n(n-a)yz$$

and the two other similar expressions are squares.

If $M=-(a+x+y+z)$, $P=y+z-x$ and corresponding expressions,

$$\left.\begin{array}{l} a^2-4xy-4xz \\ a^2-4yz-4yx \\ a^2-4zx-4zy \end{array}\right\} \text{are all squares.}$$

In particular, if $n=2a$, $a=\frac{1}{4}$, the following six expressions are made squares by putting $x+y+z=\frac{1}{4}$:

$$\begin{array}{ll} x^2+y+z, & (y+z)^2+x, \\ y^2+z+x, & (z+x)^2+y, \\ z^2+x+y, & (x+y)^2+z. \end{array}$$

If $a=2$, we make the expressions

$$\left.\begin{array}{l} 1-xy-xz \\ 1-yz-yx \\ 1-zx-xy \end{array}\right\}$$

all squares by putting $x+y+z=2$.

Problem (5) finds expressions which are made squares if

$$W=yz+zx+xy-a(x+y+z)+b=0$$

is satisfied.

Problem (6). *Given* $W=x^2+y^2+z^2-2yz-2zx-2xy-a=0$, *to find the more simple formulae which can be made squares by means of solving that equation.*

Here the general formula will be

$$P^2+M(x^2+y^2+z^2-2yz-2zx-2xy-a).$$

If $M=-1$, $P=x+y+z$,

$$4yz+4zx+4xy+a=\text{a square.}$$

If $M=-1$, $P=y+z-x$, etc.,

$$\left.\begin{array}{l} 4yz+a \\ 4zx+a \\ 4xy+a \end{array}\right\} \text{are squares.}$$

If $M=-1$, $P=y-z$, etc.,

$$\left.\begin{array}{l} a+2(y+z)x-x^2 \\ a+2(z+x)y-y^2 \\ a+2(x+y)z-z^2 \end{array}\right\} \text{are squares.}$$

In the particular case where $a = 4n$, so that

$$x^2 + y^2 + z^2 = 2yz + 2zx + 2xy + 4n,$$

$$\left.\begin{array}{r} yz + n \\ zx + n \\ xy + n \\ yz + zx + xy + n \end{array}\right\} \text{are all squares;}$$

or our formula gives the means of solving the elegant Diophantine problem:

Given any number n, to find three numbers such that the product of any pair added to n gives a square, and also the sum of the products of the pairs added to n gives a square.

By solving the equation

$$W = x^2 + y^2 + z^2 - 2yz - 2zx - 2xy - 4n = 0,$$

we obtain
$$z = x + y \pm 2\sqrt{(xy + n)}.$$

We assume, therefore, such numbers for x, y as will make $xy + n$ a square; suppose $xy + n = u^2$, and we then have two values for z, namely $z = x + y \pm 2u$, each of which along with x, y will satisfy the conditions.

In fact, if $z = x + y \pm 2u$, while $u = \sqrt{(xy + n)}$,

$$\pm\sqrt{(xz + n)} = \tfrac{1}{2}(x + z - y) = x \pm u,$$
$$\pm\sqrt{(yz + n)} = \tfrac{1}{2}(y + z - x) = y \pm u,$$
$$\pm\sqrt{(yz + zx + xy + n)} = \tfrac{1}{2}(x + y + z) = x + y \pm u.$$

(Cf. Euler's solution of Dioph. III. 10, p. 160 above.)

Problem (7). *Given*

$$W = x^2 + y^2 + z^2 - 2yz - 2zx - 2xy - 2a(x + y + z) - b = 0,$$

to find the more noteworthy expressions which can be made squares by satisfying this equation.

The general expression here is

$$P^2 + M\{x^2 + y^2 + z^2 - 2yz - 2zx - 2xy - 2a(x + y + z) - b\}.$$

If $M = -1$, $P = x + y + z + a$, we have

(a) $4yz + 4zx + 4xy + 4a(x + y + z) + a^2 + b =$ a square.

If $M = -1$, $P = x + y + z - a$,

(b) $4yz + 4zx + 4xy + a^2 + b =$ a square.

If $M = -1$, $P = y + z - x + a$, etc.,

$$(c)\quad \left.\begin{array}{r} 4yz + 4a(y + z) + a^2 + b \\ 4zx + 4a(z + x) + a^2 + b \\ 4xy + 4a(x + y) + a^2 + b \end{array}\right\} \text{are all squares.}$$

If $M=-1$, $P=y+z-x-a$, etc.,

$$(d)\quad \left.\begin{array}{l} 4yz+4ax+a^2+b \\ 4zx+4ay+a^2+b \\ 4xy+4az+a^2+b \end{array}\right\} \text{ are all squares.}$$

Cor. 1. In order to solve the problem represented by (c), equate the expression $4xy+4a(x+y)+a^2+b$ to a square u^2, whence

$$4(x+a)(y+a)=u^2-b+3a^2,$$

or

$$(x+a)(y+a)=\tfrac{1}{4}(u^2-b+3a^2);$$

x and y are then determined by splitting $\frac{1}{4}(u^2-b+3a^2)$ into two factors and equating $x+a$, $y+a$ to these factors respectively. Next, solving, for z, the equation

$$x^2+y^2+z^2-2yz-2zx-2xy-2a(x+y+z)-b=0,$$

we find, since $4xy+4a(x+y)+a^2+b=u^2$, that

$$z=x+y+a\pm u.$$

Cor. 2. If $b=-a^2$, then, by solving the equation

$$x^2+y^2+z^2=2yz+2zx+2xy+2a(x+y+z)-a^2,$$

we make all the following formulae severally squares,

$$\begin{array}{cc} yz+a(y+z), & yz+ax, \\ zx+a(z+x), & zx+ay, \\ xy+a(x+y), & xy+az, \end{array}$$

$$yz+zx+xy,$$

$$yz+zx+xy+a(x+y+z),$$

by assuming

$$z=x+y+a\pm 2\sqrt{\{xy+a(x+y)\}}=x+y+a\pm 2u,$$

where $(x+a)(y+a)$ is put equal to u^2+a^2.

An interesting case of this last problem is that in which $a=1$; and from this case we can deduce a solution of a new problem in which the corresponding expressions with x^2, y^2, z^2 in place of x, y, z are all squares. The problem is

To find three square numbers such that (1) *the product of any two added to the sum of those two,* (2) *the product of any two added to the third,* (3) *the sum of the products of pairs,* (4) *the sum of the products of pairs added to the sum of the numbers themselves, all give squares.*

We have to find values of x^2, y^2, z^2 which will make all the following expressions squares,

$$\begin{array}{cc} y^2z^2+y^2+z^2, & y^2z^2+x^2, \\ z^2x^2+z^2+x^2, & z^2x^2+y^2, \\ x^2y^2+x^2+y^2, & x^2y^2+z^2, \end{array}$$

$$y^2z^2+z^2x^2+x^2y^2,$$

$$y^2z^2+z^2x^2+x^2y^2+x^2+y^2+z^2.$$

As we have seen, all these will be squares if

$$z^2 = x^2 + y^2 + 1 \pm 2\sqrt{(x^2y^2 + x^2 + y^2)}.$$

We have also seen (Problem (1) above) that $x^2y^2 + x^2 + y^2$ becomes a square if only $y = x + 1$. Put then $y = x + 1$, when we have

$$z^2 = 2x^2 + 2x + 2 \pm 2\sqrt{(x^4 + 2x^3 + 3x^2 + 2x + 1)};$$

that is,

$$z^2 = 4(x^2 + x + 1).$$

It only remains to make $x^2 + x + 1$ a square. Equate this to $(-x+t)^2$, and we have

$$x = \frac{t^2 - 1}{2t + 1}, \text{ and } \sqrt{(x^2 + x + 1)} = \frac{t^2 + t + 1}{2t + 1},$$

whence

$$z = 2\sqrt{(x^2 + x + 1)} = \frac{2(t^2 + t + 1)}{2t + 1}.$$

Therefore the roots of the required squares are

$$x = \frac{t^2 - 1}{2t + 1}, \; y = \frac{t^2 + 2t}{2t + 1}, \; z = \frac{2t^2 + 2t + 2}{2t + 1}.$$

Or, putting $t = (r - q)/2q$, the values become

$$x = \frac{3q^2 + 2qr - r^2}{4qr}, \; y = \frac{r^2 + 2qr - 3q^2}{4qr}, \; z = \frac{r^2 + 3q^2}{2qr}.$$

Let $q = 1$, $r = 2$, and we have $x = \frac{3}{8}$, $y = \frac{5}{8}$, $z = \frac{7}{4}$; or, if we put $t = 2$ in the values expressed in terms of t, the values are $x = \frac{3}{5}$, $y = \frac{8}{5}$, $z = \frac{14}{5}$.

PROBLEM 17. *To find two fourth powers A^4, B^4 such that their sum is equal to the sum of two other fourth powers*[1].

In other words, to solve the equation $A^4 + B^4 = C^4 + D^4$, or (what is the same thing) $A^4 - D^4 = C^4 - B^4$.

It is proved, says Euler, that the sum of two fourth powers cannot be a fourth power, and it is confidently affirmed that the sum of *three* fourth powers cannot be a fourth power. But the equation $A^4 + B^4 - C^4 = D^4$ is not impossible.

First solution.

Suppose $A = p + q$, $D = p - q$, $C = r + s$, $B = r - s$;

thus the equation

$$A^4 - D^4 = C^4 - B^4$$

becomes

$$pq(p^2 + q^2) = rs(r^2 + s^2).$$

Put $p = ax$, $q = by$, $r = kx$ and $s = y$, and we obtain

$$ab(a^2x^2 + b^2y^2) = k(k^2x^2 + y^2);$$

[1] *Novi Commentarii Acad. Petropol.*, 1772, Vol. XVII. (1773), pp. 64 sqq. = *Commentationes arithmeticae*, I. pp. 473–6; *Mémoires de l'Acad. Imp. de St Pétersbourg*, XI. (1830), pp. 49 sq. = *Comment. arithm.*, II. pp. 450–6.

therefore $\dfrac{y^2}{x^2} = \dfrac{k^3 - a^3b}{ab^3 - k}$, which fraction has therefore to be made a square.

One obvious case is obtained by putting $k = ab$, for then

$$\frac{y^2}{x^2} = \frac{a^3b(b^2-1)}{ab(b^2-1)} = a^2,$$

whence $y = a$, $x = 1$, so that $p = a$, $q = ab$, $r = ab$, $s = a$, and the result is only the obvious case where $p = s$, $q = r$.

Following up this case, however, let us put $k = ab(1+z)$.

We then have

$$\frac{y^2}{x^2} = \frac{a^3b\{(b^2-1) + 3b^2z + 3b^2z^2 + b^2z^3\}}{ab(b^2-1-z)} = a^2\frac{b^2 - 1 + 3b^2z + 3b^2z^2 + b^2z^3}{b^2-1-z};$$

therefore, multiplying numerator and denominator by $b^2 - 1 - z$ and extracting the square root, we obtain

$$\frac{y}{x} = \frac{a\sqrt{\{(b^2-1)^2 + (3b^2-1)(b^2-1)z + 3b^2(b^2-2)z^2 + b^2(b^2-4)z^3 - b^2z^4\}}}{b^2-1-z}.$$

To make the expression under the radical a square, equate it to

$$\{(b^2-1) + fz + gz^2\}^2,$$

and assume f, g such that the terms in z, z^2 vanish.

In order that the term in z may vanish, $f = \frac{1}{2}(3b^2-1)$, and, in order that the term in z^2 may disappear,

$$3b^2(b^2-2) = 2(b^2-1)g + f^2 = 2(b^2-1)g + \tfrac{1}{4}(9b^4 - 6b^2 + 1),$$

whence
$$g = \frac{3b^4 - 18b^2 - 1}{8(b^2-1)}.$$

The equation to be solved is then reduced to

$$b^2(b^2-4) - 2fg = (g^2 + b^2)z,$$

or
$$z = \frac{b^2(b^2-4) - 2fg}{b^2 + g^2}.$$

Now b can be chosen arbitrarily; and, when we have chosen it and thence determined z, we can put

$$x = b^2 - 1 - z, \quad y = a(b^2 - 1 + fz + gz^2),$$

and accordingly

$$p = a(b^2-1-z), \qquad r = ab(1+z)(b^2-1-z),$$
$$q = ab(b^2-1+fz+gz^2), \quad s = a(b^2-1+fz+gz^2),$$

where we may also divide out by a.

If x, y have a common factor, we may suppose this eliminated before p, q, r, s are determined.

Ex. 1. Let $b=2$ (for b cannot be 1, since then g would be ∞).

Therefore $$f=\tfrac{11}{2},\quad g=-\tfrac{25}{24},\quad z=\tfrac{6600}{2929}.$$

As a does not enter into the calculation, we may write 1 for it; therefore

$$x=3-\frac{6600}{2929}=\frac{2187}{2929},\qquad y=3+\frac{11}{2}\cdot\frac{6600}{2929}-\frac{25}{24}\cdot\left(\frac{6600}{2929}\right)^2$$

$$=3+\frac{55407\cdot 1100}{2929^2}=\frac{3\cdot 28894941}{2929^2}.$$

But the ratio $x:y$ is what we want, and

$$\frac{y}{x}=\frac{3\cdot 28894941}{2187\cdot 2929}=\frac{28894941}{2929\cdot 729}=\frac{3210549}{2929\cdot 81}=\frac{1070183}{27\cdot 2929},$$

so that we may put

$$x=79083,\quad y=1070183.$$

Further $$k=2(1+z)=\frac{2\cdot 9529}{2929}=\frac{19058}{2929}.$$

Therefore

$$p=79083,\qquad r=27\cdot 19058=514566,$$
$$q=2\cdot 1070183=2140366,\quad s=1070183.$$

Consequently

$$A=p+q=2219449,\quad C=r+s=1584749,$$
$$B=r-s=-555617,\quad D=p-q=-2061283,$$

and $A^4+B^4=C^4+D^4$.

Ex. 2. Let $b=3$; therefore $f=13$, $g=\tfrac{5}{4}$, $z=\tfrac{200}{169}$;

$$k=3(1+z)=\frac{3\cdot 369}{169}=\frac{1107}{169}=\frac{27\cdot 41}{169};$$

further $$x=8-\frac{200}{169}=\frac{8\cdot 144}{169},$$

$$y=8+\frac{200}{169}\left(13+\frac{5}{4}\cdot\frac{200}{169}\right)=8+\frac{200}{169}\cdot\frac{2447}{169}=\frac{8\cdot 89736}{169^2}.$$

Therefore $$\frac{x}{y}=\frac{8\cdot 144\cdot 169}{8\cdot 89736}=\frac{6\cdot 169}{3739},$$

and we may put $$x=1014,\quad y=3739.$$

Accordingly $$p=1014,\quad r=\frac{27\cdot 41}{169}\cdot 1014=6642,$$

$$q=11217,\quad s=3739,$$

and therefore $$A=12231,\quad C=10381,$$

$$B=2903,\quad D=-10203,$$

and again $A^4+B^4=C^4+D^4$.

Another solution in smaller numbers.

In the second of the papers quoted Euler says that, while investigating quite different matters, he accidentally came across four much smaller numbers satisfying the conditions, namely,

$$A = 542, \quad B = 103, \quad C = 359, \quad D = 514,$$

which are such that $A^4 + B^4 = C^4 + D^4$.

He then develops two methods of analysis leading to this particular solution; but, while they illustrate the extraordinary ingenuity which he brought to bear on such problems, they are perhaps of less general interest than the above.

INDEX.

[The references are to pages.]

I. GREEK.

II. ENGLISH.

CATALOG OF DOVER BOOKS

BOOKS EXPLAINING SCIENCE AND MATHEMATICS

General

WHAT IS SCIENCE?, Norman Campbell. This excellent introduction explains scientific method, role of mathematics, types of scientific laws. Contents: 2 aspects of science, science & nature, laws of science, discovery of laws, explanation of laws, measurement & numerical laws, applications of science. 192pp. 5⅜ x 8. S43 Paperbound **$1.25**

THE COMMON SENSE OF THE EXACT SCIENCES, W. K. Clifford. Introduction by James Newman, edited by Karl Pearson. For 70 years this has been a guide to classical scientific and mathematical thought. Explains with unusual clarity basic concepts, such as extension of meaning of symbols, characteristics of surface boundaries, properties of plane figures, vectors, Cartesian method of determining position, etc. Long preface by Bertrand Russell. Bibliography of Clifford. Corrected, 130 diagrams redrawn. 249pp. 5⅜ x 8. T61 Paperbound **$1.60**

SCIENCE THEORY AND MAN, Erwin Schrödinger. This is a complete and unabridged reissue of SCIENCE AND THE HUMAN TEMPERAMENT plus an additional essay: "What is an Elementary Particle?" Nobel laureate Schrödinger discusses such topics as nature of scientific method, the nature of science, chance and determinism, science and society, conceptual models for physical entities, elementary particles and wave mechanics. Presentation is popular and may be followed by most people with little or no scientific training. "Fine practical preparation for a time when laws of nature, human institutions . . . are undergoing a critical examination without parallel," Waldemar Kaempffert, N. Y. TIMES. 192pp. 5⅜ x 8. T428 Paperbound **$1.35**

FADS AND FALLACIES IN THE NAME OF SCIENCE, Martin Gardner. Examines various cults, quack systems, frauds, delusions which at various times have masqueraded as science. Accounts of hollow-earth fanatics like Symmes; Velikovsky and wandering planets; Hoerbiger; Bellamy and the theory of multiple moons; Charles Fort; dowsing, pseudoscientific methods for finding water, ores, oil. Sections on naturopathy, iridiagnosis, zone therapy, food fads, etc. Analytical accounts of Wilhelm Reich and orgone sex energy; L. Ron Hubbard and Dianetics; A. Korzybski and General Semantics; many others. Brought up to date to include Bridey Murphy, others. Not just a collection of anecdotes, but a fair, reasoned appraisal of eccentric theory. Formerly titled IN THE NAME OF SCIENCE. Preface. Index. x + 384pp. 5⅜ x 8. T394 Paperbound **$1.50**

A DOVER SCIENCE SAMPLER, edited by George Barkin. 64-page book, sturdily bound, containing excerpts from over 20 Dover books, explaining science. Edwin Hubble, George Sarton, Ernst Mach, A. d'Abro, Galileo, Newton, others, discussing island universes, scientific truth, biological phenomena, stability in bridges, etc. Copies limited; no more than 1 to a customer. FREE

POPULAR SCIENTIFIC LECTURES, Hermann von Helmholtz. Helmholtz was a superb expositor as well as a scientist of genius in many areas. The seven essays in this volume are models of clarity, and even today they rank among the best general descriptions of their subjects ever written. "The Physiological Causes of Harmony in Music" was the first significant physiological explanation of musical consonance and dissonance. Two essays, "On the Interaction of Natural Forces" and "On the Conservation of Force," were of great importance in the history of science, for they firmly established the principle of the conservation of energy. Other lectures include "On the Relation of Optics to Painting," "On Recent Progress in the Theory of Vision," "On Goethe's Scientific Researches," and "On the Origin and Significance of Geometrical Axioms." Selected and edited with an introduction by Professor Morris Kline. xii + 286pp. 5⅜ x 8½. T799 Paperbound **$1.45**

BOOKS EXPLAINING SCIENCE AND MATHEMATICS

Physics

CONCERNING THE NATURE OF THINGS, Sir William Bragg. Christmas lectures delivered at the Royal Society by Nobel laureate. Why a spinning ball travels in a curved track; how uranium is transmuted to lead, etc. Partial contents: atoms, gases, liquids, crystals, metals, etc. No scientific background needed; wonderful for intelligent child. 32pp. of photos, 57 figures. xii + 232pp. 5⅜ x 8. T31 Paperbound **$1.35**

THE RESTLESS UNIVERSE, Max Born. New enlarged version of this remarkably readable account by a Nobel laureate. Moving from sub-atomic particles to universe, the author explains in very simple terms the latest theories of wave mechanics. Partial contents: air and its relatives, electrons & ions, waves & particles, electronic structure of the atom, nuclear physics. Nearly 1000 illustrations, including 7 animated sequences. 325pp. 6 x 9. T412 Paperbound **$2.00**

PHILOSOPHY OF SCIENCE AND MATHEMATICS

FOUNDATIONS OF SCIENCE: THE PHILOSOPHY OF THEORY AND EXPERIMENT, N. R. Campbell. A critique of the most fundamental concepts of science in general and physics in particular. Examines why certain propositions are accepted without question, demarcates science from philosophy, clarifies the understanding of the tools of science. Part One analyzes the presuppositions of scientific thought: existence of the material world, nature of scientific laws, multiplication of probabilities, etc.: Part Two covers the nature of experiment and the application of mathematics: conditions for measurement, relations between numerical laws and theories, laws of error, etc. An appendix covers problems arising from relativity, force, motion, space, and time. A classic in its field. Index. xiii + 565pp. 5⅝ x 8⅜.
S372 Paperbound **$2.95**

THE NATURE OF PHYSICAL THEORY, P. W. Bridgman. Here is how modern physics looks to a highly unorthodox physicist—a Nobel laureate. Pointing out many absurdities of science, and demonstrating the inadequacies of various physical theories, Dr. Bridgman weighs and analyzes the contributions of Einstein, Bohr, Newton, Heisenberg, and many others. This is a non-technical consideration of the correlation of science and reality. Index. xi + 138pp. 5⅜ x 8.
S33 Paperbound **$1.25**

THE VALUE OF SCIENCE, Henri Poincaré. Many of the most mature ideas of the "last scientific universalist" covered with charm and vigor for both the beginning student and the advanced worker. Discusses the nature of scientific truth, whether order is innate in the universe or imposed upon it by man, logical thought versus intuition (relating to math, through the works of Weierstrass, Lie, Klein, Riemann), time and space (relativity, psychological time, simultaneity), Hertz's concept of force, interrelationship of mathematical physics to pure math, values within disciplines of Maxwell, Carnot, Mayer, Newton, Lorentz, etc. Index. iii + 147pp. 5⅜ x 8.
S469 Paperbound **$1.35**

SCIENCE AND HYPOTHESIS, Henri Poincaré. Creative psychology in science. How such concepts as number, magnitude, space, force, classical mechanics were developed, and how the modern scientist uses them in his thought. Hypothesis in physics, theories of modern physics. Introduction by Sir James Larmor. "Few mathematicians have had the breadth of vision of Poincaré, and none is his superior in the gift of clear exposition," E. T. Bell. Index. 272pp. 5⅜ x 8.
S221 Paperbound **$1.35**

PHILOSOPHY AND THE PHYSICISTS, L. S. Stebbing. The philosophical aspects of modern science examined in terms of a lively critical attack on the ideas of Jeans and Eddington. Discusses the task of science, causality, determinism, probability, consciousness, the relation of the world of physics to that of everyday experience. Probes the philosophical significance of the Planck-Bohr concept of discontinuous energy levels, the inferences to be drawn from Heisenberg's Uncertainty Principle, the implications of "becoming" involved in the 2nd law of thermodynamics, and other problems posed by the discarding of Laplacean determinism. 285pp. 5⅜ x 8.
T480 Paperbound **$1.65**

THE PHILOSOPHICAL WRITINGS OF PEIRCE, edited by Justus Buchler. (Formerly published as THE PHILOSOPHY OF PEIRCE.) This is a carefully balanced exposition of Peirce's complete system, written by Peirce himself. It covers such matters as scientific method, pure chance vs. law, symbolic logic, theory of signs, pragmatism, experiment, and other topics. Introduction by Justus Buchler, Columbia University. xvi + 368pp. 5⅜ x 8.
T217 Paperbound **$2.00**

LANGUAGE, TRUTH AND LOGIC, A. Ayer. A clear introduction to the Vienna and Cambridge schools of Logical Positivism. It sets up specific tests by which you can evaluate validity of ideas, etc. Contents: Function of philosophy, elimination of metaphysics, nature of analysis, a priori, truth and probability, etc. 10th printing. "I should like to have written it myself," Bertrand Russell. Index. 160pp. 5⅜ x 8.
T10 Paperbound **$1.25**

MATHEMATICS AND SCIENCE: LAST ESSAYS (DERNIÈRES PENSÉES), Henri Poincaré. Translated by J. W. Bolduc. A posthumous volume of articles and lectures by the great French mathematician, philosopher, scientist. Here are nine pieces, never before translated into English, on such subjects as The Evolution of Laws, Space and Time, Space and 3 Dimensions, The Logic of infinity in Mathematics (discussing Russell's theory of types), Mathematics and Logic, The Quantum Theory and its Modern Applications, Relationship Between Matter and Ether, Ethics and Science and The Moral Alliance. First English translation of Dernières Pensées. New index. viii + 128pp. 5⅜ x 8½.
S1101 Paperbound **$1.25**

THE PSYCHOLOGY OF INVENTION IN THE MATHEMATICAL FIELD, J. Hadamard. Where do ideas come from? What role does the unconscious play? Are ideas best developed by mathematical reasoning, word reasoning, visualization? What are the methods used by Einstein, Poincaré, Galton, Riemann? How can these techniques be applied by others? Hadamard, one of the world's leading mathematicians, discusses these and other questions. xiii + 145pp. 5⅜ x 8.
T107 Paperbound **$1.25**

EXPERIMENT AND THEORY IN PHYSICS, Max Born. A Nobel laureate examines the nature and value of the counterclaims of experiment and theory in physics. Synthetic versus analytical scientific advances are analyzed in the work of Einstein, Bohr, Heisenberg, Planck, Eddington, Milne, and others by a fellow participant. 44pp. 5⅜ x 8. S308 Paperbound **75¢**

THE PHILOSOPHY OF SPACE AND TIME, H. Reichenbach. An important landmark in the development of the empiricist conception of geometry, covering the problem of the foundations of geometry, the theory of time, the consequences of Einstein's relativity, including: relations between theory and observations; coordinate and metrical properties of space; the psychological problem of visual intuition of non-Euclidean structures; and many other important topics in modern science and philosophy. The majority of ideas require only a knowledge of intermediate math. Introduction by R. Carnap. 49 figures. Index. xviii + 296pp. 5⅜ x 8. S443 Paperbound **$2.00**

OBSERVATION AND INTERPRETATION IN THE PHILOSOPHY OF PHYSICS: WITH SPECIAL REFERENCE TO QUANTUM MECHANICS, Edited by S. Körner. A collection of papers by philosophers and physicists arising out of a symposium held at Bristol, England in 1957 under the auspices of the Colston Research Society. One of the most important contributions to the philosophy of science in recent years. The discussions center around the adequacy or inadequacy of quantum mechanics in its orthodox formulations. Among the contributors are A. J. Ayer, D. Bohm, K. Popper, F. Bopp, S. Körner, J. P. Vigier, M. Polanyi, P. K. Feyerabend, W. C. Kneale. W. B. Gallie, G. Ryle, Sir Charles Darwin, and R. B. Braithwaite. xiv + 218pp. 5⅜ x 8½. S131 Paperbound **$1.60**

SPACE AND TIME IN CONTEMPORARY PHYSICS: AN INTRODUCTION TO THE THEORY OF RELATIVITY AND GRAVITATION, Moritz Schlick. Exposition of the theory of relativity by the leader of the famed "Vienna Circle." Its essential purpose is to describe the physical doctrines of special and general relativity with particular reference to their philosophical significance. Explanations of such topics as the geometrical relativity of space, the connection with inertia and gravitation, the measure-determination of the space-time continuum, the finite universe, etc., with their philosophical ramifications. Index. xii + 89pp. 5⅜ x 8½. T1008 Paperbound **$1.00**

SUBSTANCE AND FUNCTION, & EINSTEIN'S THEORY OF RELATIVITY, Ernst Cassirer. Two books bound as one. Cassirer establishes a philosophy of the exact sciences that takes into consideration newer developments in mathematics, and also shows historical connections. Partial contents: Aristotelian logic, Mill's analysis, Helmholtz & Kronecker, Russell & cardinal numbers, Euclidean vs. non-Euclidean geometry, Einstein's relativity. Bibliography. Index. xxi + 465pp. 5⅜ x 8. T50 Paperbound **$2.25**

PRINCIPLES OF MECHANICS, Heinrich Hertz. This last work by the great 19th century physicist is not only a classic, but of great interest in the logic of science. Creating a new system of mechanics based upon space, time, and mass, it returns to axiomatic analysis, to understanding of the formal or structural aspects of science, taking into account logic, observation, and a priori elements. Of great historical importance to Poincaré, Carnap, Einstein, Milne. A 20-page introduction by R. S. Cohen, Wesleyan University, analyzes the implications of Hertz's thought and the logic of science. Bibliography. 13-page introduction by Helmholtz. xlii + 274pp. 5⅜ x 8. S316 Clothbound **$3.50**
S317 Paperbound **$1.85**

THE ANALYSIS OF MATTER, Bertrand Russell. How do our senses concord with the new physics? This volume covers such topics as logical analysis of physics, prerelativity physics, causality, scientific inference, physics and perception, special and general relativity, Weyl's theory, tensors, invariants and their physical interpretation, periodicity and qualitative series. "The most thorough treatment of the subject that has yet been published," THE NATION. Introduction by L. E. Denonn. 422pp. 5⅜ x 8. T231 Paperbound **$1.95**

FOUNDATIONS OF GEOMETRY, Bertrand Russell. Analyzing basic problems in the overlap area between mathematics and philosophy, Nobel laureate Russell examines the nature of geometrical knowledge, the nature of geometry, and the application of geometry to space. It covers the history of non-Euclidean geometry, philosophic interpretations of geometry—especially Kant—projective and metrical geometry. This is most interesting as the solution offered in 1897 by a great mind to a problem still current. New introduction by Prof. Morris Kline of N. Y. University. xii + 201pp. 5⅜ x 8. S232 Clothbound **$3.25**
S233 Paperbound **$1.75**

IDENTITY AND REALITY, Emile Meyerson. Called by Einstein a "brilliant study in the theory of knowledge," this book by the renowned Franco-German thinker is a major treatise in the philosophy of science and epistemology. Thorough, critical inquiries into causality, scientific laws, conservation of matter and energy, the unity of matter, Carnot's principle, the irrational, the elimination of time. Searches out the solutions of epistemological questions that form the bases of the scientific method. Authorized translation by Kate Loewenberg. Author's prefaces. Editor's preface. Appendices. Index. 495pp. 5⅜ x 8½. T65 Paperbound **$2.25**

ESSAYS IN EXPERIMENTAL LOGIC, John Dewey. This stimulating series of essays touches upon the relationship between inquiry and experience, dependence of knowledge upon thought, character of logic; judgments of practice, data and meanings, stimuli of thought, etc. Index. viii + 444pp. 5⅜ x 8. T73 Paperbound **$1.95**

MATHEMATICS—INTERMEDIATE TO ADVANCED

General

INTRODUCTION TO APPLIED MATHEMATICS, Francis D. Murnaghan. A practical and thoroughly sound introduction to a number of advanced branches of higher mathematics. Among the selected topics covered in detail are: vector and matrix analysis, partial and differential equations, integral equations, calculus of variations, Laplace transform theory, the vector triple product, linear vector functions, quadratic and bilinear forms, Fourier series, spherical harmonics, Bessel functions, the Heaviside expansion formula, and many others. Extremely useful book for graduate students in physics, engineering, chemistry, and mathematics. Index. 111 study exercises with answers. 41 illustrations. ix + 389pp. 5⅜ x 8½.
S1042 Paperbound **$2.00**

OPERATIONAL METHODS IN APPLIED MATHEMATICS, H. S. Carslaw and J. C. Jaeger. Explanation of the application of the Laplace Transformation to differential equations, a simple and effective substitute for more difficult and obscure operational methods. Of great practical value to engineers and to all workers in applied mathematics. Chapters on: Ordinary Linear Differential Equations with Constant Coefficients;; Electric Circuit Theory; Dynamical Applications; The Inversion Theorem for the Laplace Transformation; Conduction of Heat; Vibrations of Continuous Mechanical Systems; Hydrodynamics; Impulsive Functions; Chains of Differential Equations; and other related matters. 3 appendices. 153 problems, many with answers. 22 figures. xvi + 359pp. 5⅜ x 8½.
S1011 Paperbound **$2.25**

APPLIED MATHEMATICS FOR RADIO AND COMMUNICATIONS ENGINEERS, C. E. Smith. No extraneous material here!—only the theories, equations, and operations essential and immediately useful for radio work. Can be used as refresher, as handbook of applications and tables, or as full home-study course. Ranges from simplest arithmetic through calculus, series, and wave forms, hyperbolic trigonometry, simultaneous equations in mesh circuits, etc. Supplies applications right along with each math topic discussed. 22 useful tables of functions, formulas, logs, etc. Index. 166 exercises, 140 examples, all with answers. 95 diagrams. Bibliography. x + 336pp. 5⅜ x 8.
S141 Paperbound **$1.75**

Algebra, group theory, determinants, sets, matrix theory

ALGEBRAS AND THEIR ARITHMETICS, L. E. Dickson. Provides the foundation and background necessary to any advanced undergraduate or graduate student studying abstract algebra. Begins with elementary introduction to linear transformations, matrices, field of complex numbers; proceeds to order, basal units, modulus, quaternions, etc.; develops calculus of linears sets, describes various examples of algebras including invariant, difference, nilpotent, semi-simple. "Makes the reader marvel at his genius for clear and profound analysis," Amer. Mathematical Monthly. Index. xii + 241pp. 5⅜ x 8.
S616 Paperbound **$1.50**

THE THEORY OF EQUATIONS WITH AN INTRODUCTION TO THE THEORY OF BINARY ALGEBRAIC FORMS, W. S. Burnside and A. W. Panton. Extremely thorough and concrete discussion of the theory of equations, with extensive detailed treatment of many topics curtailed in later texts. Covers theory of algebraic equations, properties of polynomials, symmetric functions, derived functions, Horner's process, complex numbers and the complex variable, determinants and methods of elimination, invariant theory (nearly 100 pages), transformations, introduction to Galois theory, Abelian equations, and much more. Invaluable supplementary work for modern students and teachers. 759 examples and exercises. Index in each volume. Two volume set. Total of xxiv + 604pp. 5⅜ x 8.
S714 Vol I Paperbound **$1.85**
S715 Vol II Paperbound **$1.85**
The set **$3.70**

COMPUTATIONAL METHODS OF LINEAR ALGEBRA, V. N. Faddeeva, translated by **C. D. Benster.** First English translation of a unique and valuable work, the only work in English presenting a systematic exposition of the most important methods of linear algebra—classical and contemporary. Shows in detail how to derive numerical solutions of problems in mathematical physics which are frequently connected with those of linear algebra. Theory as well as individual practice. Part I surveys the mathematical background that is indispensable to what follows. Parts II and III, the conclusion, set forth the most important methods of solution, for both exact and iterative groups. One of the most outstanding and valuable features of this work is the 23 tables, double and triple checked for accuracy. These tables will not be found elsewhere. Author's preface. Translator's note. New bibliography and index. x + 252pp. 5⅜ x 8.
S424 Paperbound **$1.95**

ALGEBRAIC EQUATIONS, E. Dehn. Careful and complete presentation of Galois' theory of algebraic equations; theories of Lagrange and Galois developed in logical rather than historical form, with a more thorough exposition than in most modern books. Many concrete applications and fully-worked-out examples. Discusses basic theory (very clear exposition of the symmetric group); isomorphic, transitive, and Abelian groups; applications of Lagrange's and Galois' theories; and much more. Newly revised by the author. Index. List of Theorems. xi + 208pp. 5⅜ x 8.
S697 Paperbound **$1.45**

ALGEBRAIC THEORIES, L. E. Dickson. Best thorough introduction to classical topics in higher algebra develops theories centering around matrices, invariants, groups. Higher algebra, Galois theory, finite linear groups, Klein's icosahedron, algebraic invariants, linear transformations, elementary divisors, invariant factors; quadratic, bi-linear, Hermitian forms, singly and in pairs. Proofs rigorous, detailed; topics developed lucidly, in close connection with their most frequent mathematical applications. Formerly "Modern Algebraic Theories." 155 problems. Bibliography. 2 indexes. 285pp. 5⅜ x 8. S547 Paperbound **$1.50**

LECTURES ON THE ICOSAHEDRON AND THE SOLUTION OF EQUATIONS OF THE FIFTH DEGREE, Felix Klein. The solution of quintics in terms of rotation of a regular icosahedron around its axes of symmetry. A classic & indispensable source for those interested in higher algebra, geometry, crystallography. Considerable explanatory material included. 230 footnotes, mostly bibliographic. 2nd edition, xvi + 289pp. 5⅜ x 8. S314 Paperbound **$1.85**

LINEAR GROUPS, WITH AN EXPOSITION OF THE GALOIS FIELD THEORY, L. E. Dickson. The classic exposition of the theory of groups, well within the range of the graduate student. Part I contains the most extensive and thorough presentation of the theory of Galois Fields available, with a wealth of examples and theorems. Part II is a full discussion of linear groups of finite order. Much material in this work is based on Dickson's own contributions. Also includes expositions of Jordan, Lie, Abel, Betti-Mathieu, Hermite, etc. "A milestone in the development of modern algebra," W. Magnus, in his historical introduction to this edition. Index. xv + 312pp. 5⅜ x 8. S482 Paperbound **$1.95**

INTRODUCTION TO THE THEORY OF GROUPS OF FINITE ORDER, R. Carmichael. Examines fundamental theorems and their application. Beginning with sets, systems, permutations, etc., it progresses in easy stages through important types of groups: Abelian, prime power, permutation, etc. Except 1 chapter where matrices are desirable, no higher math needed. 783 exercises, problems. Index. xvi + 447pp. 5⅜ x 8. S300 Paperbound **$2.25**

THEORY OF GROUPS OF FINITE ORDER, W. Burnside. First published some 40 years ago, this is still one of the clearest introductory texts. Partial contents: permutations, groups independent of representation, composition series of a group, isomorphism of a group with itself, Abelian groups, prime power groups, permutation groups, invariants of groups of linear substitution, graphical representation, etc. 45pp. of notes. Indexes. xxiv + 512pp. 5⅜ x 8. S38 Paperbound **$2.45**

CONTINUOUS GROUPS OF TRANSFORMATIONS, L. P. Eisenhart. Intensive study of the theory and geometrical applications of continuous groups of transformations; a standard work on the subject, called forth by the revolution in physics in the 1920's. Covers tensor analysis, Riemannian geometry, canonical parameters, transitivity, imprimitivity, differential invariants, the algebra of constants of structure, differential geometry, contact transformations, etc. "Likely to remain one of the standard works on the subject for many years . . . principal theorems are proved clearly and concisely, and the arrangement of the whole is coherent," MATHEMATICAL GAZETTE. Index. 72-item bibliography. 185 exercises. ix + 301pp. 5⅜ x 8. S781 Paperbound **$1.85**

THE THEORY OF GROUPS AND QUANTUM MECHANICS, H. Weyl. Discussions of Schroedinger's wave equation, de Broglie's waves of a particle, Jordan-Hoelder theorem, Lie's continuous groups of transformations, Pauli exclusion principle, quantization of Maxwell-Dirac field equations, etc. Unitary geometry, quantum theory, groups, application of groups to quantum mechanics, symmetry permutation group, algebra of symmetric transformation, etc. 2nd revised edition. Bibliography. Index. xxii + 422pp. 5⅜ x 8. S269 Paperbound **$2.25**

APPLIED GROUP-THEORETIC AND MATRIX METHODS, Bryan Higman. The first systematic treatment of group and matrix theory for the physical scientist. Contains a comprehensive, easily-followed exposition of the basic ideas of group theory (realized through matrices) and its applications in the various areas of physics and chemistry: tensor analysis, relativity, quantum theory, molecular structure and spectra, and Eddington's quantum relativity. Includes rigorous proofs available only in works of a far more advanced character. 34 figures, numerous tables. Bibliography. Index. xiii + 454pp. 5⅜ x 8⅜. S1147 Paperbound **$2.50**

THE THEORY OF GROUP REPRESENTATIONS, Francis D. Murnaghan. A comprehensive introduction to the theory of group representations. Particular attention is devoted to those groups—mainly the symmetric and rotation groups—which have proved to be of fundamental significance for quantum mechanics (esp. nuclear physics). Also a valuable contribution to the literature on matrices, since the usual representations of groups are groups of matrices. Covers the theory of group integration (as developed by Schur and Weyl), the theory of 2-valued or spin representations, the representations of the symmetric group, the crystallographic groups, the Lorentz group, reducibility (Schur's lemma, Burnside's Theorem, etc.), the alternating group, linear groups, the orthogonal group, etc. Index. List of references. xi + 369pp. 5⅜ x 8½. S1112 Paperbound **$2.35**

THEORY OF SETS, E. Kamke. Clearest, amplest introduction in English, well suited for independent study. Subdivision of main theory, such as theory of sets of points, are discussed, but emphasis is on general theory. Partial contents: rudiments of set theory, arbitrary sets and their cardinal numbers, ordered sets and their order types, well-ordered sets and their cardinal numbers. Bibliography. Key to symbols. Index. vii + 144pp. 5⅜ x 8. S141 Paperbound **$1.35**

THEORY AND APPLICATIONS OF FINITE GROUPS, G. A. Miller, H. F. Blichfeldt, L. E. Dickson. Unusually accurate and authoritative work, each section prepared by a leading specialist: Miller on substitution and abstract groups, Blichfeldt on finite groups of linear homogeneous transformations, Dickson on applications of finite groups. Unlike more modern works, this gives the concrete basis from which abstract group theory arose. Includes Abelian groups, prime-power groups, isomorphisms, matrix forms of linear transformations, Sylow groups, Galois' theory of algebraic equations, duplication of a cube, trisection of an angle, etc. 2 Indexes. 267 problems. xvii + 390pp. 5⅜ x 8. S216 Paperbound **$2.00**

THE THEORY OF DETERMINANTS, MATRICES, AND INVARIANTS, H. W. Turnbull. Important study includes all salient features and major theories. 7 chapters on determinants and matrices cover fundamental properties, Laplace identities, multiplication, linear equations, rank and differentiation, etc. Sections on invariants gives general properties, symbolic and direct methods of reduction, binary and polar forms, general linear transformation, first fundamental theorem, multilinear forms. Following chapters study development and proof of Hilbert's Basis Theorem, Gordan-Hilbert Finiteness Theorem, Clebsch's Theorem, and include discussions of apolarity, canonical forms, geometrical interpretations of algebraic forms, complete system of the general quadric, etc. New preface and appendix. Bibliography. xviii + 374pp. 5⅜ x 8. S699 Paperbound **$2.25**

AN INTRODUCTION TO THE THEORY OF CANONICAL MATRICES, H. W. Turnbull and A. C. Aitken. All principal aspects of the theory of canonical matrices, from definitions and fundamental properties of matrices to the practical applications of their reduction to canonical form. Beginning with matrix multiplications, reciprocals, and partitioned matrices, the authors go on to elementary transformations and bilinear and quadratic forms. Also covers such topics as a rational canonical form for the collineatory group, congruent and conjunctive transformation for quadratic and hermitian forms, unitary and orthogonal transformations, canonical reduction of pencils of matrices, etc. Index. Appendix. Historical notes at chapter ends. Bibliographies. 275 problems. xiv + 200pp. 5⅜ x 8. S177 Paperbound **$1.55**

A TREATISE ON THE THEORY OF DETERMINANTS, T. Muir. Unequalled as an exhaustive compilation of nearly all the known facts about determinants up to the early 1930's. Covers notation and general properties, row and column transformation, symmetry, compound determinants, adjugates, rectangular arrays and matrices, linear dependence, gradients, Jacobians, Hessians, Wronskians, and much more. Invaluable for libraries of industrial and research organizations as well as for student, teacher, and mathematician; very useful in the field of computing machines. Revised and enlarged by W. H. Metzler. Index. 485 problems and scores of numerical examples. iv + 766pp. 5⅜ x 8. S670 Paperbound **$3.00**

THEORY OF DETERMINANTS IN THE HISTORICAL ORDER OF DEVELOPMENT, Sir Thomas Muir. Unabridged reprinting of this complete study of 1,859 papers on determinant theory written between 1693 and 1900. Most important and original sections reproduced, valuable commentary on each. No other work is necessary for determinant research: all types are covered—each subdivision of the theory treated separately; all papers dealing with each type are covered; you are told exactly what each paper is about and how important its contribution is. Each result, theory, extension, or modification is assigned its own identifying numeral so that the full history may be more easily followed. Includes papers on determinants in general, determinants and linear equations, symmetric determinants, alternants, recurrents, determinants having invariant factors, and all other major types. "A model of what such histories ought to be," NATURE. "Mathematicians must ever be grateful to Sir Thomas for his monumental work," AMERICAN MATH MONTHLY. Four volumes bound as two. Indices. Bibliographies. Total of lxxxiv + 1977pp. 5⅜ x 8. S672-3 The set, Clothbound **$12.50**

Calculus and function theory, Fourier theory, infinite series, calculus of variations, real and complex functions

FIVE VOLUME "THEORY OF FUNCTIONS' SET BY KONRAD KNOPP

This five-volume set, prepared by Konrad Knopp, provides a complete and readily followed account of theory of functions. Proofs are given concisely, yet without sacrifice of completeness or rigor. These volumes are used as texts by such universities as M.I.T., University of Chicago, N. Y. City College, and many others. "Excellent introduction . . . remarkably readable, concise, clear, rigorous," JOURNAL OF THE AMERICAN STATISTICAL ASSOCIATION.

ELEMENTS OF THE THEORY OF FUNCTIONS, Konrad Knopp. This book provides the student with background for further volumes in this set, or texts on a similar level. Partial contents: foundations, system of complex numbers and the Gaussian plane of numbers, Riemann sphere of numbers, mapping by linear functions, normal forms, the logarithm, the cyclometric functions and binomial series. "Not only for the young student, but also for the student who knows all about what is in it," MATHEMATICAL JOURNAL. Bibliography. Index. 140pp. 5⅜ x 8. S154 Paperbound **$1.35**

THEORY OF FUNCTIONS, PART I, Konrad Knopp. With volume II, this book provides coverage of basic concepts and theorems. Partial contents: numbers and points, functions of a complex variable, integral of a continuous function, Cauchy's integral theorem, Cauchy's integral formulae, series with variable terms, expansion of analytic functions in power series, analytic continuation and complete definition of analytic functions, entire transcendental functions, Laurent expansion, types of singularities. Bibliography. Index. vii + 146pp. 5⅜ x 8. S156 Paperbound **$1.35**

THEORY OF FUNCTIONS, PART II, Konrad Knopp. Application and further development of general theory, special topics. Single valued functions, entire, Weierstrass, Meromorphic functions. Riemann surfaces. Algebraic functions. Analytical configuration, Riemann surface. Bibliography. Index. x + 150pp. 5⅜ x 8. S157 Paperbound **$1.35**

PROBLEM BOOK IN THE THEORY OF FUNCTIONS, VOLUME 1, Konrad Knopp. Problems in elementary theory, for use with Knopp's THEORY OF FUNCTIONS, or any other text, arranged according to increasing difficulty. Fundamental concepts, sequences of numbers and infinite series, complex variable, integral theorems, development in series, conformal mapping. 182 problems. Answers. viii + 126pp. 5⅜ x 8. S158 Paperbound **$1.35**

PROBLEM BOOK IN THE THEORY OF FUNCTIONS, VOLUME 2, Konrad Knopp. Advanced theory of functions, to be used either with Knopp's THEORY OF FUNCTIONS, or any other comparable text. Singularities, entire & meromorphic functions, periodic, analytic, continuation, multiple-valued functions, Riemann surfaces, conformal mapping. Includes a section of additional elementary problems. "The difficult task of selecting from the immense material of the modern theory of functions the problems just within the reach of the beginner is here masterfully accomplished," AM. MATH. SOC. Answers. 138pp. 5⅜ x 8. S159 Paperbound **$1.35**

A COURSE IN MATHEMATICAL ANALYSIS, Edouard Goursat. Trans. by E. R. Hedrick, O. Dunkel. Classic study of fundamental material thoroughly treated. Exceptionally lucid exposition of wide range of subject matter for student with 1 year of calculus. Vol. 1: Derivatives and Differentials, Definite Integrals, Expansion in Series, Applications to Geometry. Problems. Index. 52 illus. 556pp. Vol. 2, Part I: Functions of a Complex Variable, Conformal Representations, Doubly Periodic Functions, Natural Boundaries, etc. Problems. Index. 38 illus. 269pp. Vol. 2, Part 2: Differential Equations, Cauchy-Lipschitz Method, Non-linear Differential Equations, Simultaneous Equations, etc. Problems. Index. 308pp. 5⅜ x 8.

Vol. 1 S554 Paperbound **$2.50**
Vol. 2 part 1 S555 Paperbound **$1.85**
Vol. 2 part 2 S556 Paperbound **$1.85**
3 vol. set **$6.20**

MODERN THEORIES OF INTEGRATION, H. Kestelman. Connected and concrete coverage, with fully-worked-out proofs for every step. Ranges from elementary definitions through theory of aggregates, sets of points, Riemann and Lebesgue integration, and much more. This new revised and enlarged edition contains a new chapter on Riemann-Stieltjes integration, as well as a supplementary section of 186 exercises. Ideal for the mathematician, student, teacher, or self-studier. Index of Definitions and Symbols. General Index. Bibliography. x + 310pp. 5⅝ x 8⅜. S572 Paperbound **$2.25**

THEORY OF MAXIMA AND MINIMA, H. Hancock. Fullest treatment ever written; only work in English with extended discussion of maxima and minima for functions of 1, 2, or n variables, problems with subsidiary constraints, and relevant quadratic forms. Detailed proof of each important theorem. Covers the Scheeffer and von Dantscher theories, homogeneous quadratic forms, reversion of series, fallacious establishment of maxima and minima, etc. Unsurpassed treatise for advanced students of calculus, mathematicians, economists, statisticians. Index. 24 diagrams. 39 problems, many examples. 193pp. 5⅜ x 8. S665 Paperbound **$1.50**

AN ELEMENTARY TREATISE ON ELLIPTIC FUNCTIONS, A. Cayley. Still the fullest and clearest text on the theories of Jacobi and Legendre for the advanced student (and an excellent supplement for the beginner). A masterpiece of exposition by the great 19th century British mathematician (creator of the theory of matrices and abstract geometry), it covers the addition-theory, Landen's theorem, the 3 kinds of elliptic integrals, transformations, the q-functions, reduction of a differential expression, and much more. Index. xii + 386pp. 5⅜ x 8. S728 Paperbound **$2.00**

THE APPLICATIONS OF ELLIPTIC FUNCTIONS, A. G. Greenhill. Modern books forego detail for sake of brevity—this book offers complete exposition necessary for proper understanding, use of elliptic integrals. Formulas developed from definite physical, geometric problems; examples representative enough to offer basic information in widely useable form. Elliptic integrals, addition theorem, algebraical form of addition theorem, elliptic integrals of 2nd, 3rd kind, double periodicity, resolution into factors, series, transformation, etc. Introduction. Index. 25 illus. xi + 357pp. 5⅜ x 8. S603 Paperbound **$1.75**

THE THEORY OF FUNCTIONS OF REAL VARIABLES, James Pierpont. A 2-volume authoritative exposition, by one of the foremost mathematicians of his time. Each theorem stated with all conditions, then followed by proof. No need to go through complicated reasoning to discover conditions added without specific mention. Includes a particularly complete, rigorous presentation of theory of measure; and Pierpont's own work on a theory of Lebesgue integrals, and treatment of area of a curved surface. Partial contents, Vol. 1: rational numbers, exponentials, logarithms, point aggregates, maxima, minima, proper integrals, improper integrals, multiple proper integrals, continuity, discontinuity, indeterminate forms. Vol. 2: point sets, proper integrals, series, power series, aggregates, ordinal numbers, discontinuous functions, sub-, infra-uniform convergence, much more. Index. 95 illustrations. 1229pp. 5⅜ x 8. S558-9, 2 volume set, paperbound **$4.90**

FUNCTIONS OF A COMPLEX VARIABLE, James Pierpont. Long one of best in the field. A thorough treatment of fundamental elements, concepts, theorems. A complete study, rigorous, detailed, with carefully selected problems worked out to illustrate each topic. Partial contents: arithmetical operations, real term series, positive term series, exponential functions, integration, analytic functions, asymptotic expansions, functions of Weierstrass, Legendre, etc. Index. List of symbols. 122 illus. 597pp. 5⅜ x 8. S560 Paperbound **$2.45**

MODERN OPERATIONAL CALCULUS: WITH APPLICATIONS IN TECHNICAL MATHEMATICS, N. W. McLachlan. An introduction to modern operational calculus based upon the Laplace transform, applying it to the solution of ordinary and partial differential equations. For physicists, engineers, and applied mathematicians. Partial contents: Laplace transform, theorems or rules of the operational calculus, solution of ordinary and partial linear differential equations with constant coefficients, evaluation of integrals and establishment of mathematical relationships, derivation of Laplace transforms of various functions, etc. Six appendices deal with Heaviside's unit function, etc. Revised edition. Index. Bibliography. xiv + 218pp. 5⅜ x 8½. S192 Paperbound **$1.75**

ADVANCED CALCULUS, E. B. Wilson. An unabridged reprinting of the work which continues to be recognized as one of the most comprehensive and useful texts in the field. It contains an immense amount of well-presented, fundamental material, including chapters on vector functions, ordinary differential equations, special functions, calculus of variations, etc., which are excellent introductions to these areas. For students with only one year of calculus, more than 1300 exercises cover both pure math and applications to engineering and physical problems. For engineers, physicists, etc., this work, with its 54 page introductory review, is the ideal reference and refresher. Index. ix + 566pp. 5⅜ x 8.
S504 Paperbound **$2.45**

ASYMPTOTIC EXPANSIONS, A. Erdélyi. The only modern work available in English, this is an unabridged reproduction of a monograph prepared for the Office of Naval Research. It discusses various procedures for asymptotic evaluation of integrals containing a large parameter and solutions of ordinary linear differential equations. Bibliography of 71 items. vi + 108pp. 5⅜ x 8. S318 Paperbound **$1.35**

INTRODUCTION TO ELLIPTIC FUNCTIONS: with applications, F. Bowman. Concise, practical introduction to elliptic integrals and functions. Beginning with the familiar trigonometric functions, it requires nothing more from the reader than a knowledge of basic principles of differentiation and integration. Discussion confined to the Jacobian functions. Enlarged bibliography. Index. 173 problems and examples. 56 figures, 4 tables. 115pp. 5⅜ x 8.
S922 Paperbound **$1.25**

ON RIEMANN'S THEORY OF ALGEBRAIC FUNCTIONS AND THEIR INTEGRALS: A SUPPLEMENT TO THE USUAL TREATISES, Felix Klein. Klein demonstrates how the mathematical ideas in Riemann's work on Abelian integrals can be arrived at by thinking in terms of the flow of electric current on surfaces. Intuitive explanations, not detailed proofs given in an extremely clear exposition, concentrating on the kinds of functions which can be defined on Riemann surfaces. Also useful as an introduction to the origins of topological problems. Complete and unabridged. Approved translation by Frances Hardcastle. New introduction. 43 figures. Glossary. xii + 76pp. 5⅜ x 8½. S1072 Paperbound **$1.25**

COLLECTED WORKS OF BERNHARD RIEMANN. This important source book is the first to contain the complete text of both 1892 Werke and the 1902 supplement, unabridged. It contains 31 monographs, 3 complete lecture courses, 15 miscellaneous papers, which have been of enormous importance in relativity, topology, theory of complex variables, and other areas of mathematics. Edited by R. Dedekind, H. Weber, M. Noether, W. Wirtinger. German text. English introduction by Hans Lewy. 690pp. 5⅜ x 8. S226 Paperbound **$2.85**

THE TAYLOR SERIES, AN INTRODUCTION TO THE THEORY OF FUNCTIONS OF A COMPLEX VARIABLE, P. Dienes. This book investigates the entire realm of analytic functions. Only ordinary calculus is needed, except in the last two chapters. Starting with an introduction to real variables and complex algebra, the properties of infinite series, elementary functions, complex differentiation and integration are carefully derived. Also biuniform mapping, a thorough two part discussion of representation and singularities of analytic functions, overconvergence and gap theorems, divergent series, Taylor series on its circle of convergence, divergence and singularities, etc. Unabridged, corrected reissue of first edition. Preface and index. 186 examples, many fully worked out. 67 figures. xii + 555pp. 5⅜ x 8.
S391 Paperbound **$2.75**

INTRODUCTION TO BESSEL FUNCTIONS, Frank Bowman. A rigorous self-contained exposition providing all necessary material during the development, which requires only some knowledge of calculus and acquaintance with differential equations. A balanced presentation including applications and practical use. Discusses Bessel Functions of Zero Order, of Any Real Order; Modified Bessel Functions of Zero Order; Definite Integrals; Asymptotic Expansions; Bessel's Solution to Kepler's Problem; Circular Membranes; much more. "Clear and straightforward . . . useful not only to students of physics and engineering, but to mathematical students in general," Nature. 226 problems. Short tables of Bessel functions. 27 figures. Index. x + 135pp. 5⅜ x 8. S462 Paperbound **$1.35**

ELEMENTS OF THE THEORY OF REAL FUNCTIONS, J. E. Littlewood. Based on lectures given at Trinity College, Cambridge, this book has proved to be extremely successful in introducing graduate students to the modern theory of functions. It offers a full and concise coverage of classes and cardinal numbers, well-ordered series, other types of series, and elements of the theory of sets of points. 3rd revised edition. vii + 71pp. 5⅜ x 8.
S171 Clothbound **$2.85**
S172 Paperbound **$1.25**

TRANSCENDENTAL AND ALGEBRAIC NUMBERS, A. O. Gelfond. First English translation of work by leading Soviet mathematician. Thue-Siegel theorem, its p-adic analogue, on approximation of algebraic numbers by numbers in fixed algebraic field; Hermite-Lindemann theorem on transcendency of Bessel functions, solutions of other differential equations; Gelfond-Schneider theorem on transcendency of alpha to power beta; Schneider's work on elliptic functions, with method developed by Gelfond. Translated by L. F. Boron. Index. Bibliography. 200pp. 5⅜ x 8. S615 Paperbound **$1.75**

ELLIPTIC INTEGRALS, H. Hancock. Invaluable in work involving differential equations containing cubics or quartics under the root sign, where elementary calculus methods are inadequate. Practical solutions to problems that occur in mathematics, engineering, physics: differential equations requiring integration of Lamé's, Briot's, or Bouquet's equations; determination of arc of ellipse, hyperbola, lemniscate; solutions of problems in elastica; motion of a projectile under resistance varying as the cube of the velocity; pendulums; many others. Exposition is in accordance with Legendre-Jacobi theory and includes rigorous discussion of Legendre transformations. 20 figures. 5 place table. Index. 104pp. 5⅛ x 8.
S484 Paperbound **$1.25**

LECTURES ON THE THEORY OF ELLIPTIC FUNCTIONS, H. Hancock. Reissue of the only book in English with so extensive a coverage, especially of Abel, Jacobi, Legendre, Weierstrasse, Hermite, Liouville, and Riemann. Unusual fullness of treatment, plus applications as well as theory, in discussing elliptic function (the universe of elliptic integrals originating in works of Abel and Jacobi), their existence, and ultimate meaning. Use is made of Riemann to provide the most general theory. 40 page table of formulas. 76 figures. xxiii + 498pp.
S483 Paperbound **$2.55**

THE THEORY AND FUNCTIONS OF A REAL VARIABLE AND THE THEORY OF FOURIER'S SERIES, E. W. Hobson. One of the best introductions to set theory and various aspects of functions and Fourier's series. Requires only a good background in calculus. Provides an exhaustive coverage of: metric and descriptive properties of sets of points; transfinite numbers and order types; functions of a real variable; the Riemann and Lebesgue integrals; sequences and series of numbers; power-series; functions representable by series sequences of continuous functions; trigonometrical series; representation of functions by Fourier's series; complete exposition (200pp.) on set theory; and much more. "The best possible guide," Nature. Vol. I: 88 detailed examples, 10 figures. Index. xv + 736pp. Vol. II: 117 detailed examples, 13 figures. Index. x + 780pp. 6⅛ x 9¼.
Vol. I: S387 Paperbound **$3.00**
Vol. II: S388 Paperbound **$3.00**

ALMOST PERIODIC FUNCTIONS, A. S. Besicovitch. This unique and important summary by a well-known mathematician covers in detail the two stages of development in Bohr's theory of almost periodic functions: (1) as a generalization of pure periodicity, with results and proofs; (2) the work done by Stepanoff, Wiener, Weyl, and Bohr in generalizing the theory. Bibliography. xi + 180pp. 5⅜ x 8. S18 Paperbound **$1.75**

THE ANALYTICAL THEORY OF HEAT, Joseph Fourier. This book, which revolutionized mathematical physics, is listed in the Great Books program, and many other listings of great books. It has been used with profit by generations of mathematicians and physicists who are interested in either heat or in the application of the Fourier integral. Covers cause and reflection of rays of heat, radiant heating, heating of closed spaces, use of trigonometric series in the theory of heat, Fourier integral, etc. Translated by Alexander Freeman. 20 figures. xxii + 466pp. 5⅜ x 8. S93 Paperbound **$2.00**

AN INTRODUCTION TO FOURIER METHODS AND THE LAPLACE TRANSFORMATION, Philip Franklin. Concentrates upon essentials, enabling the reader with only a working knowledge of calculus to gain an understanding of Fourier methods in a broad sense, suitable for most applications. This work covers complex qualities with methods of computing elementary functions for complex values of the argument and finding approximations by the use of charts; Fourier series and integrals with half-range and complex Fourier series; harmonic analysis; Fourier and Laplace transformations, etc.; partial differential equations with applications to transmission of electricity; etc. The methods developed are related to physical problems of heat flow, vibrations, electrical transmission, electromagnetic radiation, etc. 828 problems with answers. Formerly entitled "Fourier Methods." Bibliography. Index. x + 289pp. 5⅜ x 8.
S452 Paperbound **$1.85**

THE FOURIER INTEGRAL AND CERTAIN OF ITS APPLICATIONS, Norbert Wiener. The only book-length study of the Fourier integral as link between pure and applied math. An expansion of lectures given at Cambridge. Partial contents: Plancherel's theorem, general Tauberian theorem, special Tauberian theorems, generalized harmonic analysis. Bibliography. viii + 201pp. 5⅜ x 8. S272 Paperbound **$1.50**

Differential equations, ordinary and partial; integral equations

INTRODUCTION TO THE DIFFERENTIAL EQUATIONS OF PHYSICS, L. Hopf. Especially valuable to the engineer with no math beyond elementary calculus. Emphasizing intuitive rather than formal aspects of concepts, the author covers an extensive territory. Partial contents: Law of causality, energy theorem, damped oscillations, coupling by friction, cylindrical and spherical coordinates, heat source, etc. Index. 48 figures. 160pp. 5⅜ x 8.
S120 Paperbound **$1.25**

INTRODUCTION TO THE THEORY OF LINEAR DIFFERENTIAL EQUATIONS, E. G. Poole. Authoritative discussions of important topics, with methods of solution more detailed than usual, for students with background of elementary course in differential equations. Studies existence theorems, linearly independent solutions; equations with constant coefficients; with uniform analytic coefficients; regular singularities; the hypergeometric equation; conformal representation; etc. Exercises. Index. 210pp. 5⅜ x 8. S629 Paperbound **$1.65**

DIFFERENTIAL EQUATIONS FOR ENGINEERS, P. Franklin. Outgrowth of a course given 10 years at M. I. T. Makes most useful branch of pure math accessible for practical work. Theoretical basis of D.E.'s; solution of ordinary D.E.'s and partial derivatives arising from heat flow, steady-state temperature of a plate, wave equations; analytic functions; convergence of Fourier Series. 400 problems on electricity, vibratory systems, other topics. Formerly "Differential Equations for Electrical Engineers." Index 41 illus. 307pp. 5⅜ x 8.
S601 Paperbound **$1.65**

DIFFERENTIAL EQUATIONS, F. R. Moulton. A detailed, rigorous exposition of all the non-elementary processes of solving ordinary differential equations. Several chapters devoted to the treatment of practical problems, especially those of a physical nature, which are far more advanced than problems usually given as illustrations. Includes analytic differential equations; variations of a parameter; integrals of differential equations; analytic implicit functions; problems of elliptic motion; sine-amplitude functions; deviation of formal bodies; Cauchy-Lipschitz process; linear differential equations with periodic coefficients; differential equations in infinitely many variations; much more. Historical notes. 10 figures. 222 problems. Index. xv + 395pp. 5⅜ x 8. S451 Paperbound **$2.00**

DIFFERENTIAL AND INTEGRAL EQUATIONS OF MECHANICS AND PHYSICS (DIE DIFFERENTIAL- UND INTEGRALGLEICHUNGEN DER MECHANIK UND PHYSIK), edited by P. Frank and R. von Mises. Most comprehensive and authoritative work on the mathematics of mathematical physics available today in the United States: the standard, definitive reference for teachers, physicists, engineers, and mathematicians—now published (in the original German) at a relatively inexpensive price for the first time! Every chapter in this 2,000-page set is by an expert in his field: Carathéodory, Courant, Frank, Mises, and a dozen others. Vol I, on mathematics, gives concise but complete coverages of advanced calculus, differential equations, integral equations, and potential, and partial differential equations. Index. xxiii + 916pp. Vol. II (physics): classical mechanics, optics, continuous mechanics, heat conduction and diffusion, the stationary and quasi-stationary electromagnetic field, electromagnetic oscillations, and wave mechanics. Index. xxiv + 1106pp. Two volume set. Each volume available separately. 5⅝ x 8⅜. S787 Vol I Clothbound **$7.50**
S788 Vol II Clothbound **$7.50**
The set **$15.00**

LECTURES ON CAUCHY'S PROBLEM, J. Hadamard. Based on lectures given at Columbia, Rome, this discusses work of Riemann, Kirchhoff, Volterra, and the author's own research on the hyperbolic case in linear partial differential equations. It extends spherical and cylindrical waves to apply to all (normal) hyperbolic equations. Partial contents: Cauchy's problem, fundamental formula, equations with odd number, with even number of independent variables; method of descent. 32 figures. Index. iii + 316pp. 5⅜ x 8. S105 Paperbound **$1.75**

THEORY OF DIFFERENTIAL EQUATIONS, A. R. Forsyth. Out of print for over a decade, the complete 6 volumes (now bound as 3) of this monumental work represent the most comprehensive treatment of differential equations ever written. Historical presentation includes in 2500 pages every substantial development. Vol. 1, 2: EXACT EQUATIONS, PFAFF'S PROBLEM; ORDINARY EQUATIONS, NOT LINEAR: methods of Grassmann, Clebsch, Lie, Darboux; Cauchy's theorem; branch points; etc. Vol. 3, 4: ORDINARY EQUATIONS, NOT LINEAR; ORDINARY LINEAR EQUATIONS: Zeta Fuchsian functions, general theorems on algebraic integrals, Brun's theorem, equations with uniform periodic coffiecients, etc. Vol. 4, 5: PARTIAL DIFFERENTIAL EQUATIONS: 2 existence-theorems, equations of theoretical dynamics, Laplace transformations, general transformation of equations of the 2nd order, much more. Indexes. Total of 2766pp. 5⅜ x 8. S576-7-8 Clothbound: the set **$15.00**

PARTIAL DIFFERENTIAL EQUATIONS OF MATHEMATICAL PHYSICS, A. G. Webster. A keystone work in the library of every mature physicist, engineer, researcher. Valuable sections on elasticity, compression theory, potential theory, theory of sound, heat conduction, wave propagation, vibration theory. Contents include: deduction of differential equations, vibrations, normal functions, Fourier's series, Cauchy's method, boundary problems, method of Riemann-Volterra. Spherical, cylindrical, ellipsoidal harmonics, applications, etc. 97 figures. vii + 440pp. 5⅜ x 8. S263 Paperbound **$2.00**

ORDINARY DIFFERENTIAL EQUATIONS, E. L. Ince. A most compendious analysis in real and complex domains. Existence and nature of solutions, continuous transformation groups, solutions in an infinite form, definite integrals, algebraic theory, Sturmian theory, boundary problems, existence theorems, 1st order, higher order, etc. "Deserves the highest praise, a notable addition to mathematical literature," BULLETIN, AM. MATH. SOC. Historical appendix. Bibliography. 18 figures. viii + 558pp. 5⅜ x 8. S349 Paperbound **$2.75**

INTRODUCTION TO NONLINEAR DIFFERENTIAL AND INTEGRAL EQUATIONS, Harold T. Davis. A thorough introduction to this important area, of increasing interest to mathematicians and scientists. First published by the United States Atomic Energy Commission, it includes chapters on the differential equation of the first order, the Riccati equation (as a bridge between linear and nonlinear equations), existence theorems, second order equations, elliptic integrals, elliptic functions, and theta functions, second order differential equations of polynomial class, continuous analytic continuation, the phase plane and its phenomena, nonlinear mechanics, the calculus of variations, etc. Appendices on Painlevé transcendents and Van der Pol and Volterra equations. Bibliography of 350 items. 137 problems. Index. xv + 566pp. 5⅜ x 8½. S971 Paperbound **$2.00**

THEORY OF FUNCTIONALS AND OF INTEGRAL AND INTEGRO-DIFFERENTIAL EQUATIONS, Vito Volterra. Unabridged republication of the only English translation. An exposition of the general theory of the functions depending on a continuous set of values of another function, based on the author's fundamental notion of the transition from a finite number of variables to a continually infinite number. Though dealing primarily with integral equations, much material on calculus of variations is included. The work makes no assumption of previous knowledge on the part of the reader. It begins with fundamental material and proceeds to Generalization of Analytic Functions, Integro-Differential Equations, Functional Derivative Equations, Applications, Other Directions of Theory of Functionals, etc. New introduction by G. C. Evans. Bibliography and criticism of Volterra's work by E. Whittaker. Bibliography. Index of authors cited. Index of subjects. xxxx + 226pp. 5⅜ x 8. S502 Paperbound **$1.75**

LINEAR INTEGRAL EQUATIONS, W. V. Lovitt. Systematic survey of general theory, with some application to differential equations, calculus of variations, problems of math, physics. Partial contents: integral equation of 2nd kind by successive substitutions; Fredholm's equation as ratio of 2 integral series in lambda, applications of the Fredholm theory, Hilbert-Schmidt theory of symmetric kernels, application, etc. Neumann, Dirichlet, vibratory problems. Index. ix + 253pp. 5⅜ x 8. S176 Paperbound **$1.60**

Foundations of mathematics

THE CONTINUUM AND OTHER TYPES OF SERIAL ORDER, E. V. Huntington. This famous book gives a systematic elementary account of the modern theory of the continuum as a type of serial order. Based on the Cantor-Dedekind ordinal theory, which requires no technical knowledge of higher mathematics, it offers an easily followed analysis of ordered classes, discrete and dense series, continuous series, Cantor's transfinite numbers. 2nd edition. Index. viii + 82pp. 5⅜ x 8. S130 Paperbound **$1.00**

CONTRIBUTIONS TO THE FOUNDING OF THE THEORY OF TRANSFINITE NUMBERS, Georg Cantor. These papers founded a new branch of mathematics. The famous articles of 1895-7 are translated, with an 82-page introduction by P. E. B. Jourdain dealing with Cantor, the background of his discoveries, their results, future possibilities. Bibliography. Index. Notes. ix + 211 pp. 5⅜ x 8. S45 Paperbound **$1.35**

ELEMENTARY MATHEMATICS FROM AN ADVANCED STANDPOINT, Felix Klein.

This classic text is an outgrowth of Klein's famous integration and survey course at Göttingen. Using one field of mathematics to interpret, adjust, illuminate another, it covers basic topics in each area, illustrating its discussion with extensive analysis. It is especially valuable in considering areas of modern mathematics. "Makes the reader feel the inspiration of . . . a great mathematician, inspiring teacher . . . with deep insight into the foundations and interrelations," BULLETIN, AMERICAN MATHEMATICAL SOCIETY.

Vol. 1. ARITHMETIC, ALGEBRA, ANALYSIS. Introducing the concept of function immediately, it enlivens abstract discussion with graphical and geometrically perceptual methods. Partial contents: natural numbers, extension of the notion of number, special properties, complex numbers. Real equations with real unknowns, complex quantities. Logarithmic, exponential functions, goniometric functions, infinitesimal calculus. Transcendence of e and pi, theory of assemblages. Index. 125 figures. ix + 274pp . 5⅜ x 8. S150 Paperbound **$1.85**

Vol. 2. GEOMETRY. A comprehensive view which accompanies the space perception inherent in geometry with analytic formulas which facilitate precise formulation. Partial contents: Simplest geometric manifolds: line segment, Grassmann determinant principles, classification of configurations of space, derivative manifolds. Geometric transformations: affine transformations, projective, higher point transformations, theory of the imaginary. Systematic discussion of geometry and its foundations. Indexes. 141 illustrations. ix + 214pp. 5⅜ x 8. S151 Paperbound **$1.75**

ESSAYS ON THE THEORY OF NUMBERS: 1. CONTINUITY AND IRRATIONAL NUMBERS; 2. THE NATURE AND MEANING OF NUMBERS, Richard Dedekind. The two most important essays on the logical foundations of the number system by the famous German mathematician. The first provides a purely arithmetic and perfectly rigorous foundation for irrational numbers and thereby a rigorous meaning to continuity in analysis. The second essay is an attempt to give a logical basis for transfinite numbers and properties of the natural numbers. Discusses the logical validity of mathematical induction. Authorized English translations by W. W. Deman of "Stetigkeit und irrationale Zahlen" and "Was sind und was sollen die Zahlen?" vii + 115pp. 5⅜ x 8. T1010 Paperbound **$1.00**

Geometry

THE FOUNDATIONS OF EUCLIDEAN GEOMETRY, H. G. Forder. The first rigorous account of Euclidean geometry, establishing propositions without recourse to empiricism, and without multiplying hypotheses. Corrects many traditional weaknesses of Euclidean proofs, and investigates the problems imposed on the axiom system by the discoveries of Bolyai and Lobachevsky. Some topics discussed are Classes and Relations; Axioms for Magnitudes; Congruence and Similarity; Algebra of Points; Hessenberg's Theorem; Continuity; Existence of Parallels; Reflections; Rotations; Isometries; etc. Invaluable for the light it throws on foundations of math. Lists: Axioms employed, Symbols, Constructions. 295pp. 5⅜ x 8. S481 Paperbound **$2.00**

ADVANCED EUCLIDEAN GEOMETRY, R. A. Johnson. For years the standard textbook on advanced Euclidean geometry, requires only high school geometry and trigonometry. Explores in unusual detail and gives proofs of hundreds of relatively recent theorems and corollaries, many formerly available only in widely scattered journals. Covers tangent circles, the theorem of Miquel, symmedian point, pedal triangles and circles, the Brocard configuration, and much more. Formerly "Modern Geometry." Index. 107 diagrams. xiii + 319pp. 5⅜ x 8. S669 Paperbound **$1.65**

HIGHER GEOMETRY: AN INTRODUCTION TO ADVANCED METHODS IN ANALYTIC GEOMETRY, F. S. Woods. Exceptionally thorough study of concepts and methods of advanced algebraic geometry (as distinguished from differential geometry). Exhaustive treatment of 1-, 2-, 3-, and 4-dimensional coordinate systems, leading to n-dimensional geometry in an abstract sense. Covers projectivity, tetracyclical coordinates, contact transformation, pentaspherical coordinates, much more. Based on M.I.T. lectures, requires sound preparation in analytic geometry and some knowledge of determinants. Index. Over 350 exercises. References. 60 figures. x + 423pp. 5⅜ x 8. S737 Paperbound **$2.00**

CONTEMPORARY GEOMETRY, André Delachet. Translated by Howard G. Bergmann. The recent developments in geometry covered in uncomplicated fashion. Clear discussions of modern thinking about the theory of groups, the concept of abstract geometry, projective geometry, algebraic geometry, vector spaces, new kinds of metric spaces, developments in differential geometry, etc. A large part of the book is devoted to problems, developments, and applications of topology. For advanced undergraduates and graduate students as well as mathematicians in other fields who want a brief introduction to current work in geometry. 39 figures. Index. xix + 94pp. 5⅜ x 8½. S988 Paperbound **$1.00**

ELEMENTS OF PROJECTIVE GEOMETRY, L. Cremona. Outstanding complete treatment of projective geometry by one of the foremost 19th century geometers. Detailed proofs of all fundamental principles, stress placed on the constructive aspects. Covers homology, law of duality, anharmonic ratios, theorems of Pascal and Brianchon, foci, polar reciprocal figures, etc. Only ordinary geometry necessary to understand this honored classic. Index. Over 150 fully worked out examples and problems. 252 diagrams. xx + 302pp. 5⅜ x 8. S668 Paperbound **$1.75**

AN INTRODUCTION TO PROJECTIVE GEOMETRY, R. M. Winger. One of the best introductory texts to an important area in modern mathematics. Contains full development of elementary concepts often omitted in other books. Employing the analytic method to capitalize on the student's collegiate training in algebra, analytic geometry and calculus, the author deals with such topics as Essential Constants, Duality, The Line at Infinity, Projective Properties and Double Ratio, Projective Coordinates, The Conic, Collineations and Involutions in One Dimension, Binary Forms, Algebraic Invariants, Analytic Treatment of the Conic, Collineations in the Plane, Cubic Involutions and the Rational Cubic Curve, and a clear discussion of Non-Euclidean Geometry. For senior-college students and graduates. "An excellent textbook . . . very clearly written . . . propositions stated concisely," A. Emch, Am. Math. Monthly. Corrected reprinting. 928 problems. Index. 116 figures. xii + 443pp. 5⅜ x 8. S949 Paperbound **$2.00**

ALGEBRAIC CURVES, Robert J. Walker, Professor of Mathematics, Cornell University. Fine introduction to algebraic geometry. Presents some of the recently developed algebraic methods of handling problems in algebraic geometry, shows how these methods are related to the older analytic and geometric problems, and applies them to those same geometric problems. Limited to the theory of curves, concentrating on birational transformations. Contents: Algebraic Preliminaries, Projective Spaces, Plane Algebraic Curves, Formal Power Series, Transformations of a Curve, Linear Series. 25 illustrations. Numerous exercises at ends of sections. Index. x + 201pp. 5⅜ x 8½. S336 Paperbound **$1.60**

THE ADVANCED GEOMETRY OF PLANE CURVES AND THEIR APPLICATIONS, C. Zwikker. An unusual study of many important curves, their geometrical properties and their applications, including discussions of many less well-known curves not often treated in textbooks on synthetic and analytic Euclidean geometry. Includes both algebraic and transcendental curves such as the conic sections, kinked curves, spirals, lemniscates, cycloids, etc. and curves generated as involutes, evolutes, anticaustics, pedals, envelopes and orthogonal trajectories. Dr. Zwikker represents the points of the curves by complex numbers instead of two real Cartesian coordinates, allowing direct and even elegant proofs. Formerly: "Advanced Plane Geometry." 273 figures. xii + 299pp. 5⅜ x 8½. S1078 Paperbound **$2.00**

A TREATISE ON THE DIFFERENTIAL GEOMETRY OF CURVES AND SURFACES, L. P. Eisenhart. Introductory treatise especially for the graduate student, for years a highly successful textbook. More detailed and concrete in approach than most more recent books. Covers space curves, osculating planes, moving axes, Gauss' method, the moving trihedral, geodesics, conformal representation, etc. Last section deals with deformation of surfaces, rectilinear congruences, cyclic systems, etc. Index. 683 problems. 30 diagrams. xii + 474pp. 5⅜ x 8. S667 Paperbound **$2.75**

A TREATISE ON ALGEBRAIC PLANE CURVES, J. L. Coolidge. Unabridged reprinting of one of few full coverages in English, offering detailed introduction to theory of algebraic plane curves and their relations to geometry and analysis. Treats topological properties, Riemann-Roch theorem, all aspects of wide variety of curves including real, covariant, polar, containing series of a given sort, elliptic, polygonal, rational, the pencil, two parameter nets, etc. This volume will enable the reader to appreciate the symbolic notation of Aronhold and Clebsch. Bibliography. Index. 17 illustrations. xxiv + 513pp. 5⅜ x 8. S543 Paperbound **$2.75**

AN INTRODUCTION TO THE GEOMETRY OF N DIMENSIONS, D. M. Y. Sommerville. An introduction presupposing no prior knowledge of the field, the only book in English devoted exclusively to higher dimensional geometry. Discusses fundamental ideas of incidence, parallelism, perpendicularity, angles between linear space; enumerative geometry; analytical geometry from projective and metric points of view; polytopes; elementary ideas in analysis situs; content of hyper-spacial figures. Bibliography. Index. 60 diagrams. 196pp. 5⅜ x 8. S494 Paperbound **$1.50**

GEOMETRY OF FOUR DIMENSIONS, H. P. Manning. Unique in English as a clear, concise introduction. Treatment is synthetic, and mostly Euclidean, although in hyperplanes and hyperspheres at infinity, non-Euclidean geometry is used. Historical introduction. Foundations of 4-dimensional geometry. Perpendicularity, simple angles. Angles of planes, higher order. Symmetry, order, motion; hyperpyramids, hypercones, hyperspheres; figures with parallel elements; volume, hypervolume in space; regular polyhedroids. Glossary. 78 figures. ix + 348pp. 5⅜ x 8. S182 Paperbound **$2.00**

CONVEX FIGURES AND POLYHEDRA, L. A. Lyusternik. An excellent elementary discussion by a leading Russian mathematician. Beginning with the basic concepts of convex figures and bodies and their supporting lines and planes, the author covers such matters as centrally symmetric convex figures, theorems of Euler, Cauchy, Steinitz and Alexandrov on convex polyhedra, linear systems of convex bodies, planar sections of convex bodies, the Brunn-Minkowski inequality and its consequences, and many other related topics. No more than a high school background in mathematics needed for complete understanding. First English translation by T. J. Smith. 182 illustrations. Index. x + 176pp. 5⅜ x 8½. S1021 Paperbound **$1.50**

NON-EUCLIDEAN GEOMETRY, Roberto Bonola. The standard coverage of non-Euclidean geometry. It examines from both a historical and mathematical point of view the geometries which have arisen from a study of Euclid's 5th postulate upon parallel lines. Also included are complete texts, translated, of Bolyai's SCIENCE OF ABSOLUTE SPACE. Lobachevsky's THEORY OF PARALLELS. 180 diagrams. 431pp. 5⅜ x 8. S27 Paperbound **$2.00**

ELEMENTS OF NON-EUCLIDEAN GEOMETRY, D. M. Y. Sommerville. Unique in proceeding step-by-step, in the manner of traditional geometry. Enables the student with only a good knowledge of high school algebra and geometry to grasp elementary hyperbolic, elliptic, analytic non-Euclidean geometries; space curvature and its philosophical implications; theory of radical axes; homothetic centres and systems of circles; parataxy and parallelism; absolute measure; Gauss' proof of the defect area theorem; geodesic representation; much more, all with exceptional clarity. 126 problems at chapter endings provide progressive practice and familiarity. 133 figures. Index. xvi + 274pp. 5⅜ x 8. S460 Paperbound **$1.50**

INTRODUCTORY NON-EUCLIDEAN GEOMETRY, H. P. Manning. Sound elementary introduction to non-Euclidean geometry. The first two thirds (Pangeometry and the Hyperbolic Geometry) require a grasp of plane and solid geometry and trigonometry. The last sections (the Elliptic Geometry and Analytic Non-Euclidean Geometry) necessitate also basic college calculus for understanding the text. The book does not propose to investigate the foundations of geometry, but rather begins with the theorems common to Euclidean and non-Euclidean geometry and then takes up the specific differences between them. A simple and direct account of the bases of this important branch of mathematics for teachers and students. 94 figures. vii + 95pp. 5⅜ x 8. S310 Paperbound **$1.00**

ELEMENTARY CONCEPTS OF TOPOLOGY, P. Alexandroff. First English translation of the famous brief introduction to topology for the beginner or for the mathematician not undertaking extensive study. This unusually useful intuitive approach deals primarily with the concepts of complex, cycle, and homology, and is wholly consistent with current investigations. Ranges from basic concepts of set-theoretic topology to the concept of Betti groups. "Glowing example of harmony between intuition and thought," David Hilbert. Translated by A. E. Farley. Introduction by D. Hilbert. Index. 25 figures. 73pp. 5⅜ x 8. S747 Paperbound **$1.00**

Number theory

INTRODUCTION TO THE THEORY OF NUMBERS, L. E. Dickson. Thorough, comprehensive approach with adequate coverage of classical literature, an introductory volume beginners can follow. Chapters on divisibility, congruences, quadratic residues & reciprocity, Diophantine equations, etc. Full treatment of binary quadratic forms without usual restriction to integral coefficients. Covers infinitude of primes, least residues, Fermat's theorem, Euler's phi function, Legendre's symbol, Gauss's lemma, automorphs, reduced forms, recent theorems of Thue & Siegel, many more. Much material not readily available elsewhere. 239 problems. Index. I figure. viii + 183pp. 5⅜ x 8. S342 Paperbound **$1.65**

ELEMENTS OF NUMBER THEORY, I. M. Vinogradov. Detailed 1st course for persons without advanced mathematics; 95% of this book can be understood by readers who have gone no farther than high school algebra. Partial contents: divisibility theory, important number theoretical functions, congruences, primitive roots and indices, etc. Solutions to both problems and exercises. Tables of primes, indices, etc. Covers almost every essential formula in elementary number theory! Translated from Russian. 233 problems, 104 exercises. viii + 227pp. 5⅜ x 8. S259 Paperbound **$1.60**

THEORY OF NUMBERS and DIOPHANTINE ANALYSIS, R. D. Carmichael. These two complete works in one volume form one of the most lucid introductions to number theory, requiring only a firm foundation in high school mathematics. "Theory of Numbers," partial contents: Eratosthenes' sieve, Euclid's fundamental theorem, G.C.F. and L.C.M. of two or more integers, linear congruences, etc "Diophantine Analysis": rational triangles, Pythagorean triangles, equations of third, fourth, higher degrees, method of functional equations, much more. "Theory of Numbers": 76 problems. Index. 94pp. "Diophantine Analysis": 222 problems. Index. 118pp. 5⅜ x 8. S529 Paperbound **$1.35**

Numerical analysis, tables

MATHEMATICAL TABLES AND FORMULAS, Compiled by Robert D. Carmichael and Edwin R. Smith. Valuable collection for students, etc. Contains all tables necessary in college algebra and trigonometry, such as five-place common logarithms, logarithmic sines and tangents of small angles, logarithmic trigonometric functions, natural trigonometric functions, four-place antilogarithms, tables for changing from sexagesimal to circular and from circular to sexagesimal measure of angles, etc. Also many tables and formulas not ordinarily accessible, including powers, roots, and reciprocals, exponential and hyperbolic functions, ten-place logarithms of prime numbers, and formulas and theorems from analytical and elementary geometry and from calculus. Explanatory introduction. viii + 269pp. 5⅜ x 8½. S111 Paperbound **$1.00**

MATHEMATICAL TABLES, H. B. Dwight. Unique for its coverage in one volume of almost every function of importance in applied mathematics, engineering, and the physical sciences. Three extremely fine tables of the three trig functions and their inverse functions to thousandths of radians; natural and common logarithms; squares, cubes; hyperbolic functions and the inverse hyperbolic functions; $(a^2 + b^2)$ exp. ½a; complete elliptic integrals of the 1st and 2nd kind; sine and cosine integrals; exponential integrals Ei(x) and Ei(—x); binomial coefficients; factorials to 250; surface zonal harmonics and first derivatives; Bernoulli and Euler numbers and their logs to base of 10; Gamma function; normal probability integral; over 60 pages of Bessel functions; the Riemann Zeta function. Each table with formulae generally used, sources of more extensive tables, interpolation data, etc. Over half have columns of differences, to facilitate interpolation. Introduction. Index. viii + 231pp. 5⅜ x 8. S445 Paperbound **$1.75**

TABLES OF FUNCTIONS WITH FORMULAE AND CURVES, E. Jahnke & F. Emde. The world's most comprehensive 1-volume English-text collection of tables, formulae, curves of transcendent functions. 4th corrected edition, new 76-page section giving tables, formulae for elementary functions—not in other English editions. Partial contents: sine, cosine, logarithmic integral; factorial function; error integral; theta functions; elliptic integrals, functions; Legendre, Bessel, Riemann, Mathieu, hypergeometric functions, etc. Supplementary books. Bibliography. Indexed. "Out of the way functions for which we know no other source," SCIENTIFIC COMPUTING SERVICE, Ltd. 212 figures. 400pp. 5⅜ x 8. S133 Paperbound **$2.00**

JACOBIAN ELLIPTIC FUNCTION TABLES, L. M. Milne-Thomson. An easy to follow, practical book which gives not only useful numerical tables, but also a complete elementary sketch of the application of elliptic functions. It covers Jacobian elliptic functions and a description of their principal properties; complete elliptic integrals; Fourier series and power series expansions; periods, zeros, poles, residues, formulas for special values of the argument; transformations, approximations, elliptic integrals, conformal mapping, factorization of cubic and quartic polynomials; application to the pendulum problem; etc. Tables and graphs form the body of the book: Graph, 5 figure table of the elliptic function sn (u m); cn (u m); dn (u m). 8 figure table of complete elliptic integrals K, K′, E, E′, and the nome q. 7 figure table of the Jacobian zeta-function Z(u). 3 figures. xi + 123pp. 5⅜ x 8.
S194 Paperbound **$1.35**

TABLES OF INDEFINITE INTEGRALS, G. Petit Bois. Comprehensive and accurate, this orderly grouping of over 2500 of the most useful indefinite integrals will save you hours of laborious mathematical groundwork. After a list of 49 common transformations of integral expressions, with a wide variety of examples, the book takes up algebraic functions, irrational monomials, products and quotients of binomials, transcendental functions, natural logs, etc. You will rarely or never encounter an integral of an algebraic or transcendental function not included here; any more comprehensive set of tables costs at least $12 or $15. Index. 2544 integrals. xii + 154pp. 6⅛ x 9¼.
S225 Paperbound **$2.00**

SUMMATION OF SERIES, Collected by L. B. W. Jolley. Over 1100 common series collected, summed, and grouped for easy reference—for mathematicians, physicists, computer technicians, engineers, and students. Arranged for convenience into categories, such as arithmetical and geometrical progressions, powers and products of natural numbers, figurate and polygonal numbers, inverse natural numbers, exponential and logarithmic series, binomial expansions, simple inverse products, factorials, and trigonometric and hyperbolic expansions. Also included are series representing various Bessel functions, elliptic integrals; discussions of special series involving Legendre polynomials, the zeta function, Bernoulli's function, and similar expressions. Revised, enlarged second edition. New preface. xii + 251pp. 5⅜ x 8½.
S23 Paperbound **$2.25**

A TABLE OF THE INCOMPLETE ELLIPTIC INTEGRAL OF THE THIRD KIND, R. G. Selfridge, J. E. Maxfield. The first complete 6-place tables of values of the incomplete integral of the third kind, prepared under the auspices of the Research Department of the U.S. Naval Ordnance Test Station. Calculated on an IBM type 704 calculator and thoroughly verified by echo-checking and a check integral at the completion of each value of **a**. Of inestimable value in problems where the surface area of geometrical bodies can only be expressed in terms of the incomplete integral of the third and lower kinds; problems in aero-, fluid-, and thermodynamics involving processes where nonsymmetrical repetitive volumes must be determined; various types of seismological problems; problems of magnetic potentials due to circular current; etc. Foreword. Acknowledgment. Introduction. Use of table. xiv + 805pp. 5⅝ x 8⅜.
S501 Clothbound **$7.50**

PRACTICAL ANALYSIS, GRAPHICAL AND NUMERICAL METHODS, F. A. Willers. Translated by R. T. Beyer. Immensely practical handbook for engineers, showing how to interpolate, use various methods of numerical differentiation and integration, determine the roots of a single algebraic equation, system of linear equations, use empirical formulas, integrate differential equations, etc. Hundreds of shortcuts for arriving at numerical solutions. Special section on American calculating machines, by T. W. Simpson. 132 illustrations. 422pp. 5⅜ x 8.
S273 Paperbound **$2.00**

NUMERICAL INTEGRATION OF DIFFERENTIAL EQUATIONS, A. A. Bennett, W. E. Milne, H. Bateman. Republication of original monograph prepared for National Research Council. New methods of integration of differential equations developed by 3 leading mathematicians: THE INTERPOLATIONAL POLYNOMIAL and SUCCESSIVE APPROXIMATIONS by A. A. Bennett; STEP-BY-STEP METHODS OF INTEGRATION by W. W. Milne; METHODS FOR PARTIAL DIFFERENTIAL EQUATIONS by H. Bateman. Methods for partial differential equations, transition from difference equations to differential equations, solution of differential equations to non-integral values of a parameter will interest mathematicians and physicists. 288 footnotes, mostly bibliographic; 235-item classified bibliography. 108pp. 5⅜ x 8. S305 Paperbound **$1.35**

INTRODUCTION TO RELAXATION METHODS, F. S. Shaw. Fluid mechanics, design of electrical networks, forces in structural frameworks, stress distribution, buckling, etc. Solve linear simultaneous equations, linear ordinary differential equations, partial differential equations, Eigen-value problems by relaxation methods. Detailed examples throughout. Special tables for dealing with awkwardly-shaped boundaries. Indexes. 253 diagrams. 72 tables. 400pp. 5⅜ x 8.
S244 Paperbound **$2.45**

NUMERICAL SOLUTIONS OF DIFFERENTIAL EQUATIONS, H. Levy & E. A. Baggott. Comprehensive collection of methods for solving ordinary differential equations of first and higher order. All must pass 2 requirements: easy to grasp and practical, more rapid than school methods. Partial contents: graphical integration of differential equations, graphical methods for detailed solution. Numerical solution. Simultaneous equations and equations of 2nd and higher orders. "Should be in the hands of all in research in applied mathematics, teaching," NATURE. 21 figures. viii + 238pp. 5⅜ x 8.
S168 Paperbound **$1.75**

Probability theory and information theory

AN ELEMENTARY INTRODUCTION TO THE THEORY OF PROBABILITY, B. V. Gnedenko and A. Ya. Khinchin. Translated by Leo F. Boron. A clear, compact introduction designed to equip the reader with a fundamental grasp of the theory of probability. It is thorough and authoritative within its purposely restricted range, yet the layman with a background in elementary mathematics will be able to follow it without difficulty. Covers such topics as the processes involved in the calculation of probabilities, conditional probabilities and the multiplication rule, Bayes's formula, Bernoulli's scheme and theorem, random variables and distribution laws, and dispersion and mean deviations. New translation of fifth (revised) Russian edition (1960)—the only translation checked and corrected by Gnedenko. New preface for Dover edition by B. V. Gnedenko. Index. Bibliography. Appendix: Table of values of function $\phi(a)$. xii + 130pp. 5⅜ x 8½. T155 Paperbound **$1.45**

AN INTRODUCTION TO MATHEMATICAL PROBABILITY, Julian Lowell Coolidge. A thorough introduction which presents the mathematical foundation of the theory of probability. A substantial body of material, yet can be understood with a knowledge of only elementary calculus. Contains: The Scope and Meaning of Mathematical Probability; Elementary Principles of Probability; Bernoulli's Theorem; Mean Value and Dispersion; Geometrical Probability; Probability of Causes; Errors of Observation; Errors in Many Variables; Indirect Observations; The Statistical Theory of Gases; and The Principles of Life Insurance. Six pages of logarithm tables. 4 diagrams. Subject and author indices. xii + 214pp. 5⅜ x 8½. S258 Paperbound **$1.35**

A GUIDE TO OPERATIONS RESEARCH, W. E. Duckworth. A brief nontechnical exposition of techniques and theories of operational research. A good introduction for the layman; also can provide the initiate with new understandings. No mathematical training needed, yet not an oversimplification. Covers game theory, mathematical analysis, information theory, linear programming, cybernetics, decision theory, etc. Also includes a discussion of the actual organization of an operational research program and an account of the uses of such programs in the oil, chemical, paper, and metallurgical industries, etc. Bibliographies at chapter ends. Appendices. 36 figures. 145pp. 5¼ x 8½. T1129 Clothbound **$3.50**

MATHEMATICAL FOUNDATIONS OF INFORMATION THEORY, A. I. Khinchin. For the first time mathematicians, statisticians, physicists, cyberneticists, and communications engineers are offered a complete and exact introduction to this relatively new field. Entropy as a measure of a finite scheme, applications to coding theory, study of sources, channels and codes, detailed proofs of both Shannon theorems for any ergodic source and any stationary channel with finite memory, and much more are covered. Bibliography. vii + 120pp. 5⅜ x 8. S434 Paperbound **$1.35**

SELECTED PAPERS ON NOISE AND STOCHASTIC PROCESS, edited by **Prof. Nelson Wax,** U. of Illinois. 6 basic papers for newcomers in the field, for those whose work involves noise characteristics. Chandrasekhar, Uhlenbeck & Ornstein, Uhlenbeck & Ming, Rice, Doob. Included is Kac's Chauvenet-Prize winning Random Walk. Extensive bibliography lists 200 articles, up through 1953. 21 figures. 337pp. 6⅛ x 9¼. S262 Paperbound **$2.50**

THEORY OF PROBABILITY, William Burnside. Synthesis, expansion of individual papers presents numerous problems in classical probability, offering many original views succinctly, effectively. Game theory, cards, selections from groups; geometrical probability in such areas as suppositions as to probability of position of point on a line, points on surface of sphere, etc. Includes methods of approximation, theory of errors, direct calculation of probabilities, etc. Index. 136pp. 5⅜ x 8. S567 Paperbound **$1.00**

Statistics

ELEMENTARY STATISTICS, WITH APPLICATIONS IN MEDICINE AND THE BIOLOGICAL SCIENCES, F. E. Croxton. A sound introduction to statistics for anyone in the physical sciences, assuming no prior acquaintance and requiring only a modest knowledge of math. All basic formulas carefully explained and illustrated; all necessary reference tables included. From basic terms and concepts, the study proceeds to frequency distribution, linear, non-linear, and multiple correlation, skewness, kurtosis, etc. A large section deals with reliability and significance of statistical methods. Containing concrete examples from medicine and biology, this book will prove unusually helpful to workers in those fields who increasingly must evaluate, check, and interpret statistics. Formerly titled "Elementary Statistics with Applications in Medicine." 101 charts. 57 tables. 14 appendices. Index. iv + 376pp. 5⅜ x 8. S506 Paperbound **$2.00**

ANALYSIS & DESIGN OF EXPERIMENTS, H. B. Mann. Offers a method for grasping the analysis of variance and variance design within a short time. Partial contents: Chi-square distribution and analysis of variance distribution, matrices, quadratic forms, likelihood ration tests and tests of linear hypotheses, power of analysis, Galois fields, non-orthogonal data, interblock estimates, etc. 15pp. of useful tables. x + 195pp. 5 x 7⅜. S180 Paperbound **$1.45**

METHODS OF STATISTICS, L. H. C. Tippett. A classic in its field, this unusually complete systematic introduction to statistical methods begins at beginner's level and progresses to advanced levels for experimenters and poll-takers in all fields of statistical research. Supplies fundamental knowledge of virtually all elementary methods in use today by sociologists, psychologists, biologists, engineers, mathematicians, etc. Explains logical and mathematical basis of each method described, with examples for each section. Covers frequency distributions and measures, inference from random samples, errors in large samples, simple analysis of variance, multiple and partial regression and correlation, etc. 4th revised (1952) edition. 16 charts. 5 significance tables. 152-item bibliography. 96 tables. 22 figures. 395pp. 6 x 9.
S228 Clothbound **$7.50**

STATISTICS MANUAL, E. L. Crow, F. A. Davis, M. W. Maxfield. Comprehensive collection of classical, modern statistics methods, prepared under auspices of U. S. Naval Ordnance Test Station, China Lake, Calif. Many examples from ordnance will be valuable to workers in all fields. Emphasis is on use, with information on fiducial limits, sign tests, Chi-square runs, sensitivity, quality control, much more. "Well written . . . excellent reference work," Operations Research. Corrected edition of NAVORD Report 3360 NOTS 948. Introduction. Appendix of 32 tables, charts. Index. Bibliography. 95 illustrations. 306pp. 5⅜ x 8.
S599 Paperbound **$1.65**

Symbolic logic

AN INTRODUCTION TO SYMBOLIC LOGIC, Susanne K. Langer. Probably the clearest book ever written on symbolic logic for the philosopher, general scientist and layman. It will be particularly appreciated by those who have been rebuffed by other introductory works because of insufficient mathematical training. No special knowledge of mathematics is required. Starting with the simplest symbols and conventions, you are led to a remarkable grasp of the Boole-Schroeder and Russell-Whitehead systems clearly and quickly. PARTIAL CONTENTS: Study of forms, Essentials of logical structure, Generalization, Classes, The deductive system of classes, The algebra of logic, Abstraction of interpretation, Calculus of propositions, Assumptions of PRINCIPIA MATHEMATICA, Logistics, Logic of the syllogism, Proofs of theorems. "One of the clearest and simplest introductions to a subject which is very much alive. The style is easy, symbolism is introduced gradually, and the intelligent non-mathematician should have no difficulty in following the argument," MATHEMATICS GAZETTE. Revised, expanded second edition. Truth-value tables. 368pp. 5⅜ x 8.
S164 Paperbound **$1.75**

A SURVEY OF SYMBOLIC LOGIC: THE CLASSIC ALGEBRA OF LOGIC, C. I. Lewis. Classic survey of the field, comprehensive and thorough. Indicates content of major systems, alternative methods of procedure, and relation of these to the Boole-Schroeder algebra and to one another. Contains historical summary, as well as full proofs and applications of the classic, or Boole-Schroeder, algebra of logic. Discusses diagrams for the logical relations of classes, the two-valued algebra, propositional functions of two or more variables, etc. Chapters 5 and 6 of the original edition, which contained material not directly pertinent, have been omitted in this edition at the author's request. Appendix. Bibliography. Index. viii + 352pp. 5⅝ x 8⅜.
S643 Paperbound **$2.00**

INTRODUCTION TO SYMBOLIC LOGIC AND ITS APPLICATIONS, R. Carnap. One of the clearest, most comprehensive, and rigorous introductions to modern symbolic logic by perhaps its greatest living master. Symbolic languages are analyzed and one constructed. Applications to math (symbolic representation of axiom systems for set theory, natural numbers, real numbers, topology, Dedekind and Cantor explanations of continuity), physics (the general analysis of concepts of determination, causality, space-time-topology, based on Einstein), biology (symbolic representation of an axiom system for basic concepts). "A masterpiece," Zentralblatt für Mathematik und ihre Grenzgebiete. Over 300 exercises. 5 figures. Bibliography. Index. xvi + 241pp. 5⅜ x 8. S453 Paperbound **$1.85**
Clothbound **$4.00**

SYMBOLIC LOGIC, C. I. Lewis, C. H. Langford. Probably the most cited book in symbolic logic, this is one of the fullest treatments of paradoxes. A wide coverage of the entire field of symbolic logic, plus considerable material that has not appeared elsewhere. Basic to the entire volume is the distinction between the logic of extensions and of intensions. Considerable emphasis is placed on converse substitution, while the matrix system presents the supposition of a variety of non-Aristotelian logics. It has especially valuable sections on strict limitations, existence of terms, 2-valued algebra and its extension to propositional functions, truth value systems, the matrix method, implication and deductibility, general theory of propositions, propositions of ordinary discourse, and similar topics. "Authoritative, most valuable," TIMES, London. Bibliography. 506pp. 5⅜ x 8. S170 Paperbound **$2.00**

THE ELEMENTS OF MATHEMATICAL LOGIC, Paul Rosenbloom. First publication in any language. This book is intended for readers who are mature mathematically, but have no previous training in symbolic logic. It does not limit itself to a single system, but covers the field as a whole. It is a development of lectures given at Lund University, Sweden, in 1948. Partial contents: Logic of classes, fundamental theorems, Boolean algebra, logic of propositions, logic of propositional functions, expressive languages, combinatory logics, development of mathematics within an object language, paradoxes, theorems of Post and Goedel, Church's theorem, and similar topics. iv + 214pp. 5⅜ x 8. S227 Paperbound **$1.45**

THE PRINCIPLES OF SCIENCE, A TREATISE ON LOGIC AND THE SCIENTIFIC METHOD, W. S. Jevons. Treating such topics as Inductive and Deductive Logic, the Theory of Number, Probability, and the Limits of Scientific Method, this milestone in the development of symbolic logic remains a stimulating contribution to the investigation of inferential validity in the natural and social sciences. It significantly advances Boole's logic, and contains a detailed introduction to the nature and methods of probability in physics, astronomy, everyday affairs, etc. In his introduction, Ernest Nagel of Columbia University says, "[Jevons] continues to be of interest as an attempt to articulate the logic of scientific inquiry." Index. liii + 786pp. 5⅜ x 8. S446 Paperbound **$2.98**

Vector and tensor analysis

VECTOR AND TENSOR ANALYSIS, A. P. Wills. Covers the entire field of vector and tensor analysis from elementary notions to dyads and non-Euclidean manifolds (especially detailed), absolute differentiation, the Lamé operator, the Riemann-Christoffel and Ricci-Einstein tensors, and the calculation of the Gaussian curvature of a surface. Many illustrations from electrical engineering, relativity theory, astro-physics, quantum mechanics. Presupposes only a good working knowledge of calculus. Exercises at end of each chapter. Intended for physicists and engineers as well as pure mathematicians. 44 diagrams. 114 problems. Bibliography. Index. xxxii + 285pp. 5⅜ x 8. S454 Paperbound **$1.75**

APPLICATIONS OF TENSOR ANALYSIS, A. J. McConnell. (Formerly APPLICATIONS OF THE ABSOLUTE DIFFERENTIAL CALCULUS.) An excellent text for understanding the application of tensor methods to familiar subjects such as dynamics, electricity, elasticity, and hydrodynamics. Explains the fundamental ideas and notation of tensor theory, the geometrical treatment of tensor algebra, the theory of differentiation of tensors, and includes a wealth of practical material. Bibliography. Index. 43 illustrations. 685 problems. xii + 381pp. 5⅜ x 8. S373 Paperbound **$1.85**

VECTOR AND TENSOR ANALYSIS, G. E. Hay. One of the clearest introductions to this increasingly important subject. Start with simple definitions, finish the book with a sure mastery of oriented Cartesian vectors, Christoffel symbols, solenoidal tensors, and their applications. Complete breakdown of plane, solid, analytical, differential geometry. Separate chapters on application. All fundamental formulae listed & demonstrated. 195 problems, 66 figures. viii + 193pp. 5⅜ x 8. S109 Paperbound **$1.75**

VECTOR ANALYSIS, FOUNDED UPON THE LECTURES OF J. WILLARD GIBBS, by E. B. Wilson. Still a first-rate introduction and supplementary text for students of mathematics and physics. Based on the pioneering lectures of Yale's great J. Willard Gibbs, can be followed by anyone who has had some calculus. Practical approach, stressing efficient use of combinations and functions of vectors. Worked examples from geometry, mechanics, hydrodynamics, gas theory, etc., as well as practice examples. Covers basic vector processes, differential and integral calculus in relation to vector functions, and theory of linear vector functions, forming an introduction to the study of multiple algebra and matrix theory. While the notation is not always modern, it is easily followed. xviii + 436pp. 5⅜ x 8. S656 Paperbound **$2.00**

PROBLEMS AND WORKED SOLUTIONS IN VECTOR ANALYSIS, L. R. Shorter. More pages of fully-worked-out examples than any other text on vector analysis. A self-contained course for home study or a fine classroom supplement. 138 problems and examples begin with fundamentals, then cover systems of coordinates, relative velocity and acceleration, the commutative and distributive laws, axial and polar vectors, finite displacements, the calculus of vectors, curl and divergence, etc. Final chapter treats applications in dynamics and physics: kinematics of a rigid body, equipotential surfaces, etc. "Very helpful . . . very comprehensive. A handy book like this . . . will fill a great want," MATHEMATICAL GAZETTE. Index. List of 174 important equations. 158 figures. xiv + 356pp. 5⅜ x 8. S135 Paperbound **$2.00**

Prices subject to change without notice.

Dover publishes books on art, music, philosophy, literature, languages, history, social sciences, psychology, handcrafts, orientalia, puzzles and entertainments, chess, pets and gardens, books explaining science, intermediate and higher mathematics, mathematical physics, engineering, biological sciences, earth sciences, classics of science, etc. Write to:

Dept. catrr.
Dover Publications, Inc.
180 Varick Street, N.Y. 14, N.Y.